FROM LAB MATERIALS TO PRINT AND AUDIO TOOLS... RESOURCES THAT HELP YOU SUCCEED

This online tool includes 14 modules with 130 activities that give you virtual experience gathering data and performing experiments through engaging simulations. Change parameters to see what happens in each simulation, generate your own data, and write up results. Each experiment includes a general introduction followed by a series of interactive laboratory activities, each with its own set of questions. With an easy-to-use design and unparalleled flexibility, **Virtual Biology Laboratory 3.0** will make you feel like you're in a real lab!

The following experimental modules are available for purchase at academic. cengage.com/biology:

Choose from the following lab modules:

- Biochemistry
- Cell Chemistry
- Cell Division
- Cell Membranes
- Cell Respiration
- Cell Structure
- Ecology
- Evolution
- Genetics
- Microscopy
- Molecular Biology
- Pedigree Analysis
- Photosynthesis
- Population Biology

ALSO AVAILABLE

Study Guide

This interactive workbook pairs text-specific concepts with questions, illustrations, and exercises that promote active learning, as well as topic maps, study strategies, and case studies to help you study more efficiently.

BIOLOGY

Exploring the Diversity of Life

First Canadian Edition

Volume Two

Peter J. Russell

Stephen L. Wolfe

Paul E. Hertz

Cecie Starr

M. Brock Fenton
University of Western Ontario

Heather Addy
University of Calgary

Denis Maxwell
University of Western Ontario

Tom Haffie
University of Western Ontario

Ken Davey
York University (Emeritus)

NELSON / EDUCATION

NELSON / EDUCATION

Biology: Exploring the Diversity of Life, First Canadian Edition, Volume Two

by Peter J. Russell, Stephen L. Wolfe, Paul E. Hertz, Cecie Starr, M. Brock Fenton, Heather Addy, Denis Maxwell, Tom Haffie, Ken Davey

Vice President, Editorial Director:
Evelyn Veitch

Editor-in-Chief, Higher Education:
Anne Williams

Executive Editor:
Paul Fam

Senior Marketing Manager:
Sean Chamberland

Managing Editor, Development:
Alwynn Pinard

Photo Researcher:
Indu Arora

Permissions Coordinator:
Indu Arora

Content Production Manager:
Christine Gilbert

Production Service:
PrePress PMG

Copy Editor:
Holly Dickinson

Proofreader:
Martha Ghent

Indexer:
Cindy Coan

Production Coordinator:
Ferial Suleman

Design Director:
Ken Phipps

Managing Designer:
Franca Amore

Interior Design:
Dianna Little

Cover Design:
Johanna Liburd, Cover Concept;
Jennifer Leung, Cover Design

Cover Image:
Main image (bat): Photo courtesy of M. Brock Fenton

Background image (DNA double helix):
Grant Faint/Stone/Getty Images

Compositor:
PrePress PMG

Printer:
Courier

About the Cover: A flying little brown bat frozen in mid-wing stroke moves through the blackness of an underground passage. Echolocation allows the bat to collect information about its surroundings or to locate flying insects. In the background is the elegantly sinuous double helix of DNA, a widely recognized vernacular icon for life itself. The blurred DNA connotes the generative activity inherent in the molecule that carries the genetic code of all life into the future.

For, and because of, our generations of students.

About the Canadian Authors

M.B. (BROCK) FENTON received his Ph.D. from the University of Toronto in 1969. Since then, he has been a faculty member in biology at Carleton University, then at York University, and then at The University of Western Ontario. In addition to teaching parts of first-year biology, he has also taught vertebrate biology, animal biology, and conservation biology, as well as field courses in the biology and behaviour of bats. He has received awards for his teaching (Carleton University Faculty of Science Teaching Award, Ontario Confederation of University Faculty Associations Teaching Award, and a 3M Teaching Fellowship, Society for Teaching and Learning in Higher Education) in addition to recognition of his work on public awareness of science (Gordin Kaplan Award from the Canadian Federation of Biological Societies; Honourary Life Membership, Science North, Sudbury, Ontario; Canadian Council of University Biology Chairs Distinguished Canadian Biologist Award; The McNeil Medal for the Public Awareness of Science of the Royal Society of Canada; and the Sir Sanford Fleming Medal for public awareness of Science, the Royal Canadian Institute). He also received the C. Hart Merriam Award from the American Society of Mammalogists for excellence in scientific research. Bats and their biology, behaviour, evolution, and echolocation are the topic of his research, which has been funded by the Natural Sciences and Engineering Research Council of Canada (NSERC).

HEATHER ADDY is a graduate of the University of Alberta and received her Ph.D. in plant–soil relationships from the University of Guelph in 1995. During this training and in a subsequent postdoctoral fellowship focusing on mycorrhizas and other plant–fungus symbioses at the University of Alberta, she discovered a love of teaching. In 1998, she joined the Department of Biological Sciences at the University of Calgary in a faculty position that places emphasis on teaching and teaching-related scholarship. In addition to teaching introductory biology classes and an upper-level mycology class, she has led the development of investigative labs for introductory biology courses and the introduction of peer-assisted learning groups in large biology and chemistry classes. She received the Faculty of Science Award for Excellence in Teaching in 2005 and an Honourable Mention for the Student's Union Teaching Excellence Award in 2008.

DENIS MAXWELL received his Ph.D. from the University of Western Ontario in 1995. His thesis under the supervision of Norm Hüner focused on the role of the redox state of photosynthetic electron transport in photoacclimation in green algae. Following his doctorate, he was awarded an NSERC postdoctoral fellowship. He undertook postdoctoral training at the Department of Energy Plant Research Laboratory at Michigan State University, where he studied the function of the mitochondrial alternative oxidase. After taking up a faculty position at the University of New Brunswick in 2000, he moved in 2003 to the Department of Biology at The University of Western Ontario. His research program, which is supported by NSERC, is focused on understanding the role of the mitochondrion in intracellular stress sensing and signalling. In addition to research, he is passionate about teaching biology and science to first-year university students.

TOM HAFFIE is a graduate of the University of Guelph and the University of Saskatchewan in the area of microbial genetics. Currently the learning development coordinator for the Faculty of Science at the University of Western Ontario, Tom has devoted his 20-year career to teaching large biology classes in lecture, laboratory, and tutorial settings. He led the development of the innovative core laboratory course in the biology program, was an early adopter of computer animation in lectures and, most recently, has coordinated the implementation of personal response technology across campus. He holds a UWO Pleva Award for Excellence in Teaching, a UWO Fellowship in Teaching Innovation, a Province of Ontario Award for Leadership in Faculty Teaching (LIFT), and a national 3M Fellowship for Excellence in Teaching.

KEN DAVEY is a graduate of the University of Western Ontario and received his Ph.D. from Cambridge University. He is an emeritus professor of biology at York University and has by preference taught elementary courses in zoology at McGill and York and more advanced courses in invertebrate physiology, parasitology, and endocrinology. He has held a number of academic administrative positions at York. His research interests include invertebrate physiology and the endocrinology of insects and parasitic worms, supported by NSERC. Ken has accumulated a number of academic awards, including the Canadian Council of University Biology Chairs Distinguished Canadian Biologist Award and the Wigglesworth Award for Service to Entomology of the Royal Entomological Society. He is a Fellow of the Royal Society of Canada and an Officer of the Order of Canada.

About the U.S. Authors

PETER J. RUSSELL received a B.Sc. in Biology from the University of Sussex, England, in 1968 and a Ph.D. in Genetics from Cornell University in 1972. He has been a member of the Biology faculty of Reed College since 1972; he is currently a Professor of Biology. He teaches a section of the introductory biology course, a genetics course, an advanced molecular genetics course, and a research literature course on molecular virology. In 1987 he received the Burlington Northern Faculty Achievement Award from Reed College in recognition of his excellence in teaching. Since 1986, he has been the author of a successful genetics textbook; current editions are *iGenetics: A Mendelian Approach, iGenetics: A Molecular Approach,* and *Essential iGenetics.* He wrote nine of the BioCoach Activities for The Biology Place. Peter Russell's research is in the area of molecular genetics, with a specific interest in characterizing the role of host genes in pathogenic RNA plant virus gene expression; yeast is used as the model host. His research has been funded by agencies including the National Institutes of Health, the National Science Foundation, and the American Cancer Society. He has published his research results in a variety of journals, including *Genetics, Journal of Bacteriology, Molecular and General Genetics, Nucleic Acids Research, Plasmid,* and *Molecular and Cellular Biology.* He has a long history of encouraging faculty research involving undergraduates, including cofounding the biology division of the Council on Undergraduate Research (CUR) in 1985. He was Principal Investigator/Program Director of an NSF Award for the Integration of Research and Education (AIRE) to Reed College, 1998–2002.

STEPHEN L. WOLFE received his Ph.D. from Johns Hopkins University and taught general biology and cell biology for many years at the University of California, Davis. He has a remarkable list of successful textbooks, including multiple editions of *Biology of the Cell, Biology: The Foundations, Cell Ultrastructure, Molecular and Cellular Biology,* and *Introduction to Cell and Molecular Biology.*

PAUL E. HERTZ was born and raised in New York City. He received a bachelor's degree in Biology at Stanford University in 1972, a master's degree in Biology at Harvard University in 1973, and a doctorate in Biology at Harvard University in 1977. While completing field research for the doctorate, he served on the Biology faculty of the University of Puerto Rico at Rio Piedras. After spending 2 years as an Isaac Walton Killam Postdoctoral Fellow at Dalhousie University, Hertz accepted a teaching position at Barnard College, where he has taught since 1979. He was named Ann Whitney Olin Professor of Biology in 2000, and he received The Barnard Award for Excellence in Teaching in 2007. In addition to his service on numerous college committees, Professor Hertz was Chair of Barnard's Biology Department for 8 years. He has also been the Program Director of the Hughes Science Pipeline Project at Barnard, an undergraduate curriculum and research program funded by the Howard Hughes Medical Institute, since its inception in 1992. The Pipleine Project includes the Intercollegiate Partnership, a program for local community college students that facilitates their transfer to 4-year colleges and universities. He teaches one semester of the introductory sequence for Biology majors and preprofessional students as well as lecture and laboratory courses in vertebrate zoology and ecology. Professor Hertz is an animal physiological ecologist with a specific research interest in the thermal biology of lizards. He has conducted fieldwork in the West Indies since the mid-1970s, most recently focusing on the lizards of Cuba. His work has been funded by the National Science Foundation, and he has published his research in such prestigious journals as *The American Naturalist, Ecology, Nature,* and *Oecologia.*

CECIE STARR is the author of best-selling biology textbooks. Her books include multiple editions of *Unity and Diversity of Life, Biology: Concepts and Applications,* and *Biology Today and Tomorrow.* Her original dream was to be an architect. She may not be building houses, but with the same care and attention to detail, she builds incredible books: *"I invite students into a chapter through an intriguing story. Once inside, they get the great windows that biologists construct on the world of life. Biology is not just another house. It is a conceptual mansion. I hope to do it justice."*

BEVERLY MCMILLAN has been a science writer for more than 20 years and is coauthor of a college text in human biology, now in its seventh edition. She has worked extensively in educational and commercial publishing, including 8 years in editorial management positions in the college divisions of Random House and McGraw-Hill. In a multifaceted freelance career, Bev also has written or coauthored six trade books and numerous magazine and newspaper articles, as well as story panels for exhibitions at the Science Museum of Virginia and the San Francisco Exploratorium. She has worked as a radio producer and speechwriter for the University of California system and as a media relations advisor for the College of William and Mary. She holds undergraduate and graduate degrees from the University of California, Berkeley.

Preface

Welcome to an exploration of the diversity of life. The main goal of this text is to guide you on a journey of discovery about life's diversity across levels ranging from molecules to genes, cells to organs, and species to ecosystems. Along the way, we will explore many questions about the mechanisms underlying diversity as well as the consequences of diversity for our own species and for others.

At first glance, the riot of life that animates the biosphere overwhelms the minds of many who try to understand it. One way to begin to make sense of this diversity is to divide it into manageable sections on the basis of differences. In this book, we highlight the divisions between plants and animals, prokaryotes and eukaryotes, protostomes and deuterostomes, but we also consider features found in all life forms. We examine how different organisms solve the common problems of finding nutrients, energy, and mates on the third rock from our Sun. What basic evolutionary principles inform the relationships among life forms regardless of their different body plans, habitats, or life histories? Unlike many other first-year biology texts, this book has chapters integrating basic concepts such as genetic recombination, the effects of light, nutrition, and domestication across the breadth of life from microbes to mistletoe to moose. As you read this book, you will be referred frequently to other chapters for linked information that expands the ideas further.

Evolution provides a powerful conceptual lens for viewing and understanding the roots and history of diversity. We will demonstrate how knowledge of evolution helps us appreciate the changes we observe in organisms. Whether the focus is the conversion of free-living prokaryotes into mitochondria and chloroplasts or the steps involved in the domestication of rice, selection for particular traits over time can explain the current condition.

We hope that Canadian students will find the subject of biology as it is presented here accessible and engaging because it is presented in familiar contexts. We have highlighted the work of Canadian scientists, used examples of Canadian species, and referred to Canadian regulations and institutions, as well as discoveries made by Canadians.

Although many textbooks use the first few chapters to introduce and/or review background information, we have used the first chapters to convey the excitement and interest of biology itself. Within the centre of the book, we have placed important background information about biology and chemistry in the reference section entitled *The Chemical and Physical Foundations of Biology*. These pages are distinct and easy to find with their purple edges and have become affectionately known as the "Purple Pages." These pages enable information to be readily identifiable and accessible to students as they move through the textbook rather than information that is tied to a particular chapter. The purple background makes the pages easy to find when you need to check a topic. This section keeps background information out of the mainstream of the text, allowing you to focus on bigger pictures.

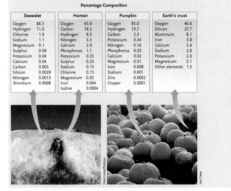

The Organization of Matter

Any substance in the universe that has mass and occupies space is defined as **matter.** The basic scientific concepts that explain how matter is organized in biological systems are no different from those for nonliving forms of matter. Living organisms are built from the same chemistry building blocks as nonliving systems and abide by the same laws of chemistry. Because of this, a basic understanding of these chemistry principles is important for our understanding of how biological systems operate.

Elements and Compounds

All matter in the universe—anything that occupies space and has mass—is composed of elements. An element is a pure substance that cannot be broken down into simpler substances by ordinary chemical or physical techniques. Ninety-two different elements occur naturally on Earth, and more than 15 artificial elements have been synthesized in the laboratory.

Living organisms are composed of about 25 elements, with only 4—carbon, hydrogen, oxygen, and nitrogen—accounting for more than 96% of the weight of living organisms. Seven other elements—calcium, phosphorus, potassium, sulphur, sodium, chlorine, and magnesium—contribute most of the remaining 4%. Nine additional elements occur in organisms in quantities so small (<0.01%) that they are known as trace elements. The proportions by mass of different elements differ markedly in seawater, the human body, a fruit, and Earth's crust.

Molecules whose component atoms are different (such as carbon dioxide) are called compounds. The chemical and physical properties of compounds are typically distinct from those of their atoms or elements. For example, we all know that water is a liquid at room temperature. We also know that water does not burn. However, the properties of the individual elements of water—hydrogen and oxygen—are quite different. Hydrogen and oxygen are gases at room temperature, and both are highly reactive.

Atoms combined chemically in fixed numbers and ratios form the molecules of living and nonliving matter. For example, the oxygen we breathe is a molecule formed from the chemical combination of two oxygen atoms; a molecule of the carbon dioxide that we exhale contains one carbon atom and two oxygen atoms. Because carbon dioxide is a molecule consisting of different elements, it is referred to as a compound.

Percentage Composition

Seawater		Human		Pumpkin		Earth's crust	
Oxygen	88.3	Oxygen	65.0	Oxygen	85.0	Oxygen	46.6
Hydrogen	11.0	Carbon	18.5	Hydrogen	10.7	Silicon	27.7
Chlorine	1.9	Hydrogen	9.5	Carbon	3.3	Aluminum	8.1
Sodium	1.1	Nitrogen	3.3	Potassium	0.34	Iron	5.0
Magnesium	0.1	Calcium	2.0	Nitrogen	0.16	Calcium	3.6
Sulphur	0.09	Phosphorus	1.1	Phosphorus	0.05	Sodium	2.8
Potassium	0.04	Potassium	0.35	Calcium	0.02	Potassium	2.6
Calcium	0.04	Sulphur	0.25	Magnesium	0.01	Magnesium	2.1
Carbon	0.003	Sodium	0.15	Iron	0.008	Other elements	1.5
Silicon	0.0029	Chlorine	0.15	Sodium	0.001		
Nitrogen	0.0015	Magnesium	0.05	Zinc	0.0002		
Strontium	0.0008	Iron	0.004	Copper	0.0001		
		Iodine	0.0004				

In addition to presenting material about biology, this book also makes a point of highlighting particular people, important molecules, interesting contexts, and examples of life in extreme conditions. Science that appears in textbooks is the product of people who have made careful and systematic observations, which led them to formulate hypotheses about these observations and, where appropriate, design and execute experiments to test these hypotheses. We illustrate this in each chapter with boxed stories about how particular people have used their ingenuity and creativity to expand our knowledge of biology. We have endeavoured to show not just the science itself but also the process behind the science.

Although biology is not simply chemistry, specific chemicals and their interactions can have dramatic effects on biological systems. From water to progesterone, amanitin, and DDT, each chapter features the activity of a relevant chemical.

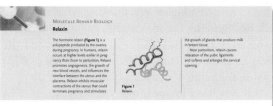

of interpubic ligaments at the time of parturition (see *Molecule Behind Biology*).

39.1 Housing and Fuelling Developing Young

Some animal parents invest significant energy in housing and feeding their developing young. This is one aspect of the genetically selfish drive to ensure that their genes are represented in future generations.

39.1a Housing: Providing a Place in Which the Embryo Can Develop

There is a recurring tendency across phyla for parents to put eggs and developing young in situations that minimize their exposure to predators and parasites while maximizing favourable conditions for growth and development. Many species of birds use nests to house their eggs and unfledged young. Parents of other species, such as some species of scorpions (see Figure 3.22a), frogs, and insects, carry their young with them, often on their backs. This allows the parent (parents) to avoid or actively deter would-be predators.

An escalation in parental investment is moving eggs and young inside the parent's body (viviparity and ovoviviparity; see Chapter 38). This approach to parental care has several different stages (see Chapter 38, *On the Road to Viviparity*). Although we associate viviparity with mammals, many species of fish are mouth-breeders, keeping eggs and, for a time, developing young in their mouths. Other fish, such as sea horses and pipefish (family Syngnathidae, order Gasterosteiformes; **Figure 39.1**), keep eggs and developing young in specialized incubation areas, called brood pouches, located on the tail or trunk of the male. "Pregnancy" in male sea horses represents an increase in parental investment. It also allows males to be confident about the paternity of the young they raise.

Some amphibians also show high levels of parental care. In Australia, female frogs, *Rheobatrachus silus*, use their stomachs as brood pouches. While the young are developing, they secrete prostaglandin E_2, which inhibits the secretion of gastric acid in the stomach and saves the developing young from being digested. On Mount Nimba in west Africa, female toads *Nectophrynoides occidentalis* harbour developing young in their uterus, where the young feed on uterine secretions in the absence of a placenta. The gestation period for these toads is nine months, and newborns are 7 to 8 mm long and weigh 30 to 60 mg. Retention of developing embryos in the oviducts has evolved independently in each of the three living groups of Amphibia: Anura, Urodela, and Gymnophiona (see Chapter 27).

39.1b Feeding: Aiding and Abetting Developing Young

Almost everyone has seen pictures of parent birds feeding their young (see Figures 40.2 and 40.4). In many species, both males and females deliver food to the nestlings. Some fruit-eating adult birds feed insects to their young

Figure 39.1
A male sea horse gives birth.

To help frame the material with an engaging context, we begin each chapter with a section called "Why It Matters." In addition, several chapters include boxed accounts of organisms thriving "on the edge" at unusual temperatures, pressures, radiation dosages, salt concentrations, etc. These brief articles explain how our understanding of "normal" can be increased through study of the "extreme."

Examining how biological systems work is another theme pervading this text and underlying the idea of diversity. We have intentionally tried to include examples that will tax your imagination, from sea slugs that steal chloroplasts for use as solar panels, to hummingbirds fuelling their hovering flight, to adaptive radiation of viruses. In each situation, we examine how biologists have explored and assessed the inner workings of organisms from gene regulation to the challenges of digesting cellulose.

Solving problems is another theme that runs through the book. Whether the topic is gene therapy to treat a disease in people, increasing crop production, or conserving endangered species, both the problem and the solution lie in biology. We will explore large problems facing planet Earth and the social implications that arise from them.

Science is by its nature a progressive enterprise in which answers to questions open new questions for consideration. Each chapter presents unanswered questions as well as questions for discussion to emphasize that biologists still have a lot to learn—topics for you to tackle should you decide to pursue a career in research.

"Study Breaks" occur after each section in the chapters. They contain questions written by students to identify some of the important features of the section. The answers are embedded in the "Review" section at the end of each chapter. Also included at the end of each chapter is a group of multiple-choice self-test questions, the answers to which can be found at the end of the book. "Questions for Discussion" at the end of each chapter challenge you to think more broadly about biology. You are encouraged to use these in discussions with other students and to explore potential answers by using the resources of the electronic library.

To maximize the chances of producing a useful text that draws in students (and instructors), we sought the advice of colleagues who teach biology (members of the Editorial Advisory Board). We also asked students (members of the Student Advisory Boards) for their advice and comments. Both groups read draft chapters and provided valuable feedback, but any mistakes are ours. The members of the Student Advisory Boards also wrote the Study Break questions found throughout the text.

We hope that you are as captivated by the biological world as we are and are drawn from one chapter to another. But don't stop there—use electronic resources to broaden your search for understanding.

multiple auxotrophic *E. coli* mutants here; the idea is the same.) As the homologous chromosomes pair, they are held together tightly by a protein framework called the **synaptonemal complex** (**Figure 10.15**, p. 220). Supported by this framework, regions of homologous chromatids exchange segments, producing new combinations of alleles (see Figure 10.14, step 2). Recall that the exchange process is very precise and involves the breakage and rejoining of DNA molecules by enzymes (Figure 10.1). When the exchange is complete toward the end of prophase I, the synaptonemal complex disassembles and disappears. If you now follow meiosis I and II through to the end in your mind, notice that each of the four resulting nuclei receives one of these four chromatids (see Figure 10.14, step 3); two receive unchanged chromatids, and two receive chromatids that have new combinations of alleles due to recombination.

The physical effect of recombination can be seen later in prophase I, when increased condensation of the chromosomes thickens the chromosomes enough to make them visible under the light microscope (see Figure 10.11, steps 3 and 4). Regions in which non-sister chromatids cross one another, called **crossovers** or **chiasmata** (singular, *chiasma* = crosspiece), clearly show that two of the four chromatids have exchanged segments. Because of the shape produced, the recombination process is also called **crossing-over**.

Note that illustrations of recombination usually show chromosomes "paired" side by side, with only the closest chromatids participating in recombination (see Figure 10.16; however, chromosomes actually pair "one on top of the other" such that any two of the four chromatids can participate in a given recombination event. Recombination takes place largely at random, at almost any position along the chromosome arms.

Several events likely occur at various locations along all chromatida.

Notice in Figure 10.14 that a recombination event does not just "switch" the alleles of a given gene in a localized area. All of the DNA sequence stretching from the site of recombination to the ends of the participating chromatids is exchanged.

Random Segregation. Random segregation of chromosomes of maternal and paternal origin accounts for the second major source of genetic variability in meiosis. Recall that the maternal and paternal members of each homologous pair are different in that they typically carry different alleles of many of the genes on that chromosome. During prometaphase I, spindle microtubules make connections to kinetochores. For each homologous pair, one chromosome makes spindle connections leading to one pole and the other chromosome connects to the opposite pole. In making these connections, all the maternal chromosomes may connect to one pole and all the paternal chromosomes may connect to the opposite pole. Or, as is most likely, a random combination of maternal and paternal chromosomes may be segregated to a given spindle pole (Figure 10.16, p. 221).

The number of possible combinations depends on the number of chromosome pairs in a species. For example, the 39 chromosome pairs in dogs allow 2^{39} different combinations of maternal and paternal chromosomes to be delivered to the poles, producing potentially 500 billion genetically different gametes from this source of variability alone. Note that this random partitioning of maternal and paternal chromosomes is responsible for the independent assortment of the alleles of two genes in Mendel's experiments with garden peas described in Chapter 11.

But some F_1 hybrids are healthy, vigorous, and fully fertile and can breed with other hybrids and with both parental species. Sometimes the F_2 generation, produced by matings between F_1 hybrids, or between F_1 hybrids and either parental species, may exhibit reduced survival or fertility, a phenomenon known as **hybrid breakdowns**. Experimental crosses between fruit fly (*Drosophila*) species may produce functional interspecific hybrids, but their offspring experience a high rate of chromosomal abnormalities and harmful types of genetic recombination. Thus, reproductive isolation is maintained between the species because there is little long-term mixing of their gene pools.

18.8 Geography of Speciation

Geography has a huge impact on whether gene pools have the opportunity to mix. Biologists define three modes of speciation based on the geographic relationship of populations as they become reproductively isolated: allopatric speciation (*allo* = different; *patria* = homeland), parapatric speciation (*para* = beside), and sympatric speciation (*sym* = together).

18.8a Allopatric Speciation: New Species Develop from Isolated Populations

Allopatric speciation can occur when a physical barrier subdivides a large population or when a small population becomes separated from a species' main geographic distribution. Allopatric speciation, probably the most common mode of speciation in large animals, occurs in two stages. First, two populations become *geographically* separated, preventing gene flow between them. Then, as the populations experience distinct mutations as well as different patterns of natural selection and genetic drift, they may accumulate genetic differences that isolate them *reproductively*.

Geographic separation sometimes occurs when a barrier divides a large population into two or more

Supplementary Materials

An extensive array of supplemental materials is available to accompany this text. These supplements are designed to make teaching and learning more effective. For more information on any of these resources, please contact your local Nelson Education sales representative or call Nelson Education Limited Customer Support at 1-800-268-2222.

Instructor Resources

These resources are available to qualified adopters. Please consult your local Nelson Education sales representative for details.

Instructor's Resource DVD

The *Instructor's Resource DVD* contains the following resources:

Instructor's Resource Manual

The *Instructor's Resource Manual* for this First Canadian Edition has been dramatically revised by Tanya Noel, Tamara Kelly, and Julie Clark from York University to include tips on teaching using cases as well as suggestions on how to present material and use technology and other resources effectively, integrating the other supplements available to both students and instructors. This manual doesn't simply reinvent what's currently in the text; it helps the instructor make the material relevant and engaging to students.

ExamView® Computerized Test Bank

Create, deliver, and customize tests (both print and online) in minutes with this easy-to-use assessment and tutorial system. ExamView® offers both a Quick Test Wizard and an Online Test Wizard that guide you step-by-step through the process of creating tests, while its "what you see is what you get" capability allows you to see the test you are creating on the screen exactly as it will print or display online. You can build tests of up to 250 questions using up to 12 question types. Using *ExamView's* complete word-processing capabilities, you can enter an unlimited number of new questions or edit existing questions.

Nelson Education Testing Advantage

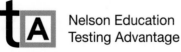
Nelson Education
Testing Advantage

In most postsecondary courses, a large percentage of student assessment is based on multiple-choice testing. Many instructors use multiple-choice testing reluctantly, believing that it is a methodology best used for testing what a student *remembers* rather than what she or he has *learned*.

Nelson Education Ltd. understands that a good-quality multiple-choice test bank can provide the means to measure *higher level thinking* skills as well as recall. Recognizing the importance of multiple-choice testing in today's classroom, we have created the Nelson Education Testing Advantage program (NETA) to ensure the value of our high-quality test banks.

The *Test Bank* to accompany *Biology*, adapted by Ivona Mladenovic of Simon Fraser University and Ian Dawe of Selkirk College, offers the Premium Nelson Education Testing Advantage. NETA was created in partnership with David DiBattista, a 3M National Teaching Fellow, professor of psychology at Brock University, and researcher in the area of multiple-choice testing. NETA ensures that subject-matter experts who author test banks have had training in two areas: avoiding common errors in test construction and developing multiple-choice test questions that "get beyond remembering" to assess higher level thinking. In addition, Professor DiBattista confirms the subject-matter expert's understanding of and adherence to the NETA principles through a review.

All Premium NETA test banks include David DiBattista's guide for instructors, "Multiple Choice Tests: Getting Beyond Remembering." This guide has been designed to assist you in using Nelson test banks to achieve your desired outcomes in your course.

Customers who adopt a Premium Nelson Education Testing Advantage title may also qualify for additional faculty training opportunities in multiple-choice testing and assessment. Please contact your local Nelson Education sales and editorial representative for more details about our Premium NETA.

Microsoft PowerPoint® Slides This one-stop lecture tool makes it easy to assemble, edit, publish, and present custom lectures. Adapted by Jane Young of the University of Northern British Columbia, this resource brings together text-specific lecture outlines, art, video, and animations, culminating in a powerful, personalized, PowerPoint® presentation.

Also included on the *Instructor's Resource DVD* are Word files of the *Test Bank*, as well as a full *Image Bank* of the art and photos from the text book. ISBN: 978-0-17-647529-1.

Student Resources

Study Guide

The *Study Guide* for the First Canadian Edition has been adapted by Colin Montpetit of the University of Ottawa, Julie Smit of the University of Windsor, and Wendy J. Keenleyside of the University of Guelph. The *Study Guide* contains unique case studies to integrate the concepts within the text, study strategies, interactive exercises, self-test questions, and more. ISBN: 978-0-17-647474-4.

CengageNOW™ CENGAGENOW™

CengageNOW Personalized Study is a diagnostic tool (featuring a chapter-specific Pretest, Study Plan, and

Post-test) that empowers students to master concepts, prepare for exams, and be more involved in class. Results to *Personalized Study* provide immediate and ongoing feedback regarding what students are mastering and why they're not to both the instructor and the student. *CengageNOW Personalized Study* links to an integrated eBook so that students can easily review topics and also contains animations, links to websites, videos, and more as part of their Study Plan. *CengageNOW* has been adapted by Dora Cavallo-Medved, University of Windsor; Todd Nickle, Mount Royal College; and Edward Andrews, Sir Wilfred Grenfell College.

CengageNOW with Premium eBook

Want to take your biology experience to the next level? Our *Premium eBook* allows students access to an integrated, interactive learning environment with advanced learning tools and a user interface that gives students control over their learning experience. *CengageNOW Personalized Study* is included with the Premium eBook for the ultimate online study experience.

JoinIn™ on TurningPoint®

Transform your lecture into an interactive student experience with JoinIn™. Combined with your choice of keypad systems, JoinIn turns your Microsoft® PowerPoint® application into audience response software. With a click on a handheld device, students can respond to multiple-choice questions, short polls, interactive exercises, and peer-review questions. You can also take attendance, check student comprehension of concepts, collect student demographics to better assess student needs, and even administer quizzes. In addition, there are interactive text-specific slide sets that you can modify and merge with any of your own PowerPoint® lecture slides. These have been adapted by Jane Young of the University of Northern British Columbia and contain poll slides and pre- and post-test slides for each chapter in the text. This tool is available to qualified adopters at **http://www.turningtechnologies.com/**.

Students and Instructors

Visit the website to accompany *Biology: Exploring the Diversity of Life*, First Canadian Edition, at **http://biologyedl.nelson.com.** This website contains quizzes, flashcards, weblinks, and more.

Prospering in Biology

Using This Book

The following are things you will need to know in order to use this text and prosper in Biology.

Names

What's in a name? People are very attached to names—their own names, the names of other people, the names of flowers and food and cars, and so on. It is not surprising that biologists would also be concerned about names. Take, for example, our use of scientific names. Scientific names are always italicized and Latinized.

Castor canadensis Kuhl is the scientific name of the Canadian beaver. *Castor* is the genus name, *canadensis* is the species name, and Kuhl is the name of the person who described the species. "Beaver" by itself is not enough because there is a European beaver, *Castor fiber*, and an extinct giant beaver, *Castoides ohioensis*. Furthermore, common names can vary from place to place (*Myotis lucifugus* is sometimes known as the "little brown bat" or the "little brown myotis").

Biologists prefer scientific names because the name (Latinized) tells you about the organism. There are strict rules about the derivation and use of scientific names. Common names are not so restricted, so they are not precise. For example, in *Myotis lucifugus*, *Myotis* means mouse-eared and *lucifugus* means flees the light; hence, this species is a mouse-eared bat that flees the light.

Birds can be an exception. There are accepted "standard" common names for birds. The American robin is *Turdus migratorius*. The common names for birds are usually capitalized because of the standardization. However, the common names of mammals are not capitalized, except for geographic names or patronyms (*geographic* = named after a country; *patronym* = named after someone; e.g., Canadian beaver or Ord's kangaroo rat, respectively).

Although a few plants that have very broad distributions may have accepted standard common names (e.g., white spruce, *Picea glauca*), most plants have many common names. Furthermore, the same common name is often used for more than one species. Several species in the genus *Taraxacum* are referred to as "dandelion." It is important to use the scientific names of plants to be sure that it is clear exactly which plant we mean. The scientific names of plants also tell us something about the plant. The scientific name for the weed quack grass, *Elymus repens*, tells us that this is a type of wild rye (*Elymus*) and that this particular species spreads or creeps (*repens* = creeping). Anyone who has tried to eliminate this plant from their garden or yard knows how it creeps! Unlike for animals, plant-naming rules forbid the use of the same word for both genus and species names for a plant; thus, although *Bison bison* is an acceptable scientific name for buffalo, such a name would never be accepted for a plant.

In this book, we present the scientific names of organisms when we mention them. We follow standard abbreviations; for example, although the full name of an organism is used the first time it is mentioned (e.g., *Castor canadensis*), subsequent references to that same organism abbreviate the genus name and provide the full species name (e.g., *C. canadensis*).

In some areas of biology, the standard representation is of the genus, for example, *Chlamydomonas*. In other cases, names are so commonly used that only the abbreviation may be used (e.g., *E. coli* for *Escherichia coli*).

Units

The units of measure used by biologists are standardized (metric or SI) units, used throughout the world in science.

Definitions

The science of biology is replete with specialized terms (sometimes referred to as "jargon") used to communicate specific information. It follows that, as with scientific names, specialized terms increase the precision with which biologists communicate among themselves and with others. Be cautious about the use of terms because jargon can be a veneer of precision. When we encounter a "slippery" term (such as species or gene), we explain why one definition for all situations is not feasible.

Time

In this book, we use C.E. (Common Era) to refer to the years since year 1 and B.C.E. (Before the Common Era) to refer to years before that.

Geologists think of time over very long periods. A geologic time scale (**see Table 1.1**) shows that the age of Earth could be measured in years, but it's challenging to think of billions of years expressed in days (or hours, etc.). With the advent of using the decay rates of radioisotopes to measure the age of rocks, geologists adopted 1950 as the baseline, the "Present," and the past is referred to as B.P. ("Before Present"). A notation of 30 000 years B.P. (^{14}C) indicates 30 000 years before 1950 using the ^{14}C method of dating.

Other dating systems are also used. Some archaeologists use PPNA (PrePottery Neolithic A, where A is the horizon or stratum). In deposits along the Euphrates River, 11 000 PPNA appears to be the same as 11 000

B.P. In this book, we use B.C.E. or B.P. as the time units, except when referring to events or species from more than 100 000 years ago. For those dates, we refer you to the geologic time scale (see Table 1.1 on page xiv).

Sources

Where does the information presented in a text or in class come from? What is the difference between what you read in a textbook or an encyclopedia and the material you see in a newspaper or tabloid? When the topic relates to science, the information should be based on material that has been published in a scholarly journal. In this context, "scholarly" refers to the process of review. Scholars submit their manuscripts reporting their research findings to the editor (or editorial board) of a journal. The editor, in turn, sends the manuscript out for comment and review by recognized authorities in the field. The process is designed to ensure that what is published is as accurate and appropriate as possible. The review process sets the scholarly journal apart from the tabloid.

There are literally thousands of scholarly journals, which, together, publish millions of articles each year. Some journals are more influential than others, for example, *Science* and *Nature*. These two journals are published weekly and invariably contain new information of interest to biologists.

To collect information for this text, we have drawn on published works that have gone through the process of scholarly review. Specific references (citations) are provided, usually in the electronic resources designed to complement the book.

A citation is intended to make the information accessible. Although there are many different formats for citations, the important elements include (in some order) the name(s) of the author(s), the date of publication, the title, and the publisher. When the source is published in a scholarly journal, the journal name, its volume number, and the pages are also provided. With the citation information, you can visit a library and locate the original source. This is true for both electronic (virtual) and real libraries.

Students of biology benefit by making it a habit to look at the most recent issues of their favourite scholarly journals and use them to keep abreast of new developments.

M. Brock Fenton
Heather Addy
Denis Maxwell
Tom Haffie
Ken Davey

London, Calgary and Toronto
February 2009

Table 1.1   The Geological Time Scale and Major Evolutionary Events

Eons (Duration drawn to scale)	Eon	Era	Period	Epoch	Millions of Years Ago	Major Evolutionary Events
Cenozoic / Mesozoic / Paleozoic	Phanerozoic	Cenozoic	Quaternary	Holocene	0.01	
				Pleistocene	1.7	Origin of humans; major glaciations
				Pliocene	5.2	Origin of ape-like human ancestors
			Tertiary	Miocene	23	Angiosperms and mammals further diversify and dominate terrestrial habitats
				Oligocene	33.4	Divergence of primates; origin of apes
				Eocene	55	Angiosperms and insects diversify; modern orders of mammals differentiate
				Paleocene	65	Grasslands and deciduous woodlands spread; modern birds and mammals diversify; continents approach current positions
		Mesozoic	Cretaceous		144	Many lineages diversify: angiosperms, insects, marine invertebrates, fishes, dinosaurs; asteroid impact causes mass extinction at end of period, eliminating dinosaurs and many other groups
			Jurassic		206	Gymnosperms abundant in terrestrial habitats; first angiosperms; modern fishes diversify; dinosaurs diversify and dominate terrestrial habitats; frogs, salamanders, lizards, and birds appear; continents continue to separate
			Triassic		251	Predatory fishes and reptiles dominate oceans; gymnosperms dominate terrestrial habitats; radiation of dinosaurs; origin of mammals; Pangaea starts to break up; mass extinction at end of period
Proterozoic						

Eon / Era	Period	Millions of years ago	Events
Phanerozoic (continued) — Paleozoic	Permian	290	Insects, amphibians, and reptiles abundant and diverse in swamp forests; some reptiles colonize oceans; fishes colonize freshwater habitats; continents coalesce into Pangaea, causing glaciation and decline in sea level; mass extinction at end of period eliminates 85% of species
	Carboniferous	354	Vascular plants form large swamp forests; first seed plants and flying insects; amphibians diversify; first reptiles appear
	Devonian	417	Terrestrial vascular plants diversify; fungi and invertebrates colonize land; first insects appear; first amphibians colonize land; major glaciation at end of period causes mass extinction, mostly of marine life
	Silurian	443	Jawless fishes diversify; first jawed fishes; first vascular plants on land
	Ordovician	490	Major radiations of marine invertebrates and fishes; major glaciation at end of period causes mass extinction of marine life
	Cambrian	543	Diverse radiation of modern animal phyla (Cambrian explosion); simple marine communities
Proterozoic		2500	High concentration of oxygen in atmosphere; origin of aerobic metabolism; origin of eukaryotic cells; evolution and diversification of protists, fungi, soft-bodied animals
Archaean		3800	Evolution of prokaryotes, including anaerobic bacteria and photosynthetic bacteria; oxygen starts to accumulate in atmosphere
		4600	Formation of Earth at start of era; Earth's crust, atmosphere, and oceans form; origin of life at end of era

Acknowledgements

We thank the many people who have worked with us on the production of this text, particularly Paul Fam, Executive Editor, whose foresight brought the idea to us and whose persistence saw the project through. Thanks go to those who reviewed the U.S. text to provide us with feedback for the Canadian edition including Logan Donaldson, York University; Robert Holmberg, Athabasca University; and Thomas H. MacRae, Dalhousie University. We also are grateful to the members of the Editorial Advisory Board and the Student Advisory Board, who provided us with valuable feedback and alternate perspectives (special acknowledgements to these individuals are listed below). We also thank Richard Walker at the University of Calgary, who began this journey with us but who was unable to continue. We thank Carl Lowenberger for contributing Chapter 44 (on defences). We are especially grateful to Alwynn Pinard, Managing Developmental Editor, and James Polley, who kept us moving through the chapters at an efficient pace, along with Tracy Duff, Project Manager, and Christine Gilbert, Content Production Manager. We thank Rosemary Tanner, who provided a thoughtful substantive edit of the entire manuscript, Holly Dickinson for her careful copy editing, and Sandra Peters, who did a cold read as a further check on our presentation. Finally, we thank Sean Chamberland, Senior Marketing Manager, for making us look good.

Brock Fenton would like to thank Allan Noon, who offered much advice about taking pictures; Laura Barclay, Jeremy McNeil, Tony Percival-Smith, C.S. (Rufus) Churcher, and David and Meg Cumming for the use of their images; and Karen Campbell for providing a critical read on the domestication chapter.

It is never easy to be in the family of an academic scientist. We are especially grateful to our families for their sustained support over the course of our careers, particularly during those times when our attentions were fully captivated by bacteria, algae, fungi, parasites, or bats. Saying "yes" to a textbook project means saying "no" to a variety of other pursuits. We appreciate the patience and understanding of those closest to us that enabled the temporary reallocation of considerable time from other endeavours and relationships.

Many of our colleagues have contributed to our development as teachers and scholars by acting as mentors, collaborators, and, on occasion, "worthy opponents." Like all teachers, we owe particular gratitude to our students. They have gathered with us around the discipline of biology, sharing their potent blend of enthusiasm and curiosity that leaves us energized and optimistic for the future.

Editorial and Student Advisory Boards

We were very fortunate to have the assistance of some extraordinary students and instructors of biology across Canada who provided us with feedback that helped shape this textbook into what you see before you. As such, we would like to say a very special thank you to the following people:

Editorial Advisory Board

Mark Brigham, University of Regina

Dion Durnford, University of New Brunswick

Wendy Keenleyside, University of Guelph

Marty Leonard, Dalhousie University

Cindy Paszkowski, University of Alberta

Carol Pollock, University of British Columbia

Kevin Scott, University of Manitoba

Paula Wilson, York University

Student Advisory Boards

University of Western Ontario (pictured above)

Rachael Danielson

Dalal Dharouj

Yvonne Dzal

Liam McGuire

Aimee McMillan

Errin Pfeiffer

Max Rachinsky

Nina Veselka

Ivana Vilimonovic

Marisol Wilcox

University of Calgary (pictured above)
Kristina Birkholz
Jobran Chebib
Liam Cummings

Aravind Ganesh
Shaista Hashem
Colleen Michael
Simon Sun
Camilla Tapp
Anita Tieu
Sahar Zaidi

University of New Brunswick
Maria Correia
Kelvin Gilliland
Jonathon Neilson
Allison Ritcey
Faith Shannon
Brittany Timberlake
Coleman Ward
Corey Willis

Thanks go as well to the high school students who participated, Meghan Harris and Lindsay Patton. Anne Duguay, a teacher from Queen Elizabeth High School in Calgary, and her student, Saskia, also participated. They provided a unique perspective on what entering students would expect from a text for an introductory course in biology. Finally, we wish to thank the student review boards from the University of Victoria, University of Toronto, Erindale Campus, Ryerson University, Sir Wilfred Grenfell College, and the University of Windsor. High school students, university students, and university instructors together provided us with an amazingly diverse array of feedback that allowed us to understand our audience and create a resource best suited to their needs.

Brief Contents

Contents

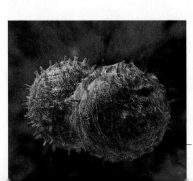

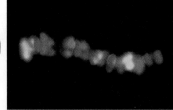
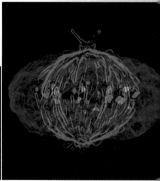

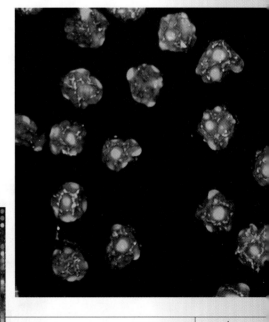

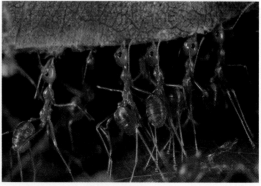

Phenotypic variation. The frog *Dendrobates pumilio* exhibits dramatic colour variation in populations that inhabit the Bocas del Toro Islands, Panama.

© Mark Moffett/Foto Natura/Minden Pictures

17 Microevolution: Genetic Changes within Populations

WHY IT MATTERS

On November 28, 1942, at the height of American involvement in World War II, a disastrous fire killed more than 400 people in Boston's Cocoanut Grove nightclub. Many more would have died later but for a new experimental drug, penicillin. A product of *Penicillium* mould, penicillin fought the usually fatal infections of *Staphylococcus aureus,* a bacterium that enters the body through damaged skin. Penicillin was the first antibiotic drug based on a naturally occurring substance that kills bacteria.

Until the disaster at the Cocoanut Grove, the production and use of penicillin had been a closely guarded military secret. But after its public debut, the pharmaceutical industry hailed penicillin as a wonder drug, promoting its use for the treatment of the many diseases caused by infectious microorganisms. Penicillin became widely available as an over-the-counter remedy, and Americans dosed themselves with it, hoping to cure all sorts of ills **(Figure 17.1, p. 374)**. But in 1945, Alexander Fleming, the scientist who discovered penicillin, predicted that some bacteria could survive low doses and that the offspring of those germs would be more resistant to its effects. In 1946—just 4 years after penicillin's use in Boston—14% of the *Staphylococcus* strains isolated

Figure 17.1

Selling penicillin. This ad, from a 1944 issue of *Life* magazine, credits penicillin with saving the lives of wounded soldiers.

bacteria that are even slightly resistant to the drug. The surviving bacteria reproduce, and resistant microorganisms—along with the genes that confer antibiotic resistance—become more common in later generations. In other words, bacterial populations change in response to antibiotics through the evolutionary process of selection. Our use of antibiotics is comparable to artificial selection by plant and animal breeders (see Chapter 49), but when we use antibiotics, we inadvertently select for the success of organisms that we are trying to eradicate.

The evolution of antibiotic resistance in bacteria is an example of **microevolution**, which is a heritable change in the genetics of a population. A **population** of organisms includes all the individuals of a single species that live together in the same place and time. Today, when scientists study microevolution, they analyze variation—the differences between individuals—in natural populations and determine how and why these variations are inherited. Darwin recognized the importance of heritable variation within populations; he also realized that natural selection can change the pattern of variation in a population from one generation to the next. Scientists have since learned that microevolutionary change results from several processes, not just natural selection, and that sometimes these processes counteract each other.

In this chapter, we first examine the extensive variation that exists within natural populations. We then take a detailed look at the most important processes that alter genetic variation within populations, causing microevolutionary change. Finally, we consider how microevolution can fine-tune the functioning of populations within their environments.

from patients in a London hospital were resistant. By 1950, more than half the strains were resistant.

Scientists and physicians have discovered numerous antibiotics since the 1940s, and many strains of bacteria have developed resistance to these drugs. *Streptococcus pneumoniae* is the leading cause of infectious death worldwide. In Canada, over 12 000 people require hospitalization for *Streptococcus* infections annually, and the rate of drug resistance nearly doubled between 1999 and 2000. In the face of such increases, it is alarming that a recent study revealed that misunderstandings about the biology of antibiotic resistance are widespread among Canadians.

How do bacteria become resistant to antibiotics? The genomes of bacteria—like those of all other organisms—vary among individuals, and some bacteria have genetic traits that allow them to withstand attack by antibiotics. When we administer antibiotics to an infected patient, we create an environment favouring

17.1 Variation in Natural Populations

In some species, individuals vary dramatically in appearance, but in most species, the members of a population look pretty much alike **(Figure 17.2)**. Even those that look alike, such as the *Cerion* snails in Figure 17.2b, are not identical, however. With a scale and a ruler, you could detect differences in their mass as well as in the length

a. European garden snails

b. Bahaman land snails

Figure 17.2

Phenotypic variation. **(a)** Shells of the European garden snail (*Cepaea nemoralis*) from a population in Scotland vary considerably in appearance. **(b)** By contrast, shells of *Cerion christophei* from a population in the Bahamas look very similar.

and diameter of their shells. With suitable techniques, you could also document variations in their individual biochemistry, physiology, internal anatomy, and behaviour. All of these are examples of **phenotypic variation**, differences in appearance or function that are passed from generation to generation.

17.1a Evolutionary Biologists Describe and Quantify Phenotypic Variation

Darwin's theory recognized the importance of heritable phenotypic variation, and today, microevolutionary studies often begin by assessing phenotypic variation within populations. Most characters exhibit **quantitative variation**: individuals differ in small, incremental ways. If you weighed everyone in your biology class, for example, you would see that mass varies almost continuously from your lightest to your heaviest classmate. Humans also exhibit quantitative variation in the length of their toes, the number of hairs on their heads, and their height, as discussed in Chapter 11.

We usually display data on quantitative variation in a bar graph or, if the sample is large enough, as a curve **(Figure 17.3)**. The width of the curve is proportional to the variability—the amount of variation—among individuals, and the *mean* describes the average value of the character. As you will see shortly, natural selection often changes the mean value of a character or its variability within populations.

Other characters, like those Mendel studied (see Section 11.1), exhibit **qualitative variation**: they exist in two or more discrete states, and intermediate forms are often absent. Snow geese, for example, have *either* blue *or* white feathers **(Figure 17.4)**. The existence of discrete variants of a character is called a **polymorphism** (*poly* = many; *morphos* = form); we describe such traits as *polymorphic*. The *Cepaea nemoralis* snail shells in Figure 17.2a are polymorphic in background colour, number of stripes, and colour of stripes. Biochemical polymorphisms, like the human A, B, AB, and O blood groups (described in Section 11.2), are also common.

We describe phenotypic polymorphisms quantitatively by calculating the percentage or *frequency* of each trait. For example, if you counted 123 blue snow geese and 369 white ones in a population of 492 geese, the frequency of the blue phenotype would be 123/492 or 0.25, and the frequency of the white phenotype would be 369/492 or 0.75.

17.1b Phenotypic Variation Can Have Genetic and Environmental Causes

Phenotypic variation within populations may be caused by genetic differences between individuals, by differences in the environmental factors that individuals experience, or by an interaction between genetics and the environment. As a result, genetic and phenotypic variations may not be perfectly correlated. Under some

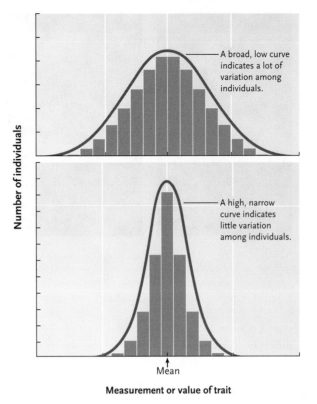

Figure 17.3

Quantitative variation. Many traits vary continuously among members of a population, and a bar graph of the data often approximates a bell-shaped curve. The mean defines the average value of the trait in the population, and the width of the curve is proportional to the variability among individuals.

circumstances, organisms with different genotypes exhibit the same phenotype. For example, the black colouration of some rock pocket mice from Arizona is caused by certain mutations in the *Mc1r* gene, but black mice from New Mexico do not share those mutations— that is, they have different genotypes—even though they exhibit the same phenotype. On the other hand, organisms with the same genotype sometimes exhibit

Figure 17.4

Qualitative variation. Individual snow geese (*Chen caerulescens*) are either blue or white. Although both colours are present in many populations, geese tend to associate with others of the same colour.

Figure 17.5

Environmental effects on phenotype. Soil acidity affects the expression of the gene controlling flower colour in the common garden plant *Hydrangea macrophylla*. When grown in acid soil, it produces deep blue flowers. In neutral or alkaline soil, its flowers are bright pink.

different phenotypes. For example, the acidity of soil influences flower colour in some plants **(Figure 17.5).**

Knowing whether phenotypic variation is caused by genetic differences, environmental factors, or an interaction of the two is important because *only genetically based variation is subject to evolutionary change*. Moreover, knowing the causes of phenotypic variation has important practical applications. Suppose, for example, that one field of wheat produced more grain than another. If a difference in the availability of nutrients or water caused the difference in yield, a farmer might choose to fertilize or irrigate the less productive field. But if the difference in productivity resulted from genetic differences between plants in the two fields, a farmer might plant only the more productive genotype. Because environmental factors can influence the expression of genes, an organism's phenotype is frequently the product of an interaction between its genotype and its environment. In our hypothetical example, the farmer may maximize yield by fertilizing and irrigating the better genotype of wheat.

How can we determine whether phenotypic variation is caused by environmental factors or by genetic differences? We can test for an environmental cause experimentally by changing one environmental variable and measuring the effects on genetically similar subjects. You can try this yourself by growing some cuttings from an ivy plant in shade and other cuttings from the same plant in full sun. Although they all have the same genotype, the cuttings grown in sun will produce smaller leaves and shorter stems.

Breeding experiments can demonstrate the genetic basis of phenotypic variation. For example, Mendel inferred the genetic basis of qualitative traits, such as flower colour in peas, by crossing plants with different phenotypes. Moreover, traits that vary quantitatively will respond to artificial selection only if the variation

has some genetic basis. For example, researchers observed that individual house mice (*Mus musculus*) differ in activity levels, as measured by how much they use an exercise wheel and how fast they run. John G. Swallow, Patrick A. Carter, and Theodore Garland Jr., then at the University of Wisconsin at Madison, used artificial selection to produce lines of mice that exhibit increased wheel-running behaviour, demonstrating that the observed differences in these two aspects of activity level have a genetic basis **(Figure 17.6).**

Breeding experiments are not always practical, however, particularly for organisms with long generation times. Ethical concerns also render these techniques unthinkable for humans. Instead, researchers sometimes study the inheritance of particular traits by analyzing genealogical pedigrees, as discussed in Section 12.2, but this approach often provides poor results for analyses of complex traits.

17.1c Several Processes Generate Genetic Variation

Genetic variation, the raw material moulded by microevolutionary processes, has two potential sources: the production of new alleles and the rearrangement of existing alleles. Most new alleles probably arise from small-scale mutations in DNA (described later in this chapter). The rearrangement of existing alleles into new combinations can result from larger scale changes in chromosome structure or number and from several forms of genetic recombination, including crossing over between homologous chromosomes during meiosis, the independent assortment of nonhomologous chromosomes during meiosis, and random fertilizations between genetically different sperm and eggs. (These processes are described in Chapter 10.)

The shuffling of *existing* alleles into new combinations can produce an extraordinary number of novel genotypes and phenotypes in the next generation. By one estimate, more than 10^{600} combinations of alleles are possible in human gametes, yet fewer than 10^{10} humans are alive today. So unless you have an identical twin, it is extremely unlikely that another person with your genotype has ever lived or ever will.

17.1d Populations Often Contain Substantial Genetic Variation

How much genetic variation actually exists within populations? In the 1960s, evolutionary biologists began to use gel electrophoresis (see Figure 16.7) to identify biochemical polymorphisms in diverse organisms. This technique separates two or more forms of a given protein if they differ significantly in shape, mass, or net electrical charge. The identification of a protein polymorphism allows researchers to infer genetic variation at the locus coding for that protein.

Figure 17.6

Using artificial selection to demonstrate that activity level in mice has a genetic basis.

QUESTION: Do observed differences in activity level among house mice have a genetic basis?

EXPERIMENT: Swallow, Carter, and Garland knew that a phenotypic character responds to artificial selection only if it has a genetic, rather than an environmental, basis. In an experiment with house mice (*Mus domesticus*), they selected for the phenotypic character of increased wheel-running activity. In four experimental lines, they bred those mice that ran the most. Four other lines, in which breeders were selected at random with respect to activity level, served as controls.

RESULTS: After 10 generations of artificial selection, mice in the experimental lines ran longer distances and ran faster than mice in the control lines. Thus, artificial selection on wheel-running activity in house mice increased **(a)** the distance that mice run per day and **(b)** their average speed. The data illustrate responses of females in four experimental lines and four control lines. Males showed similar responses.

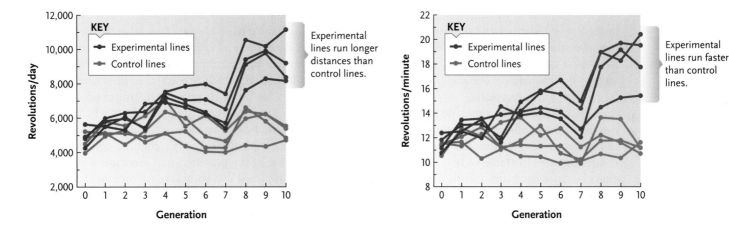

a. Distance run

b. Average speed

CONCLUSION: Because two measures of activity level responded to artificial selection, researchers concluded that variation in this behavioural character has a genetic basis.

Researchers discovered much more genetic variation than anyone had imagined. For example, nearly half the loci surveyed in many populations of plants and invertebrates are polymorphic. Moreover, gel electrophoresis actually underestimates genetic variation because it doesn't detect different amino acid substitutions if the proteins for which they code migrate at the same rate.

Advances in molecular biology now allow scientists to survey genetic variation directly, and researchers have accumulated an astounding knowledge of the structure of DNA and its nucleotide sequences. In general, studies of chromosomal and mitochondrial DNA suggest that every locus exhibits some variability in its nucleotide sequence. The variability is apparent in comparisons of individuals from a single population, populations of one species, and related species. However, some variations detected in the protein-coding regions of DNA may not affect phenotypes because, as explained in the following they do not change the amino acid sequences of the proteins for which the genes code.

STUDY BREAK

1. What is a genetic polymorphism?
2. If a population of skunks includes some individuals with stripes and others with spots, would you describe the variation as quantitative or qualitative?
3. What factors contribute to phenotypic variation in a population?

17.2 Population Genetics

To predict how certain factors may influence genetic variation, population geneticists first describe the genetic structure of a population. They then create hypotheses, which they formalize in mathematical models, to describe how evolutionary processes may change the genetic structure under specified conditions. Finally, researchers test the predictions of these models to evaluate the ideas about evolution that are embodied within them.

17.2a All Populations Have a Genetic Structure

Populations are made up of individuals, each with its own genotype. In diploid organisms, which have pairs of homologous chromosomes, an individual's genotype includes two alleles at every gene locus. The sum of all alleles at all gene loci in all individuals is called the population's **gene pool.**

To describe the structure of a gene pool, scientists first identify the genotypes in a representative sample and calculate **genotype frequencies,** the percentages of individuals possessing each genotype. Knowing that each diploid organism has two alleles (either two copies of the same allele or two different alleles) at each gene locus, a scientist can then calculate **allele frequencies,** the **relative abundances** of the different alleles. For a locus with two alleles, scientists use the symbol p to identify the frequency of one allele, and q to identify the frequency of the other allele.

The calculation of genotype and allele frequencies for the two alleles at the gene locus governing flower colour in snapdragons (genus *Antirrhinum*) is straightforward **(Table 17.1).** This locus is easy to study because it exhibits incomplete dominance (see Section 11.2). Individuals that are homozygous for the C^R allele ($C^R C^R$) have red flowers; those homozygous for the C^W allele ($C^W C^W$) have white flowers; and heterozygotes ($C^R C^W$) have pink flowers. Genotype frequencies represent how the C^R and C^W alleles are distributed among individuals. In this example, examination of the plants reveals that 45% of individuals have the $C^R C^R$ genotype, 50% have the heterozygous $C^R C^W$ genotype, and the remaining 5%

have the $C^W C^W$ genotype. Allele frequencies represent the commonness or rarity of each allele in the gene pool. As calculated in the table, 70% of the alleles in the population are C^R and 30% are C^W. Remember that for a gene locus with two alleles, there are three genotype frequencies, but only two allele frequencies (p and q). The sum of the three genotype frequencies must equal 1; so must the sum of the two allele frequencies.

17.2b The Hardy–Weinberg Principle Is a Null Model That Defines How Evolution Does Not Occur

When designing experiments, scientists often use control treatments to evaluate the effect of a particular factor. The control tells us what we would see if the experimental treatment had no effect. However, in studies that use observational rather than **experimental data,** there is often no suitable control. In such cases, investigators develop conceptual models, called **null models,** which predict what they would see if a particular factor had no effect. Null models serve as theoretical reference points against which observations can be evaluated.

Early in the twentieth century, geneticists were puzzled by the persistence of recessive traits because they assumed that natural selection replaced recessive or rare alleles with dominant or common ones. An English mathematician, G. H. Hardy, and a German physician, Wilhelm Weinberg, tackled this problem independently in 1908. Their analysis, now known as the **Hardy–Weinberg principle,** specifies the conditions under which a population of diploid organisms achieves **genetic equilibrium,** the point at which neither allele frequencies nor genotype frequencies change in succeeding generations. Their work also showed that

| Table 17.1 | Calculation of Genotype Frequencies and Allele Frequencies for the Snapdragon Flower Colour Locus | | | | |

Because each diploid individual has two alleles at each gene locus, the entire sample of 1000 individuals has a total of 2000 alleles at the C locus.

Flower Colour Phenotype	Genotype	Number of Individuals	Genotype Frequency[1]	Total Number of C^R Alleles[2]	Total Number of C^W Alleles[2]
Red	$C^R C^R$	450	450/1000 = 0.45	2 × 450 = 900	0 × 450 = 0
Pink	$C^R C^W$	500	500/1000 = 0.50	1 × 500 = 500	1 × 500 = 500
White	$C^W C^W$	50	50/1000 = 0.05	0 × 50 = 0	2 × 50 = 100
	Total	1000	0.45 + 0.50 + 0.05 = 1.0	1400	600

Calculate allele frequencies using the total of 1400 + 600 = 2000 alleles in the sample:

$$p = \text{frequency of } C^R \text{ allele} = 1400/2000 = 0.7$$
$$q = \text{frequency of } C^W \text{ allele} + 600/2000 = 0.3$$
$$p + q = 0.7 + 0.3 = 1.0$$

[1]Genotype frequency = the number of individuals possessing a particular genotype divided by the total number of individuals in the sample.
[2]Total number of C^R or C^W alleles = the number of C^R or C^W alleles present in one individual with a particular genotype multiplied by the number of individuals with that genotype.

dominant alleles need not replace recessive ones, and that the shuffling of genes in sexual reproduction does not in itself cause the gene pool to change.

The Hardy–Weinberg principle is a mathematical model that describes how genotype frequencies are established in sexually reproducing organisms. According to this model, genetic equilibrium is possible only if *all* of the following conditions are met:

1. No mutations are occurring.
2. The population is closed to migration from other populations.
3. The population is infinite in size.
4. All genotypes in the population survive and reproduce equally well.
5. Individuals in the population mate randomly with respect to genotypes.

If the conditions of the model are met, the allele frequencies of the population will never change, and the genotype frequencies will stop changing after one generation. In short, under these restrictive conditions, microevolution will *not* occur. The Hardy–Weinberg principle is thus a null model that serves as a reference point for evaluating the circumstances under which evolution *may* occur.

If a population's genotype frequencies do not match the predictions of this model or if its allele frequencies change over time, microevolution may be occurring. Determining which of the model's conditions are not met is a first step in understanding how and why the gene pool is changing.

Study Break

1. What comprises the gene pool of a population?
2. Why is the Hardy–Weinberg principle considered a null model of evolution?

17.3 The Agents of Microevolution

A population's allele frequencies will change over time if the conditions of the Hardy–Weinberg model are violated. The processes that foster microevolutionary change—which include mutation, gene flow, genetic drift, natural selection, and nonrandom mating—are summarized in **Table 17.2**.

17.3a Mutations Create New Genetic Variations

A **mutation** is a heritable change in DNA. In nature, mutations are usually rare events; during any particular breeding season, between 1 gamete in 100 000 and 1 in 1 million will include a new mutation at a particular gene locus. New mutations are so infrequent, in fact, that they exert little or no immediate

Table 17.2	Agents of Microevolutionary Change	
Agent	**Definition**	**Effect on Genetic Variation**
Mutation	A heritable change in DNA	Introduces new genetic variation into population
Gene flow	Change in allele frequencies as individuals join a population and reproduce	May introduce genetic variation from another population
Genetic drift	Random changes in allele frequencies caused by chance events	Reduces genetic variation, especially in small populations; can eliminate alleles
Natural selection	Differential survivorship or reproduction of individuals with different genotypes	One allele can replace another or allelic variation can be preserved
Nonrandom mating	Choice of mates based on their phenotypes and genotypes	Does not directly affect allele frequencies, but usually prevents genetic equilibrium

effect on allele frequencies in most populations. But over evolutionary time scales, their numbers are significant—mutations have been accumulating in **biological lineages** for billions of years. And because it is a mechanism through which entirely new genetic variations arise, *mutation is a major source of heritable variation.*

For most animals, only mutations in the germ line (the cell lineage that produces gametes) are heritable; mutations in other cell lineages have no direct effect on the next generation. In plants, however, mutations may occur in meristem cells, which eventually produce flowers as well as nonreproductive structures (see Chapter 28); in such cases, a mutation may be passed to the next generation and ultimately influence the gene pool.

Deleterious mutations alter an individual's structure, function, or behaviour in harmful ways. In mammals, for example, a protein called collagen is an essential component of most extracellular structures. Several simple mutations in humans cause forms of Ehlers–Danlos syndrome, a disruption of collagen synthesis that may result in loose skin, weak joints, or sudden death from the rupture of major blood vessels, the colon, or the uterus.

By definition, *lethal mutations* cause the death of organisms carrying them. If a lethal allele is dominant, both homozygous and heterozygous carriers suffer from its effects; if recessive, it affects only homozygous recessive individuals. A lethal mutation that causes death before the individual reproduces is eliminated from the population.

Neutral mutations are neither harmful nor helpful. Recall from Section 14.1 that in the construction of a polypeptide chain, a particular amino acid can be specified by several different codons. As a result, some DNA sequence changes—especially certain changes

Research Example: Using the Hardy–Weinberg Principle

To see how the Hardy–Weinberg principle can be applied, we will analyze the snapdragon flower colour locus using the hypothetical population of 1000 plants described in Table 17.1. This locus includes two alleles—C^R (with its frequency designated as p) and C^W (with its frequency designated as q)—and three genotypes—homozygous C^RC^R, heterozygous C^RC^W, and homozygous C^WC^W. Table 17.1 lists the number of plants with each genotype: 450 have red flowers (C^RC^R), 500 have pink flowers (C^RC^W), and 50 have white flowers (C^WC^W). It also shows the calculation of both the genotype frequencies (C^RC^R = 0.45, C^RC^W = 0.50, and C^WC^W = 0.05) and the allele frequencies ($p = 0.7$ and $q = 0.3$) for the population.

Let's assume for simplicity that each individual produces only two gametes and that both gametes contribute to the production of offspring. This assumption is unrealistic, of course, but it meets the Hardy–Weinberg requirement that all individuals in the population contribute equally to the next generation. In each parent, the two alleles segregate and end up in different gametes:

450 C^RC^R individuals produce → 900 C^R gametes

500 C^RC^W individuals produce → 500 C^R gametes + 500 C^W gametes

50 C^WC^W individuals produce → 100 C^W gametes

You can readily see that 1400 of the 2000 total gametes carry the C^R allele and 600 carry the C^W allele. The frequency of C^R gametes is 1400/2000 or 0.7, which is equal to p; the frequency of C^W gametes is 600/2000 or 0.3, which is equal to q. Thus, the allele frequencies in the gametes are exactly the same as the allele frequencies in the parent generation—it could not be

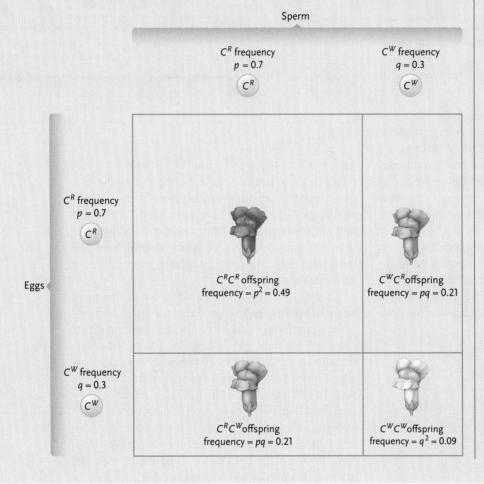

Sperm

C^R frequency $p = 0.7$ — C^R

C^W frequency $q = 0.3$ — C^W

Eggs

C^R frequency $p = 0.7$ — C^R

C^W frequency $q = 0.3$ — C^W

C^RC^R offspring frequency = p^2 = 0.49

C^WC^R offspring frequency = pq = 0.21

C^RC^W offspring frequency = pq = 0.21

C^WC^W offspring frequency = q^2 = 0.09

---

at the third nucleotide of the codon—do not alter the amino acid sequence. Not surprisingly, mutations at the third position appear to persist longer in populations than those at the first two positions. Other mutations may change an organism's phenotype without influencing its survival and reproduction. A neutral mutation might even be beneficial later if the environment changes.

Sometimes a change in DNA produces an *advantageous mutation,* which confers some benefit on an individual that carries it. However slight the advantage, natural selection may preserve the new allele and even increase its frequency over time. Once the mutation has been passed to a new generation, other agents of microevolution determine its long-term fate.

17.3b Gene Flow Introduces Novel Genetic Variants into Populations

Organisms or their gametes (for example, pollen) sometimes move from one population to another. If the immigrants reproduce, they may introduce novel alleles into the population they have joined. This phenomenon, called **gene flow**, violates the Hardy–Weinberg requirement that populations must be closed to migration.

Gene flow is common in some animal species. For example, young male baboons typically move from one local population to another after experiencing aggressive behaviour by older males. And many marine invertebrates disperse long distances as larvae carried by ocean currents.

Research Example: Using the Hardy–Weinberg Principle (*continued*)

otherwise because each gamete carries one allele at each locus.

Now assume that these gametes, both sperm and eggs, encounter each other at random. In other words, individuals reproduce without regard to the genotype of a potential mate. We can visualize the process of random mating in the mating table on the left.

We can also describe the consequences of random mating—$(p + q)$ sperm fertilizing $(p + q)$ eggs—with an equation that predicts the genotype frequencies in the offspring generation:

$$(p + q) \times (p + q) = p^2 + 2pq + q^2$$

If the population is at genetic equilibrium for this locus, p^2 is the predicted frequency of the C^RC^R genotype, $2pq$ the predicted frequency of the C^RC^W genotype, and q^2 the predicted frequency of the C^WC^W genotype. Using the gamete frequencies determined above, we can calculate the predicted genotype frequencies in the next generation:

frequency of $C^RC^R =$
$$p^2 = (0.7 \times 0.7) = 0.49$$

frequency of $C^RC^W =$
$$2pq = 2(0.7 \times 0.3) = 0.42$$

frequency of $C^WC^W =$
$$q^2 = (0.3 \times 0.3) = 0.09$$

Notice that the predicted genotype frequencies in the offspring gen-

eration have changed from those in the parent generation: the frequency of heterozygous individuals has decreased, and the frequencies of both types of homozygous individuals have increased. This result occurred because the starting population was *not already* in equilibrium at this gene locus. In other words, the distribution of parent genotypes did not conform to the predicted $p^2 + 2pq + q^2$ distribution.

The 2000 gametes in our hypothetical population produced 1000 offspring. Using the genotype frequencies we just calculated, we can predict how many offspring will carry each genotype:

490 red (C^RC^R)
420 pink (C^RC^W)
90 white (C^WC^W)

In a real study, we would examine the offspring to see how well their numbers match these predictions.

What about the allele frequencies in the offspring? The Hardy–Weinberg principle predicts that they did not change. Let's calculate them and see. Using the method shown in Table 17.1 and the prime symbol (′) to indicate offspring allele frequencies,

$$p' = ([2 \times 490] + 420)/2000 =$$
$$1400/2000 = 0.7$$

$$q' = ([2 \times 90] + 420)/2000 =$$
$$600/2000 = 0.3$$

You can see from this calculation that the allele frequencies did not change from one generation to the next, even though the alleles were rearranged to produce different proportions of the three genotypes. Thus, the population is now at genetic equilibrium for the flower colour locus; neither the genotype frequencies nor the allele frequencies will change in succeeding generations as long as the population meets the conditions specified in the Hardy–Weinberg model.

To verify this, you can calculate the allele frequencies of the gametes for this offspring generation and predict the genotype frequencies and allele frequencies for a third generation. You could continue calculating until you ran out of either paper or patience, but these frequencies will not change.

Researchers use calculations like these to determine whether an actual population is near its predicted genetic equilibrium for one or more gene loci. When they discover that a population is not at equilibrium, they infer that microevolution is occurring and can investigate the factors that might be responsible.

Dispersal agents, such as pollen-carrying wind or seed-carrying animals, are responsible for gene flow in most plant populations. For example, blue jays foster gene flow among populations of oaks by carrying acorns from nut-bearing trees to their winter caches, which may be as much as a 1.5 kilometres away **(Figure 17.7)**. Transported acorns that go uneaten may germinate and contribute to the gene pool of a neighbouring oak population.

Documenting gene flow among populations is not always easy, particularly if it occurs infrequently. Researchers can use phenotypic or genetic markers to identify immigrants in a population, but they must also demonstrate that immigrants reproduced, thereby contributing to the gene pool of their adopted population. In the San Francisco Bay area, for example, Bay checkerspot butterflies (*Euphydryas editha bayensis*)

David Neal Parks

W. Carter Johnson

Figure 17.7
Gene flow. Blue jays (*Cyanocitta cristata*) serve as agents of gene flow for oaks (genus *Quercus*) when they carry acorns from one oak population to another. An uneaten acorn may germinate and contribute to the gene pool of the population into which it was carried.

rarely move from one population to another because they are poor fliers. When adult females do change populations, it is often late in the breeding season, and their offspring have virtually no chance of finding enough food to mature. Thus, many immigrant females do not foster gene flow because they do not contribute to the gene pool of the population they join.

The evolutionary importance of gene flow depends on the degree of genetic differentiation between populations and the rate of gene flow between them. If two gene pools are very different, a little gene flow may increase genetic variability within the population that receives immigrants, and it will make the two populations more similar. But if populations are already genetically similar, even a lot of gene flow will have little effect.

17.3c Genetic Drift Reduces Genetic Variability within Populations

Chance events sometimes cause allele frequencies in a population to change unpredictably. This phenomenon, known as **genetic drift**, has especially dramatic effects on small populations, which clearly violate the Hardy–Weinberg assumption of infinite population size.

A simple analogy clarifies why genetic drift is more pronounced in small populations than in large ones. When individuals reproduce, male and female gametes often pair up randomly, as though the allele in any particular sperm or ovum was determined by a coin toss. Imagine that "heads" specifies the *R* allele and "tails" specifies the *r* allele. If the two alleles are equally common (that is, their frequencies, *p* and *q*, are both equal to 0.5), heads should be as likely an outcome as tails. But if you toss the coin 20 or 30 times to simulate random mating in a small population, you won't often see a 50:50 ratio of heads and tails. Sometimes heads will predominate and sometimes tails will—just by chance. Tossing the coin 500 times to simulate random mating in a somewhat larger population is more likely to produce a 50:50 ratio of heads and tails. And if you tossed the coin 5000 times, you would get even closer to a 50:50 ratio.

Chance deviations from expected results—which cause genetic drift—occur whenever organisms engage in sexual reproduction, simply because their population sizes are not infinitely large. But genetic drift is particularly common in small populations because only a few individuals contribute to the gene pool and because any given allele is present in very few individuals.

Genetic drift generally leads to the loss of alleles and reduced genetic variability. Two general circumstances, population bottlenecks and founder effects, often foster genetic drift.

Population Bottlenecks. On occasion, a stressful factor such as disease, starvation, or drought kills a great

Figure 17.8
Population bottleneck. Northern elephant seals (*Mirounga angustirostris*) at the Año Nuevo State Reserve in California are descended from a population that was decimated by hunting late in the nineteenth century. In this photo, two large bulls fight to control a harem of females.

Frans Lanting/Minden Pictures

many individuals and eliminates some alleles from a population, producing a **population bottleneck.** This cause of genetic drift greatly reduces genetic variation even if the population numbers later rebound.

In the late nineteenth century, for example, hunters nearly wiped out northern elephant seals (*Mirounga angustirostris*) along the Pacific coast of North America **(Figure 17.8).** Since the 1880s, when the species received protected status, the population has increased to more than 30 000, all descended from a group of about 20 survivors. Today, the population exhibits no variation in 24 proteins studied by gel electrophoresis. This low level of genetic variation, which is unique among seal species, is consistent with the hypothesis that genetic drift eliminated many alleles when the population experienced the bottleneck.

Founder Effect. When a few individuals colonize a distant locality and start a new population, they carry only a small sample of the parent population's genetic variation. By chance, some alleles may be totally missing from the new population, whereas other alleles that were rare "back home" might occur at relatively high frequencies. This change in the gene pool is called the **founder effect.**

The human medical literature provides some of the best-documented examples of the founder effect. For example, populations in the Charlevoix and Saguenay-Lac-Saint-John regions of northeastern Quebec show an unusually high incidence of myotonic dystrophy. This dominant disorder is characterized by progressive muscle weakness and wasting, often arising in early adulthood. Whereas the frequency of people carrying an allele for this trait ranges from 1 in 5000 to 1 in 50 000 in other parts of the world, this region of Quebec shows a frequency as high as 1 in 550. Analysis of the age of the founder effect suggests that the allele was brought into the

MOLECULE BEHIND BIOLOGY

Warfarin

Coumarins are anticoagulant compounds that interfere with the metabolism of vitamin K by inhibiting an enzyme called vitamin K epoxide reductase. This vitamin is required for the synthesis of prothrombin and other essential blood-clotting factors. Warfarin is a tasteless and colourless synthetic derivative of coumarin that was first developed as a rat poison in the mid-1900s **(Figure 1)**.

Warfarin was very effective when first introduced because the frequency of susceptible alleles was high in wild rodent populations. The vast majority of individuals had susceptible genotypes and therefore died from reduced clotting ability. However, those few rats carrying dominant resistance alleles tended to survive and reproduce. (Perhaps their vitamin K epoxide reductase gene had suffered a spontaneous mutation that resulted in an altered enzyme that warfarin could no longer bind to.) With continued exposure to warfarin, populations tend to accumulate resistant alleles and expand in spite of exposure to the pesticide.

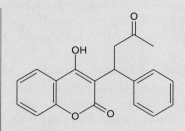

Figure 1
Warfarin, an anticoagulant rat poison.

region about nine generations ago, about the time of settlement of the area by Europeans at the turn of the seventeenth century.

Conservation Implications. Genetic drift has important implications for **conservation biology**. By definition, endangered species experience severe population bottlenecks, which result in the loss of genetic variability. Moreover, the small number of individuals available for captive breeding programs may not fully represent a species' genetic diversity. Without such variation, no matter how large a population may become in the future, it will be less resistant to diseases or less able to cope with environmental change.

For example, scientists believe that an environmental catastrophe produced a population bottleneck in the African cheetah (*Acinonyx jubatus*) 10 000 years ago. Cheetahs today are remarkably uniform in genetic make-up. Their populations are highly susceptible to diseases; they also have a high proportion of sperm cell abnormalities and a reduced reproductive capacity. Thus, limited genetic variation, as well as small numbers, threatens populations of endangered species.

17.3d Natural Selection Shapes Genetic Variability by Favouring Some Traits over Others

Recall that the Hardy–Weinberg relationship is just a theoretical model that predicts how given allele frequencies would give rise to respective genotypic frequencies in a population over time. However, the conditions necessary for Hardy–Weinberg equilibrium, such as the requirement for all genotypes to survive and reproduce equally well, are seldom met in nature. You know from Section 20 that heritable traits enable some individuals to survive better and reproduce more than others. **Natural selection** is the process by which such traits become more common in subsequent generations. Thus, natural selection violates a requirement of the Hardy–Weinberg equilibrium.

Although natural selection can change allele frequencies, *it is the phenotype of an individual organism, rather than any particular allele, that is successful or not.* When individuals survive and reproduce, their alleles—both favourable and unfavourable—are passed to the next generation. Of course, an organism with harmful or lethal dominant alleles will probably die before reproducing, and all the alleles it carries will share that unhappy fate, even those that are advantageous.

To evaluate reproductive success, evolutionary biologists consider **relative fitness**, the number of surviving offspring that an individual produces compared with the number left by others in the population. Thus, a particular allele will increase in frequency in the next generation if individuals carrying that allele leave *more* offspring than individuals carrying other alleles. Differences in the *relative* success of individuals are the essence of natural selection.

Natural selection tests fitness differences at nearly every stage of the life cycle. One plant may be fitter than others in the population because its seeds survive colder conditions, because the arrangement of its leaves captures sunlight more efficiently, or because its flowers are more attractive to pollinators. However, natural selection exerts little or no effect on traits that appear during an individual's postreproductive life. For example, Huntington disease, a dominant-allele disorder that first strikes humans after the age of 40, is not subject to strong selection. Carriers of the disease-causing allele reproduce before the onset of the condition, passing it to the next generation.

Biologists measure the effects of natural selection on phenotypic variation by recording changes in the mean and variability of characters over time (see Figure 17.3). Three modes of natural selection have been identified: directional selection, stabilizing selection, and disruptive selection **(Figure 17.9).**

Directional Selection. Traits undergo **directional selection** when individuals near one end of the phenotypic spectrum have the highest relative fitness. Directional selection shifts a trait away from the existing mean and toward the favoured extreme (see Figure 17.9a).

After selection, the trait's mean value is higher or lower than before.

Directional selection is extremely common. For example, predatory fish promote directional selection for larger body size in guppies when they selectively feed on the smallest individuals in a guppy population. And most cases of artificial selection, including the experiment on the activity levels of house mice, are directional, aimed at increasing or decreasing specific phenotypic traits. Humans routinely use directional selection to produce domestic animals and crops with desired characteristics, such

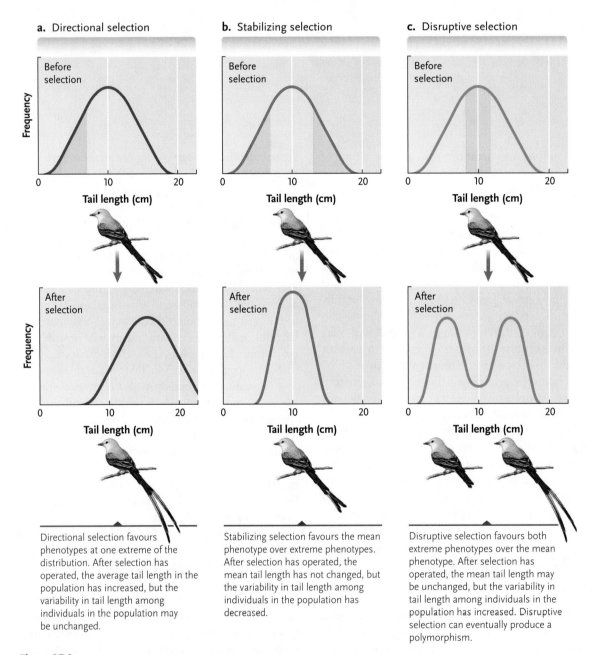

a. Directional selection

b. Stabilizing selection

c. Disruptive selection

Directional selection favours phenotypes at one extreme of the distribution. After selection has operated, the average tail length in the population has increased, but the variability in tail length among individuals in the population may be unchanged.

Stabilizing selection favours the mean phenotype over extreme phenotypes. After selection has operated, the mean tail length has not changed, but the variability in tail length among individuals in the population has decreased.

Disruptive selection favours both extreme phenotypes over the mean phenotype. After selection has operated, the mean tail length may be unchanged, but the variability in tail length among individuals in the population has increased. Disruptive selection can eventually produce a polymorphism.

Figure 17.9

Three modes of natural selection. This hypothetical example uses tail length of birds as the quantitative trait subject to selection. The yellow shading in the top graphs indicates phenotypes that natural selection does *not* favour. Notice that the area under each curve is constant because each curve presents the frequencies of all phenotypes in the population. When stabilizing selection **(b)** reduces variability in the trait, the curve becomes higher and narrower.

as the small size of chihuahuas and the intense "bite" of chili peppers.

Stabilizing Selection. Traits undergo **stabilizing selection** when individuals expressing intermediate phenotypes have the highest relative fitness (see Figure 17.9b). By eliminating phenotypic extremes, stabilizing selection reduces genetic and phenotypic variation and increases the frequency of intermediate phenotypes. Stabilizing selection is probably the most common mode of natural selection, affecting many familiar traits. For example, very small and very large human newborns are less likely to survive than those born at an intermediate mass **(Figure 17.10)**.

Warren G. Abrahamson and Arthur E. Weis of Bucknell University have shown that opposing forces of directional selection can sometimes produce an overall pattern of stabilizing selection **(Figure 17.11, p. 386)**. The gallmaking fly (*Eurosta solidaginis*) is a small insect that feeds on the tall goldenrod plant (*Solidago altissima*). When a fly larva hatches from its egg, it bores into a goldenrod stem, and the plant responds by producing a spherical growth deformity called a gall. The larva feeds on plant tissues inside the gall. Galls vary dramatically in size; genetic experiments indicate that gall size is a heritable trait of the fly, although plant genotype also has an effect.

Fly larvae inside galls are subjected to two opposing patterns of directional selection. On the one hand, a tiny wasp (*Eurytoma gigantea*) parasitizes gallmaking flies by laying eggs in fly larvae inside their galls. After hatching, the young wasps feed on the fly larvae, killing them in the process. However, adult wasps are so small that they cannot easily penetrate the thick walls of a large gall; they generally lay eggs in fly larvae occupying small galls. Thus, wasps establish directional selection favouring flies that produce large galls, which are less likely to be parasitized. On the other hand, several bird species open galls to feed on mature fly larvae; these predators preferentially open large galls, fostering directional selection in favour of small galls.

In about one-third of the populations surveyed in central Pennsylvania, wasps and birds attacked galls with equal frequency, and flies producing galls of intermediate size had the highest survival rate. The smallest and largest galls—as well as the genetic predisposition to make very small or very large galls—were eliminated from the population.

Disruptive Selection. Traits undergo **disruptive selection** when extreme phenotypes have higher relative fitness than intermediate phenotypes (see Figure 17.9c). Thus, alleles producing extreme phenotypes become more common, promoting polymorphism. Under natural conditions, disruptive selection is much less common than directional selection and stabilizing selection.

Figure 17.10
Evidence for stabilizing selection in humans.

HYPOTHESIS: Human birth mass has been adjusted by natural selection.

NULL HYPOTHESIS: Natural selection has not affected human birth mass.

METHOD: Two noted human geneticists, Luigi Cavalli-Sforza and Sir Walter Bodmer of Stanford University, collected data on the variability in human birth mass, a character exhibiting quantitative variation, and on the mortality rates of babies born at different weights. The researchers then searched for a relationship between birth mass and mortality rate by plotting both data sets on the same graph. A lack of correlation between birth mass and mortality rate would support the **null hypothesis**.

RESULTS: When plotted together on the same graph, the bar graph (birth mass) and the curve (mortality rate) illustrate that the mean birth mass is very close to the optimum birth mass (the mass at which mortality is lowest). The two data sets also show that few babies are born at the very low and very high mass associated with high mortality.

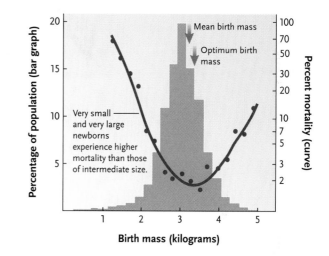

CONCLUSION: The shapes and positions of the birth mass bar graph and the mortality rate curve suggest that stabilizing selection has adjusted human birth weight to an average of 3.8 kilograms.

Peter Grant of Princeton University, one of the world's expert on the ecology and evolution of the Galápagos finches, has analyzed a likely case of disruptive selection on the size and shape of the bill in a population of cactus finches (*Geospiza conirostris*) on the island of Genovesa. During normal weather cycles, the finches feed on ripe cactus fruits, seeds, and exposed insects. During drought years, when food is scarce, they also search for insects by stripping bark from the branches of bushes and trees.

During the long drought of 1977, about 70% of the cactus finches on Genovesa died; the survivors exhibited unusually high variability in their bills **(Figure 17.12, p. 386)**. Grant suggested that this morphological variability allowed birds to specialize on particular foods.

Figure 17.11

How opposing forces of directional selection produce stabilizing selection.

HYPOTHESIS: The size of galls made by larvae of the gallmaking fly (*Eurosta solidaginis*) is governed by conflicting selection pressures established by parasitic wasps and predatory birds.

PREDICTION: Gallmaking flies that produce galls of intermediate size will be more likely to survive than those that make either small galls or large galls.

METHOD: Abrahamson and his colleagues surveyed galls made by the larvae of the gallmaking fly in Pennsylvania. They measured the diameters of the galls they encountered, and for those galls in which the larvae had died, they determined whether they had been killed by **(a)** a parasitic wasp (*Eurytoma gigantea*) or **(b)** a predatory bird, such as the downy woodpecker (*Dendrocopus pubescens*).

a. *Eurytoma gigantea,* a parasitic wasp

Forrest W. Buchanan/Visuals Unlimited

b. *Dendrocopus pubescens,* a predatory bird

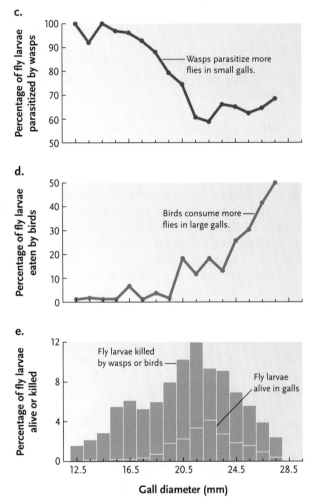

Gregory K. Scott/Photo Researchers, Inc.

RESULTS: Tiny wasps are more likely to parasitize gallmaking fly larvae inside small galls **(c),** fostering directional selection in favour of large galls. By contrast, birds usually feed on fly larvae inside large galls **(d),** fostering directional selection in favour of small galls. These opposing patterns of directional selection create stabilizing selection for the size of galls that the fly larvae make **(e).**

c. Percentage of fly larvae parasitized by wasps — Wasps parasitize more flies in small galls.

d. Percentage of fly larvae eaten by birds — Birds consume more flies in large galls.

e. Percentage of fly larvae alive or killed — Fly larvae killed by wasps or birds; Fly larvae alive in galls. Gall diameter (mm)

CONCLUSION: Because wasps preferentially parasitize fly larvae in small galls, and birds preferentially eat fly larvae in large galls, the opposing forces of directional selection establish an overall pattern of stabilizing selection in favour of medium-sized galls.

Figure 17.12

Disruptive selection. Cactus finches (*Geospiza conirostris*) on Genovesa exhibit extreme variability in the size and shape of their bills.

Geospiza conirostris

Heather Angel/Natural Visions

Birds with long bills open cactus fruits to feed on the fleshy pulp.

Birds with intermediate bills may be favoured during nondrought years when many types of food are available.

Birds with deep bills strip bark from trees to locate insects.

Figure 17.13
Sexual selection in action.

QUESTION: Is the long tail of the male long-tailed widowbird (*Euplectes progne*) the product of intrasexual selection, intersexual selection, or both?

EXPERIMENT: Andersson counted the number of females that associated with individual male widowbirds in the grasslands of Kenya. He then shortened the tails of some individuals by cutting the feathers, lengthened the tails of others by gluing feather extensions to their tails, and left a third group essentially unaltered as a control. One month later, he again counted the number of females associating with each male and compared the results from the three groups.

RESULTS: Males with experimentally lengthened tails attracted more than twice as many mates as males in the control group, and males with experimentally shortened tails attracted fewer. Andersson observed no differences in the ability of altered males and control group males to maintain their display areas.

© 2008 Josef Hlasak

CONCLUSION: Female widowbirds clearly prefer males with experimentally lengthened tails to those with normal tails or experimentally shortened tails. Tail length had no obvious effect on the interactions between males. Thus, the long tail of male widowbirds is the product of intersexual selection.

Birds that stripped bark from branches to look for insects had particularly deep bills, and birds that opened cactus fruits to feed on the fleshy interior had especially long bills. Thus, birds with extreme bill phenotypes appeared to feed efficiently on specific resources, establishing disruptive selection on the size and shape of their bills. The selection may be particularly strong when drought limits the variety and overall availability of food. However, intermediate bill morphologies may be favoured during nondrought years when insects and small seeds are abundant.

17.3e Sexual Selection Often Exaggerates Showy Structures in Males

Darwin hypothesized that a special process, which he called **sexual selection**, has fostered the evolution of showy structures—such as brightly coloured feathers, long tails, or impressive antlers—as well as elaborate courtship behaviour in the males of many animal species. Sexual selection encompasses two related processes. As the result of *intersexual selection* (that is,

selection based on the interactions between males and females), males produce these otherwise useless structures simply as a result of females finding them irresistibly attractive in the past. Under *intrasexual selection* (that is, selection based on the interactions between members of the same sex), males use their large body size, antlers, or tusks to intimidate, injure, or kill rival males. In many species, sexual selection is the most probable cause of **sexual dimorphism**, differences in the size or appearance of males and females.

Behavioural aspects of sexual selection are described further in Chapter 40.

Like directional selection, sexual selection pushes phenotypes toward one extreme. But the products of sexual selection are sometimes bizarre—such as the ridiculously long tail feathers of male African widowbirds. How could evolutionary processes favour the production of such costly structures? Malte Andersson of the University of Gothenburg, Sweden, conducted a field experiment to determine whether the long tail feathers were the product of either intersexual selection or intrasexual selection **(Figure 17.13)**.

17.3f Nonrandom Mating Can Influence Genotype Frequencies

To fulfill the assumptions of the Hardy–Weinberg model requires individuals to select mates randomly with respect to their genotypes. This requirement is, in fact, often met; humans, for example, generally marry one another in total ignorance of their genotypes for digestive enzymes or blood types.

Nevertheless, many organisms mate nonrandomly, selecting a mate with a particular phenotype and underlying genotype. Snow geese, for example, usually select mates of their own colour, and a tall woman is more likely to marry a tall man than a short man. If no one phenotype is preferred by all potential mates, nonrandom mating does not establish selection for one phenotype over another. But because individuals with similar genetically based phenotypes mate with each other, the next generation will contain fewer heterozygous offspring than the Hardy–Weinberg model predicts.

Inbreeding is a special form of nonrandom mating in which individuals that are genetically related mate with each other. Self-fertilization in plants (see Chapter 30) and a few animals (see Chapter 38) is an extreme example of inbreeding because offspring are produced from the gametes of a single parent. However, other organisms that live in small, relatively closed populations often mate with related individuals. Because relatives often carry the same alleles, inbreeding generally increases the frequency of homozygous genotypes and decreases the frequency of heterozygotes. Thus, recessive phenotypes are often expressed. For example, the high incidence of Ellis–van Creveld syndrome among the Old Order Amish population is caused by inbreeding. Although the founder effect originally established the disease-causing allele in this population, inbreeding increases the likelihood that it will be expressed. Most human societies discourage matings between genetically close relatives, thereby reducing inbreeding and the production of recessive homozygotes.

STUDY BREAK

1. Which agents of microevolution tend to increase genetic variation within populations, and which ones tend to decrease it?
2. In what way does nonrandom mating affect the predictions of the Hardy–Weinberg equation?

17.4 Maintaining Genetic and Phenotypic Variation

Evolutionary biologists continue to discover extraordinary amounts of genetic and phenotypic variation in most natural populations. How can so much variation persist in the face of stabilizing selection and genetic drift?

17.4a Diploidy Can Hide Recessive Alleles from the Action of Natural Selection

The diploid condition reduces the effectiveness of natural selection in eliminating harmful recessive alleles from a population. Although such alleles are disadvantageous in the homozygous state, they may have little or no effect on heterozygotes. Thus, recessive alleles can be protected from natural selection by the phenotypic expression of the dominant allele.

In most cases, the masking of recessive alleles in heterozygotes makes it almost impossible to eliminate them completely through selective breeding. Experimentally, we can prevent homozygous recessive organisms from mating. But, as the frequency of a recessive allele decreases, an increasing proportion of its remaining copies is "hidden" in heterozygotes **(Table 17.3)**. Thus, the diploid state preserves recessive alleles at low frequencies, at least in large populations. In small populations, a combination of natural selection and genetic drift can eliminate harmful recessive alleles.

17.4b Natural Selection Can Maintain Balanced Polymorphisms

A **balanced polymorphism** is one in which two or more phenotypes are maintained in fairly stable proportions over many generations. Natural selection preserves balanced polymorphisms when heterozygotes have higher relative fitness, when different alleles are favoured in different environments, and when the rarity of a phenotype provides an advantage.

Table 17.3	Masking of Recessive Alleles in Diploid Organisms

When a recessive allele is common in a population (top rows), most copies of the allele are present in homozygotes. But when the allele is rare (bottom rows), most copies of it exist in heterozygotes. Thus, rare alleles that are completely recessive are protected from the action of natural selection because they are masked by dominant alleles in heterozygous individuals.

Frequency of Allele *a*	Genotype Frequencies*			% of Allele *a* Copies in	
	AA	*Aa*	*aa*	*Aa*	*aa*
0.99	0.0001	0.0198	0.9801	1	99
0.90	0.0100	0.1800	0.8100	10	90
0.75	0.0625	0.3750	0.5625	25	75
0.50	0.2500	0.5000	0.2500	50	50
0.25	0.5625	0.3750	0.0625	75	25
0.10	0.8100	0.1800	0.0100	90	10
0.01	0.9801	0.0198	0.0001	99	1

*Population is assumed to be in genetic equilibrium.

Heterozygote Advantage. A balanced polymorphism can be maintained by **heterozygote advantage**, when heterozygotes for a particular locus have higher relative fitness than either homozygote. The best-documented example of heterozygote advantage is the maintenance of the *HbS* (sickle) allele, which codes for a defective form of hemoglobin in humans. As you learned in Chapter 11, hemoglobin is an oxygen-transporting molecule in red blood cells. The hemoglobin produced by the *HbS* allele differs from normal hemoglobin (coded by the *HbA* allele) by just one amino acid. In *HbS/HbS* homozygotes, the faulty hemoglobin forms long fibrous chains under low oxygen conditions, causing red blood cells to assume a sickle shape (as shown in Figure 11.1). Homozygous *HbS/HbS* individuals often die of sickle cell disease before reproducing, yet in tropical and subtropical Africa, *HbS/HbA* heterozygotes make up nearly 25% of many populations.

Why is the harmful allele maintained at such high frequency? It turns out that sickle cell disease is most common in regions where malarial parasites infect red blood cells in humans **(Figure 17.14).** When heterozygous *HbA/HbS* individuals contract malaria, their infected red blood cells assume the same sickle shape as those of homozygous *HbS/HbS* individuals. The sickled cells lose potassium, killing the parasites, which limits their spread within the infected individual. Heterozygous individuals often survive malaria because the parasites do not multiply quickly inside them; their immune systems can effectively fight the infection; and they retain a large population of uninfected red blood cells. Homozygous *HbA/HbA* individuals are also subject to malarial infection, but because their infected cells do not sickle, the parasites multiply rapidly, causing a severe infection with a high mortality rate.

Therefore, *HbA/HbS* heterozygotes have greater resistance to malaria and are more likely to survive severe infections in areas where malaria is prevalent. Natural selection preserves the *HbS* allele in these populations because heterozygotes in malaria-prone areas have higher relative fitness than homozygotes for the normal *HbA* allele.

Selection in Varying Environments. Genetic variability can also be maintained within a population when different alleles are favoured in different places or at different times. For example, the shells of European garden snails range in colour from nearly white to pink, yellow, or brown and may be patterned by one to five stripes of varying colour (see Figure 17.2a). This polymorphism, which is relatively stable through time, is controlled by several gene loci. The variability in colour and in striping pattern can be partially explained by selection for camouflage in different habitats.

Predation by song thrushes (*Turdus ericetorum*) is a major agent of selection on the colour and pattern of these snails in England. When a thrush finds a snail, it smacks it against a rock to break the shell. The bird eats the snail but leaves the shell near its "anvil."

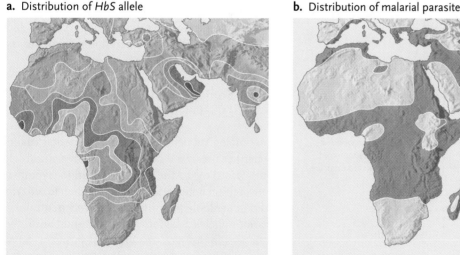

a. Distribution of *HbS* allele

b. Distribution of malarial parasite

KEY

Allele frequencies of *HbS* allele

>0.14	
0.12–0.14	0.08–0.10
0.11–0.12	0.04–0.06
0.06–0.08	0.00–0.02
0.02–0.04	

Regions with malaria

Figure 17.14
Heterozygote advantage. The distribution of the *HbS* allele **(a),** which causes sickle cell disease in homozygotes, roughly matches the distribution of the malarial parasite *Plasmodium falciparum* **(b)** in southern Europe, Africa, the Middle East, and India. Gene flow among human populations has carried the *HbS* allele to some malaria-free regions.

Figure 17.15
Habitat variation in colour and striping patterns of European garden snails.

HYPOTHESIS: Genetically based variation in the shell colour and striping patterns of the European garden snail (*Cepaea nemoralis*) differ substantially from one type of vegetation to another because birds and other visual predators establish strong selection for camouflage in local populations.

PREDICTION: Snails with plain, dark-coloured shells will be most abundant in woodland habitats, but snails with striped, light-coloured shells will be most abundant in hedges and fields.

METHOD: Two British researchers, A. J. Cain and P. M. Shepard, surveyed the distribution of colour and striping patterns of snails in many local populations. They plotted the data on a graph showing the percentage of snails with yellow shells versus the percentage of snails with striped shells, noting the vegetation type where each local population lived.

RESULTS: The shell colour and striping patterns of snails living in a particular vegetation type tend to be clustered on the graph, reflecting phenotypic differences that enable the snails to be camouflaged in different habitats. Thus, the alleles that control these characters vary from one local population to another.

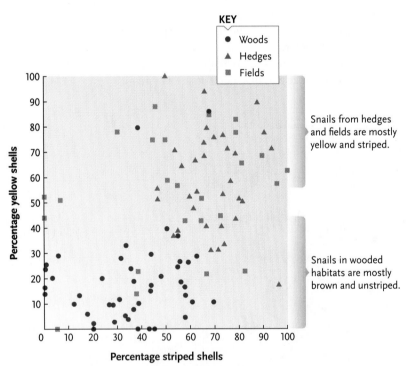

CONCLUSION: Variations in the colour and striping patterns of the shells of European garden snails allow most snails to be camouflaged in whatever habitat they occupy. Because these traits are genetically based, the frequencies of the alleles that control them also differ among snails living in different vegetation types. Natural selection therefore favours different alleles in different local populations, maintaining genetic variability in populations that span several vegetation types.

Researchers used the broken shells near an anvil to compare the phenotypes of captured snails with a random sample of the entire snail population. Their analyses indicated that thrushes are visual predators, usually capturing snails that are easy to find. Thus, well-camouflaged snails survive, and the alleles that specify their phenotypes increase in frequency.

The success of camouflage varies with habitat, however; local subpopulations of the snail, which occupy different habitats, often differ markedly in shell colour and pattern. The predators eliminate the most conspicuous individuals in each habitat; thus, natural selection differs from place to place **(Figure 17.15)**. In woods where the ground is covered with dead leaves, snails with unstriped pink or brown shells predominate. In hedges and fields, where the vegetation includes thin stems and grass, snails with striped yellow shells are the most common. In populations that span several habitats, selection preserves different alleles in different places, thus maintaining variability in the population as a whole.

Frequency-Dependent Selection. Sometimes genetic variability is maintained in a population simply because rare phenotypes—whatever they happen to be—have higher relative fitness than more common phenotypes. The rare phenotype will increase in frequency until it becomes so common that it loses its advantage. Such phenomena are examples of **frequency-dependent selection** because the selective advantage enjoyed by a particular phenotype depends on its frequency in the population.

Predator–prey interactions can establish frequency-dependent selection because predators often focus their attention on the most common types of prey (see Chapter 46 and **Figure 17.16**).

17.4c Some Genetic Variations May Be Selectively Neutral

Many biologists believe that some genetic variations are neither preserved nor eliminated by natural selection. According to the **neutral variation hypothesis**, some of the genetic variation at loci coding for enzymes and other soluble proteins is **selectively neutral.** Even if various alleles code for slightly different amino acid sequences in proteins, the different forms of the proteins may function equally well. In those cases, natural selection would not favour some alleles over others.

Biologists who support the neutral variation hypothesis do not question the role of natural selection in producing complex anatomical structures or useful biochemical traits. They also recognize that selection reduces the frequency of harmful alleles. But they argue that we should not simply assume that every genetic variant that persists in a population has been preserved by natural selection. In practice, it is often very difficult to test the natural variation hypothesis because the fitness effects of different alleles are often subtle and vary with small changes in the environment.

The neutral variation hypothesis helps explain why we see different levels of genetic variation in different populations. It proposes that genetic variation is directly proportional to a population's size and the length of time over which variations have accumulated. Small populations experience fewer mutations than large populations simply because they include fewer replicating genomes. Small populations also lose rare alleles more readily through genetic drift. Thus, small populations should exhibit less genetic variation than large ones, and a population, like the northern elephant seals, that has experienced a recent population bottleneck should exhibit an exceptionally low level of genetic variation. These predictions of the neutral variation hypothesis are generally supported by empirical data.

STUDY BREAK

1. How does the diploid condition protect harmful recessive alleles from natural selection?
2. What is a balanced polymorphism?
3. Why is the allele that causes sickle cell disease very rare in human populations that are native to northern Europe?

17.5 Adaptation and Evolutionary Constraints

Although natural selection preserves alleles that confer high relative fitness on the individuals that carry them, researchers are cautious about interpreting the benefits that particular traits may provide.

17.5a Scientists Construct Hypotheses about the Evolution of Adaptive Traits

An **adaptive trait** is any product of natural selection that increases the relative fitness of an organism in its environment. **Adaptation** is the accumulation of adaptive traits over time, and this book describes many examples. The change in the oxygen-binding capacity of hemoglobin in response to carbon dioxide concentration, the water-retaining structures and special photosynthetic pathways of desert plants, and the warning colouration of poisonous animals can all be interpreted as adaptive traits.

In fact, we can concoct an adaptive explanation for almost any characteristic we observe in nature. But such explanations are just fanciful stories unless they are framed as testable hypotheses about the relative fitness of different phenotypes and genotypes. Unfortunately, evolutionary biologists cannot always conduct straightforward experiments because they sometimes study traits that do not vary much

Figure 17.16
Demonstration of frequency-dependent selection.

QUESTION: How does the frequency of a prey type influence the likelihood that it will be captured by predators?

EXPERIMENT: Water boatmen (*Sigara distincta*) occur in three colour forms, which vary in the effectiveness of their camouflage. Researchers offered different proportions of the three colour forms to predatory fishes in the laboratory and recorded how many of each form were eaten.

RESULTS: When all three phenotypes were available, predatory fishes consumed a disproportionately large number of the most common form, thereby reducing its frequency in the population.

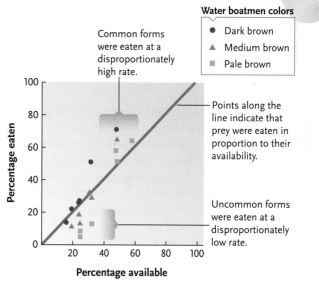

CONCLUSION: Predators tend to feed disproportionately on whatever form of their prey is most abundant, thereby reducing its frequency in the prey population.

within a population or species. In such cases, they may compare variations of a trait in closely related species living in different environments. For example, one can test how the traits of desert plants are adaptive by comparing them with traits in related species from moister habitats.

When biologists try to unravel how and why a particular characteristic evolved, they must also remember that a trait they observe today may have had a different function in the past. For example, the structure of the shoulder joint in birds allows them to move their wings first upward and backward and then downward and forward during flapping flight. But analyses of the fossil record reveal that this adaptation, which is essential for flight, did not originate in birds: some predatory nonflying dinosaurs, including the ancestors of birds, had a similarly constructed shoulder joint. Researchers hypothesize that these fast-running predators may have struck at prey with a flapping motion similar to that

PEOPLE BEHIND BIOLOGY

Dolph Schluter, University of British Columbia

This chapter closes with the idea that "genetic divergence is sometimes sufficient to cause the populations to evolve into different species." The work of Dr. Dolph Schluter, first with Darwin's finches and then with three-spine stickleback fish (*Gasterosteus aculeatus*), has helped answer important questions about "ecological speciation." Which genetic differences are ecologically determined? Under what conditions are these differences selected?

Marine sticklebacks are widespread in the oceans of the northern hemi-sphere, returning annually to freshwater streams to spawn (this lifestyle is called anadromous). Freshwater populations, believed to be derived from the anadromous population, inhabit streams and lakes. No matter where they are found in the world, the stream-dwelling fish are consistently small and lightly armoured relative to their anadromous relatives. Therefore, body size seems to be an adaptation to a particular environment.

Schluter and colleagues collected fish from geographically isolated stickleback populations and noted their choice of partners in mating trials. Females were almost twice as likely to choose mates from their own population. The data suggested that this assortive mating was on the basis of differences in body size. Experimental manipulation of body size confirmed that females preferred males that were close to them in body size, regardless of their population of origin. This work provides important evidence in support of reproductive isolation of populations (and potential speciation) on the basis of a single, ecologically related trait (body size).

used by modern birds. Thus, the structure of the shoulder may have first evolved as an adaptation for capturing prey, and only later proved useful for flapping flight. This hypothesis—however plausible it may be—cannot be tested by direct experimentation because the nonflying ancestors of birds have been extinct for millions of years. Instead, evolutionary biologists must use anatomical studies of birds and their ancestors as well as theoretical models about the mechanics of movement to challenge and refine the hypothesis.

Finally, although evolution has produced all the characteristics of organisms, not all are necessarily adaptive. Some traits may be the products of chance events and genetic drift. Others are produced by alleles that were selected for unrelated reasons (see Section 11.2). Still other characteristics result from the action of basic physical laws. For example, the seeds of many plants fall to the ground when they mature, reflecting the inevitable effect of gravity.

17.5b Several Factors Constrain Adaptive Evolution

When we analyze the structure and function of an organism, we often marvel at how well adapted it is to its environment and mode of life. However, the adaptive traits of most organisms are compromises produced by competing selection pressures. Sea turtles, for example, must lay their eggs on beaches because their embryos cannot acquire oxygen under water. Although flippers allow females to crawl to nesting sites on beaches, they are not ideally suited for terrestrial locomotion. Their structure reflects their primary function in underwater locomotion.

Moreover, no organism can be perfectly adapted to its environment because environments change over time. When selection occurs in a population, it preserves alleles that are successful under the prevailing environmental conditions. Thus, each generation is adapted to the environmental conditions under which its parents lived. If the environment changes from one generation to the next, adaptation will always lag behind.

Another constraint on the evolution of adaptive traits is historical. Natural selection is not an engineer that designs new organisms from scratch. Instead, it acts on new mutations and existing genetic variation. Because new mutations are fairly rare, natural selection works primarily with alleles that have been present for many generations. Thus, adaptive changes in the morphology of an organism are almost inevitably based on small modifications of existing structures. The bipedal (two-footed) posture of humans, for example, evolved from the quadrupedal (four-footed) posture of our ancestors. Natural selection did not produce an entirely new skeletal design to accompany this radical behavioural shift. Instead, existing characteristics of the spinal column and the musculature of the legs and back were modified, albeit imperfectly, for an upright stance.

The agents of evolution cause microevolutionary changes in the gene pools of populations. In the next chapter, we examine how microevolution in different populations can cause their gene pools to diverge. The extent of genetic divergence is sometimes sufficient to cause the populations to evolve into different species.

STUDY BREAK

1. What is an adaptive trait?
2. Why can organisms never be perfectly adapted to their environment?

What are the evolutionary forces affecting molecular variation within populations?

This question may sound like a simple restatement of the entire chapter you have just read, but it is one of the *fundamental* questions in population genetics today—and we have only begun to scratch its surface. The

Hardy–Weinberg principle provides a useful null hypothesis, but since we know that evolution happens routinely, that null hypothesis is very frequently rejected. Recent studies have attempted to address this question using theoretical models, extensive DNA sequence data, and detailed measures of recombination rate.

Review

Go to CENGAGENOW™ at http://hed.nelson.com/ to access quizzing, animations, exercises, articles, and personalized homework help.

17.1 Variation in Natural Populations

- Phenotypic traits exhibit either quantitative or qualitative variation within populations of all organisms (see Figures 17.2 and 17.3). These discrete differences are called polymorphisms.

- Genetic variation, environmental factors, or an interaction between the two cause phenotypic variation within populations. Only genetically based phenotypic variation is heritable and subject to evolutionary change.

- Genetic variation arises within populations largely through mutation and genetic recombination. Artificial selection experiments and analyses of protein and DNA sequences reveal that most populations include significant genetic variation (see Figure 17.6).

17.2 Population Genetics

- All the alleles in a population comprise its gene pool, which can be described in terms of allele frequencies and genotype frequencies.

- The Hardy–Weinberg principle of genetic equilibrium is a null model that describes the conditions under which microevolution will not occur: mutations do not occur; populations are closed to migration; populations are infinitely large; natural selection does not operate; and individuals select mates at random. Microevolution, a change in allele frequencies through time, occurs frequently in natural populations since the restrictive requirements of the model are seldom met.

17.3 The Agents of Microevolution

- Several processes cause microevolution in populations. Mutation introduces completely new genetic variation. Gene flow carries novel genetic variation into a population through the arrival and reproduction of immigrants. Genetic drift causes random changes in allele frequencies, especially in small populations. Natural selection occurs when the genotypes of some individuals enable them to survive and reproduce more than others. Nonrandom mating within a population can cause its genotype frequencies to depart from the predictions of the Hardy–Weinberg equilibrium.

- Natural selection alters phenotypic variation in one of three ways (see Figure 17.9). Directional selection increases or decreases the mean value of a trait, shifting it toward a phenotypic extreme. Stabilizing selection increases the frequency of the mean phenotype and reduces variability in the trait (see Figure 17.10). Disruptive selection increases the frequencies of extreme phenotypes and decreases the frequency of intermediate phenotypes (see Figure 17.12).

- Sexual selection promotes the evolution of exaggerated structures and behaviours (see Figure 17.13).

- Although nonrandom mating does not change allele frequencies, it can affect genotype frequencies, producing more homozygotes and fewer heterozygotes than the Hardy–Weinberg model predicts.

17.4 Maintaining Genetic and Phenotypic Variation

- Diploidy can maintain genetic variation in a population if alleles coding for recessive traits are not expressed in heterozygotes and are thus hidden from natural selection.

- Polymorphisms are maintained in populations when heterozygotes have higher relative fitness than both homozygotes (see Figure 17.14), when natural selection occurs in variable environments (see Figure 17.15), or when the relative fitness of a phenotype varies with its frequency in the population (see Figure 17.16).

- Some biologists believe that many genetic variations are selectively neutral, conferring neither advantages nor disadvantages on the individuals that carry them. The neutral variation hypothesis explains why large populations and those that have not experienced a recent population bottleneck exhibit the highest levels of genetic variation.

17.5 Adaptation and Evolutionary Constraints

- Adaptive traits increase the relative fitness of individuals carrying them. Adaptive explanations of traits must be framed as testable hypotheses.

- Natural selection cannot result in perfectly adapted organisms because most adaptive traits represent compromises among conflicting needs; because most environments are constantly changing; and because natural selection can affect only existing genetic variation.

Questions

Self-Test Questions

1. Which of the following represents an example of qualitative phenotypic variation?
   a. the lengths of people's toes.
   b. the body sizes of pigeons.
   c. human ABO blood groups.
   d. the birth mass of humans.
   e. the number of leaves on oak trees.

2. A population of mice is at Hardy–Weinberg equilibrium at a gene locus that controls fur colour. The locus has two alleles, M and m. A genetic analysis of one population reveals that 60% of its gametes carry the M allele. What percentage of mice contains both the M and m alleles?
   a. 60%
   b. 48%
   c. 40%
   d. 36%
   e. 16%

3. If the genotype frequencies in a population are 0.60 AA, 0.20 Aa, and 0.20 aa, and if the requirements of the Hardy–Weinberg principle apply, the genotype frequencies in the offspring generation will be
   a. 0.60 AA, 0.20 Aa, 0.20 aa.
   b. 0.36 AA, 0.60 Aa, 0.04 aa.
   c. 0.49 AA, 0.42 Aa, 0.09 aa.
   d. 0.70 AA, 0.00 Aa, 0.30 aa.
   e. 0.64 AA, 0.32 Aa, 0.04 aa.

4. The reason spontaneous mutations do not have an immediate effect on allele frequencies in a large population is that
   a. mutations are random events, and mutations may be either beneficial or harmful.
   b. mutations usually occur in males and have little effect on eggs.
   c. many mutations exert their effects after an organism has stopped reproducing.
   d. mutations are so rare that mutated alleles are greatly outnumbered by nonmutated alleles.
   e. most mutations do not change the amino acid sequence of a protein.

5. The phenomenon in which chance events cause unpredictable changes in allele frequencies is called
   a. gene flow.
   b. genetic drift.
   c. inbreeding.
   d. balanced polymorphism.
   e. stabilizing selection.

6. An Eastern European immigrant carrying the allele for Tay–Sachs disease settled in a small village on the St. Lawrence River. Many generations later, the frequency of the allele in that village is statistically higher than it is in the immigrant's homeland. The high frequency of the allele in the village probably provides an example of
   a. natural selection.
   b. the concept of relative fitness.
   c. the Hardy–Weinberg genetic equilibrium.
   d. phenotypic variation.
   e. the founder effect.

7. If a storm kills many small sparrows in a population, but only a few medium-sized and large ones, which type of selection is probably operating?
   a. directional selection.
   b. stabilizing selection.
   c. disruptive selection.
   d. intersexual selection.
   e. intrasexual selection.

8. Which of the following phenomena explains why the allele for sickle cell hemoglobin is common in some tropical and subtropical areas where the malaria parasite is prevalent?
   a. balanced polymorphism.
   b. heterozygote advantage.
   c. sexual dimorphism.
   d. neutral selection.
   e. stabilizing selection.

9. The neutral variation hypothesis proposes that
   a. complex structures in most organisms have not been fostered by natural selection.
   b. most mutations have a strongly harmful effect.
   c. some mutations are not affected by natural selection.
   d. natural selection cannot counteract the action of gene flow.
   e. large populations are subject to stronger natural selection than small populations.

10. Phenotypic characteristics that increase the fitness of individuals are called
    a. mutations.
    b. founder effects.
    c. heterozygote advantages.
    d. adaptive traits.
    e. polymorphisms.

Questions for Discussion

1. Most large commercial farms routinely administer antibiotics to farm animals to prevent the rapid spread of diseases through a flock or herd. Explain why you think that this practice is either wise or unwise.

2. Many human diseases are caused by recessive alleles that are not expressed in heterozygotes. Explain why it is almost impossible to eliminate such genetic traits from human populations.

3. Using two types of beans to represent two alleles at the same gene locus, design an exercise to illustrate how population size affects genetic drift.

4. In what ways are the effects of sexual selection, disruptive selection, and nonrandom mating different? How are they similar?

5. Design an experiment to test the hypothesis that the differences in size among adult guppies are determined by the amount of food they eat rather than by genetic factors.

The bacterium *Clostridium difficile*, which often is responsible for outbreaks of disease in hospitals and chronic care facilities.

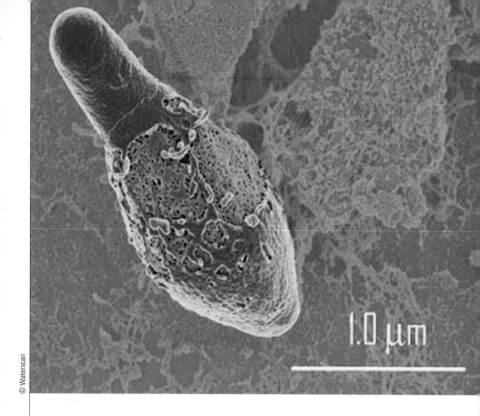

© Waterscan

1.0 µm

18 Species

' WHY IT MATTERS

Names can contribute to the precision of communication. Whether you are looking for a product in a grocery store, a book in a library, or a restaurant, knowing the name is an important first step. As noted in Chapter 1, biologists use formal scientific names to report information about organisms.

In a hospital or chronic care facility, knowing that an epidemic can be attributed to *Clostridium difficile* (*C. difficile*) helps authorities take steps to contain the outbreak and ensure that patients receive appropriate treatment. If the illness has been caused by West Nile virus, then the situation will require a different approach from prevention to treatment. Here, knowing the identity of the disease-causing agent means using the appropriate characteristics to recognize it (or the symptoms it causes).

Meanwhile, a bird watcher trying to convince colleagues about an unusual sighting in the neighbourhood understands that knowing how to recognize the bird means knowing its name. Dedicated birders will respond to the opportunity to see an Ivory-billed Woodpecker (*Campephilus principalis*) much more quickly than if you just say that you saw a crow-sized bird sitting on a tree. This woodpecker had long been thought to be extinct, so in 2007, people flocked to try to see one when it was reported that they were still alive. Although we have common names for birds, this is not true for most other organisms.

18.1 What's in a Name?

The purpose of this chapter is to explore the species concept, identify mechanisms involved in **speciation**, and develop an appreciation of the importance of names of organisms in biology. We will see how names/labels can convey a great deal of information.

Anyone who has watched an experienced shepherd work with a border collie knows that different signals (whistles) carry specific meanings that are well known to dog and handler. Use of specific signals (labels) to communicate information to other organisms is not unique to *Homo sapiens*. When a vervet monkey (*Chlorocebus pygerythrus*; **Figure 18.1**) gives the "eagle" alarm call, its fellows look skyward and move closer to the trunks of trees. When the same monkey gives a "leopard" alarm call, others within earshot look down, and those on the ground climb trees.

Communication can affect both inter- and intraspecific behaviour. Vervet monkeys use different signals (or names) for the different threats. Similarly, humans use names (signals) to distinguish between different categories of objects. "Fish" means something different from "bird," and almost everyone knows some fundamental differences between these two kinds of animals. But what about "sharks"? They are not birds, but are they really fish? When we say "eel," do we mean a fishlike creature with an elongated body? But there are "eels," bony fish with jaws, and there are "lamprey eels," jawless fish with cartilaginous skeletons (see Chapter 27).

As we have seen (see Chapter 1), biologists use scientific names, Latinized descriptions of the organism bearing the name, for precise communication. Each described species has a scientific name.

18.2 Definition of "Species"

What is a species? According to the *Stanford Encyclopedia of Philosophy* (http://plato.stanford.edu/entries/species/), "... the nature of species is controversial in biology and philosophy. Biologists disagree on the definition of the term species." A proper understanding of species is important for a number of reasons. Species are the fundamental taxonomic units of biological classification. Environmental laws are framed in terms of species (see Chapter 48). Even our concept of human nature is affected by our understanding of species.

This source goes on to say that "... The **Biological Species Concept** defines a species as a group of organisms that can successfully interbreed and produce fertile offspring. The **Phylogenetic Species Concept** (which itself has multiple versions) defines a species as a group of organisms bound by a unique ancestry. The **Ecological Species Concept** defines a species as a group of organisms that share a distinct ecological niche. These species concepts are just three of a dozen prominent species concepts in the biological literature."

How can so many definitions of "species" be used in a biological context?

There are several problems with the "Biological Species Concept" defined above. One important problem is that although the definition can work for species that reproduce sexually, it does not deal as well with the many species that reproduce asexually. By their approach to reproduction, whole groups of organisms in the biological kingdom sit outside the "conventional" definition of species. Thus, patterns of reproduction can blur the definition of species.

But try looking up the **scientific name** of West Nile virus. Are scientific names used for viruses? Prokaryotes reproduce by binary fission, yet they have scientific names. You would not want to confuse *Bacillus subtilis*, which causes food poisoning, with *Bacillus anthracis*, which causes anthrax. Similarly, the bacterium *Vibrio fisheri* is a symbiont that makes some squid bioluminescent, whereas *Vibrio cholera* has an entirely different effect, one that frequently kills people. Whatever the mode of reproduction and the comfort of fit with the Biological Species Concept, there are compelling reasons to know the species or kind of organism you are facing.

Androdioecy (*andro* = male; *dioeciocy* = male and female) and gynogenetic (*gyno* = female) species are

Figure 18.1
Vervet monkeys (*Chlorocebus pygerythrus*) are widespread in Africa and have predator-specific alarm calls.

M.B. Fenton

two interesting variations in patterns of reproduction. As the name implies, androdioecous organisms exist as natural populations of functional males and hermaphrodites but include no true females. *Krytolebias mormoratus*, the mangrove killifish (**Figure 18.2**), and clam shrimps (*Eulimnadia texana*) are androdioecous species. Gynogenetic species, as the name implies, have only females. One example is *Poecilia formosa* (Amazon molly; **Figure 18.3**). Like many other species in the genus *Poecilia*, *P. formosa* uses internal fertilization. Within these females, the eggs require mechanical stimulation by sperm to initiate development. This means that female *P. formosa* must seduce and mate with males of other species to obtain the sperm needed to achieve reproduction. Using the Biological Species Concept, neither androdioecous nor gynogenetic species are covered by the traditional definition of species. Does this mean that they are not species?

The definition also does not apply where there is **hybridization**, when two species interbreed and produce fertile offspring. Many "species" hybridize naturally in the wild. As many as 10% of the ~8000 species of birds hybridize naturally and produce fertile offspring. Hybridization between species that produces sterile offspring does not put them outside the definition of the Biological Species Concept. Sterile hybrids result when horses (*Equus calabus*) are crossed with zebras (*Equus burchellii*) and lions (*Panthera leo*) with tigers (*Panthera tigris*). Mules are the sterile hybrids resulting when a male donkey (jack) breeds with a female horse (mare), whereas hinnies are sterile hybrids resulting when a male horse (stallion) breeds with a female donkey (jennet).

Hybrid vigour is usually discussed in the context of crossbreeding between strains of domesticated organisms (see Chapter 49). Breeders of animals and plants have long used the situation to advantage, even well before the work of Gregor Mendel and the birth of the study of genetics. From the work of Peter and Rosemary Grant, we know that some species of Darwin's finches interbreed, and the hybrids are both fertile and strong competitors (see *Hybridization of Bird Species*).

Ingo Schlupp photo

Figure 18.3
Amazon molly (*Poecilia formosa*) is a gynogenetic species.

Recombination is a principal advantage of sexual reproduction (see Chapter 10), one that explains its prevalence among living organisms. Working with *Daphnia pulex*, a water flea in which some populations reproduce sexually and others reproduce asexually, researchers demonstrated the advantages of recombination. Asexually reproducing populations had a higher frequency of mutations in mitochondrial protein-coding genes than sexually reproducing populations.

STUDY BREAK

1. What is a species, according to the Biological Species Concept? Name two problems with this definition.
2. What is a species as defined by the Phylogenetic Species Concept? As defined by the Ecological Species Concept?
3. What is a hermaphrodite? What is the difference between an androdioecous species and a gynogenetic species? Name an example of each.

From Evolutionary Ecology: Sex and the Single Killifish by Elizabeth Pennisi, Science, Vol. 313, p. 1381. Reprinted with permission from AAAS.

Figure 18.2
Mangrove killifish (*Krytolebias mormoratus*) is an androdioecous species.

18.3 One Size Does Not Fit All

Anyone who has exchanged clothing or accessories with someone else will know that "one size fits all" can be a plausible strategy for people selling socks but not for those selling jeans or contact lenses. Therefore, we should not be surprised that any one definition of "species" in biology is not uniformly used or subscribed to by all biologists. Organisms are the product of evolution, a dynamic process that does not easily accommodate rigid definitions. Our concepts of species appears to be most readily applicable to static situations but not to all species in all situations.

Hybridization in Bird Species

Darwin's original descriptions of finches on the Galapágos Islands reflected the impact of his visit there on his thinking. Therefore, it is fitting that Rosemary and Peter Grant, who study Darwin's finches **(Figure 1)**, should document hybridization between different species, interbreeding that produces fertile and fit hybrids. Hybridization can be an effective way of achieving major and rapid evolution. Grant and Grant note that the discovery of superior fitness of hybrids over parent stock **(Table 1)** brings into question the designation of the parent stocks as "species." Indeed, in birds, hybridization may be a common and persistent route to rapid evolution **(Table 2).**

Biologists are obliged to be more open-mined about hybridization when given the data from birds and those from plants where polyploidy is common. Hybridization could result in major and rapid evolution. Indeed, characterization of hybridization as a gross blunder in sexual preference may be a mistake. Polyploidy is common in plants (2–7% of vascular plant species) and has been thought to be less common in animals. However, the adaptive radiation of African cichlid fish and Darwin's finches may be examples of jumps in evolution aided and abetted by hybridization.

Figure 1
Geospiza fortis, a large, ground-dwelling Darwin's finch that often interbreeds with *G. fuliginosa* and *G. scandens*.

Table 1 | A Comparison of the Breeding Success of Hybridizing and Nonhybridizing Darwin's Finches (Genus *Geospiza*) from 1983 to 1991

Pairs	Clutches (C)	Eggs (E)	Nestlings (N)	Fledglings (F)	N/E	F/C
Fortis × *fuliginosa*	31	122	107	92	0.88	2.97
Fortis × *scandens*	12	44	31	27	0.70	2.25
Fortis × *fortis*	1141	4462	3446	2953	0.77	2.59
Fuliginosa × *fuliginosa*	7	28	24	24	0.86	3.43
Scandens × *scandens*	559	2071	1550	1264	0.75	2.26

Table 2 | Incidence of Hybridization Among Bird Species Belonging to 23 Orders

Order	Species (n)	Species hybridizing n	Species hybridizing %	Pairs hybridizing (n)	Intergeneric pairs of hybridizing species n	Intergeneric pairs of hybridizing species %
Struthioniformes	10	0	0.0	0	0	0.0
Tinamiformes	47	0	0.0	0	0	0.0
Craciformes	69	2	2.9	1	0	0.0
Galiformes	214	46	21.5	46	6	13.0
Anseriformes	161	67	41.6	114	35	30.7
Tumiciformes	17	0	0.0	0	0	0.0
Piciformes	355	49	13.5	32	0	0.0
Galbulformes	51	2	3.9	1	0	0.0
Bucenotiformes	56	0	0.0	0	0	0.0
Upupiformes	10	0	0.0	0	0	0.0
Trogoniformes	39	0	0.0	0	0	0.0
Coraciformes	152	8	5.3	4	0	0.0
Coliiformes	6	2	16.7	1	0	0.0
Cuculiformes	143	4	2.8	2	0	0.0
Psittaciformes	358	27	7.5	17	5	29.4
Apodiformes	103	0	0.0	0	0	0.0
Trochiliformes	319	61	19.1	52	36	69.2
Musophagiformes	23	0	0.0	0	0	0.0
Strigiformes	291	2	0.7	1	0	0.0
Columbiformes	313	10	3.2	5	0	0.0
Gruiformes	196	17	8.7	10	3	30.0
Ciconiiformes	1027	139	13.5	92	3	3.3
Passeriformes	5712	460	8.0	320	58	18.2
Total	9672	895	9.2	698	136	19.5

The diversity of species and of their lifestyles partly reflects the mechanisms underlying the processes of speciation. The Biological Species Concept defines species in terms of population genetics and evolutionary theory in a static world. The definition alludes to the genetic *cohesiveness* of species. Populations of the same species are said to experience gene flow that mixes their genetic material and could be the "glue" holding a species together. The second part of this concept emphasizes the genetic *distinctness* of each species. Because populations of different species are reproductively isolated, they cannot exchange genetic information. In fact, the process of speciation is frequently defined as the evolution of reproductive isolation between populations.

The Biological Species Concept could explain why individuals of a species generally look alike. If phenotype reflects genotype, members of the same gene pool should share genetic traits (genotype) that determine phenotype. Individuals of different species generally do not resemble one another as closely because they share fewer genetic characteristics. In practice, biologists often use similarities or differences in morphological traits as convenient markers of genetic similarity or reproductive isolation. But remember that Linnaeus's **binomial** system predated the work of Charles Darwin and Gregor Mendel (see Chapters 11 and 20).

Biologists often describe new species and use visible morphological traits to allow other biologists to distinguish the new species from those previously known. This process dates back to Linnaeus's classification of organisms in the eighteenth century (see Chapter 20). This approach is based on the **Morphological Species Concept**, the idea that all individuals of a species share measurable traits that distinguish them from individuals of other species. The Morphological Species Concept has many practical applications. Paleontologists use morphology to identify fossils to species but also depend on information about the fossils' ages (see Chapter 19). External traits of organisms are presented in field guides, which help the users recognize species, for example, to tell yellow-throated warblers from yellow-rumped warblers **(Figure 18.4)**. Visit the **natural history** section in a bookstore to get an idea of the range of field guides available for identifying everything from butterflies to mushrooms.

Figure 18.4

Diagnostic characters. Yellow-throated Warblers (*Dendroica dominica*) and yellow-rumped Warblers (*Dendroica coronata*) can be distinguished by the colours of feathers on the throat and rump. Yellow-rumped Warblers used to be known as Myrtle Warblers. Arrows identify diagnostic differences.

18.4 Gene Flow: Four Examples

It is traditional for biologists to presume that gene flow occurs within populations of single species. For many species that reproduce sexually and whose geographic distributions are relatively continuous, this may be true. But do *Rattus norvegicus* (Norway rats; **Figure 18.5**) in London, England, look like those in London, Ontario, or Sydney, Australia, or Cape Town, South Africa, because gene flow occurs among these populations? Or do they look the same because they fill the same basic niche (role in nature) in similar, human-created habitats? You will recognize this as a variant on the nature–nurture debate. Are we what we are because of our genes or because of the environment in which we were raised?

The four examples below illustrate how ecology, habitat availability, and behaviour can affect distribution patterns and genetic differences.

Figure 18.5

Rattus norvegicus, Norway rats, a cosmopolitan species that is often commensal with humans.

STUDY BREAK

1. What contributes to the genetic cohesiveness and genetic distinctiveness of species?
2. What is the Morphological Species Concept? What are some practical applications of this concept?

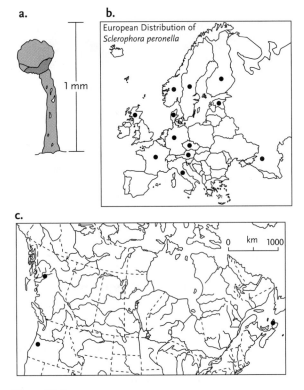

Figure 18.6
The lichen *Sclerophora peronella* (frosted glass whiskers) **(a)** and its European **(b)** and North American **(c)** distribution.

First, at one extreme are organisms such as Norway rats that occur everywhere you find humans, whereas other species, such as mosses and lichens, have very restricted distributions. The frosted glass whiskers, a lichen, is known from very few locations in the world **(Figure 18.6)**. The same is true of the cryptic paw lichen **(Figure 18.7)**. Many other organisms are widely but sparsely distributed, raising questions about gene flow as a cohesive force.

Second, the tools of modern genetics (see Chapter 16) have given biologists more opportunities to measure gene flow and document the relatedness between populations. From a genetic database, it was possible to look at the dispersal of *Balea perversa* **(Figure 18.8)**, an oviparous (egg-laying), hermaphroditic snail. Biologists showed that the distribution of snails from Tristan da Cunha to Iceland reflected the migratory pathways of birds because *B. perversa* hitchhiked with the birds (see Figure 18.8). Without knowing about the hitchhiking behaviour, the distribution of the snails and the genetic relatedness between populations would have made little sense.

Third is evidence from behaviour. In the 1960s, gel electrophoretic studies of proteins were used to examine population genetics of *Mus musculus* (house mice; see Chapter 16). At that time, examining variation in proteins was deemed to be a proxy for genetic variation, and the results demonstrated how social structures in mouse populations limited genetic exchange. The data revealed that within a single barn lived groups of mice that did not interbreed. Although these mice could interbreed, social behaviour appeared to prevent gene flow. Then, in the 1970s, Ann Eileen Miller Baker introduced some female house mice that had genetic markers into both captive and wild populations. These females bred with males, and through the progeny of these matings, the genetic markers moved rapidly through wild and captive populations. A key factor was using females to introduce the markers because males were less often assimilated into mouse populations. Genetic markers provided a more representative view of mouse population genetics than variation in allozymes.

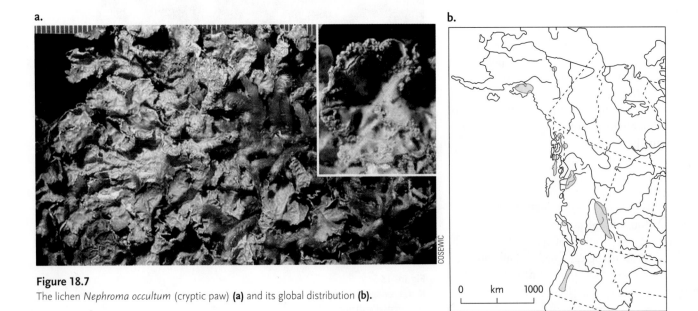

Figure 18.7
The lichen *Nephroma occultum* (cryptic paw) **(a)** and its global distribution **(b)**.

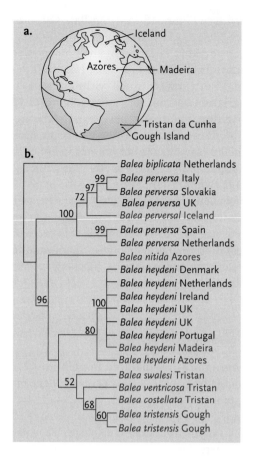

Figure 18.8

The snail, *Balea perversa* **(c),** hitchhikes on migrating birds and achieves an extensive distribution on islands in and continents adjoining the North and South Atlantic **(a, b).** Numbers on the neighbour-joining tree are bootstrap support values derived from analysis of DNA sequences of cytochrome oxidase subunit 1.

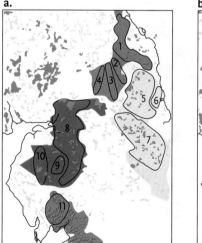

Reprinted by permission from Macmillan Publishers Ltd: Nature, "Biogeography: Molecular trails from hitch-hiking snails", by Edmund Gittenberger, Dick S. J. Groenenberg, Bas Kokshoorn and Richard C. Preece, vol. 439, p. 409, copyright (2006).

Fourth, DNA technology tools (see Chapter 16) allowed biologists to track the responses of *Sciurus vulgaris* (Eurasian red squirrel) to changes in forest availability along the border between England and Scotland **(Figure 18.9).** There, extensive pine plantations have allowed Cumbrian (northern England) populations of the squirrels to spread into isolated woodlands in Scotland. This is reflected by genetic changes **(Figure 18.10, p. 402).** This situation has changed the genetic face of *S. vulgaris* populations and demonstrates responses associated with habitat change. It also demonstrates how changes in landscape and habitat can alter genetic patterns, sometimes creating problems for those concerned about conserving biodiversity (see Chapter 48).

STUDY BREAK

Identify three different factors that can influence gene flow within populations.

Figure 18.9

Eurasian red squirrels (*Sciurus vulgaris*) (left) occur in woodlands and pine plantations in northern England (Cumbria) and adjacent Scotland. The extent of woodland coverage from low **(a)** to high **(b)** in the Kielder Forest. Three basic squirrel genetic groups are shown. Orange is the northern group, yellow is the eastern group, and blue is the western group. Coloured areas depict all woods within 1.5 km; black outlines the area over which specimens were collected. When the Kielder Forest is included, Cumbria is part of the northern genetic group.

© 4nature.at/Alamy

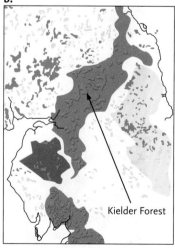

Kielder Forest

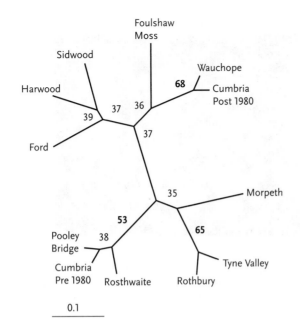

Figure 18.10
Genetic distances between populations of *S. vulgaris* in the woodlands shown in Figure 18.9.

18.5 A Dynamic Situation

The case of *Acanthinucella spirata*, a marine snail **(Figure 18.11)**, illustrates how a species can vary in space and in time. The story involves data about distribution in space (today) and in time (from 125 000 years B.P. to 2006), the morphology of their shells, and their genetics. Along 1050 km of Cali-fornia coast (see Figure 18.11, from Baja California to Tomales Bay), the 14 living populations of snails showed considerable variation in shell morphology and mitochondrial DNA sequences. Northern populations did not show as much within-population genetic variation as southern ones **(Figure 18.12)**, suggesting that the snails have expanded their range to the north. Recently colonized populations showed shell morphologies not present in either the southern populations or the 125 000-year-old fossils (Pleistocene; **Figure 18.13**).

A. spirata demonstrates how a snail can change its distribution in space and in time. Furthermore, recent expansion of snail populations coincide with novel (for the species) morphological changes. Changes in the snails appear to be in response to changes in climate (see Chapter 46).

18.6 Geographic Variation

When geographically separated populations of a species exhibit dramatic, easily recognized phenotypic variation, biologists may identify them as different **subspecies (Figure 18.14)**, which are local variants of a species. Individuals from different subspecies usually interbreed where their geographic distributions meet, and their offspring often exhibit intermediate phenotypes. Zoologists sometimes use the word "race" as shorthand for the term "subspecies." Botanists more often refer to "variants" or, for domesticated stock, "cultivars."

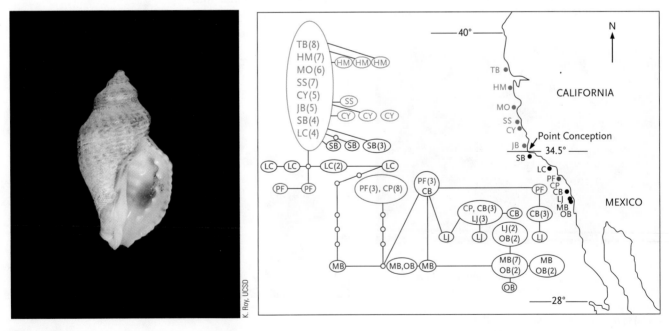

Figure 18.11
The genetic diversity of *Acanthinucella spirata* (left) from 14 populations along the coast of California (right). Locations are shown on the map, as well as a parsimony network for 33 unique cytochrome oxidase subunit 1 genes. SB and LC (blue) are located south of Point Conception. TB stands for Tomales Bay, HM for Half Moon Bay, MO for Monterey Bay, SS for San Simeon, CY for Cayucos, JB for Jalama Bay, SB for Santa Barbara, LC for Leo Carillo State Beach, PF for Point Fermin, CP for Cabrillo Beach, CB for Carlsbad, LJ for La Jolla, MB for Mission Bay, and OB for Ocean Beach.

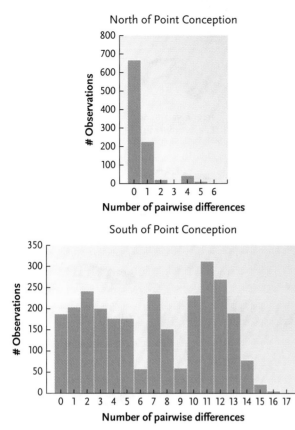

Figure 18.12
Northern and southern populations of *A. spirata* compared using pairwise base-pair differences in COI sequences.

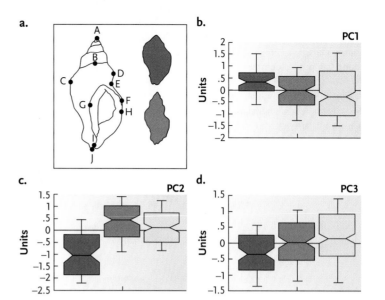

Figure 18.13
Trends in shell shape and size based on shell landmarks (A), for northern (blue), southern (red), and fossil (grey = Pleistocene) materials. The plots show scores on the first three principal components (PC in B, C, and D). PCs are statistical representations of groups of measurements.

Various patterns of geographic variation have provided insight into the speciation process. Two of the best-studied patterns are ring species and clinal variation.

18.6a Ring Species: Genes Flowing between Some Populations

Some plant and animal species have a ring-shaped geographic distribution that surrounds uninhabitable terrain. Adjacent populations of these so-called **ring species** can exchange genetic material directly, but gene flow between distant populations occurs only through intermediary populations.

The lungless salamander *Ensatina eschscholtzi*, an example of a ring species, is widely distributed in the coastal mountains and the Sierra Nevada of California, but it cannot survive in the hot, dry Central Valley **(Figure 18.15, p. 404).** Seven subspecies differ in biochemical traits, colour, size, and ecology. Individuals from adjacent subspecies often interbreed where their geographic distributions overlap, and intermediate phenotypes are fairly common. In the south, where the ring is not completely closed, the two subspecies rarely interbreed as they appear to have differentiated to an extent that they can no longer exchange genetic material.

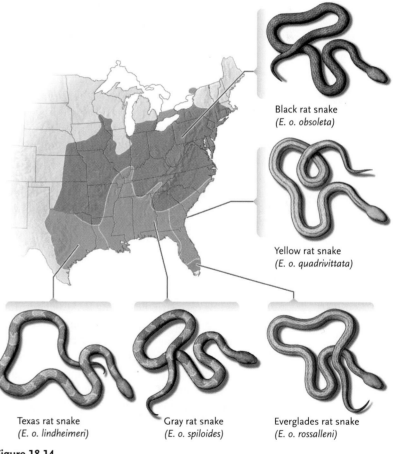

Figure 18.14
Five subspecies of rat snake (*Elaphe obsoleta*) in eastern North America differ in colour and in the presence or absence of stripes.

Are the southernmost populations of this salamander subspecies or different species? A biologist who saw *only* the southern populations, which coexist without interbreeding, might call them separate

Figure 18.15

Six of the seven subspecies of the salamander *Ensatina eschscholtzi* are distributed in a ring around California's Central Valley. However, the two subspecies that nearly close the ring in the south (marked by an arrow), the Monterey salamander and the yellow-blotched salamander, rarely interbreed.

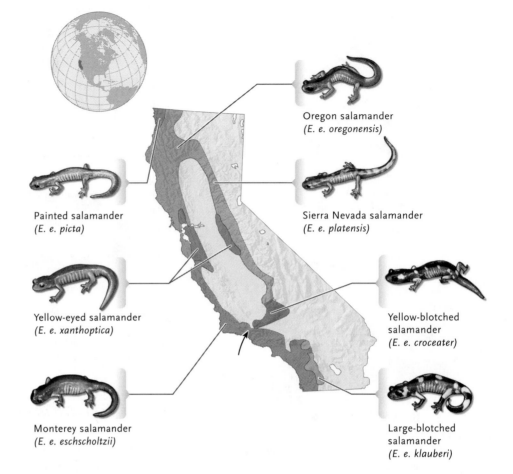

Oregon salamander
(*E. e. oregonensis*)

Painted salamander
(*E. e. picta*)

Sierra Nevada salamander
(*E. e. platensis*)

Yellow-eyed salamander
(*E. e. xanthoptica*)

Yellow-blotched salamander
(*E. e. croceater*)

Monterey salamander
(*E. e. eschscholtzii*)

Large-blotched salamander
(*E. e. klauberi*)

species. However, they still have the potential to exchange genetic material through the intervening populations that form the ring. Hence, we recognize these populations as belonging to the same species. Most likely, the southern subspecies represent an intermediate stage of new species formation.

18.6b Clinal Variation: Change along a Gradient

When a species is distributed over a large, environmentally diverse area, some traits may exhibit a **cline**, a pattern of smooth variation along the geographic gradient. Clinal variation usually results from gene flow between adjacent populations that are each adapting to slightly different conditions. Many species of birds and mammals in the northern hemisphere show clinal variation in body size and the relative length of their appendages. In general, populations living in colder environments have larger bodies and shorter appendages, a pattern usually interpreted as a mechanism to conserve heat (see Chapter 43). When a cline extends over a large geographic gradient, populations at the opposite ends of the cline may be very different.

Most species are morphologically or behaviourally distinct from other species, but local and geographic variation can mask interspecific (between species) dif-

ferences. In the next section, we consider mechanisms that establish and maintain reproductive isolation between species that are descended from a common ancestor.

STUDY BREAK

1. What is a subspecies? Do subspecies interbreed?
2. What kind of geographic distribution is characteristic of a ring species? Name an example of a ring species.

18.7 Reproductive Isolation

Reproductive isolation is fundamental to the Biological Species Concept. A **reproductive isolating mechanism** is a biological characteristic that prevents the gene pools of two species from mixing even when they are **sympatric** (occupying the same spaces at the same time). Reproductive isolation can be achieved in two basic ways **(Table 18.1)**. **Prezygotic isolating mechanisms** exert their effects before the production of a zygote, or fertilized egg, and **postzygotic isolating**

Table 18.1	Reproductive Isolating Mechanisms	
Timing Relative to Fertilization	**Mechanism**	**Mode of Action**
Prezygotic ("premating") mechanisms	Ecological isolation	Species live in different habitats
	Temporal isolation	Species breed at different times
	Behavioural isolation	Species cannot communicate
	Mechanical isolation	Species cannot physically mate
	Gametic isolation	Species have nonmatching receptors on gametes
Postzygotic ("postmating") mechanisms	Hybrid inviability	Hybrid offspring do not complete development
	Hybrid sterility	Hybrid offspring cannot produce gametes
	Hybrid breakdown	Hybrid offspring have reduced survival or fertility

mechanisms operate after zygote formation. These isolating mechanisms are not mutually exclusive, and two or more may operate simultaneously.

18.7a Prezygotic Isolating Mechanisms: Isolation before Fertilization

At least five mechanisms can prevent interspecific matings or fertilizations and the production of hybrid (mixed species) offspring. Included here are ecological, temporal, behavioural, mechanical, and gametic isolation.

Species living in the same geographic region may experience **ecological isolation** if they live in different habitats. Lions and tigers were both common in India until the mid-nineteenth century, when hunters virtually exterminated the Asian lions. However, because lions lived in open grasslands and tigers in dense forests, the two species did not encounter one another and did not interbreed. Lion–tiger hybrids are sometimes born in captivity but do not occur under natural conditions.

Species living in the same habitat can experience **temporal isolation** if they mate at different times of the day or different times of the year. The fruit flies *Drosophila persimilis* and *D. pseudoobscura* overlap extensively in their geographic distributions, but they do not interbreed, in part because *D. persimilis* mates in the morning and *D. pseudoobscura* in the afternoon. Two species of pine in California are reproductively isolated where their geographic distributions overlap:

even though both rely on the wind to carry male gametes (pollen grains) to female gametes (ova) in other cones, *Pinus radiata* releases pollen in February and *P. muricata* releases it in April.

Many animals rely on specific signals, which often differ dramatically between species, to identify the species of a potential mate. **Behavioural isolation** results when the signals used by one species are not recognized by another. Female songbirds often rely on the song, colour, and displays of males to identify members of their own species. Female fireflies identify males by their flashing patterns (**Figure 18.16**). These behaviours (collectively called *courtship displays*) may be so complicated that signals sent by one species are not recognized by another. Mate choice by females and sexual selection (see Chapters 38 and 40) generally drive the evolution of mate recognition signals. The energetic cost of producing eggs or rearing young is substantial, and mating with a male of a different

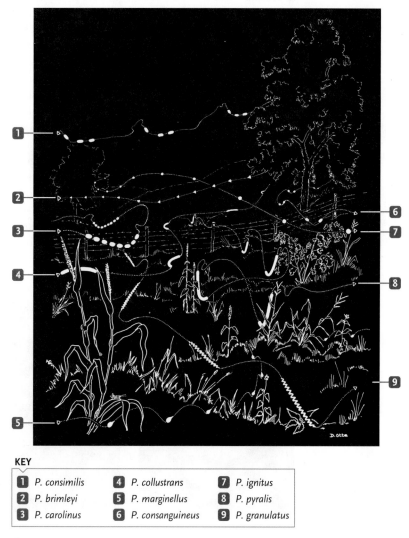

KEY

1 *P. consimilis*	**4** *P. collustrans*	**7** *P. ignitus*
2 *P. brimleyi*	**5** *P. marginellus*	**8** *P. pyralis*
3 *P. carolinus*	**6** *P. consanguineus*	**9** *P. granulatus*

Figure 18.16

Behavioural reproductive isolation. Male beetles (*Photinus* species) use bioluminescent signals to attact potential mates. The different flight paths and flashing patterns of males in nine North American species are represented here. Courtesy of James E. Lloyd. Miscellaneous Publications of the Museum of Zoology of the University of Michigan, 130:1-195, 1966.

species reduces a female's production of fertile offspring. By contrast, females that choose appropriate mates are likely to produce more surviving young. Over time, the number of males with recognizable traits, as well as the number of females able to recognize the traits, increases in the population.

Mechanical isolation results when differences in the structure of copulatory organs prevent successful mating between individuals of different species. This also could be true of other body parts. In particular, many plants have anatomical features that allow only certain pollinators, usually particular bird or insect species, to collect and distribute pollen (see Chapter 30). The flowers and nectar of two native California plants, the monkey-flowers *Mimulus lewisii* and *M. cardinalis,* attract different animal pollinators **(Figure 18.17).** *Mimulus lewisii,* pollinated by bumblebees, has shallow pink flowers with broad petals that provide a landing platform for the bees. Bright yellow streaks on the petals serve as "nectar guides," directing bumblebees to the short nectar tube and reproductive parts located among the petals. Bees enter the flowers to drink nectar and pick up and deliver pollen as they brush against the reproductive parts of the flowers. *Mimulus cardinalis,* pollinated by hummingbirds, has long red flowers with no yellow streaks, and the reproductive parts extend above the petals. The red colour attracts hummingbirds but lies outside the colour range detected by bumblebees. The nectar of *M. cardinalis* is more dilute than that of *M. lewisii,* but it is produced in much greater quantity, making it easier for hummingbirds to ingest. When a hummingbird visits *M. cardinalis* flowers, it pushes its long bill down the nectar tube, and its forehead touches the reproductive parts, picking up and delivering pollen. Where the two monkey flower species grow side by side, animal pollinators restrict their visits to either one species or the other 98% of the time, providing nearly complete reproductive isolation.

Even when individuals of different species do mate, **gametic isolation**, or incompatibility between the sperm of one species and the eggs of another, may prevent fertilization. Many marine invertebrates release gametes into the environment for external fertilization. The sperm and eggs of each species recognize one another's complementary surface proteins (see Chapter 40), but the surface proteins on the gametes of different species do not match. In animals with internal fertilization, the sperm of one species may not survive or function within the reproductive tract of another. Interspecific matings between some *Drosophila* species induce a reaction in the female's reproductive tract that blocks "foreign" sperm from reaching the eggs. Parallel physiological incompatibilities between a pollen tube and a stigma can prevent interspecific fertilization in some plants.

18.7b Postzygotic Isolating Mechanisms: Barriers after Fertilization

Despite the existence of prezygotic isolating mechanisms, sperm from one species sometimes fertilizes an egg of another species. In such cases, the two species are reproductively isolated if their offspring, called interspecific (between species) hybrids, have lower fitness than those produced by intraspecific (within species) matings. Three postzygotic isolating mechanisms (hybrid inviability, hybrid sterility, and hybrid breakdown) can reduce the fitness of hybrid individuals.

Hybrid inviability can occur because many genes govern the complex processes that transform a zygote into a mature organism (see Chapter 39). Hybrid individuals have two sets of developmental instructions, one from each parent, which may not interact properly for the successful completion of embryonic development. As a result, hybrid organisms frequently die as embryos or at an early age, a phenomenon called hybrid inviability. Domestic sheep and goats can mate and fertilize one another's ova, but the hybrid embryos die before reaching term, presumably because the developmental programs of the two parent species are incompatible.

Although some hybrids between closely related species develop into healthy and vigorous adults, they may not produce functional gametes. This **hybrid sterility** often results when the parent species differ in the number or structure of their chromosomes, which cannot pair properly during meiosis. Such hybrids have zero fitness because they leave no descendants. The most familiar example is a mule, the product of mating between a female horse ($2n = 64$) and a male donkey ($2n = 62$). Zebroids, the offspring of matings between horses and zebras, are also sterile.

Mimulus lewisii   *Mimulus cardinalis*

Reny Parker

Figure 18.17

Mechanical reproductive isolation. Because of differences in floral structure, two species of monkey-flower attract different animal pollinators. *Mimulus lewisii* attracts bumblebees, and *Mimulus cardinalis* attracts hummingbirds.

Rate of Evolutionary Change

How quickly can evolution occur? The role of the fossil record in our knowledge and understanding of evolution can leave the impression that evolution occurs over millions of years, or at least millions of generations. But this is not always true.

In 1971, five adult pairs of Italian wall lizards (*Podarcis sicula*) were introduced to Pod Kopište a 0.09 km² islet in the South Adriatic, and five other pairs to the nearby Pod Mrčaru (0.03 km²). In 1971, another lacertid lizard, *Podarcis melisellensis*, occurred on Pod Mrčaru, but they had vanished by 2007. In 2007, densities of *P. sicula* on Pod Mrčaru were significantly greater than those on Pod Kopište. Female Italian wall lizards may lay several clutches of eggs in one season, translating into a short generation time and high values of R, the intrinsic rate of population increase (see Chapter 45).

In 36 years, *P. sicula* established viable populations on both islets. In 2007, the *P. sicula* on both islets were genetically indistinguishable from the mainland source population. However, their populations had changed in morphology. Specifically, introduced lizards differed both from **source populations** and from one another in head morphology, bite strength, and digestive tracts. On Pod Mrčaru, *P. sicula* have longer, wider, and taller heads than those on Pod Kopište, corresponding with a difference in diet. *P. sicula* on Pod Mrčaru ate more plant material than those on Pod Kopište.

The changes in morphology and performance of *P. sicula* after introduction to the islets are similar to those documented among other species and families of lizards. Italian wall lizards on small islands demonstrate adaptability, a foundation for evolution. Italian wall lizards have also been introduced to Long Island, New York, where they have thrived. The situation reminds us how introduced species may adapt to and thrive in new settings. However, we will see how such introductions can pose significant problems for conservation (see Chapter 48). Adapting to life on the edge can be a recipe for success.

But some F$_1$ hybrids are healthy, vigorous, and fully fertile and can breed with other hybrids and with both parental species. Sometimes the F$_2$ generation, produced by matings between F$_1$ hybrids, or between F$_1$ hybrids and either parental species, may exhibit reduced survival or fertility, a phenomenon known as **hybrid breakdown**. Experimental crosses between fruit fly (*Drosophila*) species may produce functional interspecific hybrids, but their offspring experience a high rate of chromosomal abnormalities and harmful types of genetic recombination. Thus, reproductive isolation is maintained between the species because there is little long-term mixing of their gene pools.

STUDY BREAK

1. What is a reproductive isolating mechanism? Distinguish between two major types of reproductive isolating mechanisms.
2. Define five types of prezygotic isolating mechanisms that can prevent interspecific mating.
3. Prezygotic isolating mechanisms prevent gene pools of two species from mixing, so why do postzygotic isolating mechanisms exist? Distinguish between three types of postzygotic isolating mechanisms.

18.8 Geography of Speciation

Geography has a huge impact on whether gene pools have the opportunity to mix. Biologists define three modes of speciation based on the geographic relationship of populations as they become reproductively isolated: allopatric speciation (*allo* = different; *patria* = homeland), **parapatric speciation** (*para* = beside), and sympatric speciation (*sym* = together).

18.8a Allopatric Speciation: New Species Develop from Isolated Populations

Allopatric speciation can occur when a physical barrier subdivides a large population or when a small population becomes separated from a species' main geographic distribution. Allopatric speciation, probably the most common mode of speciation in large animals, occurs in two stages. First, two populations become *geographically* separated, preventing gene flow between them. Then, as the populations experience distinct mutations as well as different patterns of natural selection and genetic drift, they may accumulate genetic differences that isolate them *reproductively*.

Geographic separation sometimes occurs when a barrier divides a large population into two or more

MOLECULE BEHIND BIOLOGY

Champignon Scents

People associate the aroma of mushrooms (champignon scent) with edible fungi. The aroma is mainly associated with four constituents that comprise >70% of the volaties: oct-1-en-3-ol, oct-1-en-3-one, octan-3-ol, and octan-3-one **(Figure 1)**.

The floral fragrance of the orchid *Dracula chestertonii* emits the champignon scent that attracts fungus gnats to pollinate the flowers that are astonishingly mushroom-like in appearance.

Flowers in the genera *Asarum* and *Arisaema* (family Araceae) and *Aristolochia arborea* (family Aristolochiaceae) also use champignon-like scents to attract fungus gnats. Whereas *Asarum* and *Arisaema* attract pollinators, *Aristolochia arborea* **(Figure 2)** is an insectivorous plant (see Chapter 3 and Box 47.6), and the fungus gnats are food.

Precision in communication often crosses species boundaries.

Figure 2
Aristochia arborea, a carnivorous plant that uses champignon scents to attract the fungus gnats it catches and eats.

Figure 1
The four main volatile constituents of champignon scent used by *Dracula chesteronii* to attract fungus gnats that serve as its pollinators.

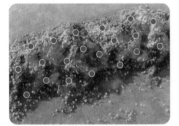 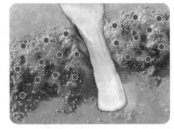 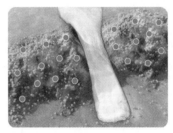 

1 At first, a population is distributed over a large geographical area.

2 A geographical change, such as the advance of a narrow glacier, separates the original population, creating a barrier to gene flow.

3 In the absence of gene flow, the separated populations evolve independently and diverge into different species.

4 When the glacier later melts, allowing individuals of the two species to come into secondary contact, they do not interbreed.

Figure 18.18
The model of allopatric speciation and secondary contact.

units **(Figure 18.18)**. Hurricanes may create new channels that divide low coastal islands and the populations inhabiting them. Uplifting mountains or landmasses, as well as advancing glaciers, can also produce barriers that subdivide populations. Movements of Earth's crust about 5 million years ago caused the uplift of the Isthmus of Panama, separating the once continuous shallow sea into the eastern tropical Pacific Ocean and the western tropical Atlantic Ocean. Populations of marine organisms such as wrasses (fish in the genus *Thalassoma*) were subdivided by this event, and pairs of closely related species now live on either side of this divide **(Figure 18.19)**.

In other cases, small populations become isolated at the edge of a species' geographic distribution. Such peripheral populations often differ genetically from the central population because they are adapted to somewhat different environments. Once a small population is isolated, genetic drift and natural selection, as well as limited gene flow from the parent population, foster further genetic differentiation. In time, the accumulated genetic differences may lead to reproductive isolation.

Isthmus of Panama

Cortez rainbow wrasse (*Thalassoma lucasanum*)

Blue-headed wrasse (*Thalassoma bifasciatum*)

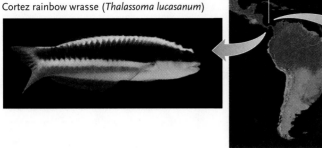

Patrice Geisel/Visuals Unlimited

Fred McConnaughey/Photo Researchers, Inc.

Tom Van Sant/The Geosphere Project, Santa Monica, CA

Figure 18.19

Geographic separation. The uplift of the Isthmus of Panama divided an ancestral wrasse population. The Cortez rainbow wrasse (*Thalassoma lucasanum*) now occupies the eastern Pacific Ocean, and the blue-headed wrassed (*T. bifasciatum*) now occupies the western Atlantic Ocean.

Populations on oceanic islands show extreme examples of this phenomenon. Founder effects, an example of genetic drift (see Chapter 17), make the populations genetically distinct. On oceanic archipelagos, such as the Galápagos and Hawaiian Islands, individuals from one island may colonize nearby islands, founding populations that differentiate into distinct species. Each island may experience multiple invasions, and the process may be repeated many times within the archipelago, leading to the evolution of a **species cluster (Figure 18.20)**. The nearly 800 species of fruit flies on the Hawaiian Islands form several species clusters.

Allopatric populations may reestablish contact when a geographic barrier is eliminated or breached (see Figure 18.18, step 4). This *secondary contact* provides a test of whether or not the populations have diverged into separate species. If their gene pools did not differentiate much during geographic separation, the populations will interbreed and merge. But if the populations have differentiated enough to be reproductively isolated, they have become separate species. Morphological and gametic isolation could involve chemical or genetic factors as well as the timing of reproduction.

During the early stages of secondary contact, prezygotic reproductive isolation may be incomplete. Some members of each population may mate with individuals from the other, producing viable, fertile offspring in areas called **hybrid zones**. Although some hybrid zones have persisted for hundreds or thousands of years, they are generally narrow, and ecological or geographic factors maintain the separation of the gene pools for the majority of individuals in both species.

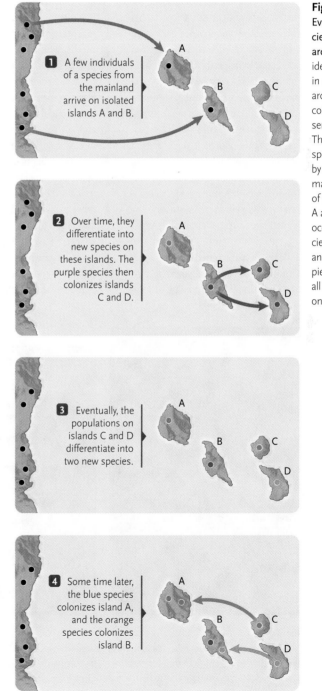

Figure 18.20

Evolution of a species cluster on an archipelago. Letters identify four islands in a hypothetical archipelago, and coloured dots represent different species. The ancestor of all species is represented by black dots on the mainland. At the end of the process, islands A and B are each occupied by two species, and islands C and D are each occupied by one species, all of which evolved on the islands.

1. A few individuals of a species from the mainland arrive on isolated islands A and B.

2. Over time, they differentiate into new species on these islands. The purple species then colonizes islands C and D.

3. Eventually, the populations on islands C and D differentiate into two new species.

4. Some time later, the blue species colonizes island A, and the orange species colonizes island B.

People Behind Biology

Jeremy N. McNeil, Visiting Professor, University of Western Ontario

Jeremy McNeil is a visiting professor in the Department of Biology at the University of Western Ontario, in London, Ontario. He and his students study reproductive behaviour, focusing on insects, particularly species that migrate. Central to their work are the signals that males use to find females and the various processes involved in mate choice. Pheromones or chemical signals (see Chapter 34) may be produced by males and/or females and are often involved in mating behaviour. In some insects, males can detect the pheromones of females from several kilometres away. Information about intraspecific communication can often be used to advantage in efforts to control insect species that are commercially important pests of plants, such as spruce trees or corn.

Pheromonostasis is the process of inhibiting pheromone production. In insects such as spruce budworms (*Choristoneura fumiferana*), males produce two kinds of sperm, one that is nucleate (eupyrene) and the other anucleate (apyrene). McNeil and two colleagues determined that in *C. fumiferana*, apyrene sperm arrive in the spermatheca (females' storage organ for sperm) three to five hours after mating. Therefore, it is possible that apyrene sperm are responsible, at least in part, for pheromonostasis. In the oblique-banded leafroller *C. rosaceana*, the timing of arrival of apyrene sperm in the spermathecae makes it unlikely that the sperm are involved in pheromonostasis. The results demonstrate variations that occur within a genus. The potential to artificially stimulate pheromonostasis could be another way to interrupt reproduction in spruce budworm moths, which are economically important pests of spruce trees.

As we have seen, chemical signals also can mediate interactions between plants and their pollinators. In many situations, these are economically important interactions. One example that McNeil and his students have explored is fruit production in cranberries (*Vaccinium macrocarpon*). In these cranberries, most reproductive stems produce one to three fruits even though there usually are five to seven flowers (**Figure 1**). Flowers higher on the reproductive stems tend to have fewer ovules than lower flowers and often abort without producing fruit. By hand-pollinating flowers along the stems, McNeil and his colleagues demonstrated that the failure of each flower to produce fruit was not a function of insufficient pollination. The upper flowers appeared to be a backup for loss of the earlier blooming lower flowers on the stem.

Chemical communication is often vital in interactions between individuals, whether interspecific or intraspecific. Another intriguing example involves insects that are nest parasites of ants. In Europe, ants (*Myrmica rubra*) adopt the larvae of Alcon blue butterflies (*Maculinea alcon*), take them into their nests, and feed them even before they feed their own young. Female butterflies lay their eggs on marsh gentian plants (*Gentiana pneumonanthe*). The eggs hatch, and young caterpillars (early instars) feed on the plants. Chemical signals from the caterpillars fool the ants. Alcon blue butterflies are social parasites (see Chapter 46) of the ants, and the interaction is an example of one mediated by semiochemicals (see Chapter 34), demonstrating yet another example of precision in interspecific communication.

a.

b.

Figure 1

(a) Cranberries (*Vaccinium macrocarpon*) are produced from individual flowers that grow on stalks. Each plant typically produces more flowers (five to seven) than fruit (one to three). Increasing production from individual plants could increase overall production **(b)**. The extra flowers (over fruit) appear to be backup for fruit loss.

If hybrid offspring have lower fitness than those produced within each population, natural selection will favour individuals that mate only with members of their own population. Recent studies of *Drosophila* suggest that this phenomenon, called **reinforcement**, enhances reproductive isolation that had begun to develop while the populations were geographically separated. Thus, natural selection may promote the evolution of prezygotic isolating mechanisms.

18.8b Parapatric Speciation: New Species Develop When Populations Span a Barrier

Isolation may occur in a situation where a single species is distributed across a discontinuity in environmental conditions, such as a major change in soil type. Although organisms from both sides of the discontinuity can interbreed freely, natural selection may favour different alleles on either side, limiting gene flow. In such cases, parapatric speciation, speciation arising between adjacent populations, may occur if hybrid offspring have low relative fitness.

Some strains of bent grass (*Agrostis tenuis*), a common pasture plant in Great Britain, have the physiological ability to grow on mine tailings where soil is heavily polluted by copper or other metals. Plants of the copper-tolerant strains grow well on polluted soils, but plants of the pasture strain do not. Conversely, copper-tolerant plants don't survive as well as pasture plants on unpolluted soils. These strains often grow within a few metres of each other where polluted and unpolluted soils form an intricate mosaic. Because bent grass is wind pollinated, pollen is readily transferred from one strain to another.

Thomas McNeilly and Janis Antonovics crossed these strains in the laboratory and determined that they are fully interfertile (pre- and post-zygotically). However, the copper-tolerant plants flower about one week earlier than nearby pasture plants, which promotes pre-zygotic (temporal) isolation of the two strains **(Figure 18.21).** If the flowering times become further separated, the two strains may attain complete reproductive isolation and become separate species.

Some biologists argue that the places where parapatric populations of bent grass interbreed are hybrid zones where allopatric populations have established secondary contact. Unfortunately, there is no way to determine whether the hybridizing populations were parapatric or allopatric in the past. Thus, a thorough evaluation of the parapatric speciation hypothesis must await the development of techniques that enable biologists to distinguish clearly between the products of allopatric and parapatric speciation.

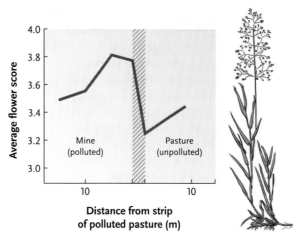

Figure 18.21

Evidence for reproductive isolation in bent grass (*Agrostis tenuis*). Comparison of flowers on bent grass growing on polluted and unpolluted soils revealed differences in flower maturity. Individual bent grass plants growing on polluted soil flowered earlier than individuals growing on unpolluted soil. The differences translated into reproductive isolation of the two populations.

18.8c Sympatric Speciation: New Species Develop in Contiguous Populations

In **sympatric speciation**, reproductive isolation evolves between distinct subgroups that arise within one population. Models of sympatric speciation do not require that the populations be either geographically or environmentally separated as their gene pools diverge. Changes in diet, behaviour, or chromosomes could effect reproductive isolation.

Insects that feed on just one or two plant species are among the animals most likely to evolve by sympatric speciation. These insects generally carry out most important life cycle activities on or near their "host" plants. Adults mate on the host plant, females lay their eggs on it, and larvae feed on the host plant's tissues, eventually developing into adults, which initiate another round of the life cycle. In many insect species, host plant choice is genetically determined. In others, individuals associate with the host plant species they ate as larvae.

Theoretically, a genetic mutation could suddenly change some insects' choice of host plant. Mutant individuals would shift their life cycle activities to the new host species and then interact primarily with others preferring the same new host, an example of ecological isolation. These individuals would collectively form a separate subpopulation, called a **host race.** Reproductive isolation could evolve between different host races if the individuals of each host race are more likely to mate with members of their own host race than with members of another. Some biologists criticize this model because it assumes that the genes controlling two traits, the insects' host plant choice and their mating preferences, change simultaneously. Moreover, host plant choice is controlled by multiple gene loci in some insect species, and it is clearly influenced by previous experience in others.

The apple maggot (*Rhagoletis pomonella*) is one of the most thoroughly studied examples of possible sympatric speciation in animals. This fly's natural host plant in eastern North America is the hawthorn (*Crataegus* species), but several new host races have appeared in just over 100 years. The larvae of a new host race were first discovered feeding on apples in New York state in the 1860s **(Figure 18.22)**. In the 1960s, a cherry-feeding host race appeared in Wisconsin.

Recent research has shown that variations at a few gene loci underlie differences in the feeding preferences of *Rhagoletis* host races. Other genetic differences cause them to develop at different rates. Moreover, adults of the three races mate during different summer months. Nevertheless, individuals show no particular preference for mates of their own host race, at least under laboratory conditions. Thus, although behavioural isolation has not developed between races, ecological and temporal isolation may separate adults in nature. Researchers are still not certain that the different host races are reproductively isolated under natural conditions.

STUDY BREAK

1. What are the three modes of speciation? What do each of their prefixes mean? How do they occur?
2. What is allopatric speciation? What are the two stages in which it occurs?
3. What is a species cluster? When does it occur?

Figure 18.22

Sympatric speciation in animals. Male and female apple maggots (*Rhagoletis pomonella*) court on a hawthorn leaf. The female will later lay her eggs on the fruit, and the offspring will feed, mate, and lay their eggs on hawthorns as well.

Dr. Jim Smith, Michigan State University

18.9 Genetic Mechanisms of Speciation

What genetic changes lead to reproductive isolation between populations, and how do these changes arise? We examine three genetic mechanisms that can lead to reproductive isolation: *genetic divergence* between allopatric populations, *polyploidy* in sympatric populations, and *chromosome alterations*, which occur independently of the geographic distributions of populations.

18.9a Genetic Divergence: When Isolated Pockets Develop in Continuous Populations

In the absence of gene flow, geographically separated populations inevitably accumulate genetic differences. Most postzygotic isolating mechanisms probably develop as accidental by-products of mutation, genetic drift, and natural selection. Natural selection cannot directly promote the evolution of reproductive isolating mechanisms between *allopatric* populations. Individuals in allopatric populations do not encounter one another and therefore have no opportunity to produce hybrids. In the absence of hybrids, natural selection cannot select against the matings that would have produced them. Natural selection may foster adaptive changes that create postzygotic reproductive isolation between populations after they reestablish contact. If postzygotic isolating mechanisms reduce the fitness of hybrids, natural selection can reinforce the evolution of prezygotic isolating mechanisms.

How much genetic divergence is necessary for speciation to occur? To understand the genetic basis of speciation in closely related species, researchers must first identify the specific causes of reproductive isolation. They then use standard techniques of genetic analysis, along with new molecular approaches such as gene mapping and sequencing, to analyze the genetic mechanisms that establish reproductive isolation. These techniques now allow researchers to determine the minimum number of genes responsible for reproductive isolation in particular pairs of species.

In cases of postzygotic reproductive isolation, mutations in a few gene loci may establish reproductive isolation. If two common species of aquarium fishes, swordtails (*Xiphophorus helleri*) and platys (*X. maculatus*), mate, two genes induce the development of lethal tumours in hybrid offspring. When hybrid sterility is the primary cause of reproductive isolation between *Drosophila* species, at least 5 to 10 gene loci are responsible. Approximately 55 gene loci contribute to postzygotic reproductive isolation between the toads *Bombina bombina* and *B. variegata*.

In cases of prezygotic reproductive isolation, some mechanisms have a surprisingly simple genetic

Mallard Ducks

Mallard Ducks   Pintail Ducks

Figure 18.23
Sexual selection and prezygotic isolation. In closely related species, such as Mallard Ducks (*Anas platyrhynchos*) and Pintails (*Anas acuta*), males have much more distinctive coloration than females, a sure sign of sexual selection.

basis. A single mutation reverses the direction of coiling (clockwise or counterclockwise) in the shells of some species of snails. Snails with shells that coil in opposite directions cannot approach each other closely enough to mate, making reproduction between them mechanically impossible.

Many traits that now function as prezygotic isolating mechanisms may originally have evolved in response to sexual selection (see Chapters 38 and 40). This evolutionary process exaggerates showy structures and courtship behaviours in males, traits that females use to identify appropriate mates. When two species encounter one another on secondary contact, these traits may also prevent interspecific mating. Many closely related species of ducks exhibit dramatic variation in the appearance of males but not females **(Figure 18.23),** an almost certain sign of sexual selection. Yet these species hybridize readily in captivity, producing offspring that are both viable and fertile. Speciation in these ducks probably resulted from geographic isolation and sexual selection without significant genetic divergence; only a few morphological and behavioural characters are responsible for their reproductive isolation. Sometimes the evolution of reproductive isolation may not require much genetic change at all.

18.9b Polyploidy: Multiples of Haploid (N) Chromosomes

Polyploidy, individuals with >2n sets of chromosomes, is common among plants, where it plays an important role in diversification and speciation. Polyploidy may also have been an important factor in the evolution of some species of fishes, amphibians, and reptiles. Polyploid individuals can arise from chromosome duplications within a single species (autopolyploidy) or through hybridization of different species (allopolyploidy). In plants, polyploids can maintain themselves for long periods of time without sexual reproduction because they reproduce vegetatively. This is not known in polyploid animals.

In **autopolyploidy (Figure 18.24),** a diploid (2n) individual may produce tetraploid (4n) offspring, each with four complete chromosome sets. Autopolyploidy occurs through an error in either mitosis or meiosis, so that gametes spontaneously receive the same

number of chromosomes as a somatic cell. Again, **unreduced gametes** do not have reduced chromosome numbers compared with somatic cells.

Tetraploids also arise when diploid pollen fertilizes diploid ovules of a self-fertilizing individual or when it fertilizes diploid eggs on another plant with unreduced gametes. Tetraploid offspring can reproduce either by self-pollination or by breeding with other tetraploid individuals. However, tetraploid plants cannot produce fertile offspring by hybridizing with its diploid parents. Fusion of a diploid gamete with a normal haploid gamete produces a triploid (3n) offspring, which is usually sterile because the odd number of chromosomes cannot segregate properly during meiosis. Thus, the tetraploid is reproductively isolated from the original diploid population. Many species of grasses, shrubs, and ornamental plants, including violets (*Viola* species), chrysanthemums (*Chrysanthemum* spp.), and nasturtiums (*Tropaelolum majus*), are autopolyploids, having anywhere from 4 to 20 complete chromosome sets.

In **allopolyploidy (Figure 18.25, p. 414),** two closely related species hybridize and subsequently form polyploid offspring. When two parent species

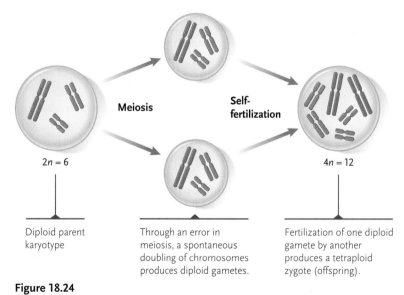

Meiosis   Self-fertilization

2n = 6   4n = 12

Diploid parent karyotype

Through an error in meiosis, a spontaneous doubling of chromosomes produces diploid gametes.

Fertilization of one diploid gamete by another produces a tetraploid zygote (offspring).

Figure 18.24
Speciation by autopolyploidy in plants. A spontaneous doubling of chromosomes during meiosis produces diploid gametes. If the plant fertilizes itself, a tetraploid zygote will be produced.

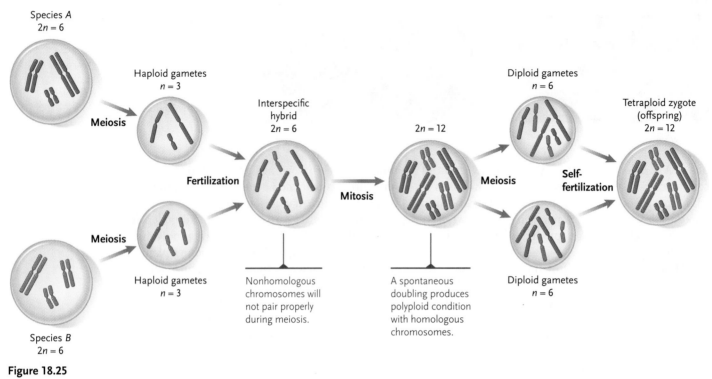

Species A
2n = 6

Haploid gametes
n = 3

Meiosis

Interspecific
hybrid
2n = 6

Fertilization

Mitosis

2n = 12

Diploid gametes
n = 6

Meiosis

Self-
fertilization

Tetraploid zygote
(offspring)
2n = 12

Meiosis

Haploid gametes
n = 3

Species B
2n = 6

Nonhomologous
chromosomes will
not pair properly
during meiosis.

A spontaneous
doubling produces
polyploid condition
with homologous
chromosomes.

Diploid gametes
n = 6

Figure 18.25

Speciation by allopolyploidy in plants. A hybrid mating between two species followed by a doubling of chromosomes during mitosis in gametes of the hybrid can instantly create sets of homologous chromosomes. Self-fertilization can then generate polyploid individuals that are reproductively isolated from both parent species.

have diverged sufficiently, their hybrid offspring are sterile because chromosomes from the two parents do not pair properly during meiosis. However, if chromosome numbers double in the interspecific hybrid, the chromosome complement of the gametes is also doubled, producing homologous chromosomes that *can* pair during meiosis. The hybrid can establish a population of a new polyploid species provided that it can produce polyploid gametes. The route to a new polyploid species can be through self-fertilization or fertilization with other doubled hybrids. When compared with speciation by genetic divergence, speciation by allopolyploidy is extremely rapid, causing a new species to arise in one generation without geographic isolation.

Even sterile polyploids are often robust, growing to a larger size than either parent species. Therefore, both autopolyploids and allopolyploids have been important to agriculture. For example, the wheat used to make flour (*Triticum aestivum*) has six sets of chromosomes (**Figure 18.26**; see Chapter 49). Other polyploid crop plants include plantains (cooking bananas), coffee, cotton, potatoes, sugarcane, and tobacco.

Plant breeders often try to increase the probability of allopolyploid formation by using chemicals that foster nondisjunction of chromosomes during mitosis (see Chapter 10). In the first such experiment, undertaken in the 1920s, scientists crossed a radish (*Raphanus sativus*) and a cabbage (*Brassica*

oleracea), hoping to develop a plant with both edible roots and leaves. Instead, the new species, *Raphanobrassica*, combined the least desirable characteristics of each parent, growing a cabbage-like root and radish-like leaves. Recent experiments have been more successful. Plant scientists have produced an allopolyploid grain, triticale, that has the disease resistance of rye and the high productivity of wheat (see Chapter 49).

18.9c Chromosome Alterations Can Lead to Genetic Isolation and Speciation

Other changes in chromosome structure or number may also foster speciation. Surveys of closely related species often uncover a substantial number of chromosome differences between them, including inversions, translocations, deletions, and duplications (see Chapter 12). These differences may foster postzygotic isolation.

Biologists use different chemical or enzymatic treatments and staining to highlight alternating light and dark bands in metaphase chromosomes. The resulting banding patterns are constant and chromosome specific, making them useful in cytogenetic mapping and karyotype analysis. In all species, banding patterns vary from one chromosome segment to another. Identical banding patterns in chromosome segments from two or more related species identify comparable portions of genomes. Banding patterns allow scientists to identify specific

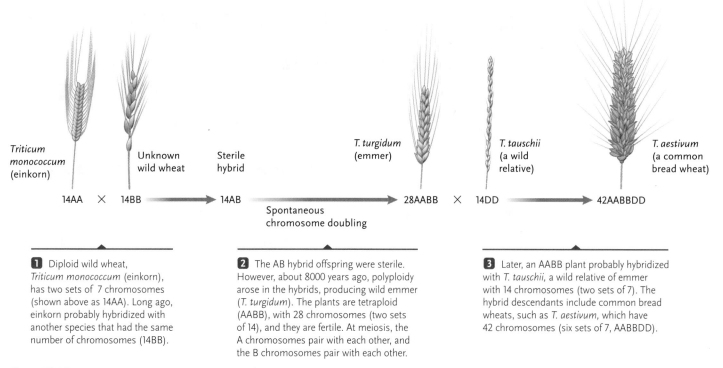

Triticum
monococcum
(einkorn)

Unknown
wild wheat

Sterile
hybrid

T. turgidum
(emmer)

T. tauschii
(a wild
relative)

T. aestivum
(a common
bread wheat)

14AA   ×   14BB   ⟶   14AB ⟶ 28AABB   ×   14DD   ⟶   42AABBDD

Spontaneous
chromosome doubling

1 Diploid wild wheat, *Triticum monococcum* (einkorn), has two sets of 7 chromosomes (shown above as 14AA). Long ago, einkorn probably hybridized with another species that had the same number of chromosomes (14BB).

2 The AB hybrid offspring were sterile. However, about 8000 years ago, polyploidy arose in the hybrids, producing wild emmer (*T. turgidum*). The plants are tetraploid (AABB), with 28 chromosomes (two sets of 14), and they are fertile. At meiosis, the A chromosomes pair with each other, and the B chromosomes pair with each other.

3 Later, an AABB plant probably hybridized with *T. tauschii*, a wild relative of emmer with 14 chromosomes (two sets of 7). The hybrid descendants include common bread wheats, such as *T. aestivum*, which have 42 chromosomes (six sets of 7, AABBDD).

Figure 18.26

The evolution of wheat (*Triticum*). Cultivated wheat grains more than 11 000 years old have been found in the eastern Mediterranean region. Researchers believe that speciation in wheat occurred through hydridization and polyploidy (see also Chapter 49).

chromosome segments and compare their positions in the chromosomes of different species.

In 1982, Jorge J. Younis and Om Prakash compared the chromosome structures of humans and their closest relatives among the apes, chimpanzees (*Pan troglodytes*), gorillas (*Gorilla gorilla*), and orangutans (*Pongo pygmaeus*). Nearly all of the 1000 bands that Younis and Prakash identified were present in all taxa, but whole sections of chromosomes have been rearranged over evolutionary time **(Figure 18.27, p. 416).** Humans have a diploid chromosome complement of 46 chromosomes, whereas chimpanzees, gorillas, and orangutans have 48. The difference can be traced to the fusion (joining together) of two ancestral chromosomes into chromosome 2 of humans. The ancestral chromosomes are separate in the other three species.

Moreover, banding patterns suggest that the position of the centromere in human chromosome 2 closely matches that of a centromere in one chimpanzee chromosome **(Figure 18.28, p. 416),** reflecting a close evolutionary relationship. But this centromere falls within an inverted region of the chromosome in gorillas and orangutans, reflecting their **evolutionary divergence** from chimpanzees and humans. Humans and chimps have different centromeric inversions in six other chromosomes.

How might such chromosome rearrangements promote speciation? In 2003, Arcadi Navarro and Nick H. Barton compared the rates of evolution in protein-coding genes within rearranged chromosome segments of humans and chimpanzees with those in genes outside rearranged segments. Proteins evolved more than twice as quickly in rearranged chromosome segments. Chromosome rearrangements inhibit chromosome pairing and recombination during meiosis. Therefore, new genetic variations favoured by natural selection would be conserved within the rearranged segments. These variations accumulate over time, contributing to genetic divergence between populations with the rearrangement and those without it. Chromosome rearrangements can be a trigger for speciation. Once a chromosome rearrangement becomes established within a population, that population will diverge more rapidly from populations lacking the rearrangement than if the rearrangement did not exist. The genetic divergence eventually causes reproductive isolation.

As important, however, are the more general genetic similarities between humans and closely related species. In 1975, genetic evidence suggested that the genomes of humans and chimps were 99% similar. Yet few people would mistake humans for chimps. Humans walk upright and have bigger brains, whereas chimps are resistant to AIDS—the list goes on and on. Genetic similarity between the two species reflects base substitutions (see Chapter 27). There are obvious differences between the brains of the two species, and in the cortex, 17.4% of the connections are specific to humans. Differences in the genomes between species can inform us about genetic isolation, but they do not provide a quantitative

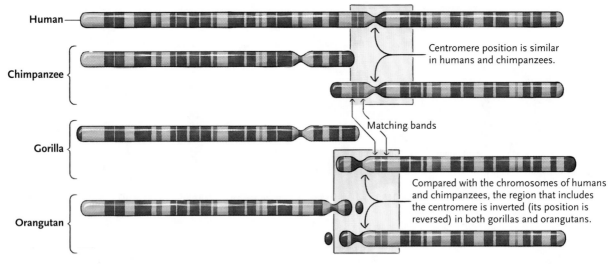

Figure 18.27

Banding patterns in chromosomes revealed by Giemsa stain. Comparison of the banding patterns of humans, chimpanzees, orangutans, and gorillas provides evidence of genetic changes associated with the evolution of these species.

Centromere position is similar in humans and chimpanzees.

Matching bands

Compared with the chromosomes of humans and chimpanzees, the region that includes the centromere is inverted (its position is reversed) in both gorillas and orangutans.

measure of differences between species (see Figure 18.28). For more discussion of humans and chimps, see Chapter 27.

STUDY BREAK

1. How does genetic divergence occur between geographically separated populations? Why does natural selection not promote the evolution of reproductive isolating mechanisms between allopatric populations?
2. In what organisms is polyploidy most common? What is the difference between autopolyploidy and allopolyploidy?

18.10 Back to the Species Concept in Biology

At this point, the dynamics of speciation should be obvious to you. Perhaps you are now better able to appreciate how species reflect the richness of biology. Species are the products of evolution, the very essence of biodiversity. But you also will know that it is naive to believe that one definition of species will apply across biology. Be cautious of evidence that does not make sense, of claims that do not seem entirely credible. Differences and similarities between humans and chimps (for example) are no better expressed by a few linear measurements of bones or organs than they are by genomes.

Figure 18.28

Through evolution, the gain (+) in the number of copies of some genes and the loss (−) of others have contributed to human–chimp differences. Shown here are gain and loss data for rodents (mouse and rat) and primates (human and chimpanzee). These changes contributed to differences between these animals.

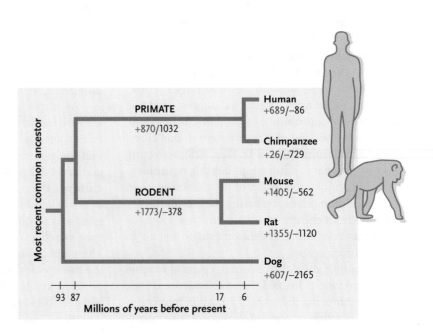

Should gardeners be permitted to use introduced plants in their gardens? How would you define "introduced"?

How do data on the distribution and genetics of starlings (*Sturnis vulgaris*) and Italian wall lizards influence your concept of species?

Review

Go to CENGAGENOW™ at http://hed.nelson.com/ to access quizzing, animations, exercises, articles, and personalized homework help.

18.1 What's in a "Name?"

- Biologists use names to precisely identify species, subspecies, or varieties. Other animals also use "names" or signals to refer to different organisms.

- Biologists use almost any available feature to identify species. Traditionally, morphological features were most important, but now behavioural and genetic features also are commonly used.

18.2 Definition of "Species"

- According to the Biological Species Concept, a species is a group of organisms that can interbreed and produce fertile offspring; however, this definition does not deal with organisms that reproduce asexually, nor does it apply well to species that hybridize and produce fertile offspring. Other species concepts are phylogenetic (a species is a group of organisms bound by a unique evolutionary ancestry) and ecological (a species is a group of organisms sharing a distinct ecological niche).

- Androdioecous species are composed of males and hermaphrodites (which produce both sperm and eggs), whereas gynogenetic species consist only of females. The egg of gynogenetic species requires mechanical stimulation by sperm donated from males of other species to begin development and achieve reproduction.

- Sexual reproduction involves genetic recombination. In *Daphnia pulex*, mutations in mitochondrial protein-coding genes are more frequent in individuals reproducing asexually compared with those reproducing sexually, demonstrating an advantage of recombination, the reduction in the number of mutations.

18.3 One Size Does Not Fit All

- Gene flow among individuals in a population of conspecifics mixes their genetic material and is said to act like "glue" holding that species together. Individuals of different species are genetically isolated, but species that produce fertile hybrids may not be naturally isolated (are they, in fact, species?).

- According to the Morphological Species Concept, individuals of the same species share measurable traits that distinguish them from individuals of other species. Paleontologists use morphology to identify fossils to species, as do naturalists identifying animals and plants in the field.

18.4 Gene Flow: Four Examples

- Distribution influences gene flow, and sparsely distributed species may experience less gene flow than those with a continuous distribution. Species may depend on other species for dispersal (hitchhike). Social behaviour also can limit gene flow within continuous populations. Changes in habitat continuity affect gene flow, and a discontinuous habitat may inhibit gene flow between populations.

18.6 Geographic Variation

- Subspecies are local variants of a species that consist of usually geographically separated populations exhibiting recognizable phenotypic and/or genotypic variations. Subspecies may interbreed where their distributions overlap. Terms such as variants, cultivars, or breeds are used to identify distinct populations.

- In ring species, adjacent populations exchange genetic material directly, and gene flow between distant populations occurs only through the intermediate populations. Clinal changes are smooth patterns of variation along a geographic gradient. Clines occur when there is gene flow between adjacent populations that are adapting to slightly different conditions.

18.7 Reproductive Isolation

- Reproductive isolating mechanisms are biological characteristics preventing gene pools of two sympatric species from mixing. Prezygotic isolating mechanisms prevent fertilization. Postzygotic isolating mechanisms operate after fertilization.

- Ecological isolation occurs between species that live in different habitats in the same area. Temporal isolation occurs between species living in the same habitat but mating at different times (of the day or year). Behavioural isolation results when the signals used by one species to identify a potential mate are not recognized by the other species. Mechanical isolation occurs when differences in the structure of reproductive organs or other body parts prevent interbreeding of species. Gametic isolation occurs when the sperm of one species are incompatible with the eggs of another.

- When sperm from one species does fertilize an egg of another species, postzygotic isolating mechanisms may reduce the fitness of hybrids. Hybrid inviability results when developmental programs of the two parent species are incompatible. Some hybrids develop into healthy adults but cannot produce functional gametes. Hybrid breakdown happens when hybrids are healthy and fully fertile, but their offspring exhibit reduced fitness.

18.8 Geography of Speciation

- Allopatric, parapatric, and sympatric speciation reflect the meanings of *allo* = different, *para* = beside, and *sym* = together.

- Allopatric speciation occurs when a physical barrier subdivides a large population or when a small population becomes separated from the species' main geographic distribution. A species cluster results after founding populations colonize an island or isolated land mass. Secondary contact occurs when allopatric populations reestablish contact after a barrier between them is eliminated.

- Parapatric speciation occurs when a species is distributed across a discontinuity in environmental conditions so that natural selection favours different alleles and phenotypes on either side of the discontinuity.

- Sympatric speciation occurs among subgroups of a population. Neither geographic nor reproductive isolation is necessary for sympatric speciation to occur. Changes in diet, behaviour, or chromosomes can cause sympatric speciation.

18.9 Genetic Mechanisms of Speciation

- Geographically separated populations experience no gene flow, allowing accumulation of genetic differences. Natural selection cannot directly promote speciation between allopatric populations.

- Polyploidy, multiples of N (haploid) chromosomes, is more common in plants than in animals. Autopolyploidy arises from chromosome duplications within a single species. It results when an error in mitosis or meiosis causes individuals to spontaneously receive the same number of chromosomes as a somatic cell. Polyploid individuals are produced when unreduced gametes join in fertilization. Allopolyploidy results from the hybridization of different species. Polyploidy is often important in the development of domesticated species.

Questions

Self-Test Questions

1. The Biological Species Concept defines species on the basis of
   a. reproductive characteristics.
   b. genetic characteristics.
   c. morphological characteristics.
   d. behavioural characteristics.
   e. all of the above.

2. Biologists can apply the Biological Species Concept most confidently to species that
   a. reproduce asexually.
   b. lived in the past.
   c. are allopatric.
   d. hybridize in captivity.
   e. reproduce sexually.

3. A _____ occurs when there are smooth changes in populations distributed along a geographic gradient.
   a. ring species
   b. subspecies
   c. cline
   d. hybridization zone
   e. subspecies

4. Gene flow in marine snails (*Balea perversa*) is directly assisted by
   a. ocean currents.
   b. migrating birds.
   c. migrating whales.
   d. shipping.
   e. none of the above.

5. Prezygotic isolating mechanisms
   a. reduce the fitness of hybrid offspring.
   b. generally prevent individuals of different species from mating.
   c. are found only in animals.
   d. are found only in plants.
   e. are observed only in organisms that reproduce asexually.

6. In allopatric speciation, geographic separation of two populations
   a. is sufficient for speciation to occur.
   b. occurs only after speciation is complete.
   c. allows gene flow between them.
   d. reduces the relative fitness of hybrid offspring.
   e. inhibits gene flow between them.

7. Adjacent populations producing hybrid offspring with low relative fitness may be undergoing
   a. clinal isolation.
   b. parapatric speciation.
   c. allopatric speciation.
   d. sympatric speciation.
   e. geographic isolation.

8. Lack of gene flow is a major contributor to speciation in
   a. rodents.
   b. birds.
   c. lichens.
   d. polyploids.
   e. hermaphrodites.

9. Which of the following could be an example of allopolyploidy?
   a. One parent has 32 chromosomes, the other has 10, and their offspring have 42.
   b. Gametes and somatic cells have the same number of chromosomes.
   c. Chromosome number increases by one in a gamete and in the offspring it produces.
   d. Chromosome number decreases by one in a gamete and in the offspring it produces.
   e. Chromosome number in the offspring is exactly half of what it is in the parents.

10. Which of the following genetic characteristics is shared by humans and chimpanzees?
   a. They have the same number of chromosomes.
   b. The position of the centromere on human chromosome 2 matches the position of a centromere on a chimpanzee chromosome.
   c. A fusion of ancestral chromosomes formed chromosome 2 in humans.
   d. Centromeres on all of their chromosomes fall within inverted chromosome segments.
   e. All of the above.

Questions for Discussion

1. Domestic dogs (*Canis familiaris*) and cats (*Felis cattus*) each represent a single species. How do you explain differences in the range of size and appearance in these two species? Do they interbreed with other species? How does this reconcile with the definition of species? (See also Chapter 49.)

2. How do genetic differences between humans and other species of great apes translate into evolution in this group? (See also Chapter 27.)

3. If intermediate populations in a ring species go extinct, eliminating the possibility of gene flow between populations at the two ends of the ring, would you now identify those remaining populations as full species? Explain your answer.

4. What will happen when the genetic integrity of a species is extensively compromised? Consider the case of peregrine falcons (*Falco peregrinus*). This species was listed as endangered, but widespread reintroductions, reproductive success, and reduced levels of DDT have brought it back from the brink of extinction. Some of the reintroductions were from stock not native to the areas of reintroduction. Or consider the case of wild grapes (*Vitus vinifera*) contaminated by genes from domesticated grapes, or grey wolves (*Canis lupis*) and red wolves (*Canis rufus*) contaminated by genes from coyotes (*Canis latrans*).

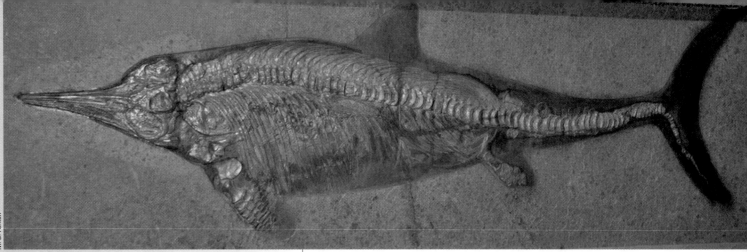

M. B. Fenton

An ichthyosaur (*Stenopterygius* spp.) from Germany on display in the Royal Tyrrell Museum in Drumheller, Alberta. Although this specimen is about 2 m long, the largest ichthyosaurs were up to 15 m in length. As adults, the smallest were about 70 cm long.

19 Evolution and Classification

WHY IT MATTERS

Understanding and documenting the diversity of life is a major challenge to biologists. This exercise means determining evolutionary relationships between organisms and deciding if similar structures or similar-looking structures are grounds for grouping species together. In other words, if they look the same, are they closely related in an evolutionary sense? Before you dismiss this as an easy exercise, remember that when first discovered, fossil ichthyosaurs were thought to be the remains of fish. Only later were they recognized as reptiles. Small wonder: ichthyosaurs have fishlike bodies, but so do dolphins and other whales (Cetacea), and they are mammals. Many aquatic vertebrates have fishlike bodies—think of sharks (cartilaginous fishes) and tunas (bony fishes). But these are two very different kinds of "fish." Other fish have very different bodies—think of eels, flatfish, anglerfish, or sea horses.

There is a tendency among organisms living under the same conditions to develop similar body forms. This can be called parallel or convergent evolution, depending on the evolutionary relatedness of the organisms involved. Convergent evolution refers to more distantly related organisms, parallel to more closely related ones. How do you tell?

Cacti and euphorbs are two groups of desert plants that can be strikingly similar in appearance **(Figure 19.1)**. But cacti and euphorbs are not closely related in an evolutionary sense. Similarity in appearance does not always mean relatedness. The same applies to earthworms (phylum Annelida) and caecilians (phylum Chordata), two terrestrial "worm-like" animals **(Figure 19.2)**. Resemblance does not necessarily mean relatedness.

Knowing what an organism is can be crucial. This sometimes means making an accurate identification by looking beyond superficial resemblances. Many people collect and eat mushrooms. Now, the fruiting bodies of many species of mushrooms are superficially similar, but you need to be sure what you are eating. There are some obvious "right" and "wrong" choices for the table **(Figure 19.3)**. Whereas true morels (*Morchella* species) are delicacies, false morels (*Gyromitra esculenta*) can be deadly because they contain gyromitrin, a hemolytic toxin (see *Molecule Behind Biology*). In

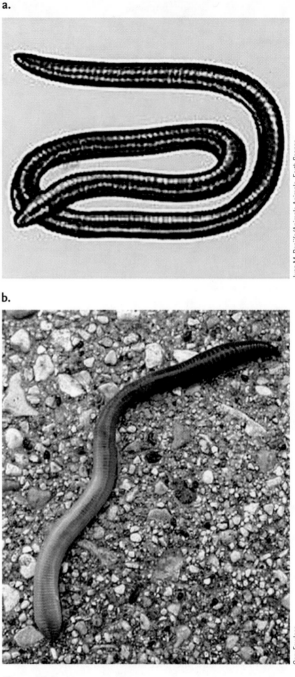

Juan M. Renjifo/Animals Animals–Earth Scenes

Figure 19.2
Two wormlike animals from different phyla. **(a)** The caecilian (Phylum Chordata) and **(b)** the earthworm (Phylum Annelida) are superficially similar, but the former has a backbone, a skull, and jaws, whereas the latter does not.

Gary Fewless

a. Cactus

Edward S. Ross

b. Spurge

Edward S. Ross

Figure 19.1
Convergent evolution in plants. **(a)** *Echinocereus* and other North American cacti (family Cactaceae) are strikingly similar to **(b)** *Euphorbia* and other African spurges (Euphorbeaceae). Convergent evolution adapted both groups to desert environments. Each has thick, water-storing stems, spiny structures that discourage animals from feeding on them, CAM photosynthesis (see Chapter 7), and stomata that open only at night.

the same spirit, choosing *Cantherellus ciabarius* (chanterelle) for dinner is epicurian, whereas *Omphalotus illudens* (jack-o'-lantern) is not. Jack-o'-lanterns are very poisonous. *Hygrophoropsis aurantiacus* (false chanterelle) looks like *C. ciabarius* and *O. illudens* but may not be poisonous. Why do they resemble one another?

If you are going mushroom hunting, know your quarry or at least work with someone who really does.

Gyromitrin

First isolated in 1885, gyromitrin **(Figure 1)** was originally known as "helvellic acid." This toxin can kill people, demonstrated by 74 of 513 fatal cases described in the medical literature between 1782 and 1965. In 1975, a case report described the death of a 53-year-old woman who had eaten some raw mushrooms she picked in the fields. The day after eating them, she was vomiting and had diarrhea. After receiving treatment in a "minor" hospital, she was transferred to a university hospital, where she was placed in the intensive care unit. She died there a few hours after being admitted. Her symptoms included a severely swollen liver, edema, necrosis, fatty degeneration in the liver, nephrosis—the list goes on.

The moral: know your mushrooms. By the way, although there is a folk tradition that toxins such as gyromitrin are neutralized by cooking, it is not wise to count on this view because human fatalities have been reported after people ate mushrooms that had been cooked and whose juices had been removed. Her case demonstrates the folly of eating raw wild mushrooms and the importance of knowing how to identify the mushrooms you pick for consumption.

Gyromitrin is the toxin produced by false morels (*Gyromitra esculenta*; see Figure 19.3b). It is important to be able to distinguish false morels from real morels (*Morchellus esculenta*; see Figure 19.3a) because eating false morels can kill you. Poisoning by gyromitrin appears to be most common in Eastern Europe and Germany.

As we have seen (see Chapter 18), other fungi use odours to attract animals to disperse spores, and rusts may use false flowers to effect fertilization (see Figure 19.4). Why do mushrooms have toxins? The topic of mushroom toxins was addressed by Discorides, a Greek surgeon, who was

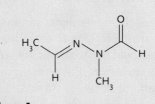

Figure 1
Gyromitrin is produced by the false morel, *Gyromitra esculenta*.

in Nero's army during the first century A.D. He is reported as saying that "of fungi there is a double difference, for either they are edible, or they are poisonous." How do toxic mushrooms signal their condition? Many species of organisms use visual, olfactory, or acoustic signals to warn would-be predators of the risks they pose (see Chapter 46). It is possible that poisonous mushrooms use olfactory cues to signal their condition. If so, humans are not the main predators of false morels.

Figure 19.3
People who know their mushrooms collect, cook, and eat **(a)** *Morchellus esculenta* and **(c)** *Cantherellus ciabrius*, a morel and a chanterelle, respectively. They never eat **(b)** *Gromitra esculenta*, the false morel, or **(e)** *Omphalotus illudens* (jack-o'-lantern) because they are deadly. They might watch someone else try **(d)** *Hygrophoropsis aurantiacus*, the false chanterelle that may (or may not) be toxic.

19.1 The Significance of Similarities and Differences

One of the excitements and satisfactions in biology is learning to look at something, recognize it, and understand just what you are seeing. Below are three cases, examples of where even an experienced biologist might be fooled. At first, this may seem strange or even preposterous when you know what a flower looks like; surely, you will always recognize one. Read on to see that things are not always as they appear.

19.1a Case 1: Fake Flowers

You may be astonished to realize that what you thought was a flower **(Figure 19.4a, b)** is actually a leaf modified by a fungus. The fungus, the rust *Puccinia monoica*, affects the growth of the leaves, changing their appearance and odour. The fungus-induced "flowers" have nectaries (glands that produce nectar; **Figure 19.4c**). Just as many biologists are fooled by the flower-like leaves, so are insects that come to pollinate the flowers. In this way, the rust effects fertilization. The rust also inhibits the formation of the plant's own flowers, minimizing confusion among pollinators. So when is a flower not a flower?

19.1b Case 2: Carnivorous Plants

In some places, there may be an abundance of water and sunlight, but nitrogen is in short supply for plants. Here we find a diversity of ways that plants trap insects to directly (or indirectly) obtain nitrogen (**Figure 19.5;** see Figure 3.21, Box 47.5). Like people trying to catch insects (but perhaps not for their nitrogen), plants use different methods, including sticky traps (flypaper), snap traps, and pitfall traps (pitchers). Flypaper traps have appeared in at least five evolutionary lines of plants and pitchers at least three times. Not all carnivorous plants share a close common ancestor.

Figure 19.4
(a) There is an obvious difference between an uninfected *Boerchera* species (left) and an infected one (right). **(b)** When infected by the fungus *Puccinia monoica*, a rust, the leaves of *Boerchera* become flower-like and **(c)** appear to produce nectar. The rust inhibits flowering so that insects visiting the "flowers" to collect nectar fertilize the rust. The insects do not visit the host plant's flowers.

19.1c Case 3: Mammals with Flat Tails Are Not Always Beavers

In 2006, the news media reported a science story about a "Mesozoic beaver" **(Figure 19.6)**. This was an exciting fossil find from China, and as long as you focused on the broad, flattened tail, the "beaver" part of the name made sense. This mammal, *Castorocauda lutrasimilis* (see **Figure 19.6a**), had modified tail vertebrae flattened like those of living beavers (rodents in the genus *Castor*) (see **Figure 19.6b**). But beavers are not the only aquatic mammals with flattened tails. Another good example is *Ornithorhynchus anatinus*, the duck-billed platypus of Australia (see **Figure 19.6c**). If you look at the skulls of the Mesozoic beaver, a modern beaver, and a platypus, the differences are striking **(Figure 19.7)**. It appears that the giant beaver (*Casteroides ohioensis*) of the North American Pleistocene may not have had a flattened tail, so there is more to being a beaver than having a flat tail!

These examples demonstrate why biologists must look closely at the details. Flowerlike structures are not always flowers. Carnivorous plants are not necessarily closely related. Looking at a mammal's tail may give you a different picture of its relationships than its skull.

The purpose of this chapter is to introduce you to classification, systematic biology, and taxonomy and give you an idea of how biologists proceed to document and understand diversity and evolution. This means giving you information about how biologists assess the importance of characters when studying evolution. Put another way, we will try to understand how biologists distinguish between parallel and convergent evolution.

STUDY BREAK

1. What is a flower? Name an example of a flowerlike structure that is not a flower.
2. How do carnivorous plants catch insects? Why?

19.2 Systematic Biology: An Overview

Systematic biology, classification, and taxonomy help us organize and understand information about the biological world. Biologists benefit from the work done on systematics and classification whether they study molecules or ecosystems or work in biotechnology or conservation. Knowing the identity of the organism of interest is the first step to finding out what already is known about it.

The science of **systematics** has two major goals. One is to reconstruct the **phylogeny** or evolutionary history of a group of organisms. Phylogenies are presented as **phylogenetic trees**, which are formal hypotheses identifying likely relationships among species. Like all hypotheses, they can be tested with data and often are revised as scientists gather new data.

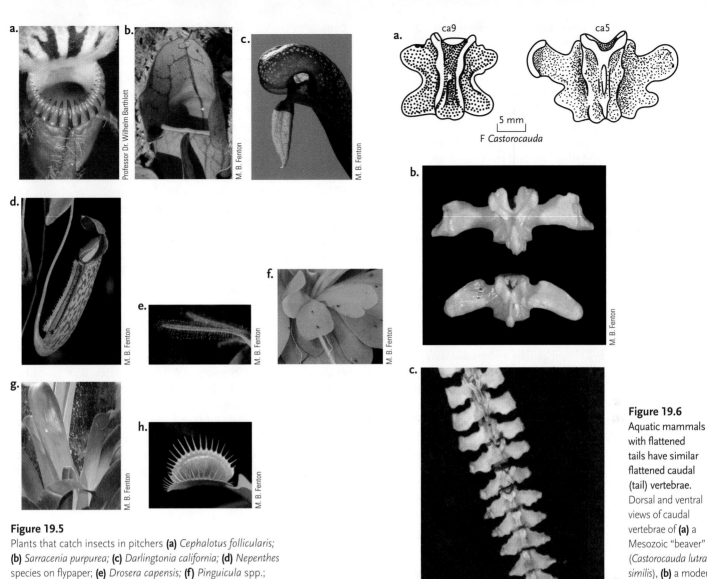

Figure 19.6
Aquatic mammals with flattened tails have similar flattened caudal (tail) vertebrae. Dorsal and ventral views of caudal vertebrae of **(a)** a Mesozoic "beaver" (*Castorocauda lutrasimilis*), **(b)** a modern beaver (*Castor canadensis*), and **(c)** a duck-billed platypus (*Ornithorhynchos anatinus*). Note the similarities in structure.

Figure 19.5
Plants that catch insects in pitchers **(a)** *Cephalotus follicularis;* **(b)** *Sarracenia purpurea;* **(c)** *Darlingtonia california;* **(d)** *Nepenthes* species on flypaper; **(e)** *Drosera capensis;* **(f)** *Pinguicula* spp.; **(g)** *Brocchinia reducta,* or in a snap trap **(h)** *Dioneae muscipula.*

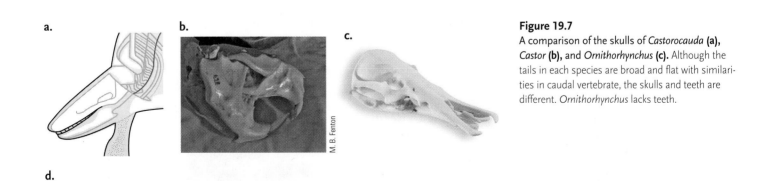

Figure 19.7
A comparison of the skulls of *Castorocauda* **(a)**, *Castor* **(b)**, and *Ornithorhynchus* **(c).** Although the tails in each species are broad and flat with similarities in caudal vertebrate, the skulls and teeth are different. *Ornithorhynchus* lacks teeth.

Accurate phylogenetic trees are essential components of the comparative method that biologists use to analyze evolutionary processes. Robust phylogenetic hypotheses allow us to distinguish similarities inherited from a common ancestor from those that evolved independently in response to similar environments.

The second goal of systematics is **taxonomy**, the identification and naming of species and their placement in a classification. A **classification** is an arrangement of organisms into hierarchical groups that reflect their relatedness. Most systematists want classifications to mirror phylogenetic history and, thus, the adaptive radiation (evolutionary history) of the group of organisms in question. This is discussed in more detail in Sections 19.4 and 19.5.

Data collected and organized by systematists allow biologists to select appropriate organisms for their work. Many biological experiments are first conducted with individuals of a single species, preferably one that is a closed genetic system that may respond uniquely to experimental conditions. If a researcher inadvertently used two species that responded differently, the mixed results probably would not make much sense. Selecting a species that is androdieocous or gynogenetic (see Chapter 18) could be a mistake—or a canny strategy depending on the research question driving the work.

STUDY BREAK

1. What evolutionary process explains why organisms living in the same conditions develop similar body forms?
2. What are two major goals of systematics, and how are they presented?
3. Why are phylogenetic trees essential for comparison and analysis of evolutionary processes?

19.3 The Linnaean System of Classification

The practice of naming and classifying organisms originated with the Swedish naturalist Carl von Linné (1707–1778), better known by his Latinized name, Carolus Linnaeus. A professor at the University of Uppsala, he developed the basic system of naming and classifying organisms still in use today. The naming of newly discovered species follows a formal process of publishing a description of the species in a scientific journal. International commissions meet periodically to settle disputes about scientific names. As we have seen (see Chapter 1), the rules for naming organisms differ between botanists and zoologists.

An effective classification, whether of organisms on Earth or of books in a library, gives users access to information. Linnaeus described and named thousands of species on the basis of their similarities and differences. Keeping track of so many species was no easy task, so he devised a **taxonomic hierarchy** for arranging organisms into ever more inclusive categories **(Figure 19.8)**. A **family** is a group of genera that closely resemble one another. Similar families are grouped into **orders**, similar orders into **classes**, similar classes into **phyla** (singular, *phylum*), and similar phyla into **kingdoms**. Finally, all life on Earth is classified into three **domains** (see Chapter 3). The organisms included within any category of the taxonomic hierarchy comprise a **taxon** (plural, *taxa*). Woodpeckers, for example, are a taxon (Picidae) at the family level, and pine trees are a taxon (*Pinus*) at the genus level.

The next step in the study of evolution is determining which species are most closely related to one another. Rather than learning the features that distinguish species A from species B, we want to know which characteristics some species have in common and can be used to place the species in the same genus and family. When Linnaeus focused on external anatomy and considered birds, he noted that all birds are oviparous (egg-laying) animals with feathered bodies, two wings, two feet, and a bony beak. Is this evidence that birds share a common ancestor?

STUDY BREAK

1. What is a taxonomic hierarchy?
2. What categories are used in the Linnaean system of classification?

Domain *Eukarya*
Kingdom *Animalia*
Phylum *Chordata*
Class *Mammalia*
Order *Rodentia*
Family *Castoridae*
Genus *Castor*
Species *Castor canadensis*

M. B. Fenton

Figure 19.8
The Linnaean hierarchy of classification. The classification of the Canadian beaver (*Castor canadensis*) reflects its similarity to other species in the genus *Castor* and its placement by family, order, class, phylum, kingdom, and domain.

19.4 From Classification to Phylogeny

For at least 200 years, systematists relied on organismal traits (mainly morphology) when analyzing evolutionary relationships and classifying organisms. In the wake of Linnaeus, they developed phylogenies based on characteristics such as chromosomal anatomy; details of physiological functioning; morphology of subcellular structures, cells, organ systems, and whole organisms; and patterns of behaviour. Today, systematists also use molecular sequences of nucleic acids and proteins as additional characters when deriving phylogenies.

19.5 Evaluating Systematic Characters

Systematists use guidelines to select characters for study. As we saw previously, there is more to being a beaver than being a mammal with a flattened tail. Systematists seek characters that are independent markers of underlying genetic similarity and differentiation. Ideally, systematists create phylogenetic hypotheses and classifications by analyzing the genetic changes that caused speciation and differentiation. But the fossil record is not complete, so often systematists must rely on phenotypic traits as indicators of genetic similarity or divergence. Systematists study traits in which phenotypic variation reflects genetic differences. They try to exclude differences caused by environmental conditions.

Useful systematic characters must be genetically *independent*, reflecting different parts of organisms' genomes. This precaution is necessary because different organismal characters can have the same genetic basis. We want to use each genetic variation only once in an analysis. For example, tropical lizards in the genus *Anolis* can climb trees because they get a grip (purchase) on the bark from small adhesive pads on the underside of their toes. The number of pads varies from species to species and toe to toe. Researchers have used the number of pads on the fourth toe of the left hind foot as a systematic character. They do not use the number of pads on the fourth toe of the right hind foot as a *separate* character because the same genes almost certainly control the number of pads on the toes of both feet. The point here is not the fine-grained detail about toes, but rather the kinds of characters that can be used when assembling a picture of adaptive radiation.

The limbs of tetrapod vertebrates are homologous characters, and they are useful in preparing phylogenies. Such phenotypic similarities between organisms reflect underlying genetic similarities.

Systematic analyses rely on the comparison of homologous characters as indicators of common ancestry and genetic relatedness.

Analogous characters are homoplasious **(homoplasies)**, phenotypic similarities that evolved independently in different lineages. For example, the flattened tails of aquatic mammals noted above appear to be homoplasious. By definition, analogous characters serve a similar function in different species. Systematists exclude homoplasies from their analyses because homoplasies provide no information about shared (genetic) ancestry.

But where their function has changed, homologous structures (inherited from a common ancestor) can differ considerably among species. The stapes, a bone in the middle ear of tetrapod vertebrates, evolved from (is homologous to) the hyomandibula, a bone that supports the jaw joint of most fishes. The structure, position, and function of the hyomandibular are different in tetrapods than they are in fishes **(Figure 19.9)**.

The situation can be complex. For example, flight in animals has evolved at least four times (bats, birds, insects, pterosaurs). Bones in the wings of flying vertebrates (bats, birds, and pterosaurs) are homologous **(Figure 19.10, p. 426)**. They have the same basic structural elements (arm, wrist, and hand) with similar spatial relationships to each other and to the bones that attach the wing to the rest of the skeleton (shoulder girdle). Wing bones of bats, birds, and pterosaurs are homologous to the forelimbs of other tetrapods.

But the large flat surfaces of bird wings are homoplasious with those of bats and pterosaurs. The flight surfaces of birds are made of feathers, whereas those of

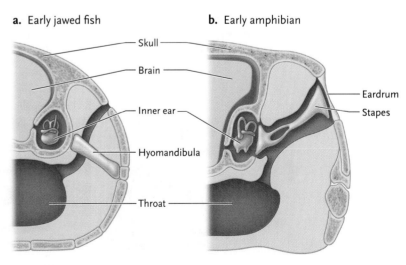

a. Early jawed fish   **b.** Early amphibian

Skull

Brain

Eardrum

Stapes

Inner ear

Hyomandibula

Throat

Figure 19.9

Homologous bones, different structures and functions. **(a)** The hyomandibula, which braced the jaw joint against the skull in early jawed fishes, is homologous to **(b)** the stapes, which transmits sound to the inner ear in four-legged vertebrates, exemplified here by an early amphibian. Both diagrams show a cross section through the head just behind the jaw joint.

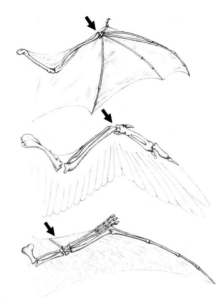

Figure 19.10
Arm, hand, and finger bones supporting the wings of a bat **(a)**, a bird **(b)**, and a pterosaur **(c)**. Note the position of the wrists (arrow). In this feature, bats and birds are more similar to one another than either is to the pterosaur.

bats and pterosaurs are made of skin. Therefore, one could assert that in their flight membranes, birds are convergent with bats and pterosaurs. When we add insects to the comparison **(Figure 19.11)**, their wings are surely convergent with those of bats, birds, and pterosaurs. In this situation, the wings of vertebrates could be considered examples of parallel evolution. If you go to the fine details, the basic elements supporting the wings of bats, birds, and pterosaurs are homologous. However, the details of the forearm, hand, and finger bones differ substantially among these three groups of animals. The example of wings illustrates that the distinction between parallel and convergent evolution is based on closeness of relationships.

Homologous characters emerge from comparable embryonic structures and grow in similar ways during development. Systematists have put great stock in embryological indications of homology on the assumption that evolution has conserved the pattern of embryonic development in related organisms. Indeed, recent discoveries in evolutionary developmental biology have revealed that some genetic controls of developmental pathways can be very similar across a wide variety of organisms (e.g., *Pax6* genes control the development of eyes; see Chapters 1 and 39).

Mosaic evolution refers to the reality that in all evolutionary lineages, some characteristics evolve slowly, whereas others evolve rapidly. Mosaic evolution is pervasive. Every species displays a mixture of **ancestral characters** (old forms of traits) and **derived characters** (new forms of traits). Derived characters provide the most useful information about evolutionary relationships because once a derived character becomes established, it is usually present in all of that species' descendants. Thus, unless they are lost or replaced by newer characters over evolutionary time, derived characters can serve as markers for entire evolutionary lineages.

Systematists score characters as either ancestral or derived only when comparing them among organisms. Thus, any particular character is derived *only in relation to* what occurs in other organisms, which could be either an older version of the same character or, in the case of an entirely new trait, the absence of it altogether.

Most species of animals lack a **vertebral column**, which is a defining feature for vertebrates, the animal lineage that includes fishes, amphibians, reptiles, birds, and mammals. Thus, when systematists compare vertebrates with all animals lacking a vertebral column, they score the absence of a vertebral column as the ancestral condition and the presence of a vertebral column as derived.

Systematists distinguish between ancestral and derived characters to ascertain in which direction a character has evolved. In some cases, the fossil record is detailed enough to provide unambiguous information about the direction of evolution. For example, biologists are confident that the presence of a vertebral

a. Caddis fly **b.** Orange palm dart butterfly **c.** Monarch butterfly

Figure 19.11
Outgroup comparison. Most adult insects, like **(a)** the caddis fly (family Limnephilidae) and **(b)** the orange palm dart butterfly (*Cephrenes auglades*, family Hesperiidae), have six walking legs. This comparison of butterflies with other insects suggests that the four walking legs of the **(c)** monarch butterfly (*Danaeus plexippus*, family Nymphalidae) represent the derived character state.

column is a derived character because fossils of the earliest animals lack backbones.

Systematists frequently use **outgroup comparison** to identify ancestral and derived characters. This involves comparing the group under study with more distantly related species not otherwise included in the analysis. Most modern butterflies have six walking legs. But some species in two families (Nymphalidae and Papillionidae) have four walking legs and two small, nonwalking legs (see Figure 19.11). Which is the ancestral character state, and which is derived? Outgroup comparison with other insects, most of which have six walking legs as adults, suggests that six walking legs is an ancestral character and four is a derived character. The same would apply when trying to understand the almost legless condition of female bagworms (Psychidae), another group of butterflies.

STUDY BREAK

1. What are outgroup comparisons?
2. How are ancestral characters different from derived ones?
3. What do *Pax 6* genes do? Where are they found?

19.6 Phylogenetic Inference and Classification

Phylogenetic trees portray the evolutionary diversification of lineages as a hierarchy that reflects the branching pattern of evolution. Each branch represents the descendants of a single ancestral species. When converting the phylogenetic tree into a classification, systematists use the **principle of monophyly.** They try to define **monophyletic taxa,** those derived from a single ancestral species **(Figure 19.12).** By contrast, **polyphyletic**

taxa include species from separate evolutionary lineages. If, based on the presence of wings, bats, birds, pterosaurs, and insects were placed in one taxonomic group (flying animals), it would be polyphyletic. A **paraphyletic taxon** includes an ancestor and some, but not all, of its descendants. The traditional taxon class Reptilia is paraphyletic (see Chapter 27).

Many systematists also strive to create parsimonious phylogenetic hypotheses. Here they include the fewest possible evolutionary changes to account for the diversity within a lineage. The justification of this approach is the **assumption of parsimony,** or that the simplest explanation should be the most accurate. This means that any particular evolutionary change is an unlikely event and presumably happened only once in any evolutionary lineage. Following this assumption, it is unlikely that the same change evolved twice in one lineage. Phylogenetic trees are representations of hypotheses that place all organisms on a single branch. For example, the portrayal of birds on a single evolutionary branch implies that feathered wings evolved once in their common ancestor. This hypothesis is more parsimonious than one proposing that feathered wings evolved independently in two or more vertebrate lineages. The monophyly of birds is not contradicted by the repeated evolution of flightlessness in this group.

19.6a Traditional Evolutionary Systematics: Using Phenotypic Similarities and Differences to Classify Organisms According to Their Evolutionary History

For a century after the publication of Charles Darwin's book *On the Origin of Species by Means of Natural Selection* (see Chapter 20), most systematists followed Linnaeus's practice of using phenotypic similarities and differences to infer evolutionary relationships. This approach, called **traditional evolutionary systematics,** groups together species that share ancestral and derived

Monophyletic taxon

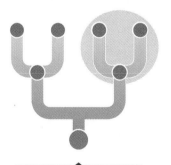

A monophyletic taxon includes an ancestral species and all of its descendants.

Polyphyletic taxon

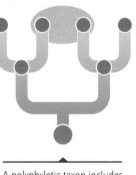

A polyphyletic taxon includes species from different evolutionary lineages.

Paraphyletic taxon

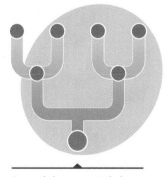

A paraphyletic taxon includes an ancestral species and only some of its descendants.

Figure 19.12

Defining taxa in a classification. Systematists can create different classifications from the same phylogenetic tree by identifying different groups of species as a single taxon (shaded).

characters. Mammals are defined by their internal skeleton, vertebral column, and four limbs—ancestral characters among tetrapod vertebrates. But mammals also have hair, mammary glands, and a four-chambered heart (see Chapter 27). These are derived characters.

Classifications produced by traditional systematics reflect evolutionary branching and morphological divergence **(Figure 19.13a)**. Among tetrapod vertebrates, the amphibian and mammalian lineages diverged early, followed shortly by the divergence of the turtle lineage and then that of other reptiles. After this, subsequent divergences produced two groups: lepidosaurs that gave rise to lizards and snakes and archosaurs that gave rise to crocodilians, dinosaurs, and birds. Although crocodilians outwardly resemble lizards, they share a more recent common ancestor with birds. Yet birds differ from crocodilians in many morphological characters.

Even though the phylogenetic tree of tetrapod vertebrates shows six living groups, the traditional classification recognizes four classes: Amphibia,

Mammalia, Reptilia, and Aves (birds). These groups (classes in classification) are given equal ranking because each represents a distinctive body plan and way of life. The class Reptilia, however, is a paraphyletic taxon because it includes *some* descendants of the common ancestor (located at A in Figure 19.13a), namely turtles, lizards, snakes, and crocodilians, but omits birds and therefore does not include all of the descendants.

Traditional evolutionary systematists justify this definition of Reptilia because it includes morphologically similar animals with close evolutionary relationships. Crocodilians are classified with lizards, snakes, and turtles because they share a common ancestry and are covered with dry, scaly skin. Traditional systematists also argue that the key innovations thought to have initiated the adaptive radiation of birds—wings, feathers, high metabolic rates, and flight—are extreme divergences from the ancestral morphology. Therefore, birds merit recognition as a separate class.

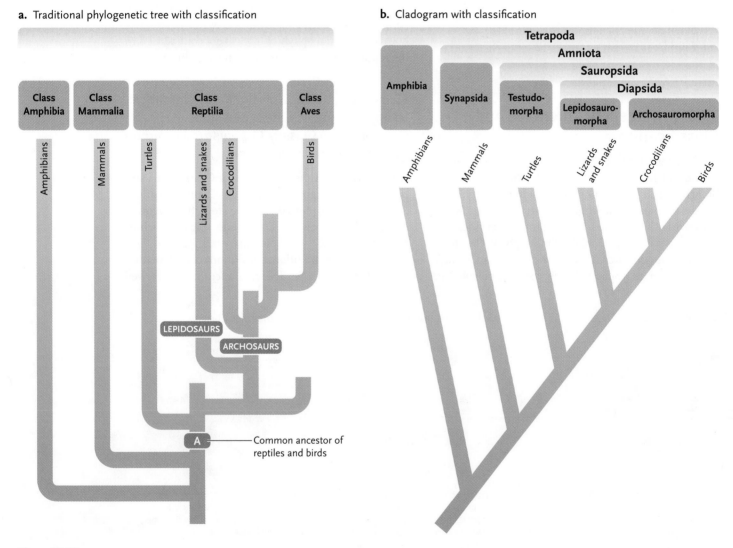

a. Traditional phylogenetic tree with classification

b. Cladogram with classification

Figure 19.13

Phylogenetic trees and classifications for tetrapod vertebrates. Traditional **(a)** and cladistic **(b)** phylogenies produce different phylogenetic trees and classifications. Classifications are presented above the trees.

19.6b Cladistics: Classifications Based on Shared Derived Characters

Cladistics emerged in the 1950s and 1960s when some researchers criticized the inherent lack of clarity in classifications based on two distinct phenomena, branching evolution and morphological divergence. After all, how can we tell *why* two groups are classified in the same higher taxon? Sometimes they have shared a recent common ancestor (e.g., lizards and snakes), but other times they have not (e.g., lizards and crocodilians).

To minimize such confusion, many systematists followed the philosophical and analytical lead of Willi Hennig, a German entomologist who wrote *Phylogenetic Systematics*, published in 1966. Hennig and his followers argued that classifications should be based solely on evolutionary relationships. **Cladistics** produces phylogenetic hypotheses and classifications that reflect only the branching pattern of evolution. Cladistics ignores morphological divergence.

Cladists group together species that *share derived characters*. Cladists argue that mammals form a monophyletic lineage, a **clade**, because they have a unique set of derived characters, including hair, mammary glands, reduction of bones in the lower jaw, and a four-chambered heart. The ancestral characters found in mammals, such as an internal skeleton, a vertebral column, and four legs, do not distinguish them from other tetrapod vertebrates, so these traits are excluded from analysis.

Phylogenetic trees produced by cladists **(cladograms)** illustrate the hypothesized sequence of evolutionary branchings, with a hypothetical ancestor at each branching point **(Figure 19.13b)**. Cladograms portray strictly monophyletic groups and are usually constructed using the **principle of parsimony**. Once a researcher identifies derived, homologous characters, constructing a cladogram is straightforward (see *Constructing a Cladogram*).

Classifications produced by cladistic analysis often differ radically from those of traditional evolutionary systematics (compare Figure 1a and b in *Constructing a Cladogram*). Pairs of higher taxa are defined directly from the two-way branching pattern of the cladogram. Thus, the clade **Tetrapoda** (the traditional amphibians, reptiles, birds, and mammals) is divided into two taxa, Amphibia (tetrapods lacking an amnion; see Chapters 27 and Chapter 39) and Amniota (tetrapods with an amnion). Amniota is subdivided into two taxa on the basis of skull morphology and other characteristics, namely Synapsida (mammals) and Sauropsida (turtles, lizards, snakes, crocodilians, and birds). Based on cranial structure, Sauropsida is further divided into Testudomorpha (turtles) and Diapsida (lizards and snakes, crocodilians, and birds). Finally, based on anatomical details, Diapsida is subdivided into two more recently evolved taxa, Lepidosauromorpha (lizards and snakes) and Archosauromorpha (crocodilians and birds). The strictly cladistic classification parallels the pattern of branching evolution that produced the organisms included in the classification. These parallels are the essence and strength of the cladistic method.

Today most biologists use the cladistic approach because of its evolutionary focus, clear goals, and precise methods. Some systematists advocate abandoning the Linnaean hierarchy for classifying and naming organisms. They propose using a strictly cladistic system, called **PhyloCode**, that identifies and names clades instead of placing organisms into the familiar taxonomic groups. However, traditional evolutionary systematics has guided most people's understanding of biological diversity.

STUDY BREAK

1. What kinds of traits are studied by systematists?
2. What is the difference between homologous and analogous characters? Which are used in systematics? Why?
3. What is mosaic evolution? Distinguish between ancestral and derived characters.

19.7 Add Molecular Data

Most systematists working on living organisms use molecular characters as part of the data set when conducting phylogenetic analyses. Molecular data include nucleotide base sequences of DNA and RNA or the amino acid sequences of the proteins for which they code. Because DNA is inherited, shared changes in molecular sequences (insertions, deletions, or substitutions) provide clues to the evolutionary relationships of organisms. Technological advances have automated many of the necessary laboratory techniques, and analytical software makes it easy to compare new data with information filed in data banks accessible over the Internet, for example, the Barcode of Life project (see Chapter 3).

Molecular sequences have some practical advantages over organismal characters. First, they provide abundant data because every amino acid in a protein and every base in a nucleic acid can serve as a separate, independent character for analysis. Moreover, because many genes have been conserved by evolution, molecular sequences can be compared between distantly related organisms that share no organismal characteristics. Molecular characters can also be used to study closely related species that have only minor morphological differences. Finally, many proteins and nucleic acids are not directly affected by the developmental or environmental factors that cause nongenetic morphological variations (see Chapter 17).

But there are drawbacks to molecular characters. There are only 4 alternative character states (the

CONSTRUCTING A CLADOGRAM

Cladograms allow systematists (and others) to visualize hypothesized evolutionary relationships by grouping together organisms that share derived characters. The cladogram also indicates where derived characters evolved.

Here we develop a cladogram for the nine extant groups of chordates, vertebrates, lampreys (Agnatha), sharks (Chondrichthyes), bony fishes (Osteichthyes), amphibians (Amphibia), reptiles (turtles, lizards and snakes, crocodilians), birds, and mammals (see also Chapter 27). We also include lancelets (marine organisms in the subphylum Cephalochordata). Lancelets serve as the outgroup in our comparison.

We have chosen characters on which to base the cladogram (Table 1), noting the presence or absence of (1) a vertebral column (backbone), (2) jaws, (3) a swim bladder or lungs, (4) paired limbs, (5) extraembryonic membranes (the amnion), (6) mammary glands, (7) dry, scaly skin, (8) two openings at the back of the skull (temporal fenestrae), (9) one opening on each side of the skull in front of the eye, and (10) feathers.

The characters are ancestral or derived in each group, but the outgroup (the lancelets) lacks all of these features. We tabulate the presence (+) and absence (−) of characters starting with lancelets and followed, in alphabetical order, by the other organisms (see Table 1).

We construct the cladogram from the information in the table, grouping organisms that share derived characters (right branch, **Figure 1a**), whereas the lancelets form the left branch because they lack the derived characters.

The remaining organisms except lancelets and lampreys have jaws. Now the right branch **(Figure 1b)** includes all living vertebrates sharing derived characters, separating them from lancelets and lampreys. The selection of different characteristics might give different outcomes. For further discussion of the evolution of chordates, see Chapter 27.

Table 1 — The Presence of Derived Characters in Lancelets and Living Chordates

	Vertebrae	Jaws	Swim Bladder or Lungs	Paired Limbs	Extra-embryonic Membranes	Mammary Glands	Dry, Scaly Skin	Two Openings at Back of Skull	One Opening in Front of Each Eye	Feathers
Lancelets	−	−	−	−	−	−	−	−	−	−
Amphibians	+	+	+	+	−	−	−	−	−	−
Birds	+	+	+	+	+	−	+	+	+	+
Bony fishes	+	+	+	−	−	−	−	−	−	−
Crocodilians	+	+	+	+	−	−	+	+	+	−
Lampreys	+	−	+	+	−	−	−	−	−	−
Lizards	+	+	+	+	−	−	+	+	−	−
Mammals	+	+	+	+	+	+	−	−	−	−
Sharks	+	+	−	−	−	−	−	−	−	−
Turtles	+	+	+	+	+	−	+	−	−	−

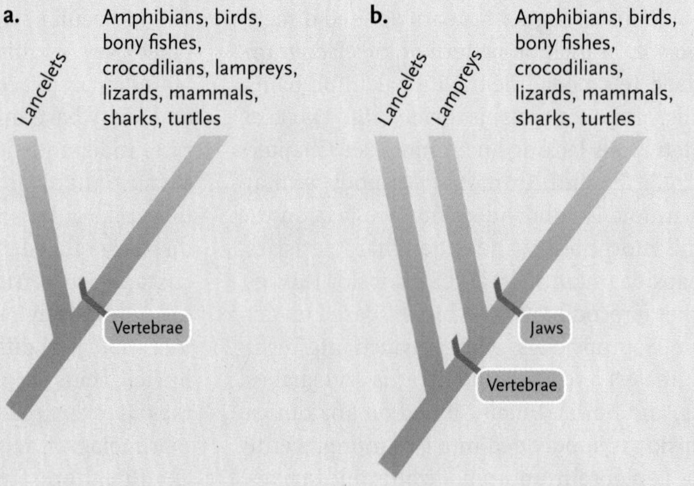

Figure 1

The first cladogram **(a)** shows the separation of lancelets from living chordates. The second cladogram **(b)** shows the separation of lancelets and lampreys from most living chordates. Lampreys are chordates, but the cladogram suggests that they are the earliest chordates. These cladograms were prepared from the data in Table 1.

a. Lancelets | Amphibians, birds, bony fishes, crocodilians, lampreys, lizards, mammals, sharks, turtles — Vertebrae

b. Lancelets | Lampreys | Amphibians, birds, bony fishes, crocodilians, lizards, mammals, sharks, turtles — Jaws, Vertebrae

4 nucleotide bases) at each position in a DNA or RNA sequence and only 20 alternative character states (the 20 amino acids) at each position in a protein (see Chapter 12). If two species have the same nucleotide base substitution at a given position in a DNA segment, their similarity may have evolved independently. As a result, systematists often find it difficult to verify that molecular similarities were inherited from a common ancestor.

For organismal characters, biologists can establish that similarities are homologous by analyzing the characters' embryonic development or details of their function. But molecular characters have no embryonic development, and biologists still do not understand the functional significance of most molecular differences. Despite these disadvantages, molecular characters represent the genome directly, and researchers use them with great success in phylogenetic analyses.

19.7a Molecular Clocks: Using Shared Mutations to Estimate Times of Divergences

Molecular phylogenetics is based on the observation that many molecules have been conserved by evolution. But different adaptive changes and neutral mutations accumulate in separate lineages from the moment they first diverge. Mutations in some types of DNA appear to arise at a relatively constant rate. Therefore, differences in the DNA sequences of two species can serve as a **molecular clock**, indexing their time of divergence. Large differences imply divergence in the distant past. Small differences suggest a more recent common ancestor.

Mosaic evolution occurs at the molecular level, so different molecules exhibit individual rates of change, and each molecule is an independent clock ticking at its own rate. Researchers study different molecules to track evolutionary divergences over different time scales.

Mitochondrial DNA (mtDNA) evolves relatively quickly; it is useful for dating evolutionary divergences that occurred within the last few million years. Studies of mtDNA have illuminated aspects of the evolutionary history of humans, as described in Chapter 27. By contrast, chloroplast DNA (cpDNA) and genes that encode ribosomal RNA evolve much more slowly, providing information about divergences that are hundreds of millions of years old.

To synchronize molecular clocks, some researchers study DNA sequences that are not parts of protein-encoding genes. Because they don't affect protein structure, mutations in these sequences are probably not often eliminated by natural selection. Thus, sequence differences between species in noncoding areas probably result from mutation alone and therefore reflect the ticking of the molecular clock more directly. Some researchers also calibrate molecular clocks to the fossil record, so that actual times of divergence can be estimated from molecular data with a fair degree of certainty.

19.7b Extracting Molecular Data: Using Segments of Nucleic Acid for Analysis

Molecular phylogenetics relies on the same basic logic that underlies analyses based on organismal characters. Species that diverged recently from a common ancestor should share many similarities in their molecular sequences, whereas more distantly related species should exhibit fewer similarities. Nevertheless, the practice of molecular phylogenetics is based on a set of distinctive methods.

After selecting a protein molecule or appropriate segment of a nucleic acid for analysis, systematists determine the exact sequence of amino acids (in the case of proteins) or nucleotide bases (in the case of DNA or RNA) that comprise the molecule.

Amino acid sequencing allows systematists to compare the **primary structure** of protein molecules directly. In Chapters 12 and 13, we learned that the amino acid sequence of a protein is determined by the sequence of nucleotide bases in the gene encoding that protein. When two species exhibit similar amino acid sequences for the same protein, systematists infer their genetic similarity and evolutionary relationship. Researchers have used sequence data from the protein cytochrome *c* to construct a phylogenetic tree for organisms as different as slime moulds, vascular plants, and humans (see *Using Amino Acid Sequences to Construct a Phylogenetic Tree*).

Most systematic studies are now based, at least in part, on DNA sequencing data, which provide a detailed view of the genetic material that is changed by evolutionary processes. The polymerase chain reaction (PCR) makes it easy for researchers to produce numerous copies of specific segments of DNA (see Chapter 16) for comparison. This technique allows scientists to sequence minute quantities of DNA taken from dried or preserved specimens in museums and even from some fossils.

19.7c Aligning Molecular Sequences: Correcting for the Effects of Insertions and Deletions

Before comparing molecular sequences from different organisms, a systematist must ensure that the homologous sequences being compared are properly "aligned." We compare nucleotide bases or amino acids at exactly the same positions in the nucleic acid or protein molecule because mutations often change along the length of a DNA sequence. This can change the relative locations of specific positions through the insertion or deletion of base pairs, making sequence comparisons more difficult. By determining where insertions or deletions have occurred, systematists can match up (align) the positions of nucleotides for comparison. Although alignments can be done "by eye," they often are done using computer programs **(Figure 19.14, p. 433)**.

USING AMINO ACID SEQUENCES TO CONSTRUCT A PHYLOGENETIC TREE

Amino acid sequences of proteins change over evolutionary time, so differences in sequences between organisms should reflect evolutionary patterns. We expect closely related species to have similar amino acid sequences compared with distantly related species. Using amino acid sequences of cytochrome c from eukaryotic organisms classified in four different kingdoms, biologists developed a phylogenetic tree. Cytochrome c is a protein in the electron transport system that has been conserved in evolution (see Chapter 6).

The amino acid sequences of cytochrome c are surprisingly similar across organisms from evolutionary lines that have been distinct for millions of years. In **Figure 1,** gold shading marks amino acids that are identical in sequences for yeast (top row), wheat (middle row), and humans (bottom row).

Using similarities and differences in cytochrome c sequences, biologists constructed a phylogenetic tree **(Figure 2).** The vertical axis gives approximate time for each evolutionary branching estimated from amino acid sequence data. The exercise demonstrates how differences in amino acid sequences can be used to construct phylogenetic trees for organisms that share virtually no organismal characters.

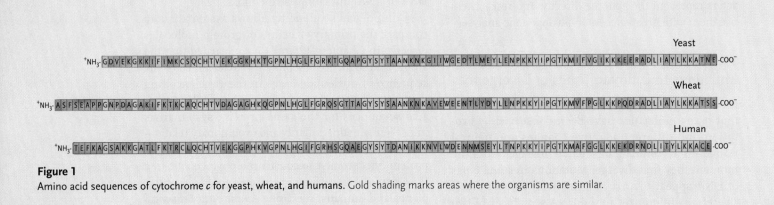

Yeast

Wheat

Human

Figure 1
Amino acid sequences of cytochrome c for yeast, wheat, and humans. Gold shading marks areas where the organisms are similar.

Figure 2
A phylogenetic tree based on differences and similarities in amino acid sequences showing a range of organisms and the estimated time of evolutionary divergence.

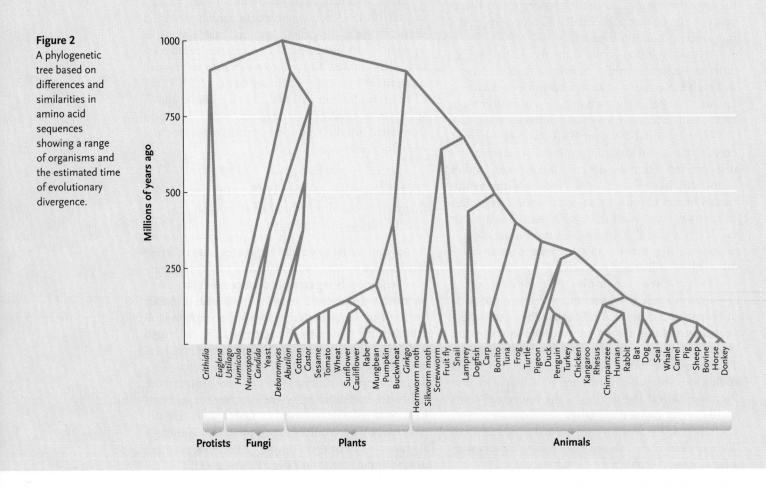

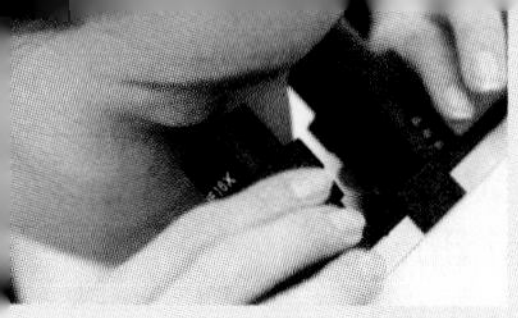

People Behind Biology

Alfred Sherwood Romer, Harvard University

Our knowledge of the evolution of vertebrate animals was strongly influenced by the work of Alfred Sherwood Romer (1894–1973). Romer's interest in fossils was sparked in his childhood by visits to the American Museum of Natural History, particularly the dinosaur exhibits there. His Ph.D. thesis, submitted to Columbia University, was a classic contribution to the study of muscles in vertebrates and led to his many contributions in the fields of functional anatomy and evolution.

His textbook *Vertebrate Paleontology* first appeared in 1933 and went through three editions, influencing the studies and academic development of many students of vertebrate evolution. He moved to Harvard University in 1945 to become director of the Biological Laboratories and the Museum of Comparative Zoology.

One of his main research foci was the evolution of pelycosaurian reptiles (see Chapter 27), and he continued to be active as a researcher after his retirement from Harvard in 1965. Romer is an example of an academic whose contributions spanned the spectrum from his own research endeavours to presenting information to students (through texts such as *Vertebrate Paleontology* and *The Vertebrate Body*) and as an academic leader in the various positions he filled. He was an enthusiastic and articulate speaker with a great talent for presenting his material in a format that was readily accessible to students.

Once the molecules are aligned, a systematist can compare the nucleotide base or amino acid sequences and determine whether mutations or other processes have produced evolutionary changes in the sequences. Similarities and differences can then be used to reconstruct a phylogenetic tree. Each phylogenetic tree is a hypothesis about evolutionary relationships, and different assumptions can yield alternative trees for any data set. Indeed, systematists have developed several approaches for comparing molecular sequences and constructing trees.

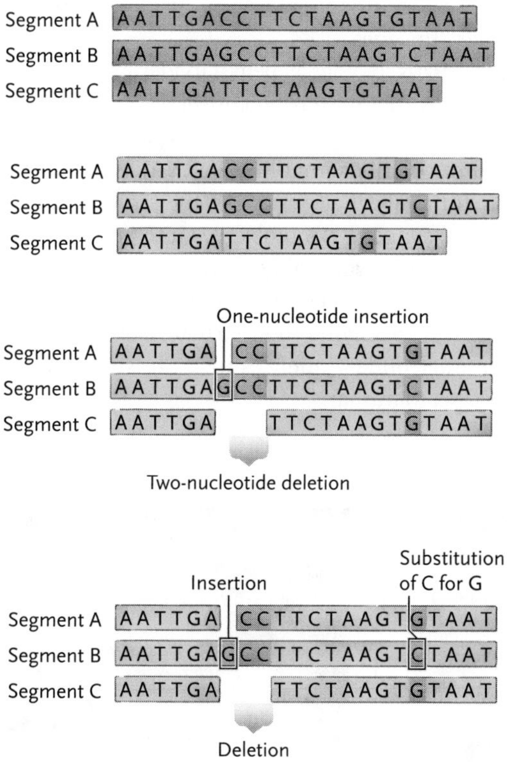

Segment A AATTGACCTTCTAAGTGTAAT
Segment B AATTGAGCCTTCTAAGTCTAAT
Segment C AATTGATTCTAAGTGTAAT
Segment A AATTGACCTTCTAAGTGTAAT
Segment B AATTGAGCCTTCTAAGTCTAAT
Segment C AATTGATTCTAAGTGTAAT
One-nucleotide insertion
Segment A AATTGA CCTTCTAAGTGTAAT
Segment B AATTGAGCCTTCTAAGTCTAAT
Segment C AATTGA TTCTAAGTGTAAT
Two-nucleotide deletion
Insertion
Substitution of C for G
Segment A AATTGA CCTTCTAAGTGTAAT
Segment B AATTGAGCCTTCTAAGTCTAAT
Segment C AATTGA TTCTAAGTGTAAT
Deletion

Figure 19.14
Insertion or deletion of base pairs can change the length of a DNA sequence and the relative locations of the specific positions along its length. Therefore, systematists "align" the sequences they are comparing to ensure that the nucleotide bases being compared are at exactly the same positions in the nucleic acid molecules. By determining where insertions or deletions have occurred, systematists match up the positions of the nucleotides. In this hypothetical example, DNA sequences were obtained from three species and aligned.

For DNA sequences, the simplest approach is to count the number of similarities and differences between each pair of organisms being compared. Systematists use data from these comparisons to estimate *genetic distances* between species and construct a phylogenetic tree by grouping together organisms exhibiting the smallest genetic distances. This approach, however, can produce phylogenies based on both ancestral and derived characters. Recall that this is the same problem involved in traditional evolutionary systematics.

Using cladistics and the principle of parsimony, molecular sequence data can be converted into a phylogenetic tree. To achieve this requires identification of ancestral and derived character states. For each position in the sequence, systematists must determine which nucleotide bases are ancestral and which are derived. As for organismal characters, analysis of homologous sequences in a designated outgroup can provide information that allows researchers to distinguish between ancestral and derived conditions. In the parsimony approach, a computer program is used to test all possible phylogenetic trees and identify the one that accounts for the diversity of organisms in the group using the fewest evolutionary changes in molecular sequences.

In recent years, researchers have faulted the parsimony approach because identical changes in nucleotides can arise independently. To avoid this problem, systematists have begun to use a series of statistical techniques collectively known as *maximum likelihood methods.* This approach reconstructs phylogenetic history from molecular sequence data by making assumptions about variations in the rate at which different segments of DNA evolve. These statistical models can take into account variations in the rates of evolution between genes or between species as well as changes in evolutionary rates over time. Maximum likelihood programs construct numerous alternative phylogenetic trees and estimate how likely it is that each tree represents the true evolutionary history. Systematists then accept the phylogenetic tree that is most likely to be true until more data are available.

STUDY BREAK

1. What are some advantages and disadvantages to using molecular data as clues to the evolutionary relationships among organisms?
2. How can the concept of a molecular clock indicate the time of divergence for traits? What are two types of DNA used for dating evolutionary divergence, and when are they used?
3. Why must molecular sequences be aligned before they are compared?

19.8 Clarifications from Molecular Phylogenetics

Analyses of morphological data sometimes produced conflicting hypotheses about the origin and relationships of flowering plants. Molecular phylogenetics have been used to resolve these conflicts. In 1999, four teams of researchers, analyzing different parts of flowering plant genomes, independently identified *Amborella trichopoda*, a bush native to the South Pacific island of New Caledonia, as a living representative of the most ancient group of flowering plants yet discovered **(Figure 19.15).** The first team to publish their results, Sarah Mathews and Michael Donoghue, studied phytochrome genes (*PHYA* and *PHYC*) that had duplicated early in the evolutionary history of this group. Other researchers, who studied chloroplast, mitochondrial, and ribosomal sequences, obtained similar results, providing strong support for this phylogenetic hypothesis.

On a grander scale, molecular phylogenetics has revolutionized our view of the entire tree of life (look back at Figure 3.7). The first efforts to create a phylogenetic tree for all forms of life were based on morphological analyses that did not resolve branches of the tree containing prokaryotes. Prokaryotes lack significant structural variability to allow earlier efforts to resolve their relationships to eukaryotes.

In the 1960s and early 1970s, biologists organized living systems into five kingdoms. Prokaryotes were grouped in the kingdom Monera. Eukaryotes were grouped into four kingdoms, Fungi, Plantae, **Animalia**, and Protista. Protista was always recognized as a polyphyletic "grab bag" of unicellular or acellular eukaryotic organisms. Phylogenetic analyses based on morphology were unable to sort Protista into distinct evolutionary lineages.

In the 1970s, biologists began to identify and analyze molecules that have been conserved by evolution over billions of years. Carl R. Woese identified the small subunit of ribosomal RNA (rRNA) as a suitable molecule for analysis. Ribosomes, the structures that translate messenger RNA molecules into proteins (see Chapter 13), are remarkably similar in all forms of life. Ribosomes are so essential to cellular processes that the genes specifying their structure exhibit similarities in nucleotide sequences in organisms ranging from bacteria to humans.

Figure 19.15

The ancestral flowering plant. DNA sequencing studies identified *Amborella trichopoda* **(a)** as a living representative of the earliest group of flowering plants. Its flower is shown in **(b)**.

a. *Amborella trichopoda* branch

Thomas J. Lemieux, University of Colorado

b. *Amborella trichopoda* flower

Sandra Floyd, University of Colorado

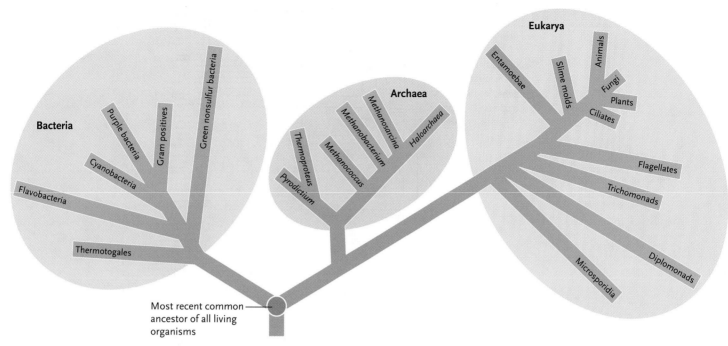

Figure 19.16

Three domains: the tree of life. Carl R. Woese's 1996 analysis of rRNA sequences suggests that all living organisms can be classified into one of three domains, identified here on branches shaded in different colours.

The phylogenetic tree based on rRNA sequences divides living organisms into three primary lineages called domains: Bacteria, Archaea, and Eukarya **(Figure 19.16)**. According to this hypothesis, two domains, Bacteria and Archaea, include prokaryotic organisms, and one, Eukarya, includes eukaryotes. Bacteria includes well-known microorganisms, and Archaea comprises microorganisms that live in physiologically harsh environments, such as hot springs or very salty habitats. Eukarya includes the familiar animals, plants, and fungi, as well as the many lineages formerly included among the Protista.

Study Break

1. What characters (features) do systematists use when constructing phylogenetic trees?
2. What constitutes a "kingdom" in biology? Name four kingdoms.

19.9 Putting It Together

Returning to the evolution of carnivory in plants, we can see how phylogeny derived from nucleotide sequence data helped clarify the situation **(Figure 19.17, p. 436)**.

The plastid gene *rbcL* encodes a large subunit of ribulolse-1,5-biphosphate carboxylase/oxygenase (rubisco). This is a primary enzyme in the Calvin cycle (see Chapter 7). Rates of substitution in *rbcL* make it well suited to parsimony analyses in seed plants. This work made it easier to understand the evolution of carnivory in plants and their adaptive radiation.

When traditional data are combined with molecular data, we can see advances in our understanding of evolution and adaptive radiation. Bats provide an interesting example. Today there are ~1100 species arrayed in 17 families and distributed worldwide aside from remote oceanic islands and the polar regions. The first known fossil bats are found in Eocene rocks, dating to about 50 million years ago. At that time, the fossil record contains the remains of species from at least 10 families of bats. From 1990 to 2005, more fossil bats have been discovered, and detailed phylogenetic analyses of molecular (living bats) and morphological data (living and fossil bats) have changed our understanding of the relationships among families **(Figure 19.18, p. 436)**. The combination of molecular evidence with detailed morphological analyses of living and fossil species is responsible for our new view of their evolution. However, the ancestors of bats remain undiscovered.

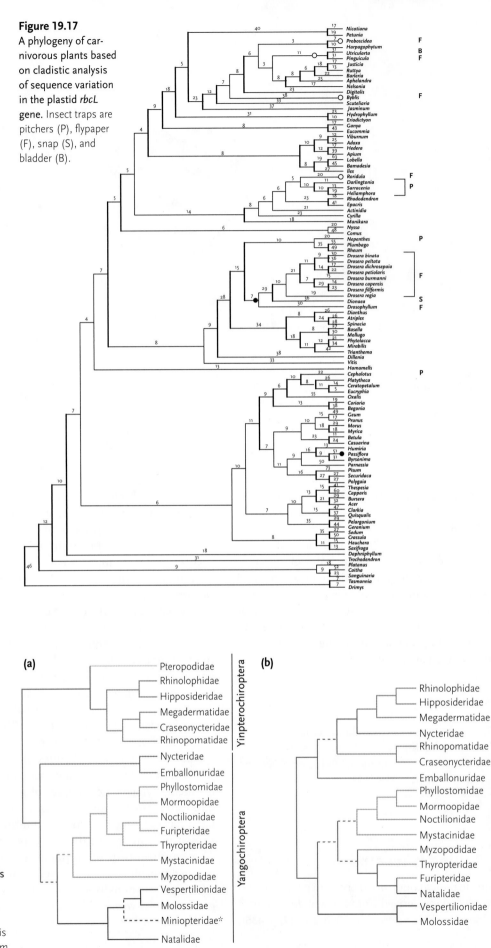

Figure 19.17

A phylogeny of carnivorous plants based on cladistic analysis of sequence variation in the plastid *rbcL* gene. Insect traps are pitchers (P), flypaper (F), snap (S), and bladder (B).

Figure 19.18

A comparison of two phylogenies of bats identifies the changes in our view of the relationships between families with the publication of additional molecular and morphological data. The newer view **(a)** is substantially different in many details from the more traditional one **(b)**.

To what extent should systematists be able to use data about the structure of chemicals used by organisms? Included could be odourants used to attract pollinators or venom used to immobilize prey.

Think back to the origin of life (see Chapter 2) and the tree of life (see Figure 3.7). Do you think that all living organisms are monophyletic? Diphyletic? Polyphyletic? What data would you use to support your point of view?

Review

Go to CENGAGENOW™ at http://hed.nelson.com/ to access quizzing, animations, exercises, articles, and personalized homework help.

19.2 Systematic Biology and Classification

- Convergent evolution refers more to distantly related organisms and parallel evolution to more closely related ones. The evolution of flight is convergent between insects (phylum Arthropoda) and vertebrates (phylum Chordata, birds, pterosaurs, and bats) and parallel within the vertebrates.

- Systematics is used to reconstruct the phylogeny (evolutionary history) of a group of organisms and is portrayed as a phylogenetic tree. Systematics also assists in the identification and naming of species and their placement in a classification. A classification arranges organisms into hierarchical groups reflecting their relatedness.

- Phylogenetic trees can be used to distinguish similarities inherited from a common ancestor from those that evolved independently (e.g., wings).

- A taxonomic hierarchy arranges organisms into ever more exclusive categories. In the Linnaean system, a family is a group of genera that closely resemble one another. Families are grouped into orders, orders into classes, etc.

- Organisms are classified based on features such as morphological traits; chromosomal anatomy; gene sequences; details of physiological functioning; morphology of subcellular structures, cells, and organ systems; and patterns of behaviour.

19.5 Evaluating Systematic Characters

- In preparing a phylogeny, systematists seek traits in which phenotypic variation reflects genetic differences rather than environmental variation. Systematists also use genetically independent traits, which reflect different parts of an organism's genome.

- Homologous characters have been inherited from a common ancestor, so phenotypic similarities between organisms reflect underlying genetic similarities. Homologous characters can differ considerably among species. Analogous (homoplasious) characters are phenotypically similar and have similar functions but evolved independently in different lineages.

- Systematists compare homologous characters to determine common ancestry and genetic relatedness. They exclude analogous structures because they provide no information about shared ancestry or genetic relatedness.

- Mosaic evolution refers to the reality that some characteristics evolve more slowly or more quickly than others. Ancestral characters are old forms of traits, and derived characters are new forms. Once a derived characteristic becomes established, it occurs in all the species' descendants and is a marker for evolutionary lineages.

- An outgroup comparison can be used to identify ancestral and derived traits because it compares the group under study with more distantly related species not otherwise included in the analysis.

19.6 Phylogenetic Inference and Classification

- A monophyletic taxon is a group of species derived from a single ancestral species. A polyphyletic taxon includes species from separate evolutionary lineages. A paraphyletic taxon includes an ancestor and some, but not all, of its descendants.

- According to the principle of parsimony, any particular evolutionary change is a rare event, unlikely to have occurred twice in one lineage. Therefore, the fewest possible evolutionary changes should be used to account for within-lineage diversity.

- Traditional evolutionary systematics groups together species that share what are considered to be ancestral and derived characters. Classifications reflect evolutionary branching and morphological divergence. Cladistics investigates branching patterns of evolution, ignoring morphological divergence. Cladistics groups together species sharing derived characters and uses cladograms based on the principle of parsimony to illustrate sequences of evolutionary branching and the ancestors at each branching point.

19.7 Add Molecular Data

- Every amino acid in a protein and every base in a nucleic acid can serve as independent characters for analysis. DNA can be compared between distantly related species sharing no organismal characteristics and between closely related species exhibiting minor morphological differences. Molecular data are not affected by developmental and environmental factors.

- It can be difficult to verify that similarities at the molecular level were inherited from a common ancestor because there are only 4 DNA bases and only 20 amino acids. The same base substitution in a given DNA segment may have evolved independently in two different species.

- Mutations in certain types of DNA appear at a constant rate, so the DNA sequences of two species can index their time of divergence, with large differences implying divergence in the distant past and small differences suggesting a more recent common ancestor.

- When molecular clocks can be calibrated to the fossil record, biologists can predict the times of evolutionary divergence. Mitochondrial DNA evolves relatively quickly, making it useful for dating evolutionary divergences that occurred within the last few million years. Choloroplast DNA evolves much more slowly, providing information about divergences that are hundreds of millions of years old.

- DNA molecules must be aligned to allow for comparison of changes in bases or amino acids. The comparisons must be made at exactly the same positions because mutations often change along the length of a DNA sequence. After alignment, sequences can be compared to determine if mutations or other processes have produced evolutionary changes in the sequences. Similarities and differences can then be used to construct phylogenetic trees.

- Maximum likelihood methods are statistical techniques used to reconstruct phylogenetic history from molecular sequence data. These methods make assumptions about variations because identical changes in nucleotides can arise independently and there are variations in the rates at which different segments of DNA evolve. Maximum likelihood methods account for variations in the rates of evolution between genes or species, as well as over time. The process involves constructing numerous phylogenetic trees and selecting the one that best represents the true evolutionary history.

Questions

Self-Test Questions

1. A phylogenetic tree portrays the _____ of a group of organisms.
   a. classification
   b. evolutionary history
   c. domain
   d. distribution
   e. all of the above

2. Species in the same genus should
   a. belong to the same family.
   b. share a recent common evolutionary history.
   c. be animals.
   d. be plants.
   e. reproduce sexually.

3. When systematists use morphological or behavioural traits to reconstruct the evolutionary history of a group of animals, they assume that
   a. phenotypic characters reflect underlying genetic similarities and differences.
   b. the animals use exactly the same traits to identify appropriate mates.
   c. these traits were responsible for speciation events in the past.
   d. the adaptive value of these traits can be explained.
   e. variations are produced by environmental effects during development.

4. Which statement best describes the concept of mosaic evolution?
   a. Some phenotypic variation is caused by environmental factors.
   b. Homologous characters are inherited from a common ancestor.
   c. Different organismal traits may reflect the same part of an organism's genome.
   d. Some characters evolve more quickly than others.
   e. The fossil record provides clues about the ancestral versions of characters.

5. Which of the following pairs of structures are homoplasious?
   a. the wing skeleton of a bird and the wing skeleton of a bat
   b. the wing of a bird and the wing of a fly
   c. the eye of a fish and the eye of a human
   d. the bones in the foot of a duck and the bones in the foot of a chicken
   e. the wing structures of a pterosaur and those of a bird

6. Which of the following does not help systematists determine which version of a morphological character is ancestral and which is derived?
   a. outgroup comparison
   b. patterns of embryonic development
   c. studies of the fossil record
   d. studies of the character in more related species
   e. dating of the character by molecular clocks

7. In a cladistic analysis, a systematist groups together organisms that share
   a. derived homologous traits.
   b. derived homoplasious traits.
   c. ancestral homologous traits.
   d. ancestral homoplasious traits.
   e. all of the above.

8. A monophyletic taxon includes
   a. an ancestor and all of its descendants.
   b. an ancestor and some of its descendants.
   c. organisms from different evolutionary lineages.
   d. an ancestor and those descendants that still resemble it.
   e. organisms that resemble each other because they live in similar environments.

9. Which of the following is not an advantage of using molecular characters in a systematic analysis?
   a. Molecular characters provide abundant data.
   b. Systematists can compare molecules among morphologically similar species.
   c. Systematists can compare molecules among species that share few morphological characters.
   d. Amino acid sequences in proteins are generally not influenced by environmental factors.
   e. Systematists can easily determine if nucleotide base substitutions in DNA are homologous.

10. To construct a cladogram by applying the principles of parsimony to molecular sequence data, one would
    a. start by making assumptions about variations in the rates at which different DNA segments evolve.
    b. group together organisms sharing the largest number of ancestral sequences.
    c. group together organisms that share derived sequences, matching the groups to those defined by morphological characters.
    d. group together organisms sharing derived sequences, minimizing the number of hypothesized evolutionary changes.
    e. identify derived sequences by studying the embryology of the organisms.

Questions for Discussion

1. Systematists use both amino acid sequences and DNA sequences to determine evolutionary relationships. Think about the genetic code (DNA structure; see Chapter 13) and explain why phylogenetic hypotheses based on DNA sequences may be more accurate than those based on amino acid sequences.

2. Traditional evolutionary systematists identify the Reptilia as one class of vertebrates, even though this taxon is paraphyletic. What are the advantages and disadvantages of defining paraphyletic taxa in a classification?

3. The table below includes information about the distribution of ancestral and derived states for six systematic characters (1 through 6) in five species (A through E). A "d" denotes the presence of the derived form of the character and an "a" the ancestral form. Construct a cladogram for the five species using the principle of parsimony. Assume that each derived character evolved only once in this group of organisms. Mark the branches of the cladogram to show where each character changed from the ancestral to the derived state.

	Character					
Species	1	2	3	4	5	6
A	a	a	a	a	a	a
B	d	a	a	a	a	d
C	d	d	d	a	a	a
D	d	d	d	a	d	a
E	d	d	a	d	a	a

A fossil ammonite

M. B. Fenton

20 Darwin, Fossils, and Developmental Biology

WHY IT MATTERS

Many cities and towns are built on the remains of earlier life. Medicine Hat, Alberta, is a good example **(Figure 20.1, p. 440)**. There the South Saskatchewan River has cut a deep valley through sediments. Every year, more and more fossils are eroded from the river's banks, providing paleontologists with a picture of life in the area over the last ~100 000 years (dating back to the Pleistocene). Many of the animals we find there as fossils do not occur in the area today. Equids, camels, several species of ground sloths, sabre-toothed cats, mammoths, and other species disappeared by 11 000 years ago. The horses (equids; see Chapter 27) there today are descendants of those reintroduced by European explorers and settlers beginning with the Spanish. Humans probably lived along the South Saskatchewan River before many of these now extinct species disappeared.

Imagine looking out and seeing a giant ground sloth (*Megalotherium*) or a sabre-toothed cat (*Smilodon*) in your garden. This would have been possible 15 000 years ago. Look at the roster of mammals (see Figure 20.1). But sharks' teeth have also been found in the deposits. Does that mean that swimmers in the South

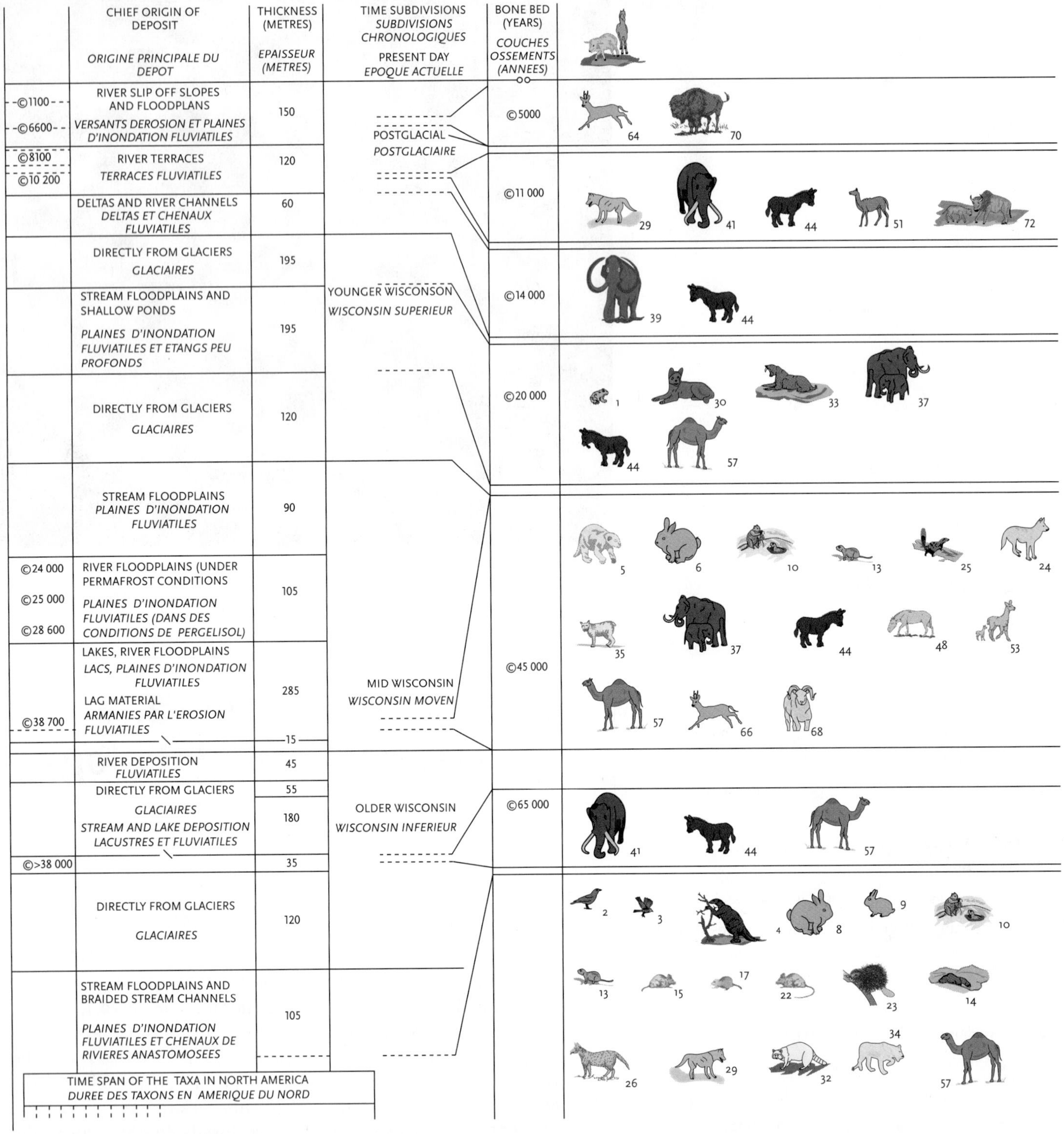

Figure 20.1

	CHIEF ORIGIN OF DEPOSIT / *ORIGINE PRINCIPALE DU DEPOT*	THICKNESS (METRES) / *EPAISSEUR (METRES)*	TIME SUBDIVISIONS / *SUBDIVISIONS CHRONOLOGIQUES*	BONE BED (YEARS) / *COUCHES OSSEMENTS (ANNEES)*
			PRESENT DAY / *EPOQUE ACTUELLE*	
–©1100– –©6600–	RIVER SLIP OFF SLOPES AND FLOODPLANS / *VERSANTS DEROSION ET PLAINES D'INONDATION FLUVIATILES*	150	POSTGLACIAL / *POSTGLACIAIRE*	©5000
©8100 ©10 200	RIVER TERRACES / *TERRACES FLUVIATILES*	120		©11 000
	DELTAS AND RIVER CHANNELS / *DELTAS ET CHENAUX FLUVIATILES*	60		
	DIRECTLY FROM GLACIERS / *GLACIAIRES*	195	YOUNGER WISCONSON / *WISCONSIN SUPERIEUR*	©14 000
	STREAM FLOODPLAINS AND SHALLOW PONDS / *PLAINES D'INONDATION FLUVIATILES ET ETANGS PEU PROFONDS*	195		
	DIRECTLY FROM GLACIERS / *GLACIAIRES*	120		©20 000
	STREAM FLOODPLAINS / *PLAINES D'INONDATION FLUVIATILES*	90		
©24 000 ©25 000 ©28 600	RIVER FLOODPLAINS (UNDER PERMAFROST CONDITIONS / *PLAINES D'INONDATION FLUVIATILES (DANS DES CONDITIONS DE PERGELISOL)*	105		©45 000
©38 700	LAKES, RIVER FLOODPLAINS / *LACS, PLAINES D'INONDATION FLUVIATILES* LAG MATERIAL / *ARMANIES PAR L'EROSION FLUVIATILES*	285 / 15	MID WISCONSIN / *WISCONSIN MOVEN*	
	RIVER DEPOSITION / *FLUVIATILES*	45		
	DIRECTLY FROM GLACIERS / *GLACIAIRES* STREAM AND LAKE DEPOSITION / *LACUSTRES ET FLUVIATILES*	55 / 180	OLDER WISCONSIN / *WISCONSIN INFERIEUR*	©65 000
©>38 000		35		
	DIRECTLY FROM GLACIERS / *GLACIAIRES*	120		
	STREAM FLOODPLAINS AND BRAIDED STREAM CHANNELS / *PLAINES D'INONDATION FLUVIATILES ET CHENAUX DE RIVIERES ANASTOMOSEES*	105		

TIME SPAN OF THE TAXA IN NORTH AMERICA / *DUREE DES TAXONS EN AMERIQUE DU NORD*

Figure 20.1

Pleistocene sequence from Medicine Hat, Alberta. Erosion of the banks of the South Saskatachewan River provides access to (right) fossil deposits. This sequence goes from the present to about 80 000 years ago and portrays the changes in the vertebrate fauna over this period. Included are (1) prairie toad; (2) grouse; (3) hawk; (4) ground sloth; (5) shasta ground sloth; (6) Hartan's ground sloth; (7) Gazin's marsh rabbit; (8) Townsend's hare; (9) eastern cottontail rabbit; (10) white-tailed prairie dog; (11) meade prairie dog; (12) meade ground squirrel; (13) ground squirrel; (14) undescribed species of pocket gopher; (15) northern pocket gopher; (16) Canadian beaver; (17) field vole; (18) extinct vole; (19) undescribed species of extinct vole; (20) Osborn's extinct tree vole; (21) Kansas southern bog lemming; (22) muskrat; (23) porcupine; (24) black-footed ferret; (25) eastern striped skunk; (26) red fox; (27) Cope's bone-eating dog; (28) coyote; (29) grey wolf; (30) dire wolf; (31) dog or wolf; (32) raccoon; (33) sabre-toothed cat; (34) Pleistocene lion; (35) Canada lynx; (36) bobcat; (37) mammoth; (38) Cook's mammoth; (39) Imperial mammoth; (40) Siberian or northern mammoth; (41) eastern horse; (42) stilt-legged ass; (43) Pacific horse; (44) Mexican ass; (45) Pacific horse; (46) Niobrara horse; (47) Scott's horse; (48) giant horse; (49) neogene horse; (50) Cope's peccary; (51) unidentified camel; (52) plains llama; (53) Steven's plains llama; (54) Holloman's plains llama; (55) camel; (56) Irvingtonian camel; (57) Western camel; (58) Nearctic deer; (59) white-tailed deer; (60) waipiti or elk; (61) caribou; (62) small caribou; (63) moose deer; (64) mountain sheep; (65) unidentified pronghorned antelope; (66) pronghorn; (67) mountain sheep; (68) woodland muskox; (69) woodland scrub ox; (70) bison; (71) giant long-horned bison; and (72) large extinct bison.

Saskatchewan River had to cope with sharks 11 000 years ago? The answer is "no." The sharks' teeth are much older than the Pleistocene sediments. They are fossils from the Cretaceous that had weathered out of their bedrocks and were redeposited during the Pleistocene (see Table 1.1).

The ground on which Medicine Hat is built contains a treasure trove of earlier life. This pattern repeats itself in many cities around the world. It can give people a sense of history that extends well beyond their current situation. The fossils bring mysteries: Why did so many animals disappear at the end of the Pleistocene? Did early humans arriving in the New World encounter these animals? We know that in the American southwest, early North Americans hunted mammoths (*Mammuthus* spp.), mastodons (*Mastodon* spp.), and ground sloths (*Megalotherium* spp.). Did this hunting pressure contribute to the extinction of large mammals in the Pleistocene?

In biology, unanswered questions outnumber answered ones.

20.1 Recognition of Evolutionary Change

It is timely to reflect on the historical development of evolutionary theory. We know that the Greek philosopher Aristotle (384–322 B.C.E.) was a keen observer of nature and natural history, the branch of biology that examines the form and variety of organisms in their natural environments. Aristotle believed that both inanimate objects and living species had fixed characteristics. Careful study of their differences and similarities enabled him to create a ladder-like classification of nature from simplest to most complex: minerals ranked below plants, plants below animals, animals below humans, and humans below the gods of the spiritual realm.

By the fourteenth century, Europeans had merged Aristotle's classification with the biblical account of creation. At that time, a prevailing view in Europe was that all of the different kinds of organisms had been specially created by a god, that species could never change or become extinct, and that new species could never arise. Biological research was dominated by **natural theology**, which sought to name and catalogue all of God's creation. Careful study of each species would identify its position and purpose in the *Scala Naturae*, or Great Chain of Being, as Aristotle's ladder of life was called. This approach to nature and history was clear in the work of Carolus Linnaeus (1707–1778), whose efforts were *ad majorem Dei gloriam* (for the greater glory of God).

In the Western world, modern science began to come of age in the fifteenth through eighteenth centuries. The English philosopher and statesman Sir Francis Bacon (1561–1626) established the importance of observation, experimentation, and inductive reasoning. Other scientists proposed mechanistic theories to explain physical events, notably Nicolaus Copernicus (1473–1543), Galileo Galilei (1564–1642), René Descartes (1596–1650), and Sir Isaac Newton (1643–1727). Three new disciplines—**biogeography**, **comparative morphology**, and geology—promoted a growing awareness of change.

A French scientist, George-Louis Leclerc (1707–1788), le Comte (Count) de Buffon, was puzzled by the existence of body parts with no apparent function. He noted, for example, that the feet of pigs and some other mammals have two toes that never touch the ground. If each species is anatomically perfect for its particular way of life, why do useless structures exist?

Buffon proposed that some animals must have *changed* since their creation. He suggested that **vestigial structures**, the useless body parts we observe today, must have functioned in ancestral organisms. Buffon offered no explanation of how functional structures became vestigial, but he clearly recognized that some species were "conceived by Nature and produced by Time."

Georges Cuvier (1769–1832), a French zoologist, realized that the layers of fossils represented organisms that had lived at successive times in the past. He suggested that abrupt changes between geologic strata marked dramatic shifts in ancient environments. Cuvier and his followers developed the theory of **catastrophism**, reasoning that each layer of fossils represented the remains of organisms that had died in a local catastrophe such as a flood. Somewhat different species then recolonized the area, and when another catastrophe struck, they formed a different set of fossils in the next higher layer.

A contemporary of Cuvier and a student of Buffon, Jean Baptiste de Lamarck (1744–1829) proposed the first comprehensive theory of **biological evolution** based on specific mechanisms. He proposed that a metaphysical "perfecting principle" caused organisms to become better suited to their environments. Simple organisms evolved into more complex ones, moving up the ladder of life. Microscopic organisms were replaced at the bottom by spontaneous generation.

Lamarck theorized that two mechanisms fostered evolutionary change. According to his *principle of use and disuse*, body parts grow in proportion to how much they are used, as anyone who "pumps iron" well knows. Conversely, unused structures get weaker and shrink, like the muscles of an arm immobilized in a cast. According to his second principle, the *inheritance of acquired characteristics*, changes that an animal acquires during its lifetime

Figure 20.2
Great blue heron,
Ardea herodias.

are inherited by its offspring. Thus, Lamarck argued that long-legged wading birds, such as herons **(Figure 20.2)**, are descended from short-legged ancestors that stretched their legs to stay dry while feeding in shallow water. Their offspring inherited slightly longer legs, and after many generations, their legs became extremely long.

Today we know that Lamarck's proposed mechanisms do not cause evolutionary change. Although muscles do grow larger through continued use, most structures do not respond in the way Lamarck predicted. Structural changes acquired during an organism's lifetime are not inherited by the next generation.

Despite the shortcomings of his theory, Lamarck made four important contributions to the development of an evolutionary world-view:

- He proposed that all species change through time.
- He recognized that changes are passed from one generation to the next.
- He suggested that organisms change in response to their environments.
- He hypothesized the existence of specific mechanisms that caused evolutionary change.

The first three of these ideas became cornerstones of Darwin's evolutionary theory. Perhaps Lamarck's most important contribution was to foster discussion. By the mid-nineteenth century, most educated Europeans were talking about evolutionary change, whether they believed in it or not.

STUDY BREAK

1. Why can one find fossil shark teeth in the bluffs at Medicine Hat?
2. What four main points did Darwin make with his theory about evolution?

20.2 Changes in Earth

In 1795, the Scottish geologist James Hutton (1726–1797) argued that slow and continuous physical processes, *acting over long periods of time*, produced Earth's major geologic features. The movement of water in a river slowly erodes the land and deposits sediments near the river's mouth. Given enough time, erosion creates deep canyons, and sedimentation creates thick topsoil on flood plains. Hutton's **gradualism**, the view that Earth changed *slowly* over its history, contrasted sharply with Cuvier's catastrophism.

The English geologist Charles Lyell (1797–1875) championed and extended Hutton's ideas in an influ-

ential series of books, *Principles of Geology*. Lyell argued that the geologic processes that sculpted Earth's surface over long periods of time, such as volcanic eruptions, earthquakes, erosion, and the formation and movement of glaciers, are exactly the same as the processes we observe today. This concept, **uniformitarianism**, undermined any remaining notions of an unchanging Earth. Because geologic processes proceed very slowly, it must have taken millions of years, not just a few thousand, to mould the landscape into its current configuration.

STUDY BREAK

What is the theory of catastrophism?

20.3 Charles Darwin

Charles Darwin (1809–1882) changed biologists' view of evolution. But around 1830, Charles Darwin wondered what to do with his life. Raised in a wealthy English household, Darwin had always collected shells and studied the habits of insects and birds. He preferred hunting and fishing to classical studies. Despite his lacklustre performance as a student, Darwin was expected to continue the family tradition of practising medicine. He abandoned medical studies after two years and followed his interest in natural history.

20.3a HMS *Beagle*: Darwin's Voyage

In 1831, Darwin set sail as a dining companion for the captain of HMS *Beagle*, first going westward to map the coastline of South America and then on to circumnavigate the globe **(Figure 20.3)**. When the ship's naturalist quit his post mid-journey, Darwin replaced him in an unofficial capacity. For nearly five years, Darwin toured the world, and because he suffered from seasickness, he seized every chance to go ashore. He collected plants and animals in Brazilian rain forests and fossils in Patagonia. He hiked the grasslands of the pampas and climbed the Andes in Chile. Armed with the first volume of Lyell's *Principles of Geology*, Darwin was primed to apply gradualism and uniformitarianism to the living world.

Darwin observed fascinating patterns in the distributions of species on the Galápagos Islands **(Figure 20.4)**. There he found strange and wonderful creatures, including giant tortoises and lizards that dived into the sea to eat algae. Darwin noted that the animals on different islands varied slightly in form. Indeed, experienced sailors could easily identify

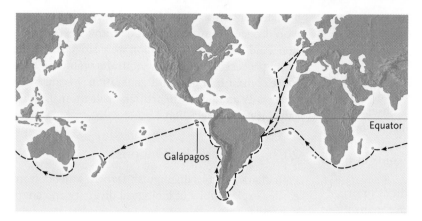

Figure 20.3
Darwin's voyage—map of the path followed by HMS *Beagle*.

nearest continent? Darwin later hypothesized that the plants and animals of the Galápagos were descended from South American ancestors and that each species had changed after being isolated on a particular island.

20.3b Selective Breeding and Heredity: Like Begets Like

Having grown up in the country, Darwin was well aware that "like begets like": offspring resemble their parents. Plant and animal breeders had applied this basic truth of inheritance for thousands of years. By selectively breeding individuals with favourable characteristics, breeders enhanced those traits in future generations. Darwin was well aware of this process, which he called **artificial selection** (see Chapter 49), but he puzzled over how it could operate in nature.

a tortoise's island of origin by the shape of its shell. Moreover, many species resembled those on the distant South American mainland. Why did so many different organisms occupy one small island cluster? Why did these species resemble others from the

a. The Galápagos

b. Galápagos tortoise

c. Marine iguana

d. Blue-footed booby

Figure 20.4
The Galápagos Islands. Between 3 and 5 million years ago, volcanic eruptions created the Galápagos Islands **(a)** about 1000 km west of Ecuador. The islands were named for the giant tortoises **(b)** found there (in Spanish, *galdpa* means tortoise). This tortoise (*Geochelone elephantopus*) is native to Isla Santa Cruz. Marine iguanas **(c,** *Amblyrhynchus cristatus*) dive into the Pacific Ocean to feed on algae. A male blue-footed booby **(d,** *Sula nebouxii*) engages in courtship display.

20.3c Struggle For Existence: Survival of the Fittest

Darwin had a revelation about how selective breeding could occur naturally when he read Thomas Malthus's famous *Essay on the Principles of Population*. Malthus, an English clergyman and economist, observed that England's population was growing much faster than its agricultural capacity. This situation meant that individuals competed for food, and some of them would inevitably starve.

Darwin applied Malthus's argument to organisms in nature. Species typically produce many more offspring than are needed to replace the parent generation, yet the world is not overrun with sunflowers, tortoises, or bears. Darwin even calculated that if its reproduction went unchecked, a single pair of elephants (the slowest breeding animal known) would leave roughly 19 million descendants after only 750 years. Happily for us (and all other species that might be underfoot), the world is not so crowded with elephants. Instead, some members of every population survive and reproduce, whereas others die without reproducing.

20.3d Darwin's Inferences: The Theory of Evolution by Natural Selection

Darwin's discovery of a mechanism for evolutionary change required him to infer the nature of a process that no one previously had envisioned or documented **(Table 20.1)**. First, individuals within populations vary in size, form, colour, behaviour, and other characteristics. Second, many of these variations are hereditary. What if variations in hereditary traits enabled some individuals to survive and reproduce more readily than others? Organisms with favourable traits would leave many young, whereas those that lacked favourable traits would die, leaving few, if any, descendants. Thus, favourable hereditary traits would become more common in the next generation. And if the next generation were subjected to the same process of selection, the traits would be even more common in the third generation. Because this process is analogous to artificial selection, Darwin called it **natural selection.**

20.3e Darwin's Innovations

Four characteristics distinguish Darwin's theory from earlier explanations of biological diversity and adaptive traits:

1. Darwin provided purely physical rather than spiritual explanations about the origins of biological diversity.
2. Darwin recognized that evolutionary change occurs in groups of organisms rather than in individuals. Some members of a group survive and reproduce more successfully than others do.
3. Darwin described evolution as a multistage process. Variations arise within groups, natural selection eliminates unsuccessful variations, and the next generation inherits successful variations.
4. Like Lamarck, Darwin understood that evolution occurs because some organisms function better than others *in a particular environment.*

One of the most interesting parts of the story of Darwin's development and publication of his theory is its parallel with work by Alfred Russell Wallace. On June 18, 1858, Darwin received a letter from Wallace outlining his ideas about how species change over time. To his credit, Darwin forwarded Wallace's manuscript to Charles Lyell, who had been encouraging Darwin to publish his theory. On July 1, 1858, papers by Darwin and Wallace were presented to the Linnaean Society of London. On November 24,

Table 20.1	Darwin's Observations and Inferences about Evolution by Means of Natural Selection	
Observations	**Inferences**	
Most organisms produce more than one or two offspring.	Individuals within a population compete for limited resources.	A population's characteristics will change over the generations as advantageous, heritable characteristics become more common.
Populations do not increase in size indefinitely.		
Food and other resources are limited for most populations.		
Individuals within populations exhibit variability in many characteristics.	Hereditary characteristics may allow some individuals to survive longer and reproduce more than others.	
Many variations have a genetic basis that is inherited by subsequent generations.		

1859, Darwin's book *On the Origin of Species by Means of Natural Selection* was published.

Just as species on different continents converge in their appearance, so do similar theories and ideas in biology arise from different biologists.

20.3f Darwin's Impact on Biological Thought and Society

It would be hard to overestimate the impact of Darwin's theory on Western thought. In *On the Origin of Species*, he proposed a logical mechanism for evolutionary change and provided enough supporting evidence to convince the educated public. Darwin argued that all the organisms that have ever lived arose through **descent with modification**, the evolutionary alteration and diversification of ancestral species. Darwin proposed natural selection as the mechanism that drives evolutionary change. In fact, most of *On the Origin of Species* was an explanation of how natural selection acted on the variability within groups of organisms, preserving favourable traits and eliminating unfavourable ones. Remember that as he wrote, Darwin knew nothing about Mendelian genetics (see Chapter 11). He had no clear idea of how variation arose or how it was passed from one generation to the next.

Evolution was a popular topic in Victorian England, and Darwin's theory received both praise and ridicule. Although he had not speculated about the evolution of humans in *On the Origin of Species*, many readers were quick to extrapolate Darwin's ideas to our own species. Needless to say, certain influential Victorians were not amused by the suggestion that humans and apes shared a common ancestry. The problem of this perception lingers still.

STUDY BREAK

1. How did historical thinkers pave the way for the acceptance of the theory of evolution by the scientific community?
2. How did Lyell's ideas influence Darwin's development of the theory of evolution by natural selection?
3. What makes Darwin's theory a scientific theory?

20.4 The Fossil Record

Paleontology is our primary source of data about the evolutionary history of many organisms. Paleontologists discover, describe, and name species of fossils (e.g., the ichthyosaur shown in Figure 19.1). They also analyze the morphology and ecology (deduced from the sediments and the other species in them) of extinct organisms. Most fossils are found in sedimentary rocks, which formed when rain and runoff eroded the land, carrying fine particles of rock and soil downstream to a swamp, a lake, or the sea. Particles settled to the bottom as sediments, forming successive layers over millions of years. The weight of newer sediments compressed the older layers beneath them into a solid matrix: sand into sandstone and silt or mud into shale. When organisms were buried in the sediments, their fossils formed within that layer.

The process of fossilization is a race against time because usually the soft remains of organisms are quickly consumed by scavengers or decomposed by microorganisms. Thus, fossils usually preserve the details of hard structures—bones, teeth, and shells of animals or wood, leaves, and pollen of plants. During fossilization, dissolved minerals replace some of an organism's parts, molecule by molecule **(Figure 20.5a, p. 446)**. Other fossils are moulds, casts, or impressions **(Figure 20.5b)**. In environments where oxygen is scarce, decomposition does not occur and even soft-bodied organisms may be preserved. The Burgess Shale, a deposit in the Canadian Rockies, is rich in extremely well-preserved soft-bodied animals (see Chapter 26). Amber, the fossilized resin of coniferous trees, can include the remains of insects, plants, tiny lizards, and frogs **(Figure 20.5c)**. Other organisms are preserved in glacial ice, coal, tar pits, or the highly acidic water of peat bogs **(Figure 20.5d)**. Sometimes organisms are well enough preserved that their internal anatomy and cell structure, even food in their digestive tracts, can be examined. Biologists have obtained and analyzed DNA from a 40-million-year-old magnolia leaf.

Still, the odds are against almost anything being fossilized, let alone against the discovery of fossils by paleontologists. The ~300 000 described fossil species represent less than 1% of the estimated number of species that have ever lived. Inevitably, absence of skeletons and hard parts means that fossil jellyfish (Cnidaria) are much less common than fossil trilobites (Arthropoda; see Chapter 26), even if both kinds of organisms were equally abundant in the same Ordovician sea. Fossils rarely form in habitats where sediments do not accumulate (e.g., mountain forests) or where soils are acidic (e.g., many forests). Furthermore, although most fossils are composed of stone, they do not last forever. Many are deformed by pressure from overlying rocks **(Figure 20.6, p. 447)** or destroyed by geologic processes (erosion) or disturbances, such as volcanic eruptions. The effects of erosion mean that fossils from older rocks are less common than those in younger rocks because the latter have been around for less time and therefore exposed to less erosion.

a. Petrified wood

b. An invertebrate

c. Insects in amber

d. Mammoth in permafrost

Figure 20.5
In petrified wood **(a)** from Dinosaur Provincial Park in Alberta, minerals have replaced the wood of dead trees molecule by molecule.
(b) The soft tissues of an invertebrate (genus *Dickinsonia*) from the Proterozoic preserved as an impression in very fine sediments;
(c) a 20-million-year-old fly (left) and a wasp were trapped in the oozing resin of a coniferous tree and are now encased in amber; **(d)** a frozen
baby mammoth, genus *Mammuthus*, that lived about 40 000 years ago was discovered embedded in ice in Siberia in 1977.

20.4a Dating: How Old Is That Fossil in Relative or in Absolute Time?

Scientists can assign relative and absolute dates to geologic strata and the fossils they contain. Sediments found in any one place form distinctive strata (layers) that usually differ in colour, mineral composition, particle size, and thickness **(Figure 20.7)**. If they have not been disturbed, the strata are arranged in the order in which they formed, with the youngest layers on top. But strata sometimes have been uplifted, warped, or even inverted by geologic processes.

Geologists of the early nineteenth century deduced that the fossils discovered in a particular sedimentary stratum, no matter where it is found, represent organisms that lived and died at roughly the same time in the past. Because each stratum formed at a specific time, the sequence of fossils in the lowest (oldest) to the highest (newest) strata reveals their *relative ages*. Geologists used the sequence of strata and their distinctive fossil assemblages to establish the geologic time scale (see Table 1.1).

The geologic time scale provides a relative dating system for sedimentary strata rather than actual ages of rocks and fossils. **Radiometric** dating involves the use of isotopes and sometimes allows actual ages (with error bars) to be associated with different rock strata. Radiometric dating exploits the fact that isotopes begin to decay (break down into more stable elements) from the moment they form. Isotopes decay at steady rates; thus, rocks containing isotopes can be dated (see Chapter 3) when the amounts of isotopes can be measured and the rates of decay are known.

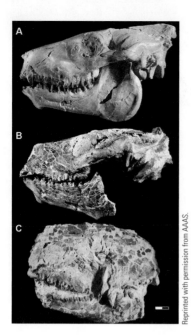

Reprinted with permission from AAAS.

Figure 20.6
Fossils can be distorted. These fossil mammals (creodonts) are from the Day Formation in Oregon. The three fossils are of the same species.

David Noble/FPG/Getty Images

Figure 20.7
Geologic strata in the Grand Canyon. Millions of years of sedimentation in an old ocean basin produced layers of rock that differ in colour and particle size. Tectonic forces later lifted the land above sea level, and the flow of the Colorado River carved this natural wonder.

This approach to dating is limited by the half-life of the isotope, which is the amount of time it takes half of the initial amount of isotope to decay into more stable elements.

Radiometric dating works best with volcanic rocks, which form when lava cools and solidifies. But most fossils are found in sedimentary rocks.

To date sedimentary fossils, scientists determine the age of volcanic rocks from the same strata. Using this method, investigators have linked fossils to deposits that are hundreds of millions of years old.

Fossils that still contain organic matter, such as the remains of bones or wood, can be dated directly by measuring the amount of the isotope ^{14}C. Living organisms absorb traces of ^{14}C and large quantities of the stable ^{12}C from the environment and incorporate them into biological molecules. As long as an organism is still alive, its ^{14}C content remains constant because any ^{14}C that decays is replaced by the uptake of other ^{14}C atoms. But as soon as the organism dies, no further replacement occurs, and ^{14}C begins its steady radioactive decay. Scientists use the ratio of ^{14}C to ^{12}C present in a fossil to determine its age.

STUDY BREAK

1. What is the difference between absolute and relative dates?
2. How are isotopes used in dating rocks?

20.5 Earth History, Biogeography, and Convergent Evolution

Living organisms are affected profoundly by prevailing climates and environmental conditions. Organisms also affect their surroundings, a striking example being the development of oxygenic photosynthesis (see Section 2.4). A more modest example is the impact of a beaver dam on a stream. Environments on Earth are affected by shifts in geography and climate, whether brief or prolonged, and by catastrophic events. Major geologic shifts occur because the planet's crust is in motion.

20.5a Continental Drift: Movements in Space and Time

According to the theory of **plate tectonics**, Earth's crust is broken into irregularly shaped plates of rock that float on its semisolid mantle **(Figure 20.8, p. 448).** Currents in the mantle cause the plates, and the continents embedded in them, to move, a phenomenon called **continental drift**. About 250 million years ago, Earth's landmasses coalesced into a single supercontinent named Pangea. Later continental drift separated Pangea into a northern continent, Laurasia, and a southern continent, Gondwana. Laurasia and Gondwana subsequently broke into the continents we know today **(Figure 20.9, p. 449).**

J. Tuzo Wilson, Director of the Ontario Science Centre

In 1963, Canadian geophysicist J. Tuzo Wilson (1908–1993) published a paper suggesting that the Hawaiian Islands and other volcanic island chains formed because of "hot spots" in Earth's mantle. With this concept, Tuzo Wilson explained the presence of active volcanoes thousands of kilometres from the boundaries between tectonic plates. His manuscript was rejected by many major international journals because it was too radical. The hot spot theory, published in the relatively obscure journal *Canadian Journal of Physics*, is one of the milestone papers in the development of our understanding of the theory of plate tectonics.

In 1965, Tuzo published two more papers that further advanced this theory. He asserted that a third type of plate boundary connects oceanic ridges and trenches. This third type of boundary can end abruptly and transform into major faults. The San Andreas Fault zone in California is now recognized as an example of the third type of plate boundary.

Tuzo Wilson was an accomplished teacher, but he also contributed to science in other ways. He was the first principal of Erindale College, which became the University of Toronto, Mississauga, and later was the director of the Ontario Science Centre.

Tuzo Wilson was a geophysicist whose work had a strong impact on our understanding of evolution and biogeography.

Drifting continents induced global changes in Earth's climate. The movement of continents toward the poles encouraged the formation of glaciers, which caused temperature and rainfall to decrease worldwide. Earth's average temperature has fluctuated widely because of complex continental movements.

Unpredictable events have also changed physical environments on Earth. Massive volcanic eruptions and asteroid impacts have occasionally altered the planet's atmosphere and climate drastically. These cataclysmic events have sometimes caused the extinction of many forms of life in relatively short periods of geologic time.

More than a century after Darwin published his observations, the theory of plate tectonics refocused attention on biogeography. Historical biogeographers try to explain how organisms acquired their geographic distributions over evolutionary time.

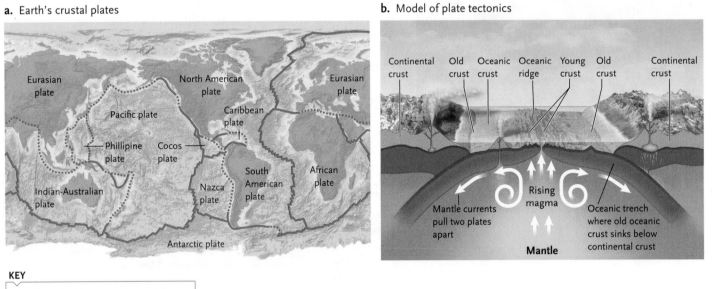

a. Earth's crustal plates

b. Model of plate tectonics

KEY
—— Oceanic ridge ⋯⋯⋯ Oceanic trench

Figure 20.8

Plate tectonics. Earth's crust **(a)** is broken into large rigid plates. New crust is added at oceanic ridges (red), and old crust is recycled into the mantle at oceanic trenches (blue). Oceanic ridges **(b)** form where pressure in the mantle forces magma (molten rock) through fissures in the sea floor. Mantle currents pull the plates apart on either side of the ridge, forcing the sea floor to move laterally away from the ridge. This phenomenon, sea-floor spreading, is widening the Atlantic Ocean about 3 cm per year. Oceanic trenches form where plates collide. The heavier oceanic crust sinks below the lighter continental crust and is recycled into the mantle, a process called subduction. The highest mountain ridges (including the Rockies, Himalayas, Alps, and Andes) formed where subduction uplifted continental crust. Earthquakes and volcanoes are also common near trenches.

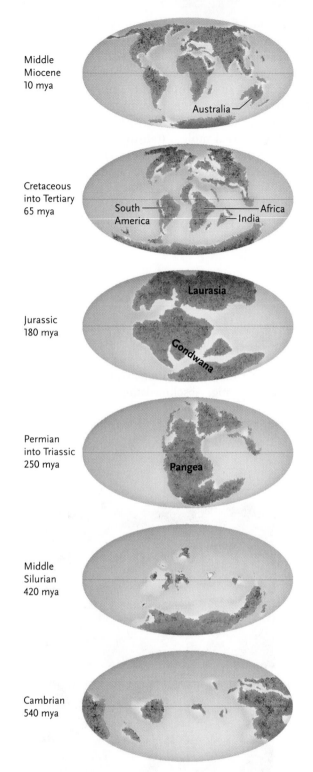

Middle
Miocene
10 mya

Australia

Cretaceous
into Tertiary
65 mya

South
America

Africa

India

Jurassic
180 mya

Laurasia

Gondwana

Permian
into Triassic
250 mya

Pangea

Middle
Silurian
420 mya

Cambrian
540 mya

Figure 20.9

History of long-term changes in the positions of continents. Earth's many landmasses coalesced during the Permian, forming the supercontinent Pangea. About 180 million years ago, Pangea separated into Gondwana and Laurasia. Then Gondwana began to break apart. Africa and India pulled way first, opening the South Atlantic and Indian Oceans. Australia separated from Antarctica about 55 million years ago and slowly drifted northward. South America separated from Antartica shortly thereafter. Laurasia remained nearly intact until 43 million years ago when North America and Greenland together separated from Europe and Asia. Movement of the continents also changed the shapes and sizes of the oceans.

Continuous and Disjunct Distributions Many species have a **continuous distribution**, living in suitable habitats throughout large areas. For example, herring gulls (*Larus argentatus*) live along the coastlines of all northern continents. Continuous distributions usually require no special historical explanations. Other groups exhibit **disjunct distributions**. Here, closely related species live in widely separated locations. Magnolia trees (*Magnolia* spp.) occur in parts of North, Central, and South America, as well as in China and Southeast Asia, but nowhere in between.

Dispersal and vicariance create disjunct distributions. **Dispersal** is the movement of organisms away from their place of origin; it can produce a disjunct distribution if a new population becomes established on the far side of a geographic barrier. **Vicariance** is the fragmentation of a continuous geographic distribution by external factors. Over the course of evolutionary history, dispersal and vicariance have together influenced the geographic distributions of organisms on a very grand scale.

20.5b Biogeographic Regions: Regional Influences on Flora and Fauna

Pangea's breakup was a powerful vicariant experience for species that were widespread in the Mesozoic. The subsequent geographic isolation of continents fostered the evolution of distinctive regional **biotas** (all organisms living in a region). Alfred Russel Wallace used biotas to define six **biogeographic regions** that we still recognize today **(Figure 20.10)**.

The Australian and Neotropical realms have been geographically isolated since the Mesozoic. Each contains many **endemic species** (those that occur nowhere else on Earth). The Australian region, in particular, has had no complete land connection to any other continent for approximately 55 million years. The biota of the Australian region reflects this isolation, especially the mammals. Of the 247 species of living terrestrial mammals native to Australia, 64% of them are marsupials, unlike the situation

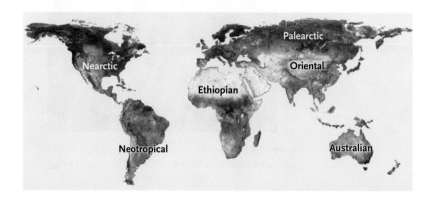

Figure 20.10

Wallace's biogeographic realms. Each realm contains a distinctive biota.

on any other continent. There are also two species of monotremes (egg-laying mammals). The rest of the native mammal species are placentals: mostly bats (77 species), but some rodents (10 species) and one carnivore, the dingo (*Canis familiaris*). The dingo arrived with humans, whereas the rodents apparently arrived on their own. For more about mammals, see Chapter 27.

In comparison, the biotas of the Nearctic and Palearctic realms (including mammals) are fairly similar. North America and Eurasia were frequently connected by land bridges; eastern North America was attached to Western Europe until the breakup of Laurasia 43 million years ago, and northwestern North America has had periodic contact with northeastern Asia over the Bering land bridge during much of the last 60 million years.

20.5c Convergences in Life Forms: Parallel and Convergent Evolution

Distantly related species living in different biogeographic realms can be similar in appearance. We have seen that cacti can be almost identical to spurges (see Figure 19.2). But these lineages arose independently long after the continents had separated. Cacti and spurges did not inherit their similarities from a shared ancestor; rather, their overall resemblance is the product of **convergent evolution**, the evolution of similar adaptations in distantly related organisms that occupy similar environments.

A comparison of some mammals provides impressive examples of convergence between marsupials and placental mammals. *Canis lupis*, the grey wolf of the Palearctic, is strikingly similar to the extinct *Thylacinus cynocephalus* (marsupial wolf or thalacine, **Figure 20.11**). Similarly, in the Pleistocene, *Thylacoleo carnifex* was a lion-like Australian marsupial. Sabre-toothed "lions" lived among South American marsupials (*Thylacosmilus* of the Pliocene), whereas *Smilodon*, a Pleistocene placental sabre-toothed lion, lived in the Northern Hemisphere (and spread into South America) **(Figure 20.12)**. Other exceptional examples are *Notorytes typhlops*, a marsupial mole from Australia, compared with "real moles" (family Talpidae), which are placentals from the Northern Hemisphere, or "golden moles" (family Chrysochloridae), which are placentals from Africa.

Carnivorous plants such as living flypaper and pitcher plants are other variations on the themes of convergent and parallel evolution (see Figure 19.6).

STUDY BREAK

1. What conditions lead to fossilization? How would these affect the sample of fossils available?
2. What techniques for dating fossils provide relative dating? Absolute dating?
3. What historical conditions lead to continuous distributions? Disjunct distributions?

a.

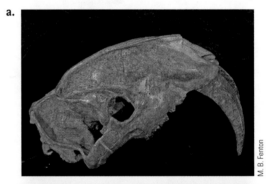

b.

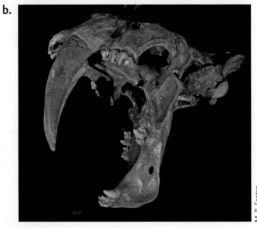

M. B. Fenton

Figure 20.12
Convergent evolution. **(a)** Sabre-toothed marsupial lion (*Thylacosmilus atrox*) of South America, compared with the **(b)** placental sabre-toothed cat (*Smilodon* spp.) from North America.

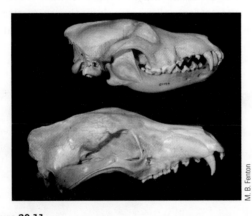

M. B. Fenton

Figure 20.11
Convergent evolution. Wolf-like mammals such as *Canis lupis* (top) and *Thylacinus cynocephalus* (bottom). The grey wolf occurs widely in the Northern Hemisphere, whereas the now extinct thalacine (marsupial wolf) formerly occurred in Tasmania.

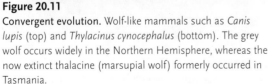

20.6 Interpreting Evolutionary Lineages

As newly discovered fossils demanded the reinterpretation of old hypotheses, biologists have refined their ideas about the history of life. The evolution of horses is a case in point.

20.6a Evolution of Horses: An Adaptive Radiation

The earliest known ancestors of modern horses were first identified by Othniel C. Marsh a year after Darwin published *On the Origin of Species*. These early horses, *Hyracotherium*, stood 25 to 50 cm high at the shoulder. Each of their toes (four on the front feet and three on the hind) was capped with a tiny hoof, but the animals walked on soft pads, as dogs do today. Their faces were short, their teeth were small, and they browsed on soft leaves in woodland habitats.

In 1879, Marsh published his analysis of 60 million years of horse family history. He described their evolution in a series of stages from the tiny *Hyracotherium* through intermediates (*Mesohippus* spp., *Merychippus* spp., and *Pliohippus* spp.) to the modern *Equus* **(Figure 20.13a, p. 452)**. Marsh inferred a pattern of descent characterized by gradual, directional evolution in several skeletal features. Changes in the legs and feet allowed horses to run faster, and changes in the face and teeth accompanied a switch in diet from soft leaves to tough grasses. The pattern of evolution appeared to progress from living in wooded habitats to open grasslands.

The fossil record for horses is superb, and we now have fossils of more than 100 extinct species from five continents. These fossils reveal a macroevolutionary history that differs from Marsh's interpretation. *Hyracotherium* was not gradually transformed into *Equus* along a linear track. Rather, the evolutionary tree for horses was highly branched **(Figure 20.13b)**, and *Hyracotherium*'s descendants differed in size, numbers of toes, tooth structure, and other traits. Although there were many branches of the horse lineage in the Miocene and Pliocene epochs, today only one genus (*Equus*) remains, and it includes several species. Today's horses and their close relatives (donkeys and zebras) are the surviving tips of one evolutionary line.

When we study extinct organisms, we tend to focus on traits that characterize modern species. Marsh had assumed that the differences between *Hyracotherium* and *Equus* were typical of the changes that characterized the group's evolutionary history. But not all fossil horses were larger **(Figure 20.13c)**, had fewer toes, or were better adapted to feed on grass than their ancestors. Furthermore, if a branch other than

Equus survived today, Marsh's description of trends in horse evolution could have been very different. All evolutionary lineages have extinct branches. Any attempt to trace a linear evolutionary path, as Marsh did for horses and many people do for humans, imposes artificial order on an inherently disorderly history. This is a variation on the problem of defining a species where we impose a set of conditions on a natural continuum.

20.6b Time for Evolution to Occur: Rapid or Slow Change?

Which evolutionary processes produce the numerous branches of a lineage such as the horse lineage? Over what time scale does a lineage evolve? To put this in perspective, remember the example of *Acanthinucella spirata*, a marine gastropod from the California coast (see Figure 18.12), or the Italian wall lizard (see Section 18.11).

Evolution can occur by gradual changes, by anagenesis or by cladogenesis. **Anagenesis** is the accumulation of changes in a lineage as it adapts to changing environments. If morphological changes are large, we may give the organisms different names at different times in their history. One might say that Species A from the late Mesozoic evolved into Species B from the middle Cenozoic **(Figure 20.14a, p. 453)**. Anagenesis does not increase the number of species; it is the evolutionary transformation of an existing species rather than the production of new ones.

Evolution also occurs by **cladogenesis**, the evolution of two or more descendant species from a common ancestor. If the fossilized remains of the descendants are distinct, paleontologists will recognize them as different species **(Figure 20.14b)**. Cladogenesis increases the number of species on Earth.

The **gradualist hypothesis** suggests that large changes result from slow, continuous accumulations of small changes over time. If this hypothesis is correct, in any lineage we expect to find a series of transitional fossils documenting gradual evolution. However, we rarely find evidence of gradual changes in any lineage. Most species appear suddenly in a particular stratum, persist for some time with little change, and then disappear from the fossil record. Then another species, a variant on the first with different traits, suddenly appears in the next higher stratum.

Alternatively, evolution also can occur rapidly, as predicted by the **punctuated equilibrium hypothesis** proposed in the early 1970s by Niles Eldredge and Stephen Jay Gould. The punctuated equilibrium hypothesis suggested that speciation occurs in isolated populations at the edge of a species' geographic distribution. Marginal populations experience substantial genetic drift and distinctive patterns of natural selection. According to this hypothesis,

a. Marsh's reconstruction of horse evolution

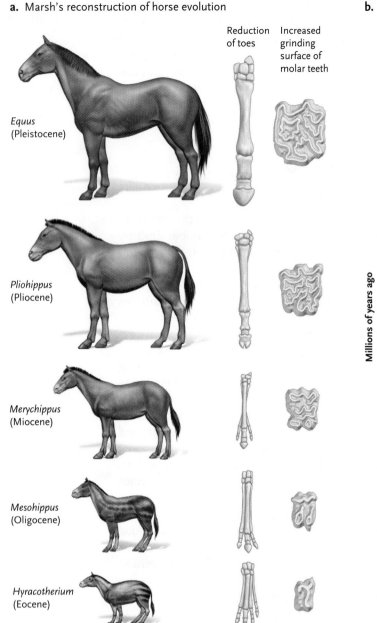

Reduction of toes

Increased grinding surface of molar teeth

Equus (Pleistocene)

Pliohippus (Pliocene)

Merychippus (Miocene)

Mesohippus (Oligocene)

Hyracotherium (Eocene)

b. Modern reconstruction of horse evolution

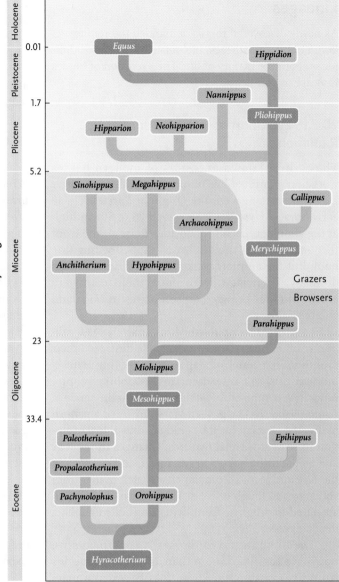

Millions of years ago

Holocene — 0.01 — Pleistocene — 1.7 — Pliocene — 5.2 — Miocene — 23 — Oligocene — 33.4 — Eocene

Equus
Hippidion
Nannippus
Pliohippus
Hipparion
Neohipparion
Sinohippus
Megahippus
Callippus
Archaeohippus
Merychippus
Anchitherium
Hypohippus
Grazers
Browsers
Parahippus
Miohippus
Mesohippus
Paleotherium
Epihippus
Propalaeotherium
Pachynolophus
Orohippus
Hyracotherium

c. Changes in body size of horse species over time

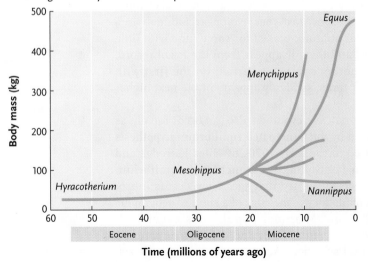

Body mass (kg)

Equus
Merychippus
Mesohippus
Hyracotherium
Nannippus

Time (millions of years ago)

Eocene — Oligocene — Miocene

Figure 20.13

Evolution of horses. Marsh depicted the evolution of horses **(a)** as a linear pattern of descent characterized by an increase in body size, a reduction in the number of toes, increased fusion of bones in the lower leg, elongation of the face, and an increase in the sizes of grinding (molar) teeth. Recent studies **(b)** indicated that the horse family included numerous evolutionary branches with variable morphology. Although many branches of the lineage developed larger bodies, some remained as small as the earliest horses **(c)**.

a. Anagenesis

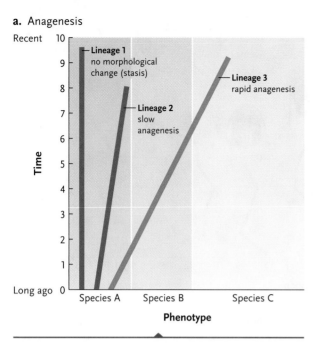

Three lineages begin with the same phenotype, identified as fossil Species A, at time 0. The rate of evolutionary change is shown by the angle of the line for each lineage: lineage 1 undergoes no change over time, lineage 2 changes slowly, and lineage 3 changes so rapidly that its phenotype shifts far to the right in the graph. Paleobiologists might assign different names to the fossils of lineage 3 at different times in its history—Species A at time 1, Species B at times 2 through 6, and Species C at times 7 through 9—even though no additional species evolved. By contrast, fossils of lineages 1 and 2 change so little over time that they would be identified as Species A throughout their evolutionary history.

b. Cladogenesis

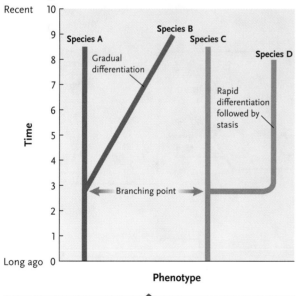

Each branching point represents a new line of descent. The branching may show either gradual (left) or rapid (right) morphological differentiation from the parent species.

Figure 20.14

Patterns of evolution. In these hypothetical examples, the vertical axis represents geologic time and the horizontal axis represents variation in a phenotypic trait.

morphological variations arise rapidly during clado-genesis. Thus, most species exhibit long periods of morphological equilibrium (stasis), punctuated by brief periods of cladogenesis and rapid morphological evolution. If this hypothesis is correct, transitional forms are uncommon in the fossil record because they live only for short periods of time in small, localized populations. Darwin had used a similar line of reasoning to explain puzzling gaps in the fossil record.

The fossil record supports both hypotheses. Data from work on Ordovician trilobites (Arthropoda) support the gradualist hypothesis. The number of "ribs" in the tail regions of trilobites changed continuously over 3 million years. The change was so gradual that a sample from any given stratum is almost always intermediate between samples from the strata just above and below it. The changes in rib number probably evolved without cladogenesis **(Figure 20.15, p. 454)**.

A punctuated pattern is evident in the evolutionary history of *Metrarabdotus*, a genus of ectoprocts from the Caribbean Sea. Ectoprocts are small colonial animals that build hard skeletons **(Figure 20.16, p. 454)**, the details of which are well preserved in fossils. Alan Cheetham measured 46 morphological traits in fossils of 18 *Metrarabdotus* species. He used a single statistic to summarize the morphological differences between populations of a single species over time and between ancestral species and their descendants. He found that most species did not change much over millions of years, but new species, which were morphologically different from their ancestors, often appeared quite suddenly (see Figure 20.16).

The punctuationalist and gradualist hypotheses are extremes along a continuum of possible macroevolutionary patterns. The mode and tempo of evolution vary among lineages, and both viewpoints are validated by data on some organisms but not on others. Some of the most interesting results have come from work focused on morphological changes within lineages and on long-term changes in the number of living species (e.g., *Acanthinucella spirata*; see Figure 18.12).

STUDY BREAK

1. Why would it be a mistake to classify a fossil as an ancestor to an extant species based on the possession of intermediate traits?
2. Which sort of evolution does not increase the number of species? How does it work?
3. Compare the gradualist hypothesis with the punctuated equilibrium hypothesis. Why should a biologist consider both hypotheses when looking at the evolution of a species?

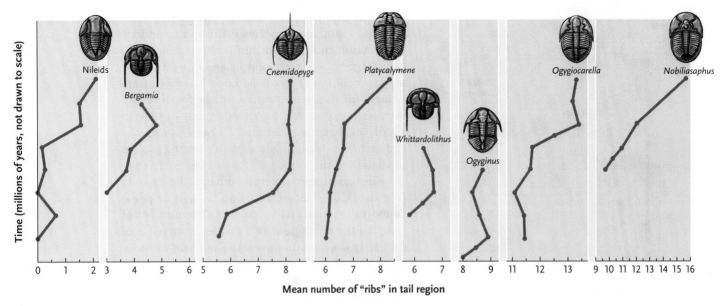

Figure 20.15

The gradualist hypothesis predicts that in morphology, the fossils from any layer of rock (stratum) will be intermediate between those in strata above and below (younger and older, respectively). Analysis of the number of riblike structures in the tail regions of 15 000 trilobites from northern Wales revealed gradual changes as illustrated in this figure. The fossils had been deposited over 3 million years in the Ordovician.

Figure 20.16

Changes in the morphology of 18 fossil species of ectoprocts (genus *Metrarabdotus*) from the Dominican Republic support the punctuated equilibrium hypothesis. Although the morphology of most fossil species of *Metrarabdotus* changed relatively little, new species often appeared "suddenly" in the fossil record. The dashed lines represent gaps in the fossil record. The time scale is shown on the vertical axis.

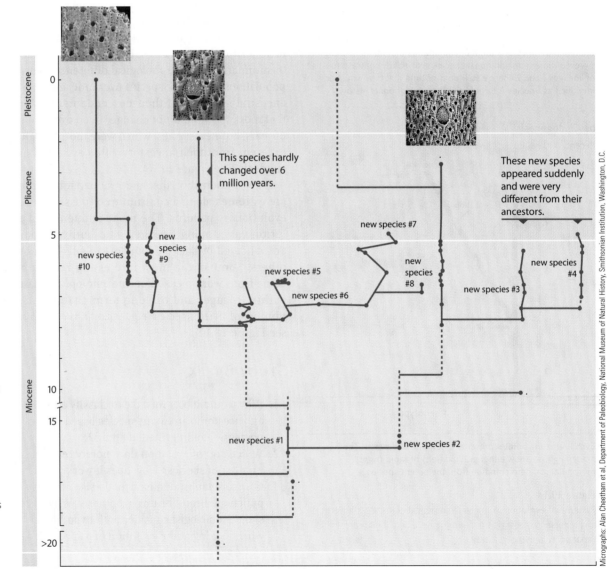

Micrographs: Alan Cheetham et al, Department of Paleobiology, National Museum of Natural History, Smithsonian Institution, Washington, D.C.

20.7 Macroevolutionary Trends in Morphology

Some evolutionary lineages exhibit trends toward larger size and greater morphological complexity. Others are marked by the development of novel structures.

Body size affects most aspects of an organism's physiology and ecology. When we look at the entire history of life, some organisms have become larger over time, but others have not. Within some evolutionary lineages, increases in body size are common, but not universal. The nineteenth-century paleobiologist Edward Drinker Cope noted this trend in vertebrates, now known as *Cope's Rule*. Although Cope's Rule also applies to some lineages of invertebrates and plants, no truly broad survey has been done to test the generality of the hypothesis underlying it. Insects appear to be a major exception to Cope's Rule. Most insects have remained small since their appearance in the Devonian, perhaps reflecting the prevalence of a life history strategy that permits production of large numbers of offspring and thus the ability to withstand high levels of mortality (see Chapter 45).

20.7a Novel Features: Innovation in Evolution

Novel morphological structures, such as the wings of birds, often appear suddenly in the fossil record. How do novel features evolve? Scientists have identified several mechanisms, including preadaptation, allometric growth, and heterochrony.

Preadaptations are said to occur when a trait that is adaptive in one context is also advantageous in another. In this situation, the trait may be enhanced by natural selection, modifying and enhancing the feature to enhance its new function. Such preadaptations are lucky accidents; they never evolve *in anticipation* of future evolutionary needs.

John Ostrom described how some evolutionary lines of carnivorous dinosaurs, the immediate ancestors of *Archaeopteryx* and modern birds, were preadapted for flight **(Figure 20.17)**. Some of these small, agile, nonflying creatures were bipedal, with light hollow bones and long forelimbs that they used to capture prey. Feathers appeared in some of these lineages, where they probably served in **thermoregulation** (either as heat shields or insulation). The collection of traits developed because they conferred high levels of activity and mobility, combined with access to elusive prey, such as flying insects. Other branches of carnivorous dinosaurs related to birds were active and predatory but did not fly. At least one was a large bipedal predator, the size of *Tyrannosaurus* (see Figure 20.17). We have no fossils of animals that were intermediate between *Archaeopteryx* and its ancestors, just as we lack fossils of animals whose descendants were on their way to becoming pterosaurs or bats. The absence of intermediate forms does not mean that they did not exist. In 1990, most biologists would have considered feathers to be a diagnostic feature of birds. Within

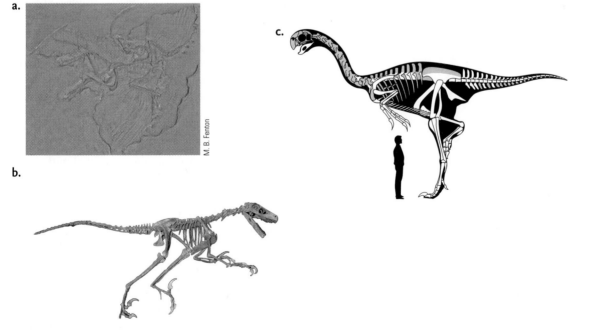

M. B. Fenton

Figure 20.17

Bird-like fossils. **(a)** Skeleton of *Archaeopteryx lithographica* from the German Jurassic. Bird-like features include a furculum (wishbone) and feathers. **(b)** This bird-like dinosaur, *Saurornitholestes langstoni*, from the Cretaceous of western Canada, probably had feathers and was closely related to birds but did not fly. **(c)** This bird-like dinosaur, *Gigantoraptor erlianensis*, from the Late Cretaceous of China, probably had feathers and was closely related to birds but did not fly. The human silhouette puts *Gigantoraptor* in perspective.

10 years, it was obvious that other species of carnivorous dinosaurs had feathers but were not birds (see Chapter 27).

20.7b Allometric Growth: Changes in Shape through Differential Growth

Allometric growth occurs when different parts of the body grow at different rates. Allometry can result in changes in the morphology of individuals

Figure 20.18
Examples of allometric growth.

a. Allometric growth in humans

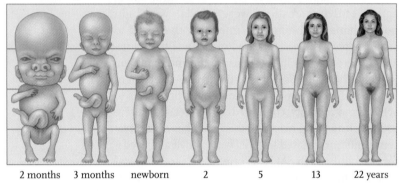

| 2 months | 3 months | newborn | 2 | 5 | 13 | 22 years |

Humans exhibit allometric growth from prenatal development until adulthood. Our heads grow more slowly than other body parts; our legs grow faster.

b. Differential growth in the skulls of chimpanzees and humans

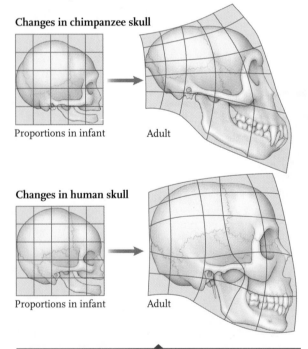

Changes in chimpanzee skull

Proportions in infant   Adult

Changes in human skull

Proportions in infant   Adult

Although the skulls of newborn humans and chimpanzees are remarkably similar, differential patterns of growth make them diverge during development. Imagine that the skulls are painted on a blue rubber sheet marked with a grid. Stretching the sheet deforms the grid in particular ways, mimicking the differential growth of various parts of the skull.

over time (*allo* = different; *metro* = measure). Allometric growth occurs in humans. The relative sizes of different body parts change because human heads, torsos, and limbs grow at different rates **(Figure 20.18a)**. Allometric growth also occurred in dinosaurs. It can create morphological differences in closely related species. The skulls of chimpanzees and humans are similar in newborns but markedly different in adults **(Figure 20.18b)**. Some regions of the chimp skull grow much more quickly than others, whereas the proportions of the human skull change much less. Differences in the adult skulls may simply reflect changes in one or a few genes that regulate the pattern of growth.

20.7c Heterochrony: Timing of Developmental Events and Larval Stages

Heterochrony, changes in the timing of developmental events (*hetero* = different; *chronos* = time), can cause the morphology of closely related species to differ. At least two phenomena can be involved, neoteny and **pedomorphosis** (*paedo* = child; *morpho* = form). We use the ability to reproduce to distinguish juveniles (no reproduction) from adults (reproduction). Neoteny occurs when larvae acquire the ability to reproduce. Pedomorphosis occurs when adults retain juvenile characters. In many protostomes, larvae contain totipotent cells that develop into adults (see Chapter 26).

Metamorphosis, the change from a juvenile form to an adult form, can involve significant reorganization of internal organs. The distinctiveness of larval versus adult forms is obvious in some insects and in many other protostomes (see Chapter 26). Metamorphosis also occurs in many species of salamanders and frogs, coincident with the change from aquatic (juvenile) to terrestrial (adult) forms. Populations of several salamander species are pedomorphic because the organisms grow to adult size and become reproductively mature without changing to the adult form **(Figure 20.19)**.

The evolutionary change associated with pedomorphosis can be surprisingly simple. In amphibians, including salamanders, the hormone thyroxine induces metamorphosis (see Chapter 35). Pedomorphosis could result from a mutation that either reduces thyroxine production or limits the responsiveness of some developmental processes to thyroxine concentration.

Changes in developmental rates also influence the morphology of plants **(Figure 20.20)**. The flower of a larkspur species, *Delphinium decorum*, includes a ring of petals that guide bees to its nectar tube and other structures on which bees can perch. By contrast, *D. nudicaule*, a more recently evolved species, has tight flowers that attract hummingbird pollinators, which

Figure 20.19

Pedomorphosis in salamanders. Some populations of the small-mouthed salamander *Amblystoma talpoideum* undergo metamorphosis, losing their gills and developing lungs (left). Other populations are pedomorphic (right); they retain juvenile morphological characters such as gills after attaining sexual maturity.

a. *D. decorum*

b. *D. nudicaule*

c.

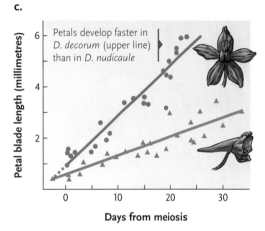

Petals develop faster in *D. decorum* (upper line) than in *D. nudicaule*

Petal blade length (millimetres)

Days from meiosis

Figure 20.20

Delphinium decorum flowers are pollinated by bees **(a)** and *D. nudicaule* flowers by hummingbirds **(b)**. Using days since completion of meiosis in pollen grains, it is clear in the graph that the rate of petal growth differs between the two species **(c)**. Petals of *D. decorum* develop faster and are pollinated by bees.

can hover in front of the flowers. Slower development in *D. nudicaule* flowers causes the structural difference. A mature flower in the descendant species resembles an unopened (juvenile) flower of the ancestral species.

STUDY BREAK

1. What is a preadaptation?
2. How can allometric growth lead to novel structures?
3. What is pedomorphosis?

20.8 Evolutionary Developmental Biology

Historically, evolutionary biologists studied evolutionary history by comparing the embryos of different species, often independently from scientists studying embryonic development. Therefore, we did not see the development of a coherent picture of specific developmental mechanisms contributing to morphological innovations. Since the late 1980s, advances in molecular genetics have allowed scientists to explore the genomes of organisms in great detail, fostering a new approach to these studies. **Evolutionary developmental biology**, "evo-devo" for short, asks how evolutionary changes in genes regulating embryonic development can lead to changes in body shape and form.

The study of development helps advance the understanding of macroevolutionary trends because changes in genes that regulate development often promote evolution of morphological innovations. Moreover, the resulting changes in body plan have sometimes fostered adaptive radiations, increasing biodiversity over geologic time. In the life cycle of a multicellular organism, the many different body parts of the adult develop in a highly controlled sequence of steps specified by genetic instructions in the single cell of a fertilized egg. Developmental biologists study how regulatory genes control the development of phenotypes and their variations. (Gene regulation was described in Chapter 14). Homeotic genes are regulatory genes that code for transcription factors that bind regulatory sites on DNA, either activating or repressing the expression of other genes that contribute to an organism's form (see Chapter 13).

20.8a Genetic Tool-Kits: Controlling Growth and Development

Comparisons of genome sequence data reveal that most animals, regardless of their complexity or position in the tree of life (see Figure 3.7), share a set of several hundred homeotic genes that control their development. This "genetic tool-kit" governs the basic design of the body plan by controlling the activity of thousands of other genes. Some of the homeotic genes must be at least 500 million years old because all living animals inherited them from a common ancestor alive then. Some of the same tool-kit genes are present in plants, fungi, and prokaryotes, suggesting that those genes could date back to the earliest forms of life.

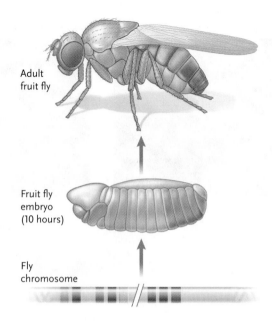

Adult
fruit fly

Fruit fly
embryo
(10 hours)

Fly
chromosome

Mouse
chromosomes

Mouse
embryo
(12 days)

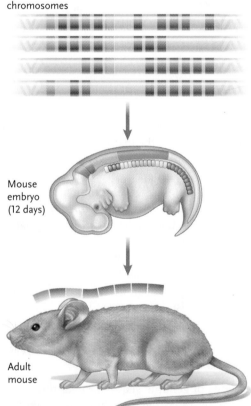

Adult
mouse

Figure 20.21

Hox genes. The linear sequence of *Hox* genes on chromosomes and their expression in different body regions have been conserved by evolution. Each colour-coded band on the chromosomes in the illustration represents a different gene in the *Hox* family. Fruit flies have one set of *Hox* genes, which are arranged on a single chromosome in the same order that they are expressed in the fruit fly embryo. Like all mammals, mice have four sets of *Hox* genes, arranged on four chromosomes that are expressed in mouse embryos in the same order as the *Hox* genes in fruit flies. The illustrations of the adult fruit fly and mouse show the adult body regions influenced by the expression of *Hox* genes in their embryos.

Structurally, tool-kit genes do not differ much among the animals that have them and generally play the same role in development in all species. Genes in the *Hox* family control the overall body plan of animals. *Hox* genes always include a 180-nucleotide sequence (a **homeobox**) that codes for a **homeodomain**, part of a protein that functions as a transcription factor. When bound to a regulatory site on a strand of DNA, the homeodomain either activates or represses a downstream gene involved in development.

Among other functions, *Hox* genes specify where appendages such as wings in flies and legs in mice will develop on the animal's body. They do so by producing transcription factors that activate the genes that produce wings or legs in the body regions where these appendages typically grow. Different *Hox* genes are expressed at different positions along the head-to-tail axis of a developing embryo. These genes are arranged on a chromosome in the same sequence in which they are expressed in the body. Remarkably, the *Hox* genes and their relative positions on chromosomes have been conserved by evolution. Nearly identical genes are found in animals as different as fruit flies (phylum Arthropoda) and mice (phylum Chordata) **(Figure 20.21)**. Genes with comparable functions control aspects of development in plants (see Chapter 31).

Pax-6 is another highly conserved and widely distributed tool-kit gene. The *Pax-6* gene triggers the formation of light-sensing organs as diverse as the eye spots in flatworms, the compound eyes of insects and other arthropods, and the camera eyes of vertebrates (see Chapter 34). Like *Hox* genes, *Pax-6* contains a homeobox, indicating that the protein for which it codes either activates or represses gene transcription. Proteins coded by *Pax-6* in different animals are so similar that when researchers genetically engineered fruit fly larvae to express the *Pax-6* gene taken from either a squid or a mouse, the flies responded by developing eyes. The induced eyes were, however, fruit fly eyes, not squid eyes or mouse eyes. Thus, *Pax-6* triggers activity in genes that carry the specific instructions for making an eye typical of the species. Apparently, the ancient genetic sequence for *Pax-6*, the master regulatory gene for eye development, has been conserved over the hundreds of millions of years since squids, fruit flies, and mice shared a common ancestor.

20.8b Evolutionary Changes in Development Switches: Changes in Gene Expression

If most animals share the same tool-kit genes, how has evolution produced different body plans among species? What makes a squid, a fruit fly, and a mouse different? Researchers in evo-devo have proposed that morphological differences among species arise when mutations alter the effects of developmental regulatory genes. As you will discover in Chapter 39, developmental programs of animals involve complex networks of many interacting genes. Continuously changing combinations of tool-kit genes may be expressed at different times and in different body regions. According to this hypothesis, the several hundred tool-kit genes encode proteins that work either as activators or repressors in a multitude of possible combinations. Thus, they can generate an unimaginably large number of different gene expression patterns, each with the potential to alter morphology.

Sean Carroll described the regulatory sites that transcription factors can bind as *switches*, like those that we use to turn lights on or off. When a combination of transcription factors turns a regulatory switch on, they activate a gene further downstream. When they turn it off, their activity represses the gene.

Although all the cells in an animal contain exactly the same set of genes, the differential expression of genes in different body regions and at different times during embryonic development causes different structures to be made. Allometric growth can result from evolutionary changes in developmental switches that cause certain body parts to grow larger or more quickly than others. Similarly, heterochrony can be explained as an evolutionary change in the switches that either delays the development of adult characteristics or speeds up the development of reproductive maturity.

If Carroll's hypothesis is correct, morphological novelties arise when evolutionary changes in developmental switches alter the expression patterns of *existing* genes. This view contrasts markedly with the explanation that most morphological novelties arise as mutations that slowly accumulate in genes that carry the blueprints for building particular structures. In this scenario, accumulated mutations eventually create *new* genes that specify the creation of new structures.

Although Carroll's hypothesis argues that changes in the genes that regulate development cause most morphological change, proponents of evo-devo recognize that mutations in developmental regulatory genes and their effects on morphology are subject to the action of the same microevolutionary processes—natural selection, genetic drift, and gene flow—that influence the frequencies of genotypes and phenotypes in populations. Thus, every morphological change induced by a mutation in a homeotic gene or in a developmental switch is tested by the success or failure of the individual that carries it.

Numerous studies have shown that changes in the expression of homeotic genes can have dramatic effects on morphology. Fancy footwork from fins to fingers explains how a change in the number and expression of *Hox* genes produced a striking alteration in the structure of vertebrate limbs (see *From Fins to Fingers*).

In another example, researchers have determined how an adaptive morphological change in a small fish, the three-spined stickleback (*Gasterosteus aculeatus*), results from the deactivation of a homeotic gene. The freshwater stickleback populations in North American lakes are the descendants of marine ancestors that colonized the lakes after the retreat of glaciers between 10 000 and 20 000 years ago. Marine sticklebacks have bony armour along their sides and prominent spines; lake-dwelling sticklebacks have greatly reduced armour and, in many populations, lack spines on their pelvic fins **(Figure 20.22)**.

Natural selection has apparently fostered these morphological differences in response to the dominant predators in each habitat. In marine environments, long spines prevent some predatory fishes from swallowing sticklebacks. But long spines are a liability in lakes, where voracious dragonfly larvae grab sticklebacks by their spines and then devour them. Freshwater sticklebacks that lack spines are more likely to escape from their clutches.

The presence or absence of spines on the pelvic fins of sticklebacks is governed by the expression of the gene *Pitx1*. Pelvic spines are part of the pelvic fin skeleton, the fishes' equivalent of a hind limb. In fact, *Pitx1* also contributes to the development of hind limbs in four-legged vertebrates as well as certain glands and sensory organs in the head. In long-spined marine sticklebacks, *Pitx1* is expressed in the embryonic buds from which pelvic fins develop, promoting the development of spines. But *Pitx1* is not expressed in the fin buds of the freshwater sticklebacks, and pelvic spines do not develop in them. However, freshwater sticklebacks have not *lost* the *Pitx1* gene, which is still expressed elsewhere in the fishes' bodies. Apparently, a mutation somehow blocks its expression in the developing pelvic fin, thereby blocking the production of pelvic spines.

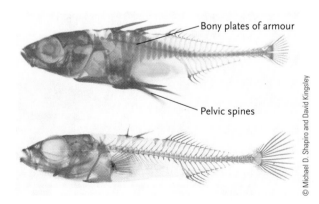

Figure 20.22

Stickleback marine populations (top) of three-spined sticklebacks (*Gasterosteus aculeatus*) have bony plates along their sides and large spines on their dorsal and pelvic fins. Many freshwater populations of the same species (bottom) lack the bony plates and spines. Pelvic spines do not develop in the freshwater fishes because they do not express the *Pitx1* gene in their fin buds during embryonic development. The skeletons of these specimens, each about 8 cm long, were dyed bright red.

From Fins to Fingers

The early embryonic development of the limbs of fishes and tetrapods is similar. The limbs start as buds of mesoderm, which thicken by increased cell division. As the buds elongate, cartilage is deposited at localized centres, the precursors of later limb bones. In fishes, bones develop along a central axis from base to tip **(Figure 1a)**. In tetrapods, centres of cartilage formation generate the long bones of the limb and the five digits of the foot (or hand; **Figure 1b**).

To assess the patterns of development and determine if the digits of tetrapods were modifications of the bones radiating from the central axis in fish, biologists used molecular techniques. In tetrapods with paired forelimbs and hind limbs, groups of homeobox genes control their development. A comparison of *HoxD* genes in zebrafish (*Danio rerio*) and previously available data from birds and mammals revealed the details of development. Using the DNA from a rodent *HoxD* gene as a probe, researchers searched for similar genes in fragmented zebrafish DNA. After cloning and sequencing, it was clear that the *HoxD-11*, *HoxD-12*, and *HoxD-13* genes in zebrafish are arranged in the same order as they are in rodents.

Paolo Sordino, Franks van der Hoeven, and Denis Duboule then tested the activity of *HoxD* genes in developing zebrafish using a nucleic acid probe that could pair with mRNA products of the genes. The probe was linked to a blue dye molecule so that the cells in which a particular *HoxD* gene was active would appear blue in the light microscope. In zebrafish, the *HoxD* genes became active in cells along the posterior side of the central axis **(Figure 1c)**. As limb development neared completion, the activity of *HoxD* genes dropped off.

Using the same approach in tetrapods, the researchers found that the *HoxD* genes were activated in two distinct phases **(Figure 1d)**. In phase 1, gene activity was restricted to the posterior half of the limb, as it had been in zebrafish. This period of activity corresponded to the development of long limb bones. In phase 2, the *HoxD* genes became active in a band of cells perpendicular to the central axis. Here, cartilage centres formed the bones of the digits that developed in an anterior–posterior band. These patterns differed from those in zebrafish, suggesting morphological novelty in tetrapods. These changes in *HoxD* activity must have preceded the development of tetrapod limbs.

A comparison of levels of activity of bone morphogenetic protein 2 (*Bmp2*) house mice (*Mus musculus*) and short-tailed fruit bats (*Carollia perspicillata*) may help explain the development of elongated fingers that support the wings of bats. Elongation of bat fingers reflects growth of cartilage, which depends on relative proliferation and differentiation of cartilage cells (chondrocytes). The developing forelimbs of bats have higher levels of *Bmp2* compared with the hind limbs of the bats or the forelimbs and hind limbs of mice.

Differences in developmental patterns reflect genetic differences.

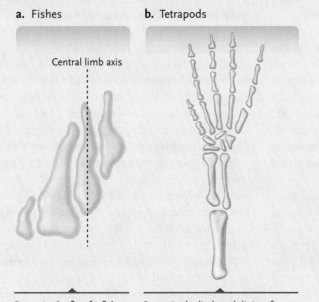

a. Fishes

Central limb axis

Bones in the fin of a fish develop from centers of cartilage formation along a central axis (dashed line).

b. Tetrapods

Bones in the limb and digits of a tetrapod also develop from centers of cartilage formation in the central axis.

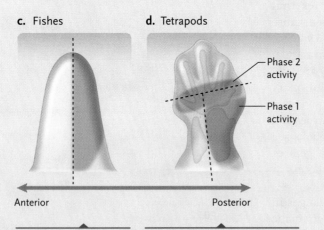

c. Fishes

Anterior — Posterior

During development of the fin in fishes, *HoxD* genes become active in cells posterior to the central axis of the fin (shown in blue).

d. Tetrapods

Phase 2 activity

Phase 1 activity

During development of the limb and digits in tetrapods, *HoxD* genes first become active in cells posterior to the central axis of the limb (blue). Later, these genes are active in a band of cells perpendicular to the central axis of the limb (green).

Figure 1
Fins versus fingers:
HoxD genes in action.

Spidroin

Spider and their webs have always fascinated people. Ancient Greeks are said to have used spider webs to staunch bleeding wounds. Some Australian aborigines used webs for fishing. In the American Civil War, a surgeon, Burt G. Wilder, built a device to hold spider webs and collected 137 metres from one cooperative spider.

Spider silk (also known as spidroin) is very strong, but its thinness makes it workable. It can stretch to 40% of its normal length and return to its original length. Spider webs may include both a supporting architecture and an overlay of sticky capture spiral.

Spiders produce more than one kind of silk. Spidroins **(Figure 1)** are the proteins comprising spider silk. Spidroins have been reported in two lineages of orb-weaving spiders (araneoids and deinopoids) and from six non–orb weavers.

Orthologues are genes that evolved from a common ancestor through speciation. In spiders, the silk proteins MaSp1 and MaSp2 are orthologues.

The dragline web silk of orb-web spiders is a composite of MaSp1 and MaSp2, and both proteins are encoded at multiple loci.

Silk gland cDNAs were characterized from both groups of orb weavers (the araneoid *Uloborus diversus* and the deinopid *Deinopis spinosa*) and other spiders **(Figure 2).** Both the araneoid and the dinopid use MaSp2, and both have flagelliform-like spigots that are used to make silk capture spirals. In the silk glands, spidroins are soluble but turn into an insoluble solid after leaving the body. The cDNA data suggest that the ancestor of orb weavers had the genetic tools for effecting orb web construction.

The fossil record of spiders reveals some information on the first appearance of webs. The first fossil webs found are from the Early Cretaceous (~110 million years old) and have been reported from Lebanon and Spain. The Spanish fossils (see Figure 2) suggest an orb web with supporting architecture and capture spiral.

The radiation of insects, probably just after that of angiosperms, is thought to predate the diversification of

Figure 3
A 2 cm-long *Nephila* (wood spider) female on its web in Costa Rica.

M. B. Fenton

spiders. Using webs, spiders were able to catch flying insects not otherwise available to predators that did not fly. Of special importance was the radiation of small flying insects (flies: Diptera; bees and wasps: Hymenoptera; and beetles: Coleoptera), the main prey of today's araneid spiders. Wood spiders **(Figure 3)** are commonly used by biologists and chemists studying webs.

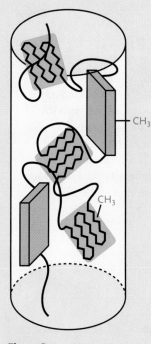

Figure 1
Spidroin.

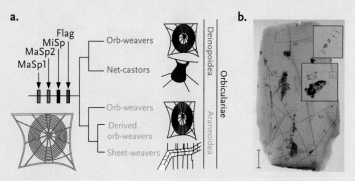

Figure 2
Relationships **(a)** of orb-weaving spiders and spidroins showing inferred ancestral web and spidroins. Orb-web frame and radii composed of MaSp1 (blue) and MaSp2 (brown) are shown with MiSp (black) capture spiral with flag. Spider web in amber **(b)** with arthropods sticking to it. Amber is from Early Cretaceous of Spain. Scale bar is 1 mm. Strands of web are identified by lettered lines.

1. Name three examples of regulatory genes.
2. Why are sticklebacks a good example of developmental biology?
3. What is allometric growth? Give an example of it.

20.9 Evolutionary Biology since Darwin

Our ideas about evolution have changed over time (evolved!) and expanded as more people enter the field, we obtain more data, and from different organisms. Having access to more data and more points of view stimulates further thought and reflection, as well as the design of new experiments. The discovery of previously unknown fossils also changes our view of evolutionary history.

Biologists and paleontologists had known for some time that dinosaurs originated 200 to 230 million years ago (Late Triassic). Before 2007, the only evidence of precursors to dinosaurs was fossils from the Middle Triassic of Argentina. The fossil record appeared to indicate that dinosaurs appeared abruptly in the Late Triassic. Writing in *Science* on July 20, 2007, Randall B. Irmis and colleagues reported Upper Triassic fossils from New Mexico (**Figure 20.23**) and suggested that the transition to a fauna dominated by dinosaurs took 15 to 20 million years.

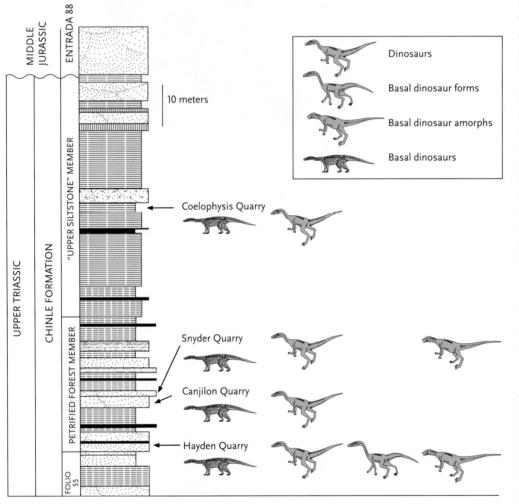

Figure 20.23
The rise of dinosaurs. Stratigraphic position of Middle Triassic fossil beds containing early dinosaurs and other reptiles.

STUDY BREAK

1. What are the general functions of tool-kit genes?
2. How can species with the same tool-kit genes have different morphologies?
3. Why is it important that flying insects predated diversification of spiders?

UNANSWERED QUESTIONS

Imagine a population of mice that includes brown and black individuals. They live in a habitat with brown soil, where predatory hawks can see black mice more easily than they can see brown ones. Design a study that would allow you to determine whether brown or black mice are better adapted to this environment. What would happen if you used different predators, for example, owls or rattlesnakes?

Find examples from popular publications or advertisements for consumer products that misrepresent the theory of biological evolution. Explain how the theory is misrepresented.

Review

Go to CENGAGENOW™ at http://hed.nelson.com/ to access quizzing, animations, exercises, articles, and personalized homework help.

20.1 Recognition of Evolutionary Change

- Well before Darwin published his theory of evolution by natural selection, changes in scientific thought and methods paved the way for its appearance. Natural theology promoted investigation of living organisms, giving rise to ideas that species had changed since their creation. Fields such as geology contributed through documentation of the fossil record and the discovery that Earth was very, very old.

- Remember the contributions of people such as Aristotle, Bacon, Buffon, Copernicus, Cuvier, Hutton, Lamarck, Linnaeus, Lyell, Malthus, Newton, and Wallace.

20.2 Changes in Earth

- Plate tectonics can be responsible for phenomena such as continental drift and have strong influences on the distribution and evolution of organisms.

- Changes in Earth's crust can also cause calamitous events, such as earthquakes, which also have implications for living organisms.

20.3 Charles Darwin

- A five-year voyage on HMS *Beagle* introduced Charles Darwin to many variations in the natural world. Darwin's theory of evolution recognized the importance of variation and provided a mechanism (natural selection) that can be tested using data from nature.

20.4 The Fossil Record

- Conditions of low oxygen or high acidity are ideal for fossilization. Hard structures such as skeletons and teeth do not readily decompose and are more often fossilized than softer structures. Some fossils are casts or moulds; in others, the original materials are replaced by dissolved minerals. The availability of fossils is highly skewed toward certain areas, certain organisms, or parts of organisms.

- Relative dating involves comparisons of deeper (older) strata to shallower (younger) strata. Radiometric dating is based on the decay rates of unstable isotopes and permits absolute dating.

20.5 Earth History, Biogeography, and Convergent Evolution

- Continuous distributions require no special explanation, but disjunct distributions result from dispersal and/or vicariance. In vicariance, external conditions fragment a continuous distribution and create new geographic barriers. Dispersing organisms may cross geographic barriers.

- Under similar environmental pressures and lifestyles, similar structures are favoured by natural selection. Therefore, structures may be morphologically similar even among unrelated species.

Sharks, tunas, ichthyosaurs, and dolphins share similar lifestyles and habitats and have similar shapes. Worms, caecilians, cacti, and spurges are other examples of organisms that resemble one another but have evolved from different ancestries.

20.6 Interpreting Evolutionary Linages

- The evolution and adaptive radiation of horses demonstrate that many species arise and disappear, revealing that the evolution of a species is not a linear process. Possession of intermediate traits may not be evidence of direct ancestry.

- In anagenesis, evolutionary changes in one species gradually change that species until it is distinct enough from the original to be considered a novel species.

- The gradualist hypothesis proposes that large changes result from small changes over time. The punctuated equilibrium hypothesis proposes that speciation occurs rapidly during cladogenesis. Evolutionary biologists must consider both hypotheses because both may be involved in the evolution of the group they study.

20.7 Macroevolutionary Trends in Morphology

- A preadapted trait evolved under pressures for one function and later was coopted for another.

- Allometric growth occurs when there are differential growth rates of different parts of the body during development. In closely related species, allometric growth can lead to significant morphological changes. The same body part may be much larger in one species than in another.

- Pedomorphosis (neoteny) is the retention of the juvenile traits in the adult. Pedomorphosis is an example of heterochrony, changes in developmental timing that can lead to novel species.

20.8 Evolutionary Developmental Biology

- *Hox* and *Pax* genes are examples of tool-kit genes. Tool-kit genes control the development of the body plan through regulation of the timing and amount of expression of many other genes important in the development of particular structures. Tool-kit genes may have different levels of activity at different times, leading to a different sequence of development and different morphology.

20.9 Evolutionary Biology since Darwin

- Many spiders use webs to catch flying insects. To attribute the function of modern spider webs to capturing insects, the flying insects would have to have been present and sufficiently abundant during the period of spider diversification. Spider silk could have been a preadaptation, originally serving some other purpose, such as defence, and been coopted for insect capture with the diversification of flying insects.

- New discoveries change our view of evolution and the history of the world, such as the discovery that the rise of dinosaurs spanned 15 to 20 million years.

Questions

Self-Test Questions

1. Which of the following statements about evolutionary studies is INCORRECT?
   a. Biologists study the products of evolution to understand processes causing it.
   b. Biologists design molecular experiments to examine evolutionary processes operating over short time periods.
   c. Biologists study inheritance of characteristics a parent acquired during its lifetime.
   d. Biologists study variation in homologous structures among related organisms.
   e. Biologists examine why a huge variety of species may inhabit a small island.

2. Which of the following ideas is NOT included in Darwin's theory?
   a. All organisms that ever existed arose through evolutionary modifications of ancestral species.
   b. Most species alive today resulted from the diversification of ancestral species.
   c. Natural selection drives some evolutionary change.
   d. Natural selection preserves favourable traits.
   e. Natural selection eliminates adaptive traits.

3. The father of taxonomy was
   a. Charles Darwin.
   b. Charles Lyell.
   c. Alfred Wallace.
   d. Carolus Linnaeus.
   e. Jean Baptiste de Lamarck.

4. The wings of birds, the forelegs of pigs, and the flippers of whales are examples of
   a. vestigial structures.
   b. homologous structures.
   c. acquired characteristics.
   d. artificial selection.
   e. uniformitarianism.

5. Which of the following statements is NOT compatible with Darwin's theory?
   a. All organisms have arisen by descent with modification.
   b. Evolution has altered and diversified ancestral species.
   c. Evolution occurs in individuals rather than in groups.
   d. Natural selection eliminates unsuccessful variations.
   e. Evolution occurs because some individuals function better than others in a particular environment.

6. Which of the following does NOT contribute to the study of evolution?
   a. population genetics
   b. inheritance of acquired characteristics
   c. the fossil record
   d. DNA sequencing
   e. comparative morphology

7. Which of the following could be an example of microevolution?
   a. a slight change in a bird population's song arising from a small genetic change in the population
   b. the evolution of many species of finch from a common ancestor
   c. the sudden disappearance of an entire genus
   d. the direct evolutionary link between living primates and humans
   e. a flood that drowns all members of a population

8. Which of the following ideas proposed by Lamarck was NOT included in Darwin's theory?
   a. Organisms change in response to their environments.
   b. Changes that an organism acquires during its lifetime are passed to its offspring.
   c. All species change with time.
   d. Changes are passed from one generation to the next.
   e. Specific mechanisms cause evolutionary change.

9. Medical advances now allow many people who suffer from genetic diseases to survive and reproduce. These advances
   a. refute Darwin's theory.
   b. support Lamarck's theory.
   c. disprove descent with modification.
   d. reduce the effects of natural selection.
   e. eliminate adaptive traits.

10. The belief that evolution is progressive or goal oriented is called
    a. gradualism.
    b. uniformitarianism.
    c. taxonomy.
    d. orthogenesis.
    e. the modern synthesis.

Questions for Discussion

1. Would Charles Darwin have had the same inspiration about natural selection and evolution had he visited other islands? Think of the situation on Hawaii, on Easter Island, or on Tristan da Cunha. Why would the island matter?

2. Recognizing the diversity of life means at least appreciating the nature of the organisms you encounter. Do you think that the fauna of the Burgess Shales (Cambrian rocks from British Columbia) is so unusual as to conceal the adaptive radiation that it represents? What is so unusual about the Burgess Shales fauna?

3. Explain why the characteristics we see in living organisms adapt them to the environments in which their ancestors lived rather than to the environments in which they live today. What are examples of this situation?

The bacterium *Escherichia coli*

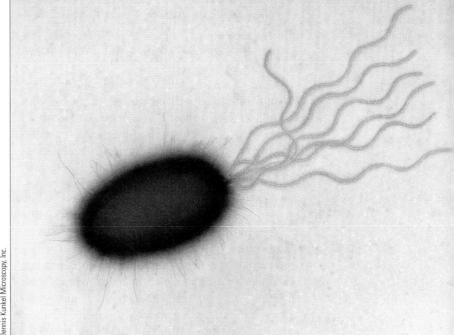

Dennis Kunkel Microscopy, Inc.

21 Prokaryotes

WHY IT MATTERS

In the spring of 2000, seven people, including a small child, in the town of Walkerton, Ontario, died and hundreds of others became ill when the town's drinking water supply was contaminated by a strain of *Escherichia coli* bacteria, known as *E. coli* O157:H7 (the letters indicate the location of bacterial **antigens**, substances that stimulate antibody production by the immune system; "O" refers to the cell wall antigen, and "H" is the flagellar antigen). This strain has been found in the intestines of healthy livestock animals such as cattle, sheep, and goats and can be passed on to humans if they eat meat from those animals that is not sufficiently cooked or if manure from infected animals contaminates groundwater that feeds into drinking water supplies, as was the case in Walkerton. Once cells of this strain colonize our intestinal tracts, they multiply and produce a toxin that kills intestinal epithelial cells, causing hemorrhaging. In some people, infection also results in hemolytic–uremic syndrome, in which red blood cells are destroyed and kidney function is compromised. Complications from this syndrome can last for the rest of the victim's life. Brett Finlay of the University of British Columbia, in collaboration with researchers from the University of Saskatchewan, has developed a vaccine against *E. coli* O157:H7 for cattle. Field trials of this vaccine are now under way; if successful, we may be able to stop our livestock from acting as carriers of this deadly strain.

But *E. coli* is also a normal and necessary inhabitant of healthy intestinal tracts because it provides us with vitamin K. In fact, without *E. coli*, our intestines would be overrun by harmful bacteria. So how did "friendly" *E. coli* become pathogenic? And why aren't antibiotics effective against the pathogenic strain of *E. coli* or against many other pathogenic bacteria? In this chapter, we explore these questions as we investigate the biology of bacteria and other prokaryotes. But don't think that all or even most prokaryotes are harmful! Nothing could be further from the truth: most known prokaryotes play a crucial role in ecosystems, recycling nutrients and breaking down compounds that no other organisms can. Others carry out reactions important in food production, in industry (e.g., production of pharmaceutical products), or in **bioremediation** of polluted sites.

In this chapter, we first look at the structure and function of prokaryotes, emphasizing the features that differentiate them from other organisms, and conclude with a look at the diversity of this group of fascinating organisms.

21.1 The Full Extent of Prokaryote Diversity Is Unknown

While reading this chapter, keep in mind that everything we know so far about prokaryotes is based on a tiny fraction of the total number of species. We have isolated and identified only about 6000 species, which may be as low as 1% of the total number. There are entire habitats—such as the oceans, which make up 70% of Earth's surface—for which we know almost nothing about the prokaryote inhabitants (see *Unanswered Questions* at the end of the chapter). Why

have we only identified so few, and why are we not even sure how many prokaryotes there might be? We have been able to make detailed studies only of prokaryotes that we can grow in culture, and the vast majority of prokaryotes cannot grow on the media and conditions we can provide. As you will see later in the chapter, many prokaryotes live in very extreme conditions, and we cannot yet create favourable growth conditions in our labs. Estimates of prokaryote diversity from many habitats are thus based solely on molecular data, that is, DNA samples isolated from various habitats.

21.1a Prokaryotes Make Up Two of the Three Domains of Life

Two domains of living organisms, **Archaea** and **Bacteria**, consist of prokaryotes (the third domain, **Eukarya**, includes all eukaryotes). Bacteria are the prokaryotic organisms most familiar to us, including those responsible for diseases of humans and other animals. Archaea are not as well known as they were only discovered about 40 years ago. As you will see in this chapter, Archaea share some cellular features with eukaryotes and some with bacteria but have still other features that are unique. Many of the Archaea live under very extreme conditions that no other organisms, including bacteria, can survive.

21.2 Prokaryote Structure and Function

We begin our survey of prokaryotes by examining their cellular structure, their mode of reproduction, and how they obtain energy and nutrients.

Prokaryotes are the smallest organisms in the world **(Figure 21.1)**. Few species are more than 1 to 2 μm long; from 500 to 1000 of them would fit side

Figure 21.1
Bacillus bacteria on the point of a pin. Cells magnified **(a)** 70 times, **(b)** 350 times, and **(c)** 14 000 times.

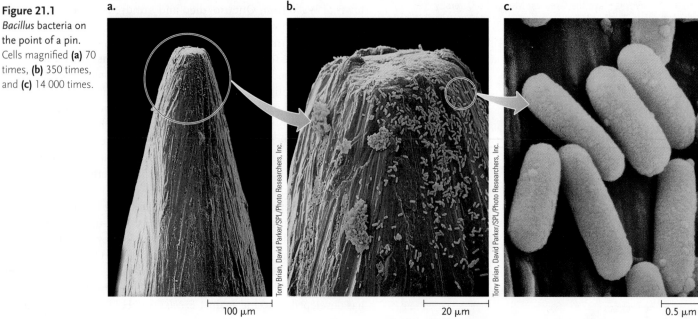

a.

b.

c.

100 μm

20 μm

0.5 μm

Tony Brian, David Parker/SPL/Photo Researchers, Inc.

by side across the dot above this letter "i." Despite the small size of prokaryotes, they dominate life on Earth: current estimates of total prokaryote diversity are in the billions of species, and their total collective mass (their **biomass**) on Earth exceeds that of animals and may be greater than that of all plant life. Prokaryotes colonize every niche on Earth that supports life—for example, huge numbers of bacteria inhabit the surfaces and cavities of a healthy human body, including the skin, mouth and nasal passages, and large intestine. Collectively, the bacteria in and on your body outnumber all the other cells in your body. It is not surprising that prokaryote diversity should be so much greater than that of eukaryotes because for about 3 billion years they were the only forms of life on Earth and so had time to diversify and expand into every habitat on Earth before the first eukaryotes appeared on the scene (see Chapter 2).

21.2a Prokaryotic Cells Appear Simple in Structure Compared with Eukaryotic Cells

Three cell shapes are common among prokaryotes: spiral, spherical (or **coccoid**; *coccus* = berry), and cylindrical (known as **rods**), but some Archaea even have square cells **(Figure 21.2).**

At first glance, a typical prokaryotic cell seems much more simple than a eukaryotic cell **(Figure 21.3, p. 468):** images taken with standard electron microscopy typically reveal little more than a cell wall and plasma membrane surrounding a cytoplasm with DNA concentrated in one region and ribosomes scattered throughout. The chromosome is not contained in a membrane-bound nucleus but is packed into an area of the cell called the **nucleoid.** Prokaryotic cells have no cytoplasmic organelles equivalent to the mitochondria, endoplasmic reticulum, or Golgi complex of eukaryotic cells (see Chapter 2). With few exceptions, the reactions carried out by these organelles in eukaryotes are distributed between the cytoplasmic solution and the plasma membrane in prokaryotes. This evident simplicity led people to regard prokaryote cells as featureless and disorganized. However, the apparent simplicity of these cells is misleading: new microscopic techniques reveal that prokaryote cells do have a cytoskeleton—not homologous to that of a eukaryote but serving some of the same functions—and have more sophisticated organization than was previously thought.

Internal Structures. The genome of most prokaryotes consists of a single, circular DNA molecule, although some, such as the causative agent of Lyme disease

a. Cocci

b. Bacilli

c. Spirilla

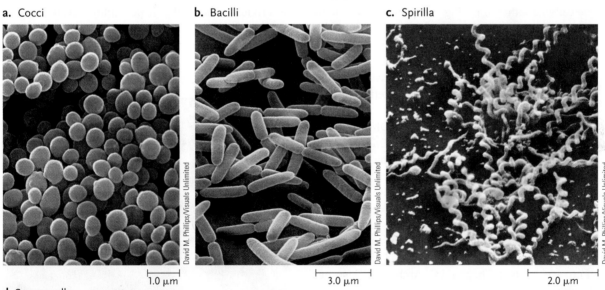

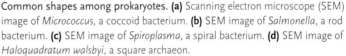

1.0 μm   3.0 μm   2.0 μm

d. Square cells

4.0 μm

Figure 21.2

Common shapes among prokaryotes. **(a)** Scanning electron microscope (SEM) image of *Micrococcus*, a coccoid bacterium. **(b)** SEM image of *Salmonella*, a rod bacterium. **(c)** SEM image of *Spiroplasma*, a spiral bacterium. **(d)** SEM image of *Haloquadratum walsbyi*, a square archaeon.

Figure 21.3
The structure of a bacterial cell.

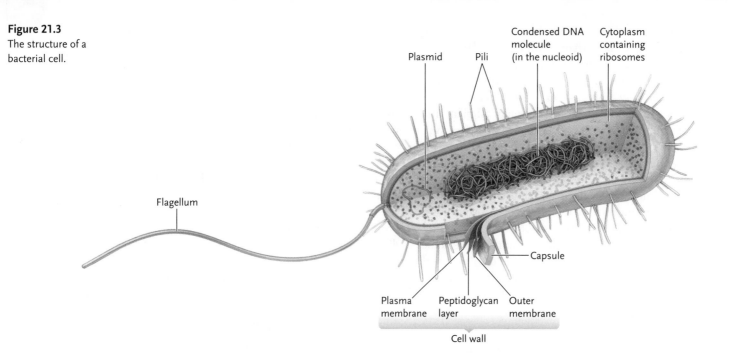

Plasmid
Pili
Condensed DNA molecule (in the nucleoid)
Cytoplasm containing ribosomes
Flagellum
Capsule
Plasma membrane
Peptidoglycan layer
Outer membrane
Cell wall

(*Borrelia burgdorferi*), have a linear chromosome. Many prokaryotes also contain small circles of DNA called **plasmids (Figure 21.4)**, which generally contain genes for nonessential but beneficial functions such as antibiotic resistance. Plasmids replicate independently of the cell's chromosomes and can be transferred from one cell to another, meaning that genes for antibiotic resistance are readily shared among prokaryotic cells, even among cells of different species. This *horizontal gene transfer* allows antibiotic resistance and other traits to spread very quickly in bacterial populations. Horizontal gene transfer also occurs when bacterial cells take up DNA from their environment (e.g., from other cells that have lysed) or when viruses transfer DNA from one bacterium to another (see Chapter 22). Evidence indicates that a virus transferred toxin-encoding genes from *Shigella dysenteriae* (which causes bloody diarrhea) to *E. coli*, resulting in the deadly O157:H7 strain.

Like eukaryotic cells, prokaryotic cells contain ribosomes. Bacterial ribosomes are smaller than eukaryotic ribosomes but carry out protein synthesis by essentially the same mechanisms as those of eukaryotes (see Chapter 14). Archaeal ribosomes resemble those of bacteria in size but differ in structure; protein synthesis in Archaea is a combination of bacterial and eukaryotic processes, with some unique archaeal features. As a result, antibiotics that stop bacterial infections by targeting ribosome activity do not interfere with archaeal protein synthesis.

Prokaryotic Cell Walls. Most prokaryotes have a cell wall that lies outside their plasma membrane. The primary component of bacterial cell walls is **peptidoglycan**, a polymer of sugars and amino acids, which forms linear chains. Peptide cross-linkages between the chains give the cell wall great strength and rigidity. The antibiotic penicillin prevents the formation of these cross-linkages, resulting in a weak cell wall that is easily ruptured, killing the cell **(Figure 21.5)**.

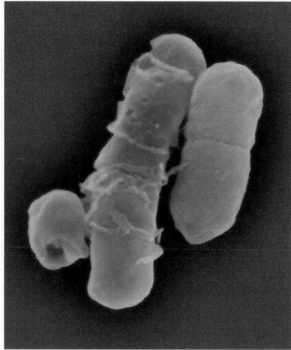

Dennis Kunkel Microscopy, Inc.

Figure 21.5
The cell on the left shows degradation of the cell wall following antibiotic treatment. The cell will eventually lyse, killing the bacterium. A cell with an intact cell wall is shown on the right.

Figure 21.4
Plasmids inside a prokaryote cell.

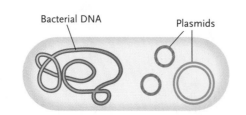

Bacterial DNA
Plasmids

Bacteria can be divided into two broad groups, Gram-positive and Gram-negative cells, based on their reaction to the **Gram stain procedure**, traditionally used as the first step in identification of an unknown bacterium. Cells are first stained with crystal violet, rinsed with ethanol, and then counterstained with safranin. Some cells retain the crystal violet and thus appear purple when viewed under the microscope; these are termed Gram-positive cells. In other bacteria, ethanol washes the crystal violet out of the cells, which are colourless until counterstained with safranin; these Gram-negative cells appear pink under the microscope. The differential response to staining is related to differences in cell wall structure: Gram-positive bacteria have cell walls composed almost entirely of a single, relatively thick peptidoglycan layer **(Figure 21.6a).** In contrast, the cell wall of Gram-negative bacteria has two distinct layers **(Figure 21.6b and c),** a thin peptidoglycan layer just outside the plasma membrane and an **outer membrane** external to the peptidoglycan layer. This outer membrane contains **lipopolysaccharides (LPS)** and thus is very different from the plasma membrane (Figure 21.6c). The outer membrane protects Gram-negative bacteria from potentially harmful substances in the environment; for example, it inhibits entry of penicillin. Therefore, **Gram-negative** cells are less sensitive to penicillin than are **Gram-positive** cells.

The cell walls of some Archaea are assembled from a molecule related to peptidoglycan but with different molecular components and bonding structure. Others have walls assembled from proteins or polysaccharides instead of peptidoglycan. Archaea have a variable response to the Gram stain, so this procedure is not useful in identification of Archaea.

The cell wall of many prokaryotes is surrounded by a layer of polysaccharides known as a **capsule (Figure 21.7, p. 470;** see also Figure 21.6). Capsules are "sticky" and play important roles in protecting cells in different environments. Cells with capsules are protected to some extent from desiccation, extreme temperatures, bacterial viruses, and harmful molecules such as antibiotics and antibodies. In many pathogenic bacteria, the presence or absence of the protective capsule differentiates infective from noninfective forms. For example, normal *Streptococcus pneumoniae* bacteria are capsulated and virulent, causing severe pneumonia in humans and other mammals. Mutant *S. pneumoniae* without capsules are nonvirulent and can easily be eliminated by the body's immune system if they are injected into mice or other animals.

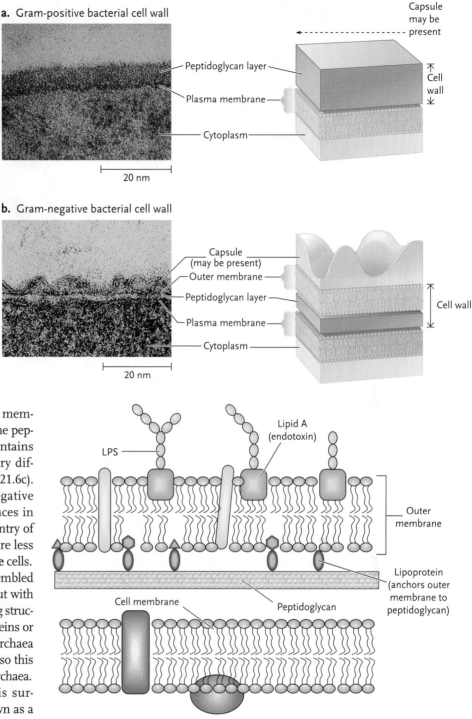

a. Gram-positive bacterial cell wall

T. J. Beveridge/Visuals Unlimited

Peptidoglycan layer
Plasma membrane
Cytoplasm

20 nm

Capsule may be present
Cell wall

b. Gram-negative bacterial cell wall

T. J. Beveridge/Visuals Unlimited

Capsule (may be present)
Outer membrane
Peptidoglycan layer
Plasma membrane
Cytoplasm

20 nm

Cell wall

LPS
Lipid A (endotoxin)
Outer membrane
Lipoprotein (anchors outer membrane to peptidoglycan)
Cell membrane
Peptidoglycan

Figure 21.6
Cell wall structure in Gram-positive and Gram-negative bacteria. **(a)** The thick cell wall in Gram-positive bacteria. **(b)** The thin cell wall of Gram-negative bacteria. **(c)** detail of Gram-negative cell wall, showing thin peptidoglycan layer and outer membrane with lipopolysaccharides (LPS).

Flagella and Pili. Many prokaryotes can move actively through liquids and across wet surfaces, most commonly via **flagella** (singular, *flagellum* = whip) extending from the cell wall (see Figure 21.3). As outlined in Chapter 2, prokaryotic flagella are very different from eukaryotic flagella in both structure and pattern of

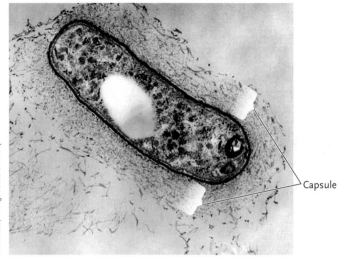

Figure 21.7

The capsule surrounding the cell wall of *Rhizobium*, a Gram-negative soil bacterium.

Frank Dazzo, Michigan State University

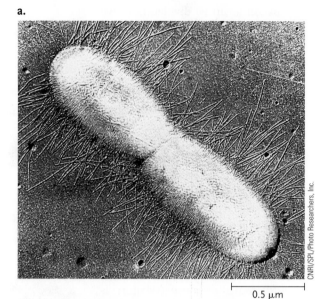

0.5 μm

CNRI/SPL/Photo Researchers, Inc.

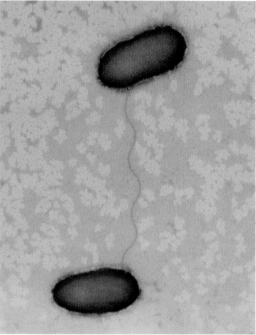

Dennis Kunkel Microscopy, Inc.

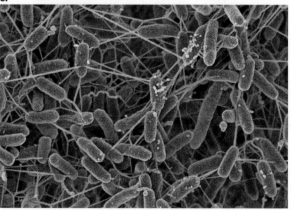

New Scientist

Figure 21.8

(a) Pili extending from the surface of a dividing *E. coli* bacterium. **(b)** Sex pilus connecting two bacterial cells. **(c)** Nanowires (pili that conduct electricity) on *Shewanella oneidensis*. Note that these nanowires are much longer than the cells.

movement. Prokaryotic flagella are made of rigid helical proteins and rotate much like the propeller of a boat. Archaean flagella are superficially similar to bacterial flagella and carry out the same function, but the two types of flagella contain different components, develop differently, and are coded for by different genes.

Some prokaryotes have rigid shafts of protein called **pili** (singular, *pilus* = "hair") extending from their cell walls **(Figure 21.8a),** which help them adhere to other cells. One type, called a *sex pilus*, not only allows bacterial cells to adhere to each other but also acts as a conduit for the transfer of plasmids from one cell to another **(Figure 21.8b).** Other types of pili enable bacteria to bind to animal cells. The bacterium that causes gonorrhea (*Neisseria gonorrhoeae*) uses pili to adhere to cells of the throat, eye, urogenital tract, or rectum in humans. In 2005, it was discovered that the pili of some bacteria (e.g., species of *Geobacter* and *Shewanella*) conduct electricity; these "nanowires" transfer electrons out of the cell onto minerals such as iron oxides in their environment **(Figure 21.8c).** Such electricity-generating bacteria hold promise for the development of microbial fuel cells as an alternative energy source (see *Unanswered Questions*).

Even though prokaryotes are simpler and less structurally diverse than eukaryotic cells, they are much more diverse metabolically, as we will now explore.

21.2b Prokaryotes Have the Greatest Metabolic Diversity of All Organisms

As outlined in Chapter 3, organisms can be grouped into four modes of nutrition based on sources of energy and carbon (see Table 3.1). From reading the chapters on photosynthesis and respiration, you are familiar with photoautotrophs such as green plants, which use light as their energy source and CO_2 as their carbon source, and **chemoheterotrophs**, which use organic molecules as sources of both energy and carbon. Humans and other animals are chemoheterotrophs, as are fungi. Two other modes of nutrition are found only in prokaryotes. **Photoheterotrophs** use light as an energy source and obtain carbon from organic molecules rather than from CO_2. **Chemoautotrophs** are commonly referred to as "lithotrophs" (*lithos* = rock, thus "rock-eaters"). As this name suggests, chemoautotrophs obtain energy by oxidizing inorganic substances such as hydrogen, iron, sulphur, ammonia, and nitrites and use CO_2 as their carbon source. Chemolithotrophs thrive in habitats such as the deep-sea hydrothermal vents **(Figure 21.9),** where reduced inorganic compounds are abundant; their ability to harness energy from these compounds makes them the foundation upon which the rest of the vent community ultimately depends, just as terrestrial organisms rely on the ability of plants and other photoautotrophs to capture light energy.

We breathe oxygen to provide the final electron acceptor for the electrons we remove from our food and pass down an electron transport chain to make ATP via aerobic respiration (Chapter 6). Some prokaryotes also use oxygen as a final electron acceptor; like us, these are aerobic organisms or **aerobes.** Aerobes may be **obligate,** that is, they cannot survive without oxygen. But some prokaryotes "breathe" metals, using metals as the final electron acceptor for electrons; these organisms obtain energy via anaerobic respiration. **Anaerobic respiration** can also involve other inorganic molecules, such as nitrate or sulphate, as the final electron acceptors. Only prokaryotes are capable of this type of respiration. **Obligate anaerobes** are poisoned by oxygen and survive either by fermentation, in which organic molecules are the final electron acceptors, or by anaerobic respiration. **Facultative anaerobes** use O_2 when it is present, but under anaerobic conditions, they live by fermentation or anaerobic respiration. As you learned in Chapter 6, prokaryotes carry out a wider range of fermentation reactions than do eukaryotes; many of these fermentations are economically important to humans, for example, in the production of foods such as cheese, yogurt, and chocolate.

21.2c Prokaryotes Play Key Roles in Biogeochemical Cycles

The ability of prokaryotes to metabolize such a wide range of substrates makes them key players in the life-sustaining recycling of elements such as carbon, oxygen, and nitrogen, among others. The pathway by which a chemical element moves through an ecosystem is known as a **biogeochemical cycle.** As an element flows through its cycle, it is transformed from one form to another; prokaryotes are crucial in many of these transformations. We will look at the **nitrogen cycle** as an example of the key role prokaryotes play in biogeochemical cycles.

Nitrogen is a component of proteins and nucleotides and so is of vital importance for all organisms. The largest source of nitrogen on Earth is the atmosphere, which is almost 80% nitrogen. Why can't we just use this atmospheric nitrogen since it is so abundant? Most organisms cannot make use of this nitrogen because they cannot break the strong triple bond between the two nitrogen atoms. Prokaryotes are the only organisms that can break this bond and convert N_2 into forms that can be used by other organisms. In this conversion process, known as **nitrogen fixation**, N_2 is reduced to ammonia (NH_3). Ammonia is quickly ionized to ammonium (NH_4^+), which prokaryote cells then use to produce nitrogen-containing molecules such as amino acids and nucleic acids. Nitrogen fixation is the only means of replenishing the nitrogen sources used by most organisms—in other words, all organisms rely on nitrogen fixed by bacteria. Examples of nitrogen-fixing bacteria include cyanobacteria and *Rhizobium* (which is symbiotic with plants; see Chapter 41).

Not all bacteria convert fixed nitrogen directly into organic molecules. Some bacteria carry out **nitrification**, the conversion of ammonium (NH_4^+) to nitrate (NO_3^-). This is carried out in two steps by two types of *nitrifying bacteria* present in soil and water, one of which converts ammonium to nitrite (NO_2^-), whereas the other converts nitrite to nitrate. Nitrate is then taken up by plants and fungi and incorporated into their organic molecules. Animals obtain

Figure 21.9
Hydrothermal vents on the ocean floor.

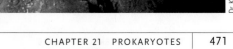

nitrogen in organic form by eating other organisms or each other.

In sum, nitrification makes nitrogen available to many other organisms, including plants, animals, and bacteria that cannot metabolize ammonia. The metabolic versatility of the prokaryotes is one factor that accounts for their abundance and persistence on the planet; another factor is their impressive reproductive capacity.

21.2d Asexual Reproduction Can Result in Rapid Population Growth

In prokaryotes, asexual reproduction is the normal mode of reproduction. In this process, a parent cell divides by binary fission into two daughter cells that are exact genetic copies of the parent **(Figure 21.10)**. Reproducing by binary fission means that, under favourable conditions, populations of prokaryotes can have very rapid exponential growth as one cell becomes two, two become four, and so on. Some prokaryotes can double their population size in only 20 minutes; thus, one cell, given ideal conditions, can produce millions of cells in only a few hours.

These short generation times, combined with the small genomes (roughly 1000 times smaller than an average eukaryote), mean that prokaryotes have higher mutation rates than do eukaryotes. This translates to roughly 1000 times more mutations per gene, per unit time, per individual than for eukaryotes. Genetic variability in prokaryotic populations, the basis for their diversity, derives largely from mutation and to a lesser degree from horizontal gene transfer (see Chapter 10). Further, the typically much larger populations of prokaryotes compared with eukaryotes contribute to the much greater genetic variability in prokaryotes. In short, prokaryotes have an enormous capacity to adapt, which is one reason for their evolutionary success.

Figure 21.10
E. coli cell dividing by binary fission.

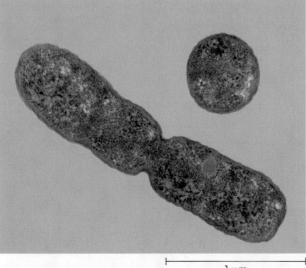

1 μm

As we have seen, the success of bacteria is beneficial to humans in many ways but can also be detrimental to us when dealing with successful pathogenic bacteria. In the next section, we investigate how some bacteria cause disease and how they are able to resist treatment with antibiotics.

21.2e Pathogenic Bacteria Cause Diseases by Different Mechanisms

Some bacteria produce **exotoxins**, toxic proteins that leak from or are secreted from the bacterium. For example, botulism food poisoning is caused by the exotoxin of the Gram-positive bacterium *Clostridium botulinum*, which grows in poorly preserved foods **(Figure 21.11)**. The botulism exotoxin, botulin, is one of the most poisonous substances known: just a few nanograms can cause severe illness. What makes botulin so toxic? It produces muscle paralysis that can be fatal if the muscles that control breathing are affected. Interestingly, botulin is used under the brand name Botox for the cosmetic removal of wrinkles and in the treatment of migraine headaches and some other medical conditions. Exotoxins produced by certain strains of *Streptococcus pyogenes* have "superantigen properties" (i.e., overactivation of the immune system) that cause necrotizing fasciitis ("flesh-eating disease"). In 1994, Lucien Bouchard, who was then premier of Quebec, lost a leg to this disease.

Other bacteria cause disease through **endotoxins**. Endotoxins are natural components of the outer membrane of Gram-negative bacteria such as *E. coli*, *Salmonella*, and *Shigella*. When a Gram-negative cell lyses, the lipopolysaccharides of the outer membrane are released; exposure to a specific component of this layer, known as lipid A, causes endotoxic shock. The endotoxin overstimulates the host's immune system, triggering inflammation and an often lethal immune response. Endotoxins have different effects depending on the bacterial species and the site of infection, which include typhoid or other fevers, diarrhea, and, in severe cases, organ failure and death.

21.2f Pathogenic Bacteria Commonly Develop Resistance to Antibiotics

An **antibiotic** is a natural or synthetic substance that kills or inhibits the growth of bacteria and other microorganisms. Prokaryotes and fungi produce these substances naturally as defensive molecules, and we have also developed ways to synthesize several types of antibiotics. Different types of antibiotics have different modes of action: for example, streptomycins, produced by soil bacteria, block protein synthesis in their targets whereas penicillins, produced by fungi, target the peptide cross-linkages in peptidoglycan, as described above.

Dennis Kunkel Microscopy, Inc.

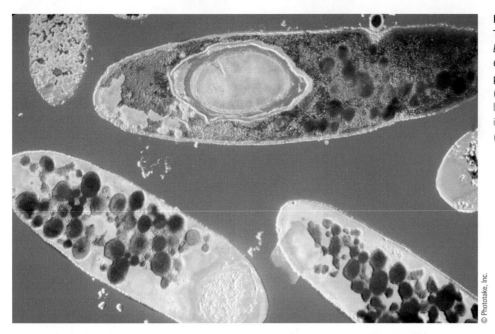

Figure 21.11
The bacterium *Clostridium butyricum*, one of the *Clostridium* species that produces the toxin botulin (colourized TEM). The large stained structure in the cells is a spore (a survival structure).

© Phototake, Inc.

How are bacteria able to block the actions of antibiotics? There are various mechanisms by which bacteria resist antibiotics **(Figure 21.12)**. For example, some bacteria are able to pump antibiotics out of the cell using membrane-bound pumps. They can also produce molecules that bind to the antibiotic or enzymes that break down the antibiotic, rendering it ineffective against its target. Alternatively, a simple mutation can result in a change in the structure of the antibiotic's target, so that the antibiotic cannot bind to it. Finally, bacteria can develop new enzymes or pathways that are not inhibited by the antibiotic.

Bacteria can develop resistance through mutations, but they can also acquire resistance via horizontal gene transfer (e.g., plasmid transfer). Taking antibiotics routinely in mild doses, or failing to complete a prescribed dosage, contributes to the development of resistance by selecting strains that can survive in the presence of the drug. Prescription of antibiotics for colds and other virus-caused diseases can also promote bacterial resistance because viruses are unaffected by antibiotics, but the presence of antibiotics in your system can lead to resistance. Antibacterial agents that may promote resistance are also commonly included in such commercial products as soaps, detergents, and deodorants. Resistance is a form of **evolutionary adaptation**; antibiotics alter the bacterium's environment, conferring a reproductive advantage on those strains best adapted to the altered conditions.

The development of resistant strains has made tuberculosis, cholera, typhoid fever, gonorrhea, and other bacterial diseases difficult to treat with antibiotics. For example, as recently as 1988, drug-resistant strains of *Streptococcus pneumoniae*, which causes pneumonia, meningitis, and middle-ear infections, were practically unknown. Now, resistant strains of *S. pneumoniae* are common and increasingly difficult to treat.

21.2g In Nature, Prokaryotes May Live in Communities Attached to a Surface

Researchers grow prokaryotes as individuals in pure cultures. We have learned a lot about prokaryotes from studies using pure cultures, but in nature, prokaryotes rarely exist as individuals or as pure cultures. Instead, many prokaryotes live in communities where they interact in a variety of ways. One important type of prokaryotic community is known

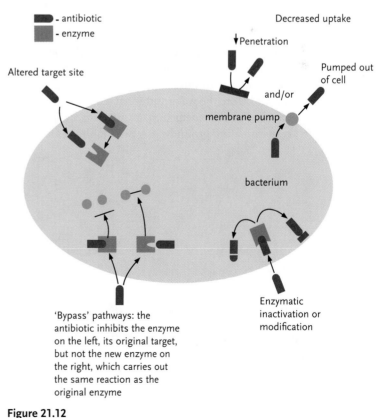

Figure 21.12
Four major mechanisms of antibiotic resistance.

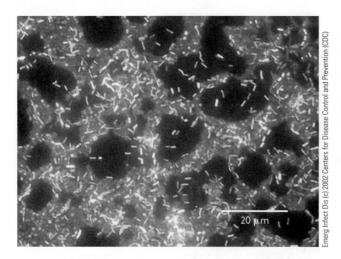

Figure 21.13
Biofilm grown on a stainless steel surface.

Emerg Infect Dis (c) 2002 Centers for Disease Control and Prevention (CDC)

20 μm

as a **biofilm**, which consists of a complex aggregation of microorganisms attached to a surface and surrounded by a film of polymers **(Figure 21.13)**. Life in a biofilm offers several benefits: organisms can adhere to hospitable surfaces, they can live on the products of other cells, conditions within the biofilm promote gene transfer between species, and the biofilm protects cells from harmful environmental conditions. Biofilms form on any surface with sufficient water and nutrients. For example, you're probably familiar with how slippery rocks in a stream can be when you try to step from one to the next; the slipperiness is due to biofilms on the rocks. Dental plaque is also a biofilm; if this biofilm spreads below the gumline, it causes inflammation of the gums (gingivitis). Regular removal of plaque by brushing, flossing, and dental checkups helps prevent gingivitis.

Biofilms have practical consequences for humans, both beneficial and detrimental. On the beneficial side, for example, biofilms on solid supports are used in sewage treatment plants for processing organic matter before the water is discharged, and they can be effective in bioremediation of toxic organic molecules contaminating groundwater. But biofilms can also be

harmful to human health. Biofilms adhere to many kinds of surgical equipment and supplies, including catheters, pacemakers, and artificial joints. Even if the bacteria colonizing these devices are not pathogenic, their presence is obviously not desirable given that these devices should be sterile. As well, many heterotrophic bacteria will become opportunistic pathogens, given the right conditions. Biofilm infections are difficult to treat because bacteria in a biofilm are up to 1000 times more resistant to antibiotics than are the same bacteria in liquid cultures.

How does a biofilm form? Imagine a surface, such as a rock in a stream, over which water is flowing **(Figure 21.14)**. Due to the nutrients in the water, the surface rapidly becomes coated with polymeric organic molecules, such as polysaccharides or glycoproteins. Once the surface is conditioned with organic molecules, free prokaryotes attach in a reversible manner in a matter of seconds (see Figure 21.14, step 1). If the cells remain attached, the association may become irreversible (step 2), at which point, the prokaryotes grow and divide on the surface (step 3). Next, the physiology of the cells changes, and they begin to secrete *extracellular polymeric substances* (EPS), a slimy, glue-like substance similar to the molecules found in bacterial capsules. EPS extends between cells in the mixture, forming a matrix that binds cells to each other and anchors the complex to the surface, thereby establishing the biofilm (step 4). The **slime layer** entraps a variety of materials, such as dead cells and insoluble minerals. The physiological change accompanying the formation of a biofilm results from marked changes in a prokaryote's gene expression pattern—in effect, the prokaryotes in a biofilm become very different organisms. Over time, other organisms are attracted to and join the biofilm; depending on the environment, these may include other bacterial species, algae, fungi, or protozoa producing diverse microbial communities (step 5). As described in the *Molecule Behind Biology* box on page 475, prokaryotes in a biofilm communicate with each other via

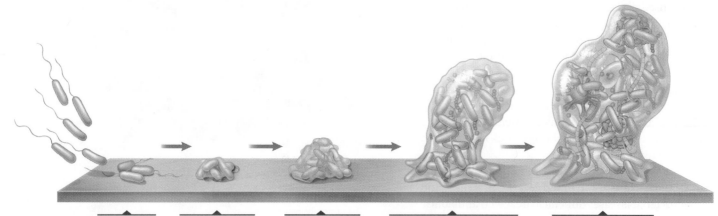

1 Reversible attachment of bacteria (sec)

2 Irreversible attachment of bacteria (sec–min)

3 Growth and division of bacteria (hr–days)

4 Production of extracellular polymer substances, leading to biofilm formation (hr–days)

5 Attachment of other organisms to biofilm (days–months)

Figure 21.14
Steps in the formation of a biofilm.

N-Acyl-I-Homoserine Lactone

Most bacteria are social organisms that interact in many ways and display social behaviours, such as hunting for food in swarms, bioluminescence (see Chapter 1), biofilm formation, and virulence in pathogenic bacteria. These behaviours happen only when a critical population density is reached, meaning that bacteria must be able to sense the presence of other cells. How does a bacterial cell know that it is not alone? Bacteria use quorum sensing to communicate; this mechanism involves the release of signalling molecules into the environment. Accumulation of signalling molecules enables the cell to determine the density of other cells around it and respond accordingly; the response occurs after the signalling molecule is perceived by specific receptors on the cell's membrane and triggers activation of specific genes. Different bacterial species use different signalling molecules; for example, many Gram-negative bacteria use N-acyl-I-homoserine lactones (a lactone is a type of cyclic ester) such as that shown in **Figure 1.** Gram-positive cells also signal each other but use small peptides rather than lactones. If we can learn to "speak" or "translate" these bacterial languages, could we interfere with the social behaviours they control? The possibility has important implications for medical science given the role of these signals in processes such as the onset of virulence in pathogenic bacteria and communication within biofilms such as those that form on medical devices implanted in patients.

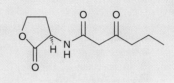

Figure 1
N-Acyl-I-homoserine lactone from *Vibrio fischeri.*

quorum sensing; in fact, this communication is part of biofilm formation—it allows cells to start secreting EPS when a high enough cell density is reached.

Much remains to be learned about how bacteria form a biofilm, how the change in gene expression during the transition is regulated, and how bacteria interact within a biofilm.

In the next two sections, we describe the major groups of prokaryotes.

STUDY BREAK

1. What distinguishes a prokaryotic cell from a eukaryotic cell?
2. What is the difference between a chemoheterotroph and a photoautotroph?
3. What is the difference between an obligate anaerobe and a facultative anaerobe?
4. What is the difference between nitrogen fixation and nitrification? Why are nitrogen-fixing prokaryotes important?
5. What is binary fission?
6. What is the difference between an endotoxin and an exotoxin? Explain how they differ with respect to how they cause disease.
7. Explain four mechanisms by which bacteria protect themselves from antibiotics.
8. What is a biofilm? Give an example of a biofilm that is beneficial to humans and one that is harmful.
9. What is quorum sensing?

21.3 The Domain Bacteria

As for other organisms, prokaryote classification has been revolutionized by molecular techniques that allow researchers to compare nucleic acid and protein sequences as tests of evolutionary relatedness. Ribosomal RNA (rRNA) sequences have been most widely used in the evolutionary studies of prokaryotes. Researchers have identified several evolutionary branches within each prokaryote domain **(Figure 21.15, p. 476),** but these classifications will likely change in the future when full genomic sequences can be compared. We discuss the major groups of the domain Bacteria in this section, and of the domain Archaea in the next section.

21.3a Molecular Studies Reveal More than a Dozen Evolutionary Branches in the Bacteria

Sequencing studies reveal that bacteria have more than 12 distinct and separate evolutionary branches. We restrict our discussion to six particularly important groups: proteobacteria, green bacteria, cyanobacteria, Gram-positive bacteria, spirochetes, and chlamydias (see Figure 21.15).

Proteobacteria: The Purple Bacteria and Their Relatives. This highly diverse group of Gram-negative bacteria likely evolved from a purple, photosynthetic ancestor. Their purple colour comes from their photosynthetic pigment, a type

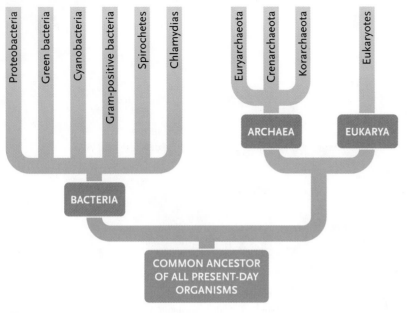

Figure 21.15
An abbreviated phylogenetic tree of prokaryotes.

100 μm

Figure 21.16
The fruiting body of *Chondromyces crocatus*, a myxobacterium.
Cells of this species collect together to form the fruiting body.

of chlorophyll distinct from that of plants. Many present-day species are either photoautotrophs (the purple sulphur bacteria) or photoheterotrophs (the purple nonsulphur bacteria); both groups carry out a type of photosynthesis that does not use water as an electron donor and does not release oxygen as a by-product.

Other present-day proteobacteria are chemoheterotrophs that are thought to have evolved as an evolutionary branch following the loss of photosynthetic capabilities in an early proteobacterium. The evolutionary ancestors of mitochondria are considered likely to have been ancient non-photosynthetic proteobacteria.

Among the chemoheterotrophs classified with the proteobacteria are *E. coli*, plant pathogenic bacteria, and bacteria that cause human diseases such as bubonic plague, gonorrhea, and various forms of gastroenteritis and dysentery. The proteobacteria also include both free-living and symbiotic nitrogen-fixing bacteria.

Myxobacteria are an unusual group of non-photosynthetic proteobacteria, which form colonies held together by the slime they produce. Enzymes secreted by the colonies digest "prey"—other bacteria, primarily—that become stuck in the slime. When environmental conditions become unfavourable, as when soil nutrients or water are depleted, myxobacteria form a fruiting body, a differentiated multicellular stage large enough to be visible to the naked eye **(Figure 21.16)**. The fruiting body contains clusters of spores that are dispersed to form new colonies when the fruiting body bursts. Quorum sensing is involved in spore formation.

Helicobacter pylori, the cause of many gastric ulcers (see *People Behind Biology* box on page 477), is also a proteobacterium.

Green Bacteria. This diverse group of photosynthetic Gram-negative bacteria is named for the chlorophyll pigments that give the cells their green colour (a different form of chlorophyll than that found in plants). Like the purple bacteria, they do not release oxygen as a by-product of photosynthesis. Also like the purple bacteria, some are photoautotrophs, whereas others are photoheterotrophs. The photoautotrophic green bacteria are fairly closely related to the Archaea and are usually found in hot springs, whereas the photoheterotrophic type is found typically in marine and high-salt environments.

Cyanobacteria. These Gram-negative photoautotrophs are blue-green in colour **(Figure 21.17)** and carry out photosynthesis by the same pathways and using the same chlorophyll as eukaryotic algae and plants. Like plants and algae, they release oxygen as a by-product of photosynthesis.

The direct ancestors of present-day cyanobacteria were the first organisms to use the water-splitting reactions of photosynthesis. As such, they were critical to the accumulation of oxygen in the atmosphere, which allowed the evolutionary development of aerobic organisms. Chloroplasts probably

Barry Marshall, University of Western Australia; Robin Warren, Royal Perth Hospital (retired)

A few hours after you eat, you go to your doctor complaining of stomach pain, abdominal bloating and nausea; most worryingly, you have started to vomit blood. Your doctor tells you that you have a gastric ulcer, a lesion in your stomach lining. If this visit to your doctor had occurred prior to the mid-1980s, your doctor would have explained that ulcers are caused by increased stomach acidity due to stress. The treatment? Drink lots of milk, take antacids, and give up alcohol and your favourite spicy foods—no more curries or chili—that would aggravate your ulcer. This view of ulcers was accepted for years until two Australian physicians, Barry Marshall and Robin Warren, demonstrated that most ulcers are caused by a bacterial infection. Marshall and Warren observed that biopsies from patients with ulcers revealed large numbers of spiral-shaped bacterial cells in inflamed tissues. Together the two physicians carried out a series of studies that demonstrated the link between ulcers and the presence of the bacterium (later named *Helicobacter pylori*) **(Figure 1).** But despite having research published in respected medical journals, the medical community did not believe Marshall and Warren's findings—how could bacteria possibly survive in the very acidic conditions of the stomach? Out of frustration, and anxious to get proper treatment for his patients, Marshall drank a culture of *H. pylori*! After about a week, he developed severe abdominal pain and vomiting, and endoscopic examination of his stomach showed regions of inflammation teeming with *H. pylori*. Much to his disappointment, he did not develop ulcers, but he had made the point that *H. pylori* is pathogenic. Marshall and Warren also showed that antibiotics were effective in treating ulcers, and in 2005, they were awarded the Nobel Prize in Medicine. So how is *H. pylori* able to survive in a stomach? It is able to burrow deep into the mucus lining the stomach by means of its numerous flagella, and it produces urease, which converts urea into CO_2 and ammonia, making the region around its cells more basic.

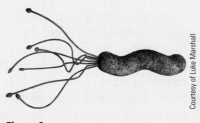

Figure 1
A high-resolution image of *Helicobacter pylori*, a causative agent of ulcers.

evolved from early cyanobacteria that were incorporated into the cytoplasm of primitive eukaryotes, which eventually gave rise to the algae and higher plants as discussed in Chapter 25. Besides releasing oxygen, present-day cyanobacteria help fix nitrogen into organic compounds in aquatic habitats and as symbiotic partners with fungi in lichens (see Chapter 24).

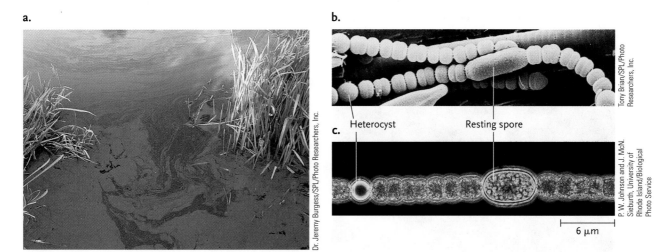

a.

b.

Heterocyst   Resting spore

c.

6 μm

Figure 21.17
Cyanobacteria. (a) A population of cyanobacteria covering the surface of a pond. **(b)** and **(c)** Chains of cyanobacterial cells. Some cells in the chains form spores. The heterocyst is a specialized cell that fixes nitrogen.

Gram-Positive Bacteria. This large group contains many species that live primarily as chemoheterotrophs. Some cause human diseases, including *Bacillus anthracis*, the causal agent of anthrax; *Staphylococcus*, which causes some forms of food poisoning, toxic shock syndrome, pneumonia, and meningitis; and *Streptococcus* **(Figure 21.18),** which causes strep throat, necrotizing fasciitis, and some forms of pneumonia. However, some Gram-positive bacteria are beneficial to humans; *Lactobacillus*, for example, carries out the lactic acid fermentation used in the production of pickles, sauerkraut, and yogurt. One unusual group of bacteria, the mycoplasmas, is placed among the Gram-positive bacteria by molecular studies even though they show a Gram-negative staining reaction. This staining reaction results because they are naked cells that secondarily lost their cell walls in evolution. Some mycoplasmas, with diameters from 0.1 to 0.2 μm, are the smallest known cells.

Spirochetes. These organisms have helically spiralled flagella embedded in their cytoplasm, causing the cells to move in a twisting, corkscrew pattern **(Figure 21.19).** Their corkscrew movements enable them to move in viscous environments such as mud and sewage, where they are common. Some spirochetes are harmless inhabitants of the human mouth; another species, *Treponema pallidum*, is the cause of syphilis. Termites have symbiotic spirochetes in their intestines that enable them to digest cellulose.

Chlamydias. These bacteria are unusual because although they are Gram-negative and have cell walls with an outer membrane, they lack peptidoglycan. All the known chlamydias are intracellular parasites that cause various diseases in animals. One bacterium of this group, *Chlamydia trachomatis*, is responsible for one of the most common sexually transmitted infections of the urinary and reproductive tracts of humans and also causes trachoma, an infection of the cornea that is the leading cause of blindness in humans.

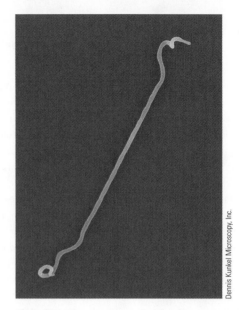

Figure 21.19
Treponema pallidum, a spirochete bacterium that is a causal agent of syphilis (scanning electron microscope image).

In this section, you have seen that bacteria thrive in nearly every habitat on Earth. However, some members of the second prokaryotic domain, the Archaea, the subject of the next section, live in habitats that are too forbidding even for the bacteria.

STUDY BREAK

1. What methodologies have been used to classify prokaryotes?
2. What were the likely characteristics of the evolutionary ancestor of present-day proteobacteria?
3. What are the differences between the way photosynthesis is carried out by photosynthetic proteobacteria and by cyanobacteria?

21.4 The Domain Archaea

The first Archaea were isolated from extreme environments, such as hot springs, hydrothermal vents on the ocean floor, and salt lakes **(Figure 21.20).** For that reason, these prokaryotes were called *extremophiles* ("extreme lovers"). Subsequently, Archaea have also been found living in less extreme environments.

Archaea share some cellular features with eukaryotes and some with bacteria and have other features that are unique **(Table 21.1).**

21.4a Archaea Have Some Unique Characteristics

Among their unique characteristics are certain features of their plasma membranes and cell walls. The lipid molecules in archaeal plasma membranes

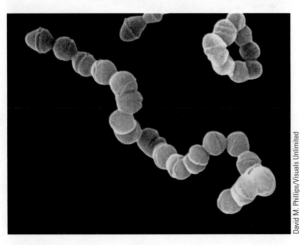

Figure 21.18
Streptococcus bacteria forming the long chains of cells typical of many species in this genus.

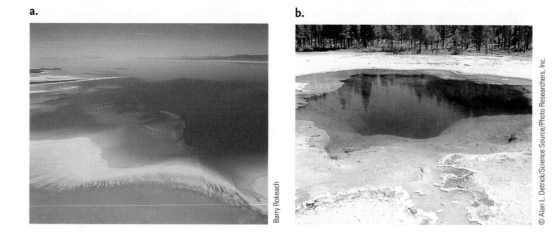

a. **b.**

Barry Rokeach

© Alan L. Detrick/Science Source/Photo Researchers, Inc.

Figure 21.20
Typically extreme archaeal habitats. **(a)** Highly saline water in Great Salt Lake, Utah, coloured red purple by archaea. **(b)** Hot, sulphur-rich water in Emerald Pool, Yellowstone National Park, coloured brightly by the oxidative activity of archaea, which convert H_2S to elemental sulphur.

are unlike those in the plasma membranes of all other organisms: there is a different linkage between glycerol and the hydrophobic tails, and the tails are isoprenes rather than fatty acids (see Chapter 5). Also, some lipids have polar head groups at both ends. Why would such seemingly minor differences be significant? These unique lipids are more resistant to disruption, making the plasma membranes better suited to extreme environments. Similarly, the unique cell walls of Archaea are more resistant to extremes than those of bacteria; some Archaea can even survive being boiled in strong detergents!

Many Archaea are chemoautotrophs, whereas others are chemoheterotrophs. No known member of the Archaea has been shown to be pathogenic.

21.4b Molecular Studies Reveal Three Evolutionary Branches in the Archaea

Based on differences in rRNA sequence data, the domain Archaea is divided into three groups (see Figure 21.15). Two major groups, the **Euryarchaeota** and the **Crenarchaeota**, contain Archaea that have been cultured in the laboratory. The third group, the

Table 21.1	Characteristics of the Bacteria, Archaea, and Eukarya		
Characteristic	Bacteria	Archaea*	Eukarya
DNA arrangement	Single, circular in most, but some linear and/or multiple	Single, circular	Multiple linear molecules
Chromosomal proteins	Prokaryotic histonelike proteins	Five eukaryotic histones	Five eukaryotic histones
Genes arranged in operons	Yes	Yes	No
Nuclear envelope	No	No	Yes
Mitochondria	No	No	Yes
Chloroplasts	No	No	Yes
Peptidoglycan in cell wall	Present	Absent; some have pseudopeptidoglycan	Absent
Membrane lipids	Unbranched; linked by ester linkages	Branched; linked by ether linkage; may have polar heads at both ends	Unbranched; linked by ester linkages
RNA polymerase	Limited variations	Multiple types	Multiple types
Ribosomal proteins	Prokaryotic	Some prokaryotic, some eukaryotic	Eukaryotic
First amino acid placed in proteins	Formylmethionine	Methionine	Methionine
Aminoacyl–tRNA synthetases	Prokaryotic	Eukaryotic	Eukaryotic
Cell division proteins	Prokaryotic	Prokaryotic	Eukaryotic
Proteins of energy metabolism	Prokaryotic	Prokaryotic	Eukaryotic

*Given that very few Archaea have been identified or cultured, the information in this table is based on an extremely small data set.

Korarchaeota, has been recognized solely on the basis of DNA taken from environmental samples.

Euryarchaeota. These organisms are found in various extreme environments. They include methanogens, extreme halophiles, and some extreme thermophiles, as described below.

Methanogens (methane generators) live in low-oxygen environments (Figure 21.21) and represent about one half of all known species of Archaea. Methanogens are obligate anaerobes that live in the anoxic (oxygen-lacking) sediments of swamps, lakes, marshes, and sewage works, as well as in more moderate environments, such as the rumen of cattle and sheep, the large intestine of dogs and humans, and the hindguts of insects such as termites and cockroaches. Methanogens generate energy by converting various substrates such as carbon dioxide and hydrogen gas or acetate into methane gas, which is released into the atmosphere.

Halophiles are salt-loving organisms. Extreme halophilic Archaea live in highly saline environments such as the Dead Sea and on foods preserved by salting. They require a minimum NaCl concentration of about 1.5 M (about 9% solution) to survive and can live in a fully saturated solution (5.5 M, or 32%). Most are aerobic chemoheterotrophs, which obtain energy from sugars, alcohols, and amino acids using pathways similar to those of bacteria. Many extreme halophiles use light as a secondary energy source, supplementing the oxidations that are their primary source of energy.

Extreme thermophiles live in extremely hot environments such as hot springs and ocean floor hydrothermal vents. Their optimal temperature range for growth is 70° to 95°C, close to the boiling point of water. By comparison, no eukaryotic organism is known to live at a temperature higher than 60°C. Some extreme thermophiles are members of the Euryarchaeota, but most belong to the Crenarchaeota, the next group that we discuss.

Crenarchaeota. This group includes most of the extreme thermophiles, which have a higher optimal temperature range than those belonging to the Euryarchaeota. For example, the most thermophilic member of this group, *Pyrobolus*, dies below 90°C, grows optimally at 106°C, and can survive an hour of autoclaving at 121°C! *Pyrobolus* lives in ocean floor hydrothermal vents, where the pressure creates water temperatures greater than the boiling point of water on Earth's surface.

Also in this group are **psychrophiles** ("cold loving"), organisms that grow optimally in cold temperatures in the range from −10 to −20°C. These organisms are found mostly in the Antarctic and Arctic oceans, which are frozen most of the year, and in the intense cold at ocean depths.

Mesophilic members of the Crenarchaeota comprise a large part of plankton found in cool, marine waters, where they are food sources for other marine organisms.

Korarchaeota. This group has been recognized solely on the basis of DNA samples obtained from marine and terrestrial hydrothermal environments. To date, no members of this group have been isolated and cultivated in the lab, and nothing is known about their physiology. Molecular data indicate that they are the oldest archaeal lineage.

Thermophilic Archaea are important commercially. For example, the thermostable DNA polymerase required for the polymerase chain reaction (PCR; you read about PCR in Chapter 16) comes from the thermophile *Thermus aquaticus*.

We began this chapter with prokaryotes, whose metabolic diversity and environmental range and ecological importance belie their structural simplicity. In the next chapter, we look at still simpler entities: viruses, viroids, and prions, which are derived from living organisms and retain only some of the properties of life.

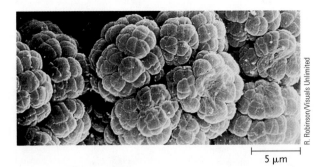

Figure 21.21
A colony of the methanogenic archaeon *Methanosarcina*, which lives in the sulphurous, waterlogged soils of marshes and swamps.

R. Robinson/Visuals Unlimited

5 μm

STUDY BREAK

1. What distinguishes members of the Archaea from members of the Bacteria and Eukarya?
2. How does a methanogen obtain its energy? In which group or groups of Archaea are methanogens found?
3. Where do extreme halophilic Archaea live? How do they obtain energy? In which group or groups of Archaea are the extreme halophiles found?
4. What are extreme thermophiles and psychrophiles?

What prokaryotes live in the world's oceans and what are their ecological roles?

Of the billions of prokaryotes on Earth, a vast number live in the open ocean and even more in the ocean sediments—these deeply buried prokaryotes may make up between a tenth to a third of all of Earth's biomass. So far, we have not been able to culture most of these organisms, so their physiology remains a mystery. Why should we care about identifying them and understanding their physiology and ecology? Aside from wanting to understand the full range of prokaryotic diversity on Earth as a goal in and of itself, there is also some urgency to understand the role these unknown organisms play in biogeochemical cycles of the ocean. As elsewhere on Earth, these prokaryotes drive the cycles of carbon and other elements in the ocean, but until we gain a clearer picture of which prokaryotes are doing what, we won't really understand these cycles, nor are we able to predict the effects of perturbations. For example, it has been proposed that one way to reduce carbon dioxide concentration in the atmosphere would be to capture CO_2 emissions and sequester them in the ocean. Without an understanding of the ocean-dwelling prokaryotes and their carbon metabolism, how can we accurately predict whether this plan will be successful or if it will lead to unforeseen problems?

Can we harness microbial reactions as a source of electricity?

If we could capture the electron flow from bacterial cells to the terminal electron acceptor, we would have a source of electricity (an electric current is just a stream of electrons). This is the theory behind a microbial fuel cell (MFC), which harnesses the power of prokaryotes to convert chemical energy into electrical energy **(Figure 1)**. MFCs have been studied for almost 100 years, but inefficiencies of the systems, such as incomplete oxidation of substrates and the requirement for electron shuttles to carry electrons from the bacteria to the electrode, meant that very little current was produced. MFCs seemed doomed to be little more than novelties, with no practical use. The discovery that some bacteria such as *Geobacter* can completely oxidize organic compounds and transfer electrons directly to an electrode means that much more efficient fuel cells are possible. Many challenges must be overcome before this technology is commercially viable, but with our pressing need for alternative sources of energy, the MFC is currently a very active area of research in both biology and engineering.

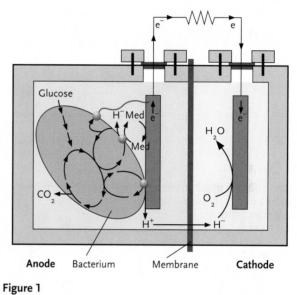

Figure 1
Schematic diagram of a microbial fuel cell.

Review

Go to CENGAGENOW™ at http://hed.nelson.com/ to access quizzing, animations, exercises, articles, and personalized homework help.

21.1 The Full Extent of Prokaryote Diversity Is Unknown

- Prokaryotes are the most abundant and diverse organisms on Earth; however, the vast majority of prokaryotes have not been described because they cannot be cultured using standard techniques.

- Prokaryotes comprise two of the three domains of life, the Archaea and the Bacteria.

21.2 Prokaryote Structure and Function

- Prokaryotic genomes typically consist of a single, circular DNA molecule packaged into the nucleoid. Many prokaryotic species also contain plasmids, which replicate independently of the chromosome and can be passed to other cells.

- Gram-positive bacterial cell walls consist of a single, relatively thick peptidoglycan layer. Gram-negative bacteria have walls consisting of a relatively thin peptidoglycan sheath surrounded by an outer lipopolysaccharide membrane.

- A polysaccharide capsule surrounds many bacteria, protecting them and helping them adhere to surfaces.

- Prokaryotes show great diversity in their modes of obtaining energy and carbon. Two of the modes of nutrition found among eukaryotes are also found in prokaryotes (chemoheterotrophy and photoautotrophy), but two other modes are unique to prokaryotes: chemoautotrophs obtain energy by oxidizing inorganic substrates and use carbon dioxide as their carbon source, and photoheterotrophs use light as a source of energy and obtain their carbon from organic molecules.

- As a group, prokaryotes can obtain energy via aerobic respiration, anaerobic respiration, and/or various forms of fermentation.

- Some prokaryotes are capable of nitrogen fixation, the conversion of atmospheric nitrogen to ammonia; others are responsible for nitrification, the conversion of ammonium to nitrate.
- Prokaryotes normally reproduce asexually by binary fission, which can result in very rapid population growth under favourable conditions.
- In nature, prokaryotes may live in an interacting community, such as a biofilm.
- Pathogenic bacteria cause disease via exotoxins and endotoxins.
- Bacteria may develop resistance to antibiotics through mutation of their own genes or by acquiring resistance genes from other bacteria.

21.3 The Domain Bacteria

- Bacteria are divided into more than a dozen evolutionary branches, including the Gram-negative proteobacteria, Gram-negative green bacteria, cyanobacteria, Gram-positive bacteria, spirochetes, and chlamydias.

21.4 The Domain Archaea

- Archaea have some features that are like those of bacteria, other features that are eukaryotic, and some that are unique (see Table 21.1).
- Archaea are classified into three groups: the Euryarchaeota (methanogens, extreme halophiles, and some extreme thermophiles); the Crenarchaeota (most of the extreme thermophiles, as well as psychrophiles and mesophiles); and the Korarchaeota, known only from DNA samples.

Questions

Self-Test Questions

1. A bacterium that uses nitrites as its only energy source was found in a deep salt mine. It is a
   a. chemoautotroph.
   b. parasite.
   c. photoautotroph.
   d. heterotroph.
   e. photoheterotroph.

2. The _____ are all oxygen-producing photoautotrophs.
   a. spirochetes
   b. chlamydias
   c. Gram-positive bacteria
   d. cyanobacteria
   e. proteobacteria

3. You would find an endotoxin associated with
   a. Gram-positive bacteria.
   b. Gram-negative bacteria.
   c. the cell wall.
   d. Both a and c are correct.
   e. Both b and c are correct.

4. Which of the following is not a property of an endospore?
   a. Resistant to boiling—must be autoclaved to be killed
   b. Metabolically inactive
   c. Can survive millions of years
   d. Provides a method to preserve bacterial DNA under harsh conditions
   e. Is a means that bacterial cells use to multiply

5. Which of the following statements about Gram-positive bacterial cell walls is true?
   1. More sensitive to effects of penicillium than are Gram-negative cell walls
   2. Are the only type of cell wall that contain peptidoglycan
   3. Have a thick peptidoglycan layer comprising about 90% of the cell wall
   4. Are quite complex relative to Gram-negative cell walls
      a. 1,2
      b. 1,3
      c. 3,4
      d. 2,4
      e. 1,4

6. Which of the following structures is not found in prokaryotic cells?
   a. chromosome
   b. cell wall
   c. ribosomes
   d. mitochondria
   e. plasma membrane

Questions for Discussion

1. You have isolated an unknown prokaryote from a soil sample. What features could you look for to help you determine if this prokaryote was a bacterium or an archaeon? Indicate how each feature would differ in an archaeon and a bacterium.

2. Some manufacturers have produced cleaning products that contain a compound that they claim can kill "99.9% of bacteria" on contact. Briefly explain to the manufacturer why this achievement is not necessarily good news.

3. In the lab, you have isolated some prokaryotic cells that belong either to a Gram-positive bacterium or an archaeon. What cellular (structural) features could you look for in order to determine which type of organism you have isolated? Indicate how that feature would differ between the two kinds of organism (assume that you have the necessary equipment to test for any cellular feature you want).

Influenza virus.

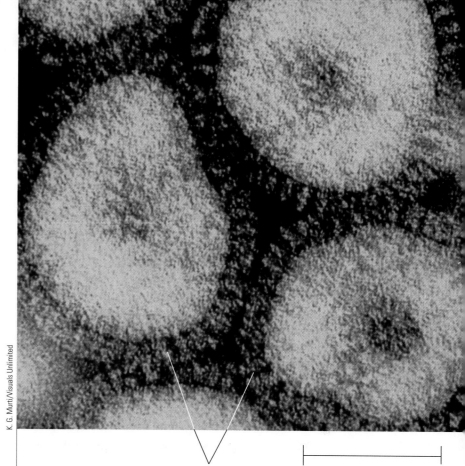

K. G. Murti/Visuals Unlimited

Envelope

50 nm

22 Viruses, Viroids, and Prions: Infectious Biological Particles

WHY IT MATTERS

Each winter in Canada, people line up for their annual flu shot. For many of us, this shot represents a gamble that we will be protected against the strains of the influenza virus (shown in the micrograph above) making the rounds that winter. Influenza is a respiratory illness that causes high fever, chills and muscle aches, sore throat, and a cough, among other symptoms. The specific strains of influenza circulating around the world change from year to year, so each year, the World Health Organization determines which strains are most likely to be prevalent during the winter flu season. A flu vaccine is then prepared containing killed viruses of those strains. Because the vaccine itself contains only killed viruses, you won't develop influenza, but your body will produce **antibodies** against the virus, protecting you against subsequent infection by any of those specific strains. (Antibodies are highly specific protein molecules, produced by the immune system, that recognize and bind to specific proteins of a pathogen, such as proteins in a virus' coat).

For most people, getting the flu means feeling awful for a few days, but for the very young, the elderly, and people with weakened immune systems, the stakes are higher: a bout of flu can be lethal. Some flu outbreaks have been devastatingly lethal to a greater proportion of the population. The worst recorded example is the flu *pandemic* (an outbreak or epidemic that spreads around the world) of 1918. A strain of influenza virus known as the Spanish flu infected almost half of the world's population, killing about 1 in every 20 people. Why was the Spanish flu so deadly? And why do we need to develop new flu vaccines so often? We investigate these questions later in this chapter. We also look at the beneficial roles played by viruses—not all are pathogenic—and investigate ways in which we may be able to harness the infective abilities of viruses for our own uses. For example, can we use viruses as vectors for gene therapy to fight diseases? We start with a look at the defining characteristics of viruses: how they are able to enter cells and take over the cell's machinery to make more copies of themselves. We also compare viruses with viroids and prions, other infectious particles.

22.1 What Is a Virus? Characteristics of Viruses

The structure of a virus is reduced to the minimum necessary to transmit its genome from one host cell to another. A virus is simply one or more nucleic acid molecules surrounded by a protein coat or **capsid** **(Figure 22.1a, b).** Some capsids may be enclosed within a membrane or **envelope** derived from their host cell's membrane **(Figure 22.1c).** So a virus is not a cell—it does not have a cytoplasm enclosed by a plasma membrane, as do all known living organisms.

Viruses also lack many of the properties of life shared by all other organisms (see Chapter 2). For example, they lack a metabolic system to provide energy for their life cycles and cannot reproduce on their own; instead, they are dependent on the host cells they infect for these functions. Many biologists do not consider viruses living organisms; instead, they are referred to as infectious biological particles.

The nucleic acid genome of a virus may be either DNA or RNA and can be composed of either a single strand or a double strand of RNA or DNA. Viral genomes range from just a few genes to over a hundred genes; all viruses have genes that encode at least their coat proteins and the enzymes required for nucleic acid replication. Many viruses also have genes that encode *recognition proteins* that become implanted in the coat surface. These coat proteins recognize and bind to the host cell, promoting entry of the virus particle or its nucleic acid core into that cell.

Most viruses take one of two basic structural forms, helical or polyhedral. In **helical viruses,** the protein subunits assemble in a rodlike spiral around the genome (see Figure 22.1a). A number of viruses that infect plant cells are helical. In **polyhedral viruses,** the coat proteins form triangular units that fit together like the parts of a geodesic sphere (see Figure 22.1b). The polyhedral viruses include forms that infect animals, plants, and bacteria. In some polyhedral viruses, protein spikes that provide host cell recognition extend from the corners, where the facets fit together. Both helical and polyhedral viruses can be enveloped in a membrane derived from the host's membrane (see Figure 22.1c and **Figure 22.2).** Recognition protein spikes extend through the membrane, allowing the virus to recognize and bind to host cells.

Although they are not considered to be alive, viruses are classified into orders, families, genera,

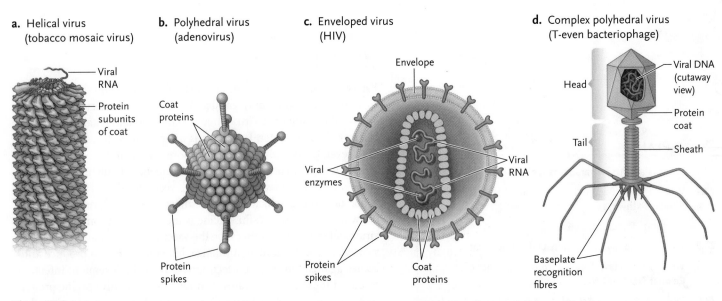

a. Helical virus (tobacco mosaic virus)

Viral RNA

Protein subunits of coat

b. Polyhedral virus (adenovirus)

Coat proteins

Protein spikes

c. Enveloped virus (HIV)

Envelope

Viral enzymes

Viral RNA

Protein spikes

Coat proteins

d. Complex polyhedral virus (T-even bacteriophage)

Head

Tail

Viral DNA (cutaway view)

Protein coat

Sheath

Baseplate recognition fibres

Figure 22.1

Viral structure. The tobacco mosaic virus in **(a)** assembles from more than 2000 identical protein subunits.

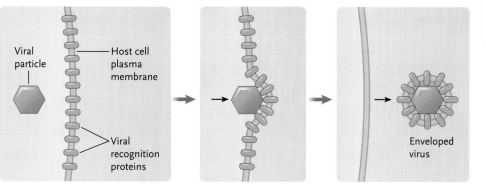

Figure 22.2
How enveloped viruses acquire their envelope.

Viral particle

Host cell plasma membrane

Viral recognition proteins

Enveloped virus

and species using several criteria, including virus size and structure, genome structure (RNA or DNA, single stranded or double stranded), and how their nucleic acid is replicated. More than 4000 species of viruses have been classified into more than 80 families. The family names end in *-viridae* and may refer either to the geographic region where the virus was first discovered or to the structure of the virus. For example, Coronaviridae, the family to which influenza virus belongs, is named for the "crown" of protein spikes on the capsid, as shown in the photomicrograph at the start of this chapter (*corona* = crown). Unlike the species names of living organisms, a virus' species name is the name of the disease it causes and can be one or two words, for example, herpesvirus or Ebola virus.

As was the case for our look at prokaryotes in the previous chapter, we have just scratched the surface of viral diversity in this chapter; for example, there are millions of viruses in every millilitre of ocean water, most of which have not been identified. As we learn more about viruses, their classification will likely change.

Every living organism is likely permanently infected by one or more kinds of viruses. Usually, a virus infects only a single species or a few closely related species. A virus may even infect only one organ system or a single tissue or cell type in its host. However, some viruses are able to infect unrelated species, either naturally or after mutating.

Of the roughly 80 viral families described to date, 21 include viruses that cause human diseases. Viruses also cause diseases of wild and domestic animals. Plant viruses cause annual losses of millions of tonnes of crops, especially cereals, potatoes, sugar beets, and sugar cane. (**Table 22.1** lists some important viral families of viruses that infect animals.) The effects of viruses on the organisms they infect range from undetectable, to merely bothersome, to seriously debilitating or lethal. For instance, some viral infections of humans, such as those causing cold sores, chickenpox, and the common cold, are usually little more than a nuisance to healthy adults. Others cause some of the most severe and deadly human diseases, including AIDS, encephalitis, and Ebola hemorrhagic fever.

However, not all viruses are harmful to people. For example, one of the primary reasons why bacteria do not completely overrun this planet is that they are destroyed in incredibly huge numbers by viruses known as **bacteriophages**, or **phages** for short (*phagein* = to eat) (see Figure 22.1d). Viruses also provide a natural means to control some insect pests, such as spruce budworm.

Viruses are vital components of ecosystems and may be the dominant "entity" in some ecosystems, such as the oceans. We don't yet fully understand their roles in these ecosystems, but it is clear that they affect nutrient cycling through their effects on prokaryotes. For example, in certain regions of the ocean, a few genera of cyanobacteria dominate the marine phytoplankton, making major contributions to global photosynthesis. Bacteriophages infect these cyanobacteria, causing high levels of mortality, thus influencing cyanobacterial population dynamics well as the release of nutrients from bacterial cells. But these viruses also help keep photosynthesis going in their cyanobacterial hosts, as recently discovered by Nicholas Mann and colleagues at the Univeristy of Warwick. As you read in Chapter 7, one of the proteins that makes up photosystem II is very susceptible to light-induced damage and so is constantly being replaced by newly synthesized molecules. As long as the cell can make new protein fast enough to keep up with damage, photosynthesis can continue; but if the rate of damage exceeds the repair rate, the rate of photosynthesis will drop. When these bacteriophages infect cyanobacteria, they shut down their host's protein synthesis. Without continued synthesis of the photosystem protein, photosynthesis should slow down following infection—but it doesn't. How is the photosynthetic rate maintained? Mann and his colleagues found that the virus' genome includes genes for this protein; expression of these viral proteins enables the repair rate to keep up with light-induced damage, allowing the cell to photosynthesize. Although the virus is doing this for "selfish" reasons (i.e., to ensure that its host has sufficient resources for the virus to complete its life cycle), the outcome of this association is that much

Table 22.1 | **Major Animal Viruses**

Viral Family	Envelope	Nucleic Acid	Diseases
Adenovirus	No	ds DNA	Respiratory infections, tumours
Flavivirus	Yes	ss RNA	Yellow fever, dengue, hepatitis C
Hepadnavirus	Yes	ds DNA	Hepatitis B
Human herpesvirus	Yes	ds DNA	
Herpes simplex I			Oral herpes, cold sores
Herpes simplex II			Genital herpes
Varicella-zoster virus			Chickenpox, shingles
Herpesvirus 4 (Epstein-Barr virus)			Infectious mononucleosis
Orthomyxovirus	Yes	ss RNA	Influenza
Papovavirus	No	ds DNA	Benign and malignant warts
Papillomavirus			Human papillomavirus (genital warts)
Paramyxovirus	Yes	ss RNA	Measles, mumps, pneumonia
Picornavirus	No	ss RNA	
Enterovirus			Polio, hemorrhagic eye disease, gastroenteritis
Rhinovirus			Common cold
Hepatitis A virus			Hepatitis A
Apthovirus			Foot-and-mouth disease in livestock
Poxvirus	Yes	ds DNA	Smallpox, cowpox
Retrovirus	Yes	ss RNA	
HTLV I, II			T-cell leukemia
HIV			AIDS
Rhabdovirus	Yes	ss RNA	Rabies, other animal diseases

ds = double-stranded; HTLV = human T lymphotropic virus; ss = single-stranded.

of the carbon fixed on Earth may be facilitated by virus-controlled photosynthesis.

STUDY BREAK

1. What is a virus?
2. List three features of viruses that distinguish them from living organisms.

22.2 Viruses Infect Bacterial, Animal, and Plant Cells by Similar Pathways

Viral particles move by random molecular motions until they contact the surface of a host cell. For infection to occur, the virus or the viral genome must then enter the cell. Inside the cell, the viral genes are expressed, leading to replication of the viral genome and assembly of progeny viruses. The viruses are then released from the host cell, a process that often ruptures the host cell, killing it.

22.2a Infection of Bacterial Cells

We have learned a great deal about the infective cycles of viruses, as well as the genetics of both viruses and bacteria, from studies of the bacteriophages infecting *Escherichia coli (E. coli)*. Some of these are **virulent bacteriophages**, which kill their host cells during each cycle of infection, whereas others are **temperate**. Temperate bacteriophages enter an inactive phase inside the host cell and can be passed on to several generations of daughter cells before becoming active and killing their host.

Virulent Bacteriophages. Among the virulent bacteriophages infecting *E. coli*, the **T-even bacteriophages** T2, T4, and T6 have been the most valuable in genetic studies. The coats of these phages are divided into a *head* and a *tail* (see Figure 22.1d). A double-stranded linear molecule of DNA is packed into the head. The tail, assembled from several different proteins, has recognition proteins at its tip that can bind to the surface of the host cell. Once the tail is attached, it functions as a sort of syringe that injects the DNA genome into the cell **(Figure 22.3).**

Infection begins when a T-even phage collides randomly with the surface of an *E. coli* cell and the tail attaches to the host cell wall **(Figure 22.4,** step 1). An enzyme present in the viral coat, *lysozyme*, then digests a hole in the cell wall through which the tail injects the DNA of the phage (step 2). The proteins of the viral coat remain outside. Throughout its life cycle within the bacterial cell, the phage uses host cell machinery to express its genes. One of the proteins produced early in the infection is an enzyme that breaks down the bacterial chromosome. The phage gene for a DNA polymerase that replicates the phage's DNA is also expressed early on. Eventually, 100 to 200 new viral DNA molecules are synthesized (step 3). Later in the infection, the host cell machinery transcribes the phage genes for the viral coat proteins (step 4). As the head and tail proteins assemble, the replicated viral DNA is packed into the heads (step 5).

When viral assembly is complete, the cell synthesizes a phage-encoded lysozyme that lyses the bacterial cell wall, causing the cell to rupture and releasing viral particles that can infect other *E. coli* cells (step 6). This whole series of events, from infection of a cell through to the release of progeny phages from the ruptured (or **lysed**) cell, is called the **lytic cycle.**

Some virulent phages (although not T-even phages) may package fragments of the host cell's

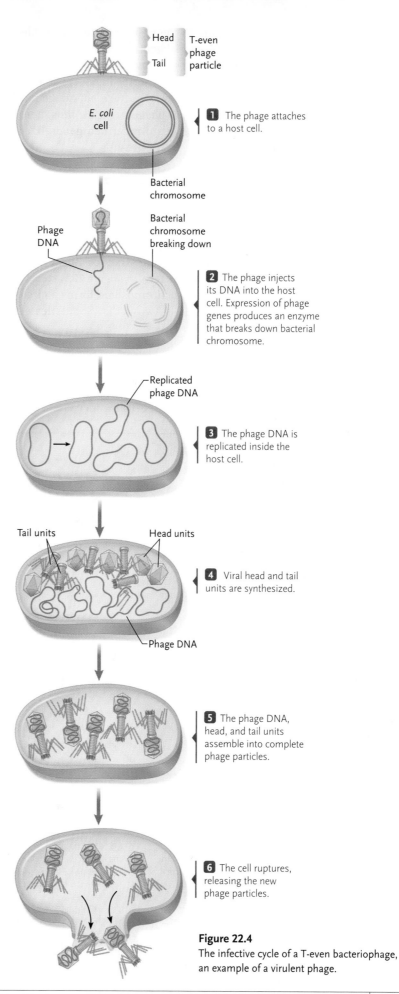

1 The phage attaches to a host cell.

2 The phage injects its DNA into the host cell. Expression of phage genes produces an enzyme that breaks down bacterial chromosome.

3 The phage DNA is replicated inside the host cell.

4 Viral head and tail units are synthesized.

5 The phage DNA, head, and tail units assemble into complete phage particles.

6 The cell ruptures, releasing the new phage particles.

Figure 22.4
The infective cycle of a T-even bacteriophage, an example of a virulent phage.

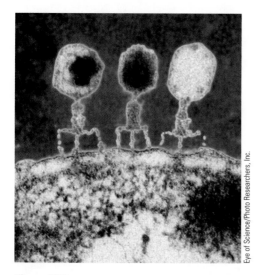

Figure 22.3
Bacteriophages injecting their DNA into *E. coli*.

DNA in the heads as the viral particles assemble. This transfer of bacterial genes from one bacterium to another via a virus is known as **transduction**. In the type of transduction described above, bacterial genes from essentially any DNA fragment can be randomly incorporated into phage particles; thus, gene transfer by this mechanism is termed **generalized transduction**.

A Scientist's Favourite Temperate *E. coli* Bacteriophage, Lambda. The infective cycle of the bacteriophage *lambda* (λ), an *E. coli* phage used extensively in research, is typical of temperate phages. Phage lambda infects *E. coli* in much the same way as the T-even phages. The phage injects its double-stranded linear DNA chromosome into the bacterium (**Figure 22.5,** step 1). Once inside, the linear chromosome forms a circle and then follows one of two paths. Sophisticated

molecular switches govern which path is followed at the time of infection.

One path is the lytic cycle, which is like the lytic cycles of virulent phages. The lytic cycle (see Figure 22.5, left side) starts with steps 1 to 2 (infection) and then goes directly to steps 7 through 9 (production and release of progeny virus) and back to step 1. A second and more common path is the **lysogenic cycle** (see Figure 22.5, right side). This cycle begins when the viral chromosome integrates into the host cell's DNA by recombination (see Figure 22.5, steps 1 through 3). The DNA of a temperate phage typically inserts at one or possibly a few specific sites in the bacterial chromosome through the action of a phage-encoded enzyme that recognizes certain sequences in the host DNA. Once integrated, the lambda genes are mostly inactive, so no phage components are made. While inserted in the host cell

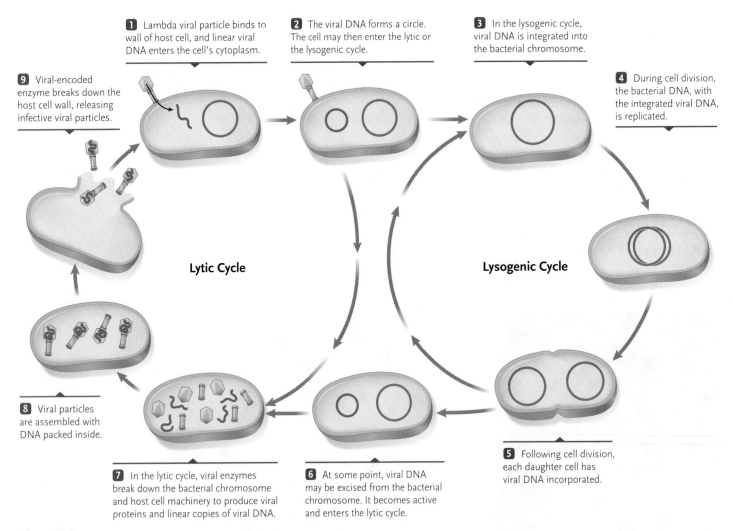

1 Lambda viral particle binds to wall of host cell, and linear viral DNA enters the cell's cytoplasm.

2 The viral DNA forms a circle. The cell may then enter the lytic or the lysogenic cycle.

3 In the lysogenic cycle, viral DNA is integrated into the bacterial chromosome.

4 During cell division, the bacterial DNA, with the integrated viral DNA, is replicated.

9 Viral-encoded enzyme breaks down the host cell wall, releasing infective viral particles.

Lytic Cycle

Lysogenic Cycle

8 Viral particles are assembled with DNA packed inside.

7 In the lytic cycle, viral enzymes break down the bacterial chromosome and host cell machinery to produce viral proteins and linear copies of viral DNA.

6 At some point, viral DNA may be excised from the bacterial chromosome. It becomes active and enters the lytic cycle.

5 Following cell division, each daughter cell has viral DNA incorporated.

Figure 22.5
The infective cycle of lambda, an example of a temperate phage, which can go through the lytic cycle or the lysogenic cycle.

DNA, the virus is known as a **prophage** (*pro* = before). When the host cell DNA replicates, so does the integrated viral DNA, which is passed on to daughter cells along with the host cell DNA (see Figure 22.5, steps 4 and 5).

What triggers the integrated prophage to become active (step 6)? Certain environmental signals, such as ultraviolet irradiation, stimulate this change, causing the prophage to enter the lytic cycle (see Figure 22.5, steps 6 through 9). Genes that were inactive in the prophage are now transcribed. Among the first viral proteins synthesized are enzymes that excise the lambda chromosome from the host chromosome. The result is a circular lambda chromosome that replicates itself and directs the production of viral DNA and coat proteins. This active stage culminates in the lysis of the host cell and the release of infective viral particles.

The excision of the prophage from its host's DNA is not always precise, resulting in the inclusion of one or more host cell genes with the viral DNA. These genes are replicated with the viral DNA and packed into the coats, and may be carried to a new host cell in the next cycle of infection. Clearly, only genes that are adjacent to the integration site(s) of a temperate phage can be cut out with the viral DNA, included in phage particles during the lytic stage, and undergo transduction. Accordingly, this mechanism of gene transfer is termed **specialized transduction.**

Infection of Animal Cells. Viruses infecting animal cells follow a pattern similar to that for bacterial cells, except that both the viral coat and the genome enter a host cell. Depending on the virus, removal of the coat to release the genome occurs during or after cell entry; the envelope does not enter the cell.

Viruses without an envelope, such as poliovirus, bind by their recognition proteins to the plasma membrane and are then taken into the host cell by endocytosis. The virus coat and genome of **enveloped viruses**, such as herpesvirus, influenza virus, and the virus causing rabies, enter the host cell by fusion of their envelope with the host cell plasma membrane.

Once inside the host cell, the genome directs the synthesis of additional viral particles by basically the same pathways as bacterial viruses. Some animal viruses, however, replicate themselves in very complex ways; one example is HIV, the virus that causes AIDS (see *Molecule Behind Biology*). Newly completed viruses that do not acquire an envelope are released by rupture of the host cell's plasma membrane, typically killing the cell. In contrast, most enveloped viruses receive their envelope as they pass through the plasma membrane, usually without breaking the membrane (see Figure 22.2). This pattern of viral release typically does not cause immediate damage to the host cell unless very high numbers of virus particles are released.

The vast majority of animal virus infections are asymptomatic because causing disease is of no benefit to the virus. However, a number of pathogenic viruses cause diseases in a variety of ways. Some viruses (e.g., herpesvirus) cause cell death when progeny viruses are released from the cell. This can lead to massive cell death, destroying vital tissues such as nervous tissue or white or red blood cells, or causing lesions in skin and mucous membranes. Other viruses release cellular molecules when infected cells break down, which can induce fever and inflammation (e.g., influenza virus). Yet other viruses alter gene function when they insert into the host cell DNA, leading to cancer and other abnormalities.

Some animal viruses enter a **latent phase**, similar to the lysogenic cycle for bacteriophages, in which the virus remains in the cell in an inactive form. The herpesviruses that cause oral and genital ulcers in humans remain in a latent phase in the cytoplasm of some body cells for the life of the individual. At times, particularly during periods of stress, the virus becomes active in some cells, directing viral replication and causing ulcers to form as cells break down during viral release.

Plant Viruses. Plant viruses may be rodlike or polyhedral. Although most include RNA as their nucleic acid, some contain DNA. None of the known plant viruses have envelopes. They enter cells through mechanical injuries to leaves and stems; they can also be transmitted from one plant to another during pollination or via herbivorous animals such as leafhoppers, aphids, and nematodes. Plant viruses can also be transmitted from one generation to the next in seeds. Once inside a cell, plant viruses replicate via the same processes as animal viruses. However, within plants, virus particles can pass from infected to healthy cells through plasmodesmata, the openings in cell walls that interconnect the cytoplasm of plant cells, and through the vascular system.

Plant viruses are generally named and classified by the type of plant they infect and their most visible effects. *Tomato bushy stunt virus*, for example, causes dwarfing and overgrowth of leaves and stems of tomato plants, and *tobacco mosaic virus* causes a mosaic-like pattern of spots on the leaves of tobacco plants. Most species of crop plants can be infected by at least one destructive virus.

The tobacco mosaic virus was the first virus to be isolated, disassembled, and reassembled in a test tube (see Figure 22.1a).

Reverse Transcriptase

Acquired immune deficiency syndrome (AIDS) is a disease caused by the human immunodeficiency virus (HIV). This disease has likely already killed about 25 million people worldwide, and the epidemic continues to grow, with infection rates in some areas of Africa as high as one in three adults. Even more concerning, infection rates are increasing in south and east Asia, some of the most densely populated regions of the world. If the epidemic continues to spread at current rates, the World Health Organization has projected AIDS as the fourth leading cause of death by 2030 (behind heart disease, other chronic diseases and car accidents). Although drug treatments to hold AIDS in check do exist, they are very expensive, and most people in developing countries cannot afford them. There is no cure for AIDS, so the millions of people currently infected will die prematurely.

HIV is a retrovirus that contains two copies of single-stranded RNA. It also carries several molecules of an enzyme, reverse transcriptase in its capsid. Replication of retroviruses is unusual: the virus' genome enters the host cell along with reverse transcriptase, which copies the viral RNA onto a complementary strand of DNA (**Figure 1**). A second strand of DNA is then synthesized, using the first strand as a template. The resulting double-stranded DNA integrates into the host cell's DNA as a provirus (comparable to the prophage described above). It is transcribed by the host cell into mRNA, which is translated to produce viral proteins, including capsid proteins and reverse transcriptase molecules. New virus particles are released from the cell to infect other cells or be passed to new hosts.

Why is HIV so lethal? The cells targeted by HIV include intestinal epithelial cells, brain cells, and cells of the immune system, including cells that produce antibodies. Obviously,

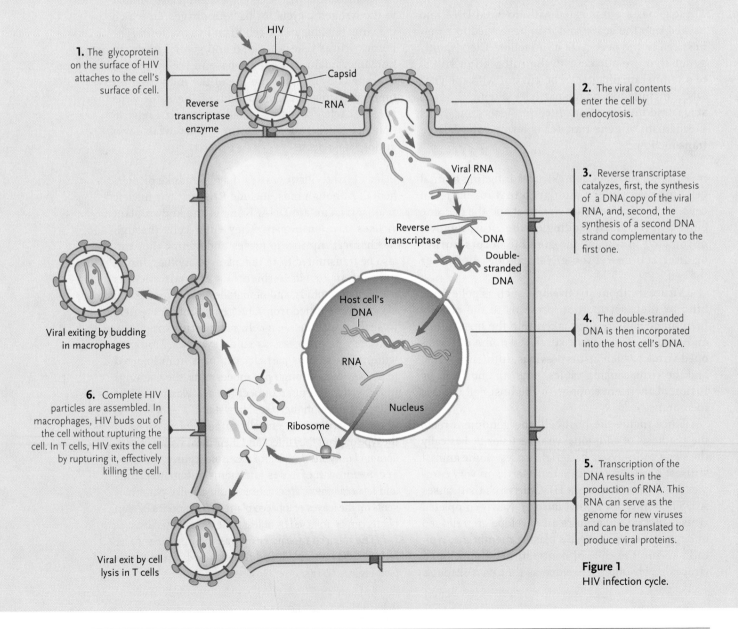

1. The glycoprotein on the surface of HIV attaches to the cell's surface of cell.

HIV

Capsid

Reverse transcriptase enzyme

RNA

2. The viral contents enter the cell by endocytosis.

Viral RNA

Reverse transcriptase

DNA

Double-stranded DNA

3. Reverse transcriptase catalyzes, first, the synthesis of a DNA copy of the viral RNA, and, second, the synthesis of a second DNA strand complementary to the first one.

Host cell's DNA

RNA

Nucleus

Ribosome

Viral exiting by budding in macrophages

6. Complete HIV particles are assembled. In macrophages, HIV buds out of the cell without rupturing the cell. In T cells, HIV exits the cell by rupturing it, effectively killing the cell.

Viral exit by cell lysis in T cells

4. The double-stranded DNA is then incorporated into the host cell's DNA.

5. Transcription of the DNA results in the production of RNA. This RNA can serve as the genome for new viruses and can be translated to produce viral proteins.

Figure 1
HIV infection cycle.

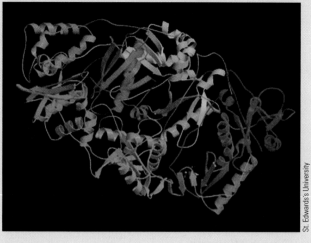

Figure 2
Reverse transcriptase.

St. Edward's University

DNA polymerase has proofreading capabilities, so the replicated DNA contains few errors. Reverse transcriptase does not have any proofreading ability, so any errors made when it catalyzes the synthesis of DNA from RNA (and there are a lot of such errors) persist. Proteins encoded by this mutated DNA will be different from those of the original virus; for example, the proteins of the viral coat will be different and so are not recognized by existing antibodies.

However, reverse transcriptase has also made important positive contributions to biomedical research. For example, retroviruses play an important role in gene therapy, in which new diseases are treated by introducing new genes into the body. Viruses are very effective vectors for introducing genes into cells. The desired genes are cloned into the viral genome, and once the virus is taken up by the cell, those genes are introduced into all cells infected by the virus. Retroviruses are particularly useful in gene therapy since the genetic material they carry is integrated into the host cell genome.

infection of these cells compromises the body's ability to fight off the virus. Some of the immune system cells are not killed by the virus but instead act as a continuing source of infection.

Because reverse transcriptase **(Figure 2)** is a unique feature of HIV, it makes a good target for drug treatment (if the drugs affect only this enzyme, they will not harm the human host). Several anti-retroviral drugs have been developed, although HIV has become resistant to some of these drugs. The search continues for a vaccine that would prevent HIV infection, but despite a years of research, no vaccine exists yet.

Why is there no vaccine, and how does HIV become resistant so quickly to drugs? The answer to both questions is that HIV mutates quickly and extensively. In a cell's normal DNA replication process,

STUDY BREAK

1. What is the difference between a virulent phage and a temperate phage?
2. What are the two types of transduction? How do they differ from each other?
3. How do plant viruses differ from animal viruses?

22.3 Viral Infections Are Typically Difficult to Treat

Viral infections are unaffected by antibiotics and other treatment methods used for bacterial infections. As a result, many viral infections are allowed to run their course, with treatment limited to relieving the symptoms while the natural immune defenses of the patient attack the virus. Some viruses, however, cause serious and sometimes deadly symptoms on infection; consequently, researchers have spent considerable effort in developing antiviral drugs to treat them. Many of these drugs fight the virus directly by targeting a stage of the viral life cycle; for example, the drug zanamivir inhibits release of influenza virus particles from cells.

The influenza virus illustrates the difficulties inherent in treating viral diseases. As mentioned at the start of the chapter, the influenza type A virus causes flu epidemics that sweep over the world each year. Why does a new vaccine have to be developed each year? One reason for the success of this virus is that its genome consists of eight separate pieces of RNA. When two different influenza viruses infect the same individual, these RNA pieces can assemble in random combinations derived from either parent virus. The new combinations can change the protein coat of the virus, making it unrecognizable to antibodies developed against either parent virus. Being "invisible" to these antibodies means that new virus strains can infect people who have already had the flu caused by a different strain or who had flu shots effective only against the parent strains of the virus. Random mutations in the RNA genome of the virus add to the variations in the coat proteins that make previously formed antibodies ineffective.

In the opening to this chapter, we learned that the 1918 influenza virus killed many of its hosts. Why was this strain so virulent? Researchers have learned that the 1918 influenza virus had mutations in the polymerase genes that replicated the viral genome in host cells, likely making this strain capable of replicating more efficiently.

Other viruses are also considered to have evolved from a virus that previously infected other animals. HIV is one of these; until the second half of the twentieth century, infections of this virus were apparently restricted almost entirely to chimpanzees and gorillas in Africa. Now the virus infects nearly 40 million people worldwide, with the greatest concentration of infected individuals in sub-Saharan Africa.

STUDY BREAK

What makes a viral infection often more difficult to treat than a bacterial infection?

22.4 Viruses May Have Evolved from Fragments of Cellular DNA or RNA

Where did viruses come from? Several different hypotheses have been proposed to explain the origin of viruses. Some biologists have suggested that because viruses can duplicate only by infecting a host cell, they probably evolved after cells appeared. They may represent "escaped" fragments of DNA molecules that once formed part of the genetic material of living cells or an RNA copy of such a fragment. In some way, the fragments became surrounded by a protective layer of protein with recognition functions and escaped from their parent cells. As viruses evolved, the information encoded in the core of the virus became reduced to a set of directions for producing more viral particles of the same kind.

More recent hypotheses suggest that viruses are very ancient, with virus-like particles predating the first cells. The first viruses originated from the "primordial gene pool"—the pool of RNA that is thought to have been the first genetic material (see Chapter 2).

Regardless of their origin, viruses have played an important role in the evolution of cellular life because of their ability to integrate their genes into their hosts and to acquire genes from their hosts, as described above. In this way, viruses can be a source of new cellular genetic material, providing new enzymes and other proteins to a cell. Viruses may also have played a more direct role in the evolution of eukaryotic cells: some biologists have suggested that the nucleus originated from a large, double-stranded DNA virus that infected prokaryote cells, resulting in the first eukaryotic cell.

STUDY BREAK

Why do some biologists think viruses must have originated after cells evolved, rather than predating cells?

22.5 Viroids and Prions Are Infective Agents Even Simpler in Structure Than Viruses

Viroids, first discovered in 1971, are small, infectious pieces of RNA. Although the RNA is single-stranded, bonding within the molecule causes it to become circular. Viroids are smaller than any virus and lack a protein coat. They also differ from viruses in that their RNA genome does not code for any proteins. Viroids are plant pathogens that can rapidly destroy entire fields of citrus, potatoes, tomatoes, coconut palms, and other crop plants. How do viroids cause such devastating diseases without synthesizing any proteins?

The manner in which viroids cause disease remains unknown. In fact, researchers believe that there is more than one mechanism. Recent research indicates that the viroid may disrupt normal RNA processing of the host cell: if the viroid's RNA sequence is complementary to mRNA of the host cell, it can bind to the host's mRNA, thus preventing normal protein synthesis and causing disease.

Prions, a loose acronym for *proti*neaceous *infec*tious particles, cause spongiform encephalopathies (SEs), degenerate diseases of the nervous system in mammals characterized by loss of motor control and erratic behaviour. The brains of affected animals are full of spongy holes **(Figure 22.6)** (hence the "spongiform" designation) and deposits of proteinaceous material. Under the microscope, aggregates of misfolded proteins, called amyloid fibres, are seen in brain tissues; the accumulation of these proteins is the likely cause of the brain damage. SEs progress slowly, meaning that animals may be sick for a long time before their symptoms become obvious, but death is inevitable.

One SE disease is *scrapie*, a brain disease that causes sheep to rub against fences, rocks, or trees until they scrape off most of their wool. In cattle, a similar disease is bovine spongiform encephalopathy (BSE), also known as "mad cow disease." Humans also have SE diseases, such as *kuru*, found among

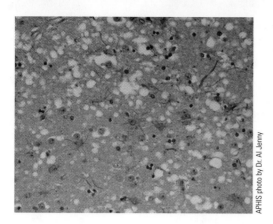

Figure 22.6

Bovine spongiform encephalopathy (BSE). The light-coloured patches in this section from a brain damaged by BSE are areas where tissue has been destroyed.

cannibals in New Guinea, who became infected by eating raw human brain during ritual feasts following the death of an individual. *Creutzfeldt-Jakob disease (CJD)* is a very rare SE disease that affects about one person in a million per year, globally. The symptoms of CJD include rapid mental deterioration, loss of vision and speech, and paralysis; autopsies show spongy holes and deposits in brain tissue similar to those of cattle with BSE. We don't know how CJD is transmitted naturally, but we know it can be transmitted inadvertently, for example, with corneal transplants.

SE diseases hit the headlines worldwide in the late 1980s when farmers in the United Kingdom reported a new disease, later determined to be BSE, spreading among their cattle. It is estimated that over 900 000 cows in the United Kingdom were affected, many of which entered the human food chain before developing symptoms. Where did BSE come from? The source was determined to be meat and bone meal fed to the cows; this meal came from the carcasses of sheep and cattle. The practice of feeding animal meal to cattle had been followed for years, but a money-saving change in processing in the early 1980s (a reduction in how long rendered material was held at high temperature) allowed the infectious agent—maybe from scrapie-infected sheep—to survive in the meat and bone meal. Worse was to come when it became evident that BSE had spread to humans who had eaten contaminated beef. This new human disease, known as variant CJD, is linked to eating meat products from cattle with BSE. Between 1996, when variant CJD was first described, and 2007, there were 208 cases from 11 countries, with the vast majority of these in the United Kingdom. Evidence from

studies of kuru suggests that it may take more than 50 years for prion diseases to develop, so there is some concern that a spike in variant CJD cases is still to come.

Concern about variant CJD explains why the discovery of even one cow with BSE can wreak havoc on a country's beef exports, as happened in Alberta in 2003. The United States closed its border to all beef from Canada within a day, followed shortly by border closings of 40 other countries. Loss of these markets caused serious economic hardship for Canadian ranchers and farmers.

What is the cause of BSE and other SE diseases, and how does this causative agent spread? As explained in *People Behind Biology*, Stanley Prusiner demonstrated that infectious proteins cause these diseases. Prions are the only known infectious agents that do not include a nucleic acid molecule, and their discovery changed some fundamental views of biology.

Our current understanding of prion infection is that prion proteins are able to survive passage through the stomach of an animal consuming them; they then enter that animal's bloodstream and proceed to the brain where they somehow interact with normal prion proteins, causing these proteins to change shape to become abnormal and infectious. As the infection spreads, neural functioning is impaired and protein fibrils accumulate, leading to the SE characteristic of these diseases.

What is the function of "normal" prion proteins? We don't know yet, but there is some evidence that normal prions may protect neurons from overactivity. In recent research, mice lacking normal prion proteins were found to have "hyperactive" neurons, which responded longer and more vigorously to stimulation, compared with neurons of mice with the normal form of prion proteins. This hyperactivity ultimately led to the destruction of the neurons. Perhaps the inability of the misfolded prion proteins to carry out their normal protective function results in dementia and the other symptoms of BSE.

In this chapter, we focused on the simplest biological entities: viruses, viroids, and prions, which possess only some of the properties of life. In the next five chapters, we investigate more structurally complex organisms: the eukaryotic kingdoms of protists, fungi, plants, and animals.

STUDY BREAK

How do viroids and prions differ from viruses? How do they differ from each other?

Stanley Prusiner, University of California

For several decades, scientists had hypothesized that a slow virus—a disease-causing virus with a long incubation period and gradual onset of pathogenicity—was responsible for scrapie and other spongiform encephalopathies. However, scientists had repeatedly examined the brains of infected animals and not found any evidence of viral infection. In 1982, Stanley Prusiner, a researcher at University of California, San Francisco, determined that the infectious agent was a protein. He pointed to the accumulation of protein fibrils in the brains of infected animals and termed this protein the prion protein (PrP). The research community mostly rejected this hypothesis because it went against all the accepted dogma of biology—genes in the form of DNA or RNA were necessary to cause disease. How could a protein make copies of itself? Prusiner located the gene for PrP and then found that prion proteins are naturally occurring membrane proteins in many types of cells, including neurons. In sheep infected with scrapie, Prusiner found "rogue" forms of the prion proteins that were abnormally folded. He proposed that these infectious prion proteins somehow interacted with "normal" prion proteins to cause misfolding of these proteins; thus, the abnormal protein structure is "infectious." The misfolded prion proteins aggregate, forming the masses of fibrils characteristic of SE diseases. In 1997, Prusiner received a Nobel Prize for his discovery of prions.

UNANSWERED QUESTIONS

Do viruses infect extremophile organisms?

As you learned in Chapter 21, prokaryotic organisms have been able to colonize every habitat on Earth, from frozen valleys of Antarctica to hydrothermal vents in deep ocean and hot springs. They can even live at depths of more than 1 kilometre in Earth's crust. So when we think of *extremophiles*—organisms that can live in conditions of extreme pH, temperature, salinity, desiccation, etc.—we usually think of prokaryotes. But there are some eukaryotic extremophiles too, such as the algae that live in Spain's Rio Tinto, a river with a pH of 2 and elevated levels of iron and copper. Do viruses infect extremophiles? If so, what type of viruses are they? What role do they play in these extreme environments?

Several lines of research indicate that viruses infect organisms living in extreme saline environments, in polar environments, at ocean depths, and in extremely hot environments. It is thought that early life forms might have been prokaryotic thermophiles, so studying the viruses that infect thermophilic archaea and bacteria might shed light on the evolution of cellular life and the origin of viruses. Recently, viruses have been found in archaea living in hot springs. Some of these viruses have morphological and molecular features unrelated to those of any other known viruses. They also show incredible genetic diversity—their genetic sequences do not match those of known viruses, and we don't yet know what most of their genes encode. Although some of these unknown proteins may carry out the same functions as known proteins, we may discover proteins with new functions.

The thermophilic viruses do not lyse their host cells and appear to persist inside their hosts in a stable state. Perhaps, like the phages that infect marine cyanobacteria, these viruses assist their hosts' survival in extreme environments.

How do prion proteins move within the brain?

The brain-wasting diseases caused by prions are not well understood, despite much research. We know that prion proteins invade nerve cells and ultimately lead to fatal degeneration of the nervous system. To understand disease progression, scientists have investigated how prion proteins move through the nervous system. Using labelled-protein techniques, researchers have tracked infectious prion proteins from sites of infection up to the brain. In mice, prion proteins move via the projections of nerve cells to points of contact with other cells. Perhaps prion proteins are able to cross into the adjacent cell. An understanding of how prions invade cells and replicate are crucial if we are to develop therapies to stop the spread of brain-wasting diseases.

Review

Go to CENGAGENOW™ at http://hed.nelson.com/ to access quizzing, animations, exercises, articles, and personalized homework help.

22.1 What Is a Virus? Characteristics of Viruses

- Viruses are non-living infective agents. A free virus particle consists of a nucleic acid genome enclosed in a protein coat. Recognition proteins enabling the virus to attach to host cells extend from the surface of infectious viruses.

22.2 Viruses Infect Bacterial, Animal, and Plant Cells by Similar Pathways

- Viruses reproduce by entering a host cell and directing the cellular machinery to make new particles of the same kind.

22.3 Viral Infections Are Typically Difficult to Treat

- Viruses are unaffected by antibiotics and most other treatment methods. As well, many viruses have great genetic variability. For these reasons, viral infections are difficult to treat.

22.4 Viruses May Have Evolved from Fragments of Cellular DNA or RNA

- There are several hypotheses about the origin of viruses. Viruses may have evolved after cells did and may have descended from nucleic acid fragments that "escaped" from a cell. Evidence for this hypothesis comes from the fact that viruses can duplicate only by infecting a host cell. On the other hand, a competing hypothesis suggests that viruses evolved before the first cells, with the first virus-like particles originating from the pool of RNA that was the first genetic material.

22.5 Viroids and Prions Are Infective Agents Even Simpler in Structure Than Viruses

- Viroids, which infect crop plants, consist of only a very small, single-stranded RNA molecule. Prions, which cause brain diseases in some animals, are infectious proteins with no associated nucleic acid. Prions are misfolded versions of normal cellular proteins, which can induce other normal proteins to misfold.

Questions

Self-Test Questions

1. Which of the following best defines a virus?
   a. A non-cellular entity containing a nucleoid region.
   b. An entity composed of proteins, nucleic acids and ribosomes.
   c. An entity composed of proteins and nucleic acids that can't replicate outside a host.
   d. A naked fragment of nucleic acid
   e. A disease-causing group of proteins

2. Most viruses form a capsid around their nucleic acid core. This capsid is composed of:
   a. protein
   b. polysaccharides
   c. antigens
   d. glycoprotein
   e. lipoprotein

3. Viral envelopes generally _____.
   a. are composed of a lipid bilayer, derived from the host cell's membrane.
   b. contain glycoproteins of viral origin.
   c. are located between virus's capsid and its nucleic acid.
   d. Both A and B are correct.
   e. A, B and C are all correct.

4. Plant viruses are different from animal viruses in that they _____.
   a. lack the ability to actively infect a host cell.
   b. lack the ability to replicate their RNA genome.
   c. are covered by a membrane envelope.
   d. are easily curable.
   e. There are NO differences between animal and plant viruses.

5. When a bacteriophage enters the lysogenic stage,
   a. the viral DNA is replicated outside the host cell.
   b. it enters the host cell and kills it immediately.
   c. it enters the host cell, picks up host DNA, and leaves the cell unharmed.
   d. it sits on the host cell plasma membrane, with which it covers itself, and then leaves the cell.
   e. it injects its DNA into the host cell DNA, and the host DNA integrates viral DNA into the host genome.

6. Reverse transcriptase synthesizes
   a. RNA from DNA.
   b. DNA from RNA.
   c. proteins from DNA.
   d. proteins from RNA.

7. Which of the following statements about prions is FALSE?
   a. Prions can only be transmitted from animals to humans.
   b. Prions contain no nucleic acids and have the same amino acid sequence as the normal protein.
   c. Prions have a different three-dimensional structure from their natural protein.
   d. Prion proteins reproduce by converting a normal protein to an infectious prion protein by misfolding it.
   e. All evidence to date indicates that prions infect mammals but not other animals.

Questions for Discussion

1. From what you have read in this chapter, would you consider viruses to be alive? Why or why not?

2. Why do animal viruses have envelopes, whereas bacteriophages do not?

3. Why is it difficult to design an effective, long-lasting vaccine for the flu virus and the HIV virus?

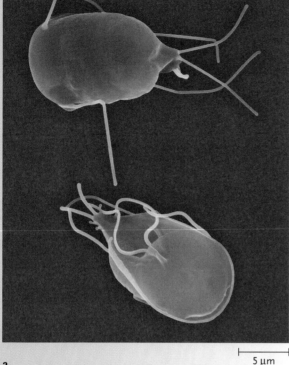

a.

| | 5 μm |

Giardia lamblia **(a)** Scanning electron microscope image; **(b)** light microscope image.

b.

| | 10 μm |

23 Protists

WHY IT MATTERS

You are on a backpacking trip in your favourite wilderness area on a hot and sunny day. You pause to take a drink of water from your water bottle but discover it is almost empty. You are very thirsty, so you refill your bottle from a nearby stream: the water is clear and cold and looks clean, and, besides, you're out in the middle of nowhere, so it must be safe to drink, right? You continue on the hike and feel fine. But a few days after you get home, you don't feel so great: you have abdominal pain, cramps, and diarrhea. Your doctor says that you have giardiasis, or "beaver fever," caused by *Giardia lamblia,* the most common intestinal parasite in North America (it is very prevalent in water bodies formed by beaver dams). What is *Giardia,* and how does it make you sick?

Giardia is a single-celled eukaryote that can exist in two forms: a dormant cyst and a motile feeding stage. When you drank from that seemingly clean stream, you ingested some cysts. The cysts can survive for months, so it is important to boil or filter water when you are out hiking or camping. As the swallowed cysts moved from your stomach into your small intestine, the cysts released the motile feeding stage, **trophozoites** (*troph* = food; *zoon* = animal), shown in the photographs at the start of this chapter. Using their multiple flagella, the trophozoites were able to swim about in your intestinal space and attach themselves to the epithelial cells of your intestine. Infection with *Giardia* can become chronic, causing inflammation and reduction of the absorptive capacity of the gut. So why doesn't your immune system detect the presence of *Giardia* and get rid of the parasite? *Giardia* can alter the proteins on its surface that your immune system relies on to recognize an invader and so escapes recognition; thus, *Giardia* infections can be persistent or recur.

Giardia is a **protist** (Greek *protistos* = the very first). Protists are a very heterogeneous collection of about 200 000 eukaryotes that are not actually closely related to each other; that is, they did not all arise from a common ancestor. Most are unicellular and microscopic, but some are large, muticellular organisms. Like their most ancient ancestors, almost all of these eukaryotic species are aquatic. **Figure 23.1** shows a number of protists, illustrating their great diversity. Traditionally, protists are grouped together into the **kingdom Protista** (sometimes called "**Protoctista**"). This kingdom has traditionally been a catch-all group that consists of those eukaryotes that are not animals, fungi, or plants.

23.1 Evolution of Protists Involved Endosymbiosis

Protists likely evolved about 1.5 to 2 billion years ago. We don't fully understand how they evolved, although we know that endosymbiosis played an important role in the process. As eukaryotes, protists contain mitochondria

a. Slime mould

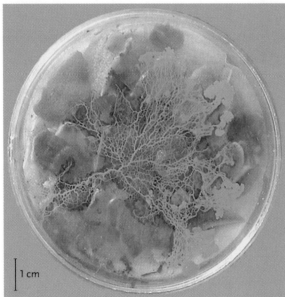

b. Ciliates

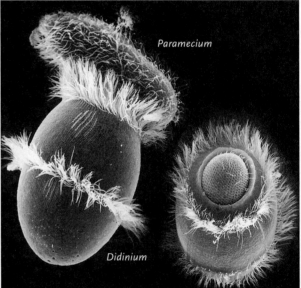

c. Brown algae

d. Green algae

Figure 23.1

A sampling of protist diversity. **(a)** *Physarum*, a plasmodial slime mould grown in organic debris in a Petri dish. **(b)** *Didinium*, a ciliate, consuming another ciliate, *Paramecium*. **(c)** *Fucus gardneri* (common rockweed), a brown alga growing in rocky intertidal zones. **(d)** *Micrasterias*, a single-celled green alga, here shown dividing in two.

(although some have very reduced versions of this organelle), and many also contain chloroplasts. As outlined in Chapter 2, mitochondria and chloroplasts are the descendants of free-living prokaryotes that, over evolutionary time, became organelles. All mitochondria are thought to have arisen from a single endosymbiotic event, but the history of chloroplasts is more complex.

The first chloroplasts evolved from free-living photosynthetic prokaryotes (cyanobacteria) ingested by eukaryote cells that had already acquired mitochondria (see Chapter 2). In some cells, the cyanobacterium was not digested but instead formed a symbiotic relationship with the engulfing host cell—it became an endosymbiont, an independent organism living inside another organism (see Figure 2.22). Over evolutionary time, the prokaryote lost genes no longer required for independent existence and transferred most of its genes to the host's nuclear genome. As explained in Chapter 2, moving some of the genes to the nucleus is thought to have given the host cell better control of overall cell function. The prokaryote had become an organelle, part of the eukaryote cell. As we'll see, some photosynthetic protists originated from this endosymbiotic event, whereas other protists were formed when a eukaryote engulfed a photosynthetic eukaryote that eventually became a chloroplast. We will return to this topic at the end of the chapter.

STUDY BREAK

How did the first chloroplasts evolve?

23.2 What Is a Protist? Characteristics of Protists

Because protists are eukaryotes, the boundary between them and prokaryotes is clear and obvious. Unlike prokaryotes, protists have a membrane-bound nucleus, with multiple, linear chromosomes. In addition to cytoplasmic organelles, including mitochondria and chloroplasts (in some species), protists have microtubules and microfilaments, which provide motility and cytoskeletal support. As well, they share characteristics of transcription and translation with other eukaryotes.

The phylogenetic relationship between protists and other eukaryotes is more complex (Figure 23.2).

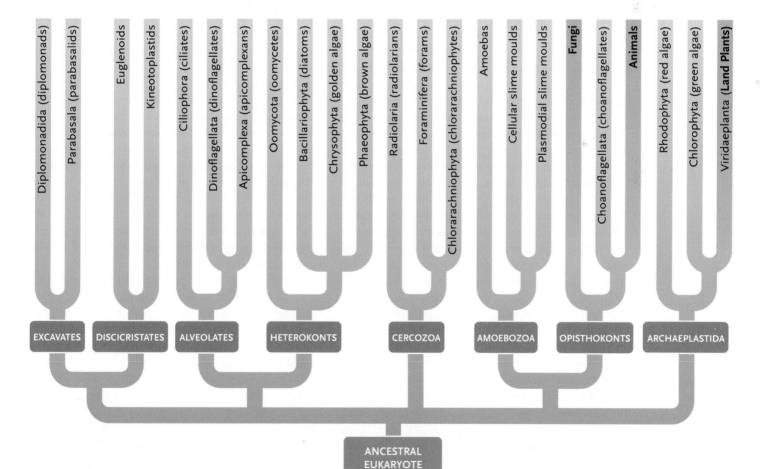

Figure 23.2

The phylogenetic relationship between the evolutionary groups within the kingdom Protista and the other eukaryotes. The Archaeplastida (boxed) include the land plants of the kingdom Plantae, and the Opisthokonts (boxed) include the animals of the kingdom Animalia and the fungi of the kingdom Fungi. The tree was constructed based on a consensus of molecular and ultrastructural data.

Over evolutionary time, the eukaryotic family tree branched out in many directions. All of the organisms in the eukaryotic lineages consist of protists except for three groups, the animals, land plants, and fungi, which arose from protist ancestors. Although some protists have features that resemble those of the fungi, plants, or animals, several characteristics are distinctive. In contrast to fungi, most protists are motile or have motile stages in their life cycles, and their cell walls are made of cellulose, not chitin.

How do photosynthesizing protists differ from plants? Unlike plants, many photoautotrophic protists can also live as heterotrophs, and some regularly combine both modes of nutrition. Protists do not retain developing embryos in parental tissue, as plants do, nor do they have highly differentiated structures equivalent to roots, stems, and leaves. Photosynthetic protists are sometimes referred to as "algae"; these protists are generally aquatic and often unicellular and microscopic (although many are multicellular). However, the different groups of algae are not closely related to each other (see Figure 23.2), so the term "algae" does not indicate any sort of relatedness among organisms referred to by that term.

How do protists differ from animals? Unlike protists, all animals are multicellular and have features such as an internal digestive tract and complex developmental stages. Protists also lack nerve cells, highly differentiated structures such as limbs and a heart, and collagen, an extracellular support protein. These features characterize many animals. The one reasonable certainty about protist classification is that the organisms lumped together in the kingdom Protista are not prokaryotes, fungi, plants, or animals.

The extreme diversity of the group has made the protists so difficult to classify that their status as a kingdom remains highly unsettled. Until recently, the protists were classified into phyla within the kingdom Protista according to criteria such as body form, modes of nutrition and movement, and forms of meiosis and mitosis. However, molecular data, now considered the most informative method for determining evolutionary relationships, show that most protists do not share a common ancestor and that many protists grouped together in a phylum are no more closely related to each other than they are to the fungi, plants, or animals.

Given this extreme diversity, some evolutionists maintain that the kingdom Protista is actually a collection of many kingdoms—perhaps as many as 30! Evolutionary lineages within the kingdoms are variously described as subkingdoms or phyla, and the existing schemes are constantly revised as new information is obtained. The tree shown in Figure 23.2 represents a current consensus, based on both structural and molecular data. Remember that such a tree represents one hypothesis about relationships among organisms; there are numerous other trees, representing alternative hypotheses.

For simplicity, we retain the Protista as a single kingdom in this book, with the understanding that it is a collection of largely unrelated organisms placed together for convenience. We refer to the major evolutionary clusterings indicated by molecular and structural comparisons as "groups" (see Figure 23.2).

STUDY BREAK

What features distinguish protists from prokaryotes? What distinguish them from fungi, plants, and animals?

23.3 Protists' Diversity Is Reflected in Their Metabolism, Reproduction, Structure, and Habitat

As you might expect from the broad range of organisms included in this kingdom, protists are highly diverse in metabolism, reproduction, structure, and habitat.

Habitat. Protists live in aqueous habitats, including aquatic or moist terrestrial locations such as oceans, freshwater lakes, ponds, streams, and moist soils and within host organisms. In bodies of water, small photosynthetic protists collectively make up the **phytoplankton** (*phytos* = plant; *planktos* = drifting), the organisms that capture the energy of sunlight in nearly all aquatic habitats. These phototrophs provide organic substances and oxygen for heterotrophic bacteria, other protists, and the small crustaceans and animal larvae that are the primary constituents of **zooplankton** (*zoe* = life, usually meaning animal life). Although protists are not animals, biologists often include them among the zooplankton. Phytoplankton and larger multicellular protists forming seaweeds collectively account for about half of the total organic matter produced by photosynthesis.

In the moist soils of terrestrial environments, protists play important roles among the detritus feeders that recycle matter from organic back to inorganic form. In their roles in phytoplankton, in zooplankton, and as detritus feeders, protists are enormously important in world ecosystems.

Protists that live in host organisms are parasites, obtaining nutrients from the host. Indeed, many of the parasites that have significant effects on human health are protists, causing diseases such as malaria, sleeping sickness, and amoebic dysentery.

Structure. Whereas most protists are single cells, others live as **colonies (Figure 23.3)** in which individual cells show little or no differentiation and are potentially independent. Within colonies, individuals use cell signalling to cooperate on tasks such as feeding or

Figure 23.3
Colonial protist (*Dinobryon*).

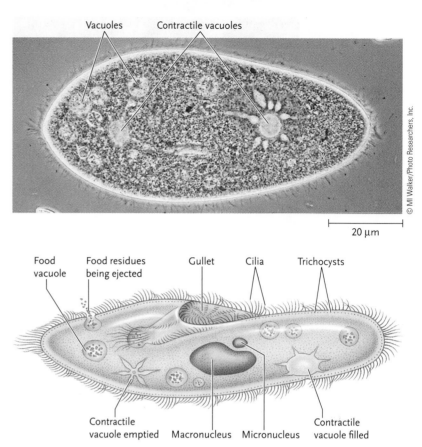

Figure 23.4
A ciliate, *Paramecium*, showing the cytoplasmic structures typical of many protists.

movement. Some protists are large multicellular organisms; for example, the giant kelp of coastal waters can rival forest trees in size.

Many single-celled and colonial protists have complex intracellular structures, some found nowhere else among living organisms **(Figure 23.4).** These unique structures reflect key aspects of the habitats in which protists live. For example, consider a single-celled protist living in a freshwater pond. Its cytoplasm is hypertonic to the water surrounding it, meaning that water flows into the cell by osmosis (see Section 5.5). How can the protist prevent itself from bursting? A specialized cytoplasmic organelle, the **contractile vacuole**, gradually fills with fluid. When this vacuole reaches its maximum size, it moves to the plasma membrane and forcibly contracts, expelling the fluid to the outside through a pore in the membrane.

The cells of some protists are supported by an external cell wall or by an internal or external shell built up from organic or mineral matter; in some, the shell takes on highly elaborate forms. Instead of a cell wall, other protists have a **pellicle**, a layer of supportive protein fibres located inside the cell just under the plasma membrane, providing strength and flexibility **(Figure 23.5).**

At some time during their lives, almost all protists move. Some move by amoeboid motion, in which

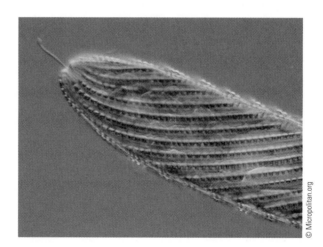

Figure 23.5
Euglena spirogyra, showing pellicle (strips of protein fibres).

the cell extends one or more lobes of cytoplasm called **pseudopodia** ("false feet"; see **Figure 23.6, p. 502**). The rest of the cytoplasm and the nucleus then flow into the pseudopodium, completing the movement. Other protists move by the beating of flagella or cilia. In some protists, cilia are arranged in complex patterns, with an equally complex network of microtubules and other cytoskeletal fibres supporting the cilia under the plasma membrane.

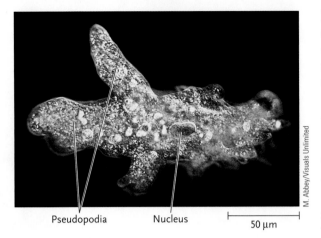

Pseudopodia   Nucleus   ⊢————⊣
                                50 μm

Figure 23.6
Amoeba proteus of the Amoebozoa is perhaps the most familiar protist of all.

Many protists can exist in more than one form, for example, as a motile form and as a nonmotile cyst that can survive unfavourable conditions. This morphological variability allows the species to live in different habitats at different stages in its life.

Metabolism. Almost all protists are aerobic organisms that live either as heterotrophs—obtaining carbon from organic molecules produced by other organisms—or as photoautotrophs, by producing organic molecules for themselves by photosynthesis (see Chapter 3). Some heterotrophic protists obtain organic molecules by engulfing part or all of other organisms (*phagocytosis*) and digesting them internally. Others absorb small organic molecules from their environment by diffusion. Some protists can live as either heterotrophs or autotrophs.

Reproduction. Reproduction may be asexual, by mitosis, or sexual, through meiotic cell division and formation of gametes. In protists that reproduce by both mitosis and meiosis, the two modes of cell division are often combined into a **life cycle** that is highly distinctive among the different protist groups. We do not yet have a complete understanding of how many protists reproduce.

STUDY BREAK

Define each of the following terms in your own words and indicate the role each plays in the life of a protist: pellicle, pseudopodia, contractile vacuole.

23.4 The Protist Groups

In this section, we look at the biological features of the groups included in Figure 23.2. Our focus is the ecological or economic importance of each group, the habitats in which you would find those organisms, and key features that differentiate the group from other protists. As you read through the information on each group, think about how the structural features of a group relate to its habitat and lifestyle.

23.4a Excavates Lack "Typical" Mitochondria

This group takes its name from the hollow (excavated) ventral feeding groove found in most members. All Excavates are single-celled animal parasites that lack mitochondria and move by means of flagella. Because they lack mitochondria, they are limited to glycolysis as an ATP source (see Chapter 6). Originally, the lack of mitochondria led biologists to consider this group as the most ancient line of protists; however, it now appears that the ancestor of this group did have mitochondria. The nuclei of Excavates contain genes derived from mitochondria, and they also have organelles that likely evolved from mitochondria. Excavates may have lost their mitochondria as an adaptation to the parasitic way of life, in which oxygen is in short supply. We consider two subgroups here, the Diplomonadida and the Parabasala.

Diplomonadida. Diplomonad means "double cell," and these organisms do look like two cells together (see the figure at the beginning of the chapter), with their two apparently identical, functional nuclei and multiple flagella arranged symmetrically around the cell's longitudinal axis. The best-known diplomonad is *Giardia lamblia,* profiled at the beginning of this chapter. Some are free-living, but many live in animal intestines; some diplomonads do not cause harm to the host, whereas others, like *Giardia,* live as parasites.

Parabasala. The sexually transmitted disease trichomoniasis is caused by the parabasalid *Trichomonas vaginalis* **(Figure 23.7a)**. The infection is usually symptomless in men, but in women, *T. vaginalis* can cause severe inflammation and irritation of the vagina and vulva. If untreated, trichomoniasis can cause infection of the uterus and fallopian tubes that can result in infertility. Luckily, drugs can easily cure the infection.

Parabasalids take their names from cytoplasmic structures associated with the nucleus, *parabasal bodies;* some biologists consider these structures to be the Golgi apparatus of these cells. Parabasalids are also characterized by a sort of fin called an **undulating membrane**, formed by a flagellum buried in a fold of the cytoplasm, in addition to freely beating flagella. The buried flagellum allows parabasalids to move through thick, viscous fluids, such as those lining human reproductive tracts.

Other parabasalids (e.g., *Trichonympha;* **Figure 23.7b**) are symbionts that live in the guts of termites

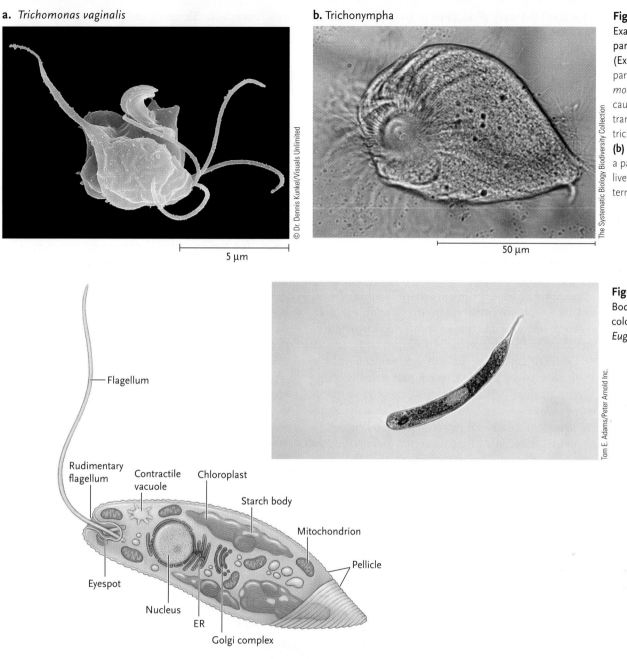

a. *Trichomonas vaginalis*

© Dr. Dennis Kunkel/Visuals Unlimited

5 μm

b. Trichonympha

The Systematic Biology Biodiversity Collection

50 μm

Figure 23.7
Examples of parabasalids (Excavates). **(a)** A parabasalid, *Trichomonas vaginalis*, that causes a sexually transmitted disease, trichomoniasis; **(b)** *Trichonympha*, a parabasalid that lives in the guts of termites.

Figure 23.8
Body plan and a colour photo of *Euglena gracilis*.

Tom E. Adams/Peter Arnold Inc.

Flagellum

Rudimentary flagellum

Contractile vacuole

Chloroplast

Starch body

Mitochondrion

Pellicle

Eyespot

Nucleus

ER

Golgi complex

and other wood-eating insects, digesting the cellulose in the wood for their hosts. As if this endosymbiotic relationship were not complex enough, biologists recently discovered that the protists themselves cannot produce the enzymes necessary to break down cellulose but instead rely on bacterial symbionts to break down the cellulose.

23.4b Discicristates Include the Euglenoids and Kinetoplastids: Highly Motile Protists

Protists of this group are sometimes referred to as *protozoa* (*proto* = first; *zoon* = animal) because they are similar to animals in that they ingest food and move by themselves. The **Discicristates** are named for their

disk-shaped mitochondrial cristae (folds of the inner mitochondrial membrane). The group includes about 1800 species, almost all single-celled, highly motile cells that swim by means of flagella. Although most are photosynthetic, some can also live as heterotrophs, and some even alternate between photosynthesis and life as a heterotroph. Other organisms in this group are parasitic.

Euglenoids. You have probably seen an example of one genus of euglenoids, *Euglena,* in your earlier biology classes **(Figure 23.8, p.504)** as they are often used to illustrate how some protists have plantlike features (photosynthesis) combined with features that we consider animal-like (movement). Euglenoids are important primary producers in freshwater ponds, streams, and lakes, and even some marine habitats. Most are autotrophs that carry out photosynthesis using the same photosynthetic pigments and mechanisms as plants. If light is not available, many of the photosynthetic euglenoids can also live as heterotrophs by absorbing organic molecules through the plasma membrane or by engulfing small particles. Other euglenoids lack chloroplasts and live entirely as heterotrophs.

The name *Euglena* roughly translates as "eyeball organism," a reference to the large *eyespot* that is an obvious feature of photosynthetic euglenoids (see Figure 23.8). The *eyespot* contains pigment granules in association with a light-sensitive structure and is part of a sensory mechanism that stimulates cells to swim toward moderately bright light or away from intensely bright light so that the organism finds optimal conditions for photosynthetic activity. In addition to an eyespot, euglenoids contain numerous organelles, including a contractile vacuole.

Rather than an external cell wall, euglenoids have a spirally grooved pellicle formed from strips of transparent, protein-rich material underneath the membrane (see Figure 23.5). In some euglenoids, the strips are arranged in a spiral pattern, allowing the cell to change its shape in a wriggling sort of motion (known as euglenoid movement) that allows the cell to change direction. Euglenoids can also swim by whiplike movements of flagella that extend from one end of the cell. Most have two flagella: one rudimentary and short, the other long.

Kinetoplastids. Sleeping sickness is a fatal disease endemic to sub-Saharan Africa. Although the disease was almost eradicated about 40 years ago, it has been making a comeback due to wars and the subsequent refugee movement and damage to health care systems. Sleeping sickness is caused by various subspecies of *Trypanosoma brucei* (**Figure 23.9**) that are transmitted from one host to another by bites of the tsetse fly. Early symptoms include fever, headaches, rashes, and anemia. Untreated, the disease damages the central nervous system, leading to a sleeplike coma and eventual death. The disease has proved difficult to control because the same trypanosomes infect wild mammals, providing an inexhaustible reservoir for the parasite. Other trypanosomes, also transmitted by insects, cause Chagas disease in Central and South America and leishmaniasis in many tropical countries. Humans with Chagas disease have an enlarged liver and spleen and may experience severe brain and heart damage; leishmaniasis causes skin sores and ulcers, as well as liver and spleen damage.

Like trypanosomes, other kinetoplastids are heterotrophs that live as animal parasites. Kinetoplastid cells are characterized by a single mitochondrion that contains a large DNA-protein deposit called a *kinetoplast* (see Figure 23.9). Most kinetoplastids also have a leading and a trailing flagellum, which are used for movement. In some cases, the trailing flagellum is attached to the side of the cell, forming an undulating membrane that allows the organism to glide along or attach to surfaces.

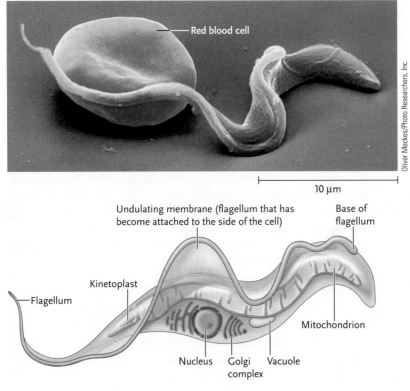

Figure 23.9
Trypansoma brucei, the parasitic kinetoplastid that causes African sleeping sickness.

Red blood cell

Oliver Meckes/Photo Researchers, Inc.

10 μm

Undulating membrane (flagellum that has become attached to the side of the cell)

Base of flagellum

Kinetoplast

Flagellum

Mitochondrion

Nucleus   Golgi complex   Vacuole

23.4c Alveolates Have Complex Cytoplasmic Structures and Move via Flagella or Cilia

This group is named for the small, membrane-bound vesicles called *alveoli* (*alvus* = belly) in a layer just under the plasma membrane. The Alveolates include two motile, primarily free-living groups, the Ciliophora and Dinoflagellata, and a nonmotile, parasitic group, the Apicomplexa.

Ciliophora: The Ciliates. Have you ever wondered how we know what we know about the details of cellular functioning? For example, how did we find out about the existence of telomeres at the ends of eukaryotic chromosomes and the function of telomerase? An important tool in these discoveries has been the use of model organisms—organisms that are easily manipulated and easily raised in the lab and for which we have abundant data, for example, genome sequences (see *The Chemical and Physical Foundations of Biology* pages). Several protists are ideal model organisms because even though they are single celled, the complexity of their structures and functions is comparable to that of humans and other animals. One ciliate, *Tetrahymena* **(Figure 23.10)**, was the organism in which telomeres and telomerase

were discovered; it was also the cell in which the first motor protein was identified, cell cycle control mechanisms were first described, and ribozymes were discovered. The involvement of ciliates with scientific research dates back several centuries as they were among the first organisms observed in the seventeenth century by the pioneering microscopist Anton van Leeuwenhoek.

Ciliophora is a large group, with nearly 10 000 known species of primarily single-celled but highly complex heterotrophic organisms that swim by means of cilia (see Figures 23.4 and 23.10). Any sample of pond water or bottom mud contains a wealth of these creatures. Some ciliates live individually, whereas others are colonial. Certain ciliates are animal parasites; others live and reproduce in their hosts as mutually beneficial symbionts. A compartment of the stomach of cattle and other grazing animals contains large numbers of symbiotic ciliates that digest the cellulose in their hosts' plant diet. The host animals then digest the excess ciliates.

The organisms in the Ciliophora have many highly developed organelles, including a mouthlike gullet lined with cilia, structures that exude toxins and other defensive materials from the cell surface, contractile vacuoles, and a complex systems of **food vacuoles**. A pellicle reinforces the cell's shape. A complex cytoskeleton anchors the cilia just below the pellicle and coordinates the ciliary beating. The cilia can stop and reverse their beating in synchrony, allowing ciliates to stop, back up, and turn if they encounter negative stimuli.

The ciliates are the only eukaryotes that have two types of nuclei in each cell: one or more small nuclei called *micronuclei* and a single larger *macronucleus* (see Figure 23.4). A **micronucleus** is a diploid nucleus that contains a complete complement of genes. It functions primarily in cellular reproduction, which may be asexual or sexual. The number of micronuclei present depends on the species. The **macronucleus** develops from a micronucleus but loses all genes except those required for basic functions (e.g., feeding,

a. Cilate

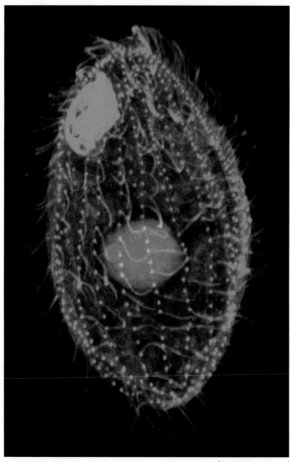

Jacek Gaertig, University of Georgia, Athens

10 µm

b. Cilia

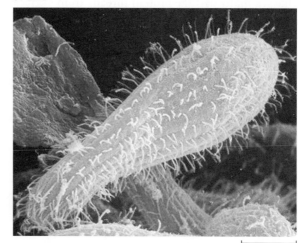

Louis De Vos, Free University of Brussels, BIODIC

10 µm

Figure 23.10
Tetrahymena, a ciliate **(a)** stained with fluorescent dye to show cilia and microtubules; **(b)** SEM image showing cilia.

Saxitoxin

Some dinoflagellates that cause red tides also produce neurotoxins. Fish that feed on the dinoflagellates and birds that feed on the fish may be killed in huge numbers by the toxins. Dinoflagellate toxins do not noticeably affect clams, oysters, and other molluscs but become concentrated in their tissues. Eating the tainted molluscs can cause paralytic shellfish poisoning in humans and other animals, characterized by nausea, vomiting, shortness of breath, and a choking feeling. The main toxin responsible is saxitoxin **(Figure 1)**, a neurotoxic alkaloid that is the most lethal non-protein toxin known—a dose of just 0.2 mg is enough to kill an average-weight person.

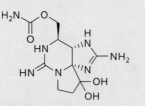

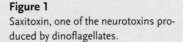

Figure 1
Saxitoxin, one of the neurotoxins produced by dinoflagellates.

Saxitoxin acts by binding to sodium channels of nerve cells, thus preventing the normal movement of sodium ions through the channel and blocking the transmission of nerve impulses.

Saxitoxin is especially deadly for mammals because it paralyzes the diaphragm and other muscles required for breathing. There is no cure, and death can occur within minutes if the person is not treated quickly; treatment involves artificial respiration to support breathing. Saxitoxin has been experimented with as a chemical weapon but also has more constructive uses. For example, it has been used to determine the components of sodium channels in cell membranes and in studies of various nerve disorders.

Other photosynthetic protists also produce blooms, and some of these also produce toxins.

---

metabolism) of the cell and for synthesis of ribosomal RNA. The macronucleus contains numerous copies of these genes, allowing it to synthesize large quantities of proteins and rRNA.

Ciliates abound in freshwater and marine habitats, where they feed voraciously on bacteria, algae, and each other. *Paramecium* and *Tetrahymena* are typical of the group (see Figures 23.4 and 23.10). Their rows of cilia drive them through their watery habitat, rotating the cell on its long axis while it moves forward or back and turns. The cilia also sweep water laden with prey and food particles into the gullet, where food vacuoles form. The ciliate digests food in the vacuoles and eliminates indigestible material through an anal pore. Contractile vacuoles with elaborate, raylike extensions remove excess water from the cytoplasm and expel it to the outside. When under attack or otherwise stressed, *Paramecium* discharges many dartlike protein threads from surface organelles called **trichocysts.**

Dinoflagellata: The Dinoflagellates. In spring and summer, the coastal waters of Canada sometimes turn reddish in colour **(Figure 23.11a).** These *red tides* are caused by a population explosion, or *bloom,* of certain **dinoflagellates** that make up a large proportion of marine phytoplankton. These protists typically have a shell formed from cellulose plates **(Figure 23.11b).** The beating of flagella, which fit into grooves in the plates, makes dinoflagellates spin like a top (*dinos* = spinning) as they swim.

Red tides are caused by conditions such as increased nutrient runoff into coastal waters (particularly from farms and industrial areas), warm ocean surface

a.

b.

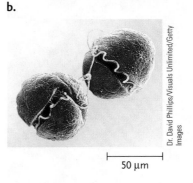

50 μm

Hong Kong Red Tide Information Network/ The Agriculture, Fisheries and Conservation Department

Dr. David Phillips/Visuals Unlimited/Getty Images

Figure 23.11
(a) Red tide caused by dinoflagellate bloom.
(b) *Karenia brevis*, a toxin-producing dinoflagellate.

temperatures, and calm water. Red tides occur in the waters of many other countries besides Canada and are more common in warmer waters. Some red tide dinoflagellates produce a toxin that interferes with nerve function in animals that ingest them (see *Molecule Behind Biology*).

More than 4000 dinoflagellate species are known, and most, like those that cause red tides, are single-celled organisms in marine phytoplankton. Their abundance in phytoplankton makes dinoflagellates a major primary producer of ocean ecosystems. You can sometimes see their abundance because some are **bioluminescent**, that is, they glow or release a

Figure 23.12
Bioluminescent dinoflagellates (*Lingulodinium polyedrum*) lighting a breaking wave at midnight.

Figure 23.13
Bleached elkhorn coral (*Acropora palmata*).

flash of light, particularly when disturbed. Dinoflagellate luminescence can make the sea glow in the wake of a boat at night and coat nocturnal surfers and swimmers with a ghostly light **(Figure 23.12).** Why do these organisms emit light? One explanation is that this burst of light would be likely to scare off predators. The production of light depends on the enzyme *luciferase* and its substrate *luciferin,* in forms similar to the system that produces light in fireflies.

Dinoflagellates live as heterotrophs or autotrophs; many can carry out both modes of nutrition. Some dinoflagellates live as symbionts in the tissues of other marine organisms such as jellyfish, sea anemones, corals, and molluscs and give these organisms their distinctive colours. Dinoflagellates in coral use the coral's carbon dioxide and nitrogenous waste while supplying 90% of the coral's carbon. The vast numbers of dinoflagellates living as photosynthetic symbionts in tropical coral reefs allow the reefs to reach massive sizes; without dinoflagellates, many coral species would die. When stressed, corals eject their endosymbionts, a phenomenon known as coral bleaching because the absence of the pigmented dinoflagellates allows the coral's calcareous skeleton to be visible **(Figure 23.13).** What causes the coral to become stressed? Increased water temperatures appear to be the main cause, although exposure to contaminants such as oil can also cause bleaching. If the stress causing the bleaching is transient, the coral usually regains its endosymbionts, but if the stress persists, the coral will die.

Apicomplexa. **Apicomplexans** are nonmotile parasites of animals. They take their name from the *apical complex,* a group of organelles at one end of a cell, which helps the cell attach to and invade host cells. Apicomplexans absorb nutrients through their plasma membranes (rather than by engulfing food particles) and lack food vacuoles. One genus, *Plasmodium,* is responsible for malaria, one of the most widespread and debilitating human diseases. About 500 million people are infected with malaria in tropical regions, including Africa, India, Southeast Asia, the Middle East, Oceania, and Central and South America. Malaria kills about 2 million people each year, twice

as many as are killed by AIDS worldwide. It is particularly deadly for children younger than six. In many countries where malaria is common, people are often infected repeatedly, with new infections occurring alongside preexisting infections.

Plasmodium is transmitted by 60 different species of mosquitoes, all members of the genus *Anopheles.* Infective cells develop inside the female mosquito, which transfers the cells to human or bird hosts **(Figure 23.14, p. 508).** The infecting parasites divide repeatedly by asexual reproduction in their hosts, initially in liver cells and then in red blood cells. Their growth causes red blood cells to rupture in regular cycles every 48 or *72 hours,* depending on the *Plasmodium* species. The ruptured red blood cells clog vessels and release the parasite's metabolic wastes, causing cycles of chills and fever.

The victim's immune system is ineffective because during most of the infective cycle, the parasite is inside body cells and thus "hidden" from antibodies. Furthermore, like *Giardia, Plasmodium* regularly changes its surface molecules, continually producing new forms that are not recognized by antibodies developed against a previous form. In this way, the parasite keeps one step ahead of the immune system, often making malarial infections essentially permanent. For a time, malaria was controlled in many countries by insecticides such as DDT. However, the mosquitoes developed resistance against the insecticides and have returned in even greater numbers than before the spraying began.

In addition to the asexual reproduction described above for *Plasmodium,* apicomplexans also reproduce sexually, forming gametes that fuse to produce cysts. As in *Giardia,* when a host organism ingests the cysts, they divide to produce infective cells. Many apicomplexans use more than one host species for different stages of their life cycle. For example, another organism in this group, *Toxoplasma,* has the sexual phase of its life cycle in cats and the asexual phases in humans, cattle, pigs, and other animals. Feces of infected cats contain cysts; humans ingesting or

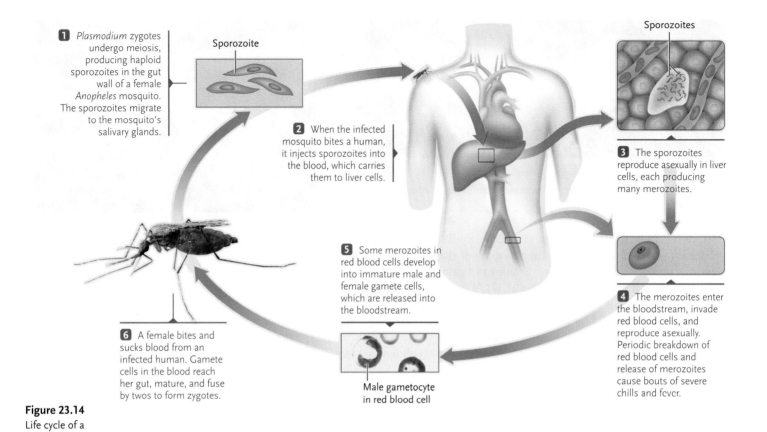

1 *Plasmodium* zygotes undergo meiosis, producing haploid sporozoites in the gut wall of a female *Anopheles* mosquito. The sporozoites migrate to the mosquito's salivary glands.

Sporozoite

2 When the infected mosquito bites a human, it injects sporozoites into the blood, which carries them to liver cells.

Sporozoites

3 The sporozoites reproduce asexually in liver cells, each producing many merozoites.

4 The merozoites enter the bloodstream, invade red blood cells, and reproduce asexually. Periodic breakdown of red blood cells and release of merozoites cause bouts of severe chills and fever.

5 Some merozoites in red blood cells develop into immature male and female gamete cells, which are released into the bloodstream.

Male gametocyte in red blood cell

6 A female bites and sucks blood from an infected human. Gamete cells in the blood reach her gut, mature, and fuse by twos to form zygotes.

Figure 23.14
Life cycle of a *Plasmodium* species that causes malaria.

inhaling the cysts develop toxoplasmosis, a disease that is usually mild in adults but can cause severe brain damage or even death to a fetus. Because of the danger of toxoplasmosis, pregnant women should avoid emptying litter boxes or otherwise cleaning up after a cat.

23.4d Heterokonts Have Two Dissimilar Flagella at Some Stage of Their Life Cycles

The Heterokonts (*hetero* = different; *kontos* = pole, referring to the flagellum) are named for their two different flagella: one smooth and a second covered with bristles, giving it a "hairy" appearance **(Figure 23.15)**. In most heterokonts, the flagella occur only on reproductive cells such as eggs and sperm. The heterokonts include the Oomycota (water moulds), Bacillariophyta (diatoms), Chrysophyta (golden algae), and Phaeophyta (brown algae). Recall that "algae" is a general term for photosynthetic protists, but the different groups of algae are not closely related to each other, so the term does not imply a phylogenetic grouping.

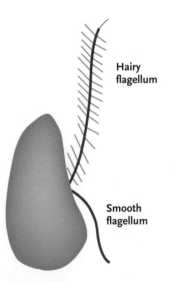

Hairy flagellum

Smooth flagellum

Figure 23.15
Heterokont protist, with smooth and "hairy" flagella.

Oomycota: Water Moulds and Downy Mildews. In Ireland, the summer of 1846 started off warm and sunny. This was a welcome change as the previous summer had been cool and damp, causing the potato crop to fail. But then the weather turned wet and cold again and within one week at the end of July, the entire potato crop was destroyed—the leaves rotting and the tubers turning to black, putrid mush **(Figure 23.16)**. Worse was to come: the unseasonably cool and damp growing seasons persisted until 1860, causing the potato crops to fail year after year. These crop failures were catastrophic because potatoes were virtually the only food source for most people. Altogether, about one-third of the Irish population died or emigrated (to Canada and the United States among other countries) due to the potato famines.

Ariena van Bruggen

Figure 23.16
Blight caused by *Phytophthora infestans* in a potato crop.

In 1861, the organism that caused the blight was identified as a water mould, *Phytophthora infestans*. Originally thought to be a fungus, *P. infestans* produces infective cells that are easily dispersed by wind and water. The blight caused by this organism has recently reemerged as a serious disease in potato-growing regions of Canada and the United States due to the migration of new strains from Mexico that are resistant to existing pesticides.

Water moulds are not fungi; they are oomycetes (**Figures 23.17a**), but they do share some features with fungi. Like fungi, oomycetes grow as microscopic, nonmotile filaments called **hyphae** (singular, hypha), forming a network called a **mycelium** (**Figure 23.17b**). Also like fungi, they are heterotrophs, which secrete enzymes that digest the complex molecules of surrounding organic matter or living tissue into simpler molecules that are small enough to be absorbed into their cells. Other features, however, set the Oomycota apart from the fungi; chief among them are differences in nucleotide sequence, which clearly indicate close evolutionary relationships to other heterokonts rather than to the fungi.

The water moulds live almost exclusively in freshwater lakes and streams or moist terrestrial habitats, where they are key decomposers. Dead animal or plant material immersed in water commonly becomes coated with cottony water moulds. Other water moulds parasitize living aquatic animals, such as the mould growing on the fish shown in Figure 23.17b. The downy mildews are parasites of land plants (**Figure 23.17c**). Oomycetes may reproduce asexually or sexually.

Bacillariophyta: Diatoms. When you look at the organisms shown in **Figure 23.18**, they may not look like living organisms at all but instead like artwork or jewels. These are bacillariophytes or **diatoms**, single-celled organisms with a glassy silica shell, which is intricately formed and beautiful in many species. The two halves of the shell fit together like the top and bottom of a Petri dish or box of chocolates (see Figure 23.18). Substances move in and out of the cell through elaborately patterned perforations in the shell. Diatom shells are common in fossil deposits. In fact, more diatoms are known as fossils than as living species—some 35 000 extinct species have been described compared with 7000 living species. For about 180 million years, diatom shells have been accumulating into thick layers of sediment at the bottom of lakes and seas.

In fact, you probably use diatoms—or their remnants—a couple of times a day when you brush your teeth. Most toothpaste contains a mild abrasive to assist in removing plaque, a bacterial biofilm that forms on your teeth. This abrasive is commonly made from grinding the fossilized shells of diatoms into a fine powder, called *diatomaceous earth*. In addition to toothpaste, diatomaceous earth is used in filters, as an insulating material, and as a

a. Water mould

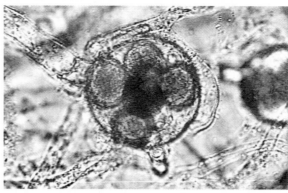

50 μm

b. Water mould infecting fish

c. Downy mildew

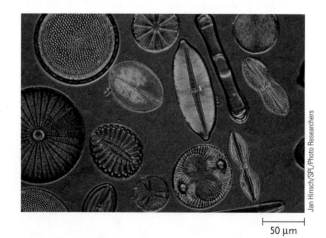

Figure 23.17
Oomycota. **(a)** The water mould *Saprolegnia parasitica*. **(b)** *S. parasitica* growing as cottony white fibres on the tail of an aquarium fish. **(c)** Downy mildew *Plasmopara viticola* growing on grapes. At times, it has nearly destroyed vineyards in Europe and North America.

pesticide. Diatomaceous earth kills crawling insects and insect larvae by abrading their exoskeleton, causing them to dehydrate and die. Insects also die when they eat the powder, but larger animals, including humans, are unaffected by it.

50 μm

Figure 23.18
Diatoms. Depending on the species, the shells are either radially or bilaterally symmetrical, as seen in this sample.

Diatoms are photoautotrophs that carry out photosynthesis by pathways similar to those of plants. They are among the primary photosynthetic organisms in marine plankton and are also abundant in freshwater habitats as both phytoplankton and bottom-dwelling species. Although most diatoms are free living, some are symbionts inside other marine protists. One diatom, *Pseudonitzschia,* produces a toxic amino acid that can accumulate in shellfish. The amino acid, which acts as a nerve poison, causes amnesic shellfish poisoning when ingested by humans; the poisoning can be fatal.

Asexual reproduction in diatoms occurs by mitosis followed by a form of cytoplasmic division in which each daughter cell receives either the top or bottom half of the parent shell. The daughter cell then secretes the missing half, which becomes the smaller, inside shell of the box. The daughter cell receiving the larger top half grows to the same size as the parent shell, but the cell receiving the smaller bottom half is limited to the size of this shell. As asexual divisions continue, the cells receiving bottom halves become progressively smaller. When a minimum size is reached, sexual reproduction is triggered. The cells produce flagellated gametes, which fuse to form a zygote. The zygote grows to normal size before secreting a completely new shell with full-sized top and bottom halves.

Although flagella are present only in gametes, many diatoms move by an unusual mechanism in which a secretion released through grooves in the shell propels them in a gliding motion.

Chrysophyta: Golden Algae. Nearly all chrysophytes are autotrophs and carry out photosynthesis using pathways similar to those of plants. Their colour is due to a brownish carotenoid pigment, fucoxanthin, which masks the green colour of the chlorophylls **(Figure 23.19a).** However, most chrysophytes can also live as heterotrophs if there is not sufficient light for photosynthesis. They switch to feeding on dissolved organic molecules or preying on bacteria and diatoms. Golden algae are important in freshwater habitats and in "nanoplankton," a community of marine phytoplankton composed of huge numbers of extremely small cells. During the spring and fall, "blooms" of golden algae are responsible for the fishy taste of many cities' drinking water.

Most golden algae are colonial forms (see Figures 23.3 and 23.20a) in which each cell of the colony bears a pair of flagella. The golden algae have glassy shells, but in the form of plates or scales rather than in the Petri dish form of the diatoms.

Phaeophyta: Brown Algae. If you were asked where in Canada you'd find forests of giant trees, you'd likely think of the temperate rain forests of the British Columbia coast. But there are also vast underwater forests in the waters off the B.C. coast, formed not by trees but by a type of brown algae known as kelp (*Macrocystis integrifolia*), which can grow to lengths of 30 m. A related species, giant kelp (*M. pyrifera*) **(Figure 23.19b),** can grow up to 60 m long. Kelps are the largest and most complex of all protists. Their tissues are differentiated into leaflike *blades,* stalklike *stipes,* and rootlike *holdfasts* that anchor them to the bottom. Hollow, gas-filled bladders give buoyancy to the stipes and blades and help keep them upright and oriented toward the sunlit upper layers of water **(Figure 23.19c).** The stipes of some kelps contain tube-like vessels, similar to the vascular elements of plants, which rapidly distribute the products of photosynthesis throughout the body of the alga. Kelps have an astonishingly fast growth rate—giant kelp can grow up to 30 cm per day!

Just as for terrestrial forests, kelp forests provide food and habitat for many marine organisms. Herds of sea otters (*Enhydra lutris*), for example, tend to live in and near kelp forests. When sea otters sleep at sea, they wrap kelp around themselves to keep from drifting away **(Figure 23.20).** Although the forest is an important habitat for the sea otters, the otters, in turn, are critical for the survival of these forests. Sea otters are one of the few predators of sea urchins, which graze on the kelp and can cause deforestation if their populations get very large. Predation by sea otters keeps sea urchin populations in control, preventing destruction of kelp forests.

Figure 23.19
Golden and brown algae. **(a)** A microscopic swimming colony of *Synura,* a golden alga. Each cell bears two flagellae, which are not visible in this light micrograph. **(b)** A forest of *Macrocystis pyrifera* (giant kelp). **(c)** Gas bladders connect kelp's stipes ("stems") to its blades ("leaves").

a. Golden alga
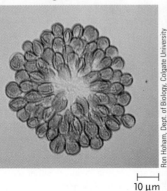
10 μm
Ron Hoham, Dept. of Biology, Colgate University

b. Giant kelp

© Phillip Colla

c. Gas bladders
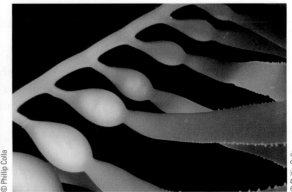
© Phillip Colla

Figure 23.20
A sea otter (*Enhydra lutris*) wrapped in kelp.

All phaeophytes (brown algae, *phaios* = brown) are photoautotrophs, but not all are as large as kelps. Nearly all of the 1500 known species inhabit temperate or cool coastal marine waters. Like golden algae, phaeophytes contain fucoxanthin, which gives them their characteristic colour. Their cell walls contain cellulose and a mucilaginous polysaccharide, alginic acid. This alginic acid, called **algin** when extracted, is an essentially tasteless substance used to thicken such diverse products as ice cream, salad dressing, jellybeans, cosmetics, and floor polish. Brown algae are also harvested as food crops and fertilizer.

Life cycles among the brown algae are typically complex and in many species consist of alternating haploid and diploid generations **(Figure 23.21)**. The large structures that we recognize as kelps and other brown seaweeds are diploid **sporophytes**, so called because they give rise to haploid spores by meiosis. The spores, which are flagellated swimming cells, germinate and divide by mitosis to form an independent, haploid **gametophyte** generation. The gametophytes give rise to haploid gametes, the egg and sperm cells. Most brown algal gametophytes are multicellular structures only a few centimetres in diameter. Cells in the gametophyte, produced by mitosis, differentiate to form nonmotile eggs or flagellated, swimming sperm cells. The sperm cells have the two different types of flagella characteristic of the heterokont protists. Fusion of egg and sperm produces a diploid zygote that grows by mitotic divisions into the sporophyte generation. This complex life cycle is very similar to that of land plants (see Chapter 25).

23.4e Cercozoa Are Amoebas with Filamentous Pseudopods

Amoeba (*amoibe* = change) is a descriptive term for a single-celled protist that moves by means of pseudopodia, as described earlier in this chapter (see Figure 23.6). Several major groups of protists contain

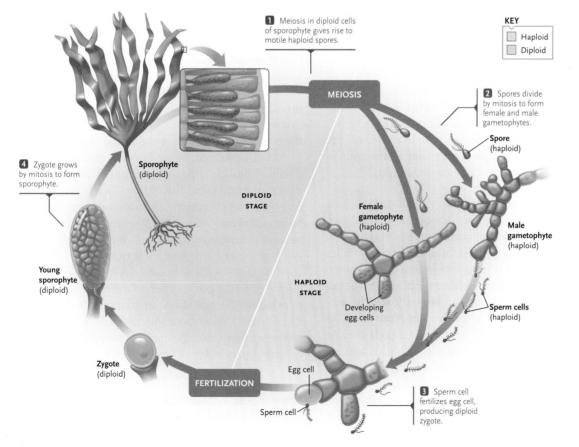

Figure 23.21
The life cycle of the brown alga *Laminaria*, which alternates between a diploid sporophyte stage and a haploid gametophyte stage.

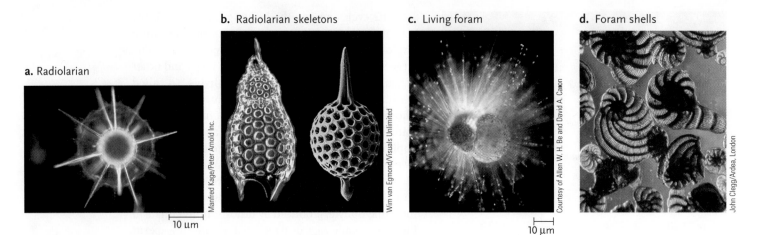

b. Radiolarian skeletons

c. Living foram

d. Foram shells

a. Radiolarian

10 μm

10 μm

Manfred Kage/Peter Arnold Inc.

Wim van Egmond/Visuals Unlimited

Courtesy of Allen W. H. Bé and David A. Caron

John Clegg/Ardea, London

Figure 23.22
(a) A living radiolarian. **(b)** The internal skeletons of two radiolarian species, possibly *Pterocorys* and *Stylosphaera*. Bundles of microtubules support the cytoplasmic extensions of the radiolarians. **(c)** A living foram, showing the cytoplasmic strands extending from its shelf. **(d)** Empty foram shells. **(e)** The body plan of a foram. Needlelike, glassy spines support the cytoplasmic extensions of the forams.

e. Foram body plan

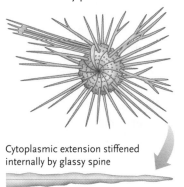

Cytoplasmic extension stiffened internally by glassy spine

amoebas, which are similar in form but are not all closely related. The cercozoan amoebas produce stiff, filamentous pseudopodia, and many produce hard outer shells, also called *tests*. We consider here two heterotrophic groups of cercozoan amoebae, the Radiolaria and the Foraminifera, and a third, photosynthesizing group, the Chlorarachniophyta.

Radiolaria. Radiolarians (*radiolus* = small sunbeam) are marine organisms characterized by a glassy internal skeleton and **axopods,** slender, raylike strands of cytoplasm supported internally by long bundles of microtubules **(Figure 23.22a, b).** This glassy skeleton is heavy—when radiolarians die, their skeletons sink to the ocean floor—so how do radiolarians keep afloat? The axopods provide buoyancy, as do the numerous vacuoles and lipid droplets in the cytoplasm. Axopods are also involved in feeding: prey stick to the axopods and are then engulfed, brought into the cell, and digested in food vacuoles.

Radiolarian skeletons that accumulate on the ocean floor become part of the sediment, which, over time, hardens into sedimentary rock. The presence of radiolarians in such rocks is very useful to the oil industry as indicators of oil-bearing strata.

Foraminifera: Forams. These organisms take their name from the perforations in their shells (*foramen* = little hole), through which extend long, slender strands of cytoplasm supported internally by a network of needlelike spines. Their shells consist of organic matter reinforced by calcium carbonate **(Figure 23.22c–e).** Most foram shells are chambered, spiral structures that, although microscopic, resemble those of molluscs.

Like radiolarians, forams live in marine environments. Some species are planktonic, but they are most abundant on sandy bottoms and attached to rocks along the coasts. Forams feed in a manner similar to that of radiolarians: they engulf prey that adhere to the strands and conduct them through the holes in the shell into the central cytoplasm, where they are digested in food vacuoles. Some forams have algal symbionts that carry out photosynthesis, allowing them to live as both heterotrophs and autotrophs.

Marine sediments are typically packed with the shells of dead forams. The sediments may be hundreds of feet thick: the White Cliffs of Dover in England are composed primarily of the shells of ancient forams. Most of the world's deposits of limestone and marble contain foram shells; the great pyramids of ancient Egypt are built from blocks cut from fossil foram deposits. Because distinct species lived during different geologic periods, they are widely used to establish the age of sedimentary rocks containing their shells. Similar to radiolarian species, oil prospectors use forams as indicators of hydrocarbon deposits because layers of forams often overlie oil deposits.

Chlorarachniophyta. Chlorarachniophytes are amoebas that contain chloroplasts and thus are photosynthetic. However, they combine this mode of nutrition with heterotrophy, engulfing food with the many filamentous pseudopodia that extend from the cell surface.

23.4f Amoebozoa Includes Slime Moulds and Most Amoebas

The Amoebozoa includes most of the amoebas (others are in the Cercozoa) as well as the cellular and plasmodial slime moulds. All members of this group use pseudopods for locomotion and feeding for all or part of their life cycles.

Amoebas. Amoebas of the Amoebozoa are single-celled organisms that are abundant in marine and freshwater environments and in the soil. All amoebas are microscopic, although some species can grow up to 5 mm in size and so are visible with the naked eye. Some amoebas are parasitic, such as the 45 species that infect the human digestive tract. One of these parasites, *Entamoeba histolytica,* causes amoebic dysentery. Cysts of this amoeba contaminate water supplies and soil in regions with inadequate sewage treatment. When ingested, a cyst breaks open to release an amoeba that feeds and divides rapidly in the digestive tract. Enzymes released by the amoebas destroy cells lining the intestine, producing the ulcerations, painful cramps, and debilitating diarrhea characteristic of the disease. Amoebic dysentery afflicts millions of people worldwide; in less developed countries, it is a leading cause of death among infants and small children.

However, most amoebas are heterotrophs that feed on bacteria, other protists, and bits of organic matter. Unlike the stiff, supported pseudopodia of cercozoans, pseudopods of amoebas extend and retract at any point on their body surface and are unsupported by any internal cellular organization—amoebas are thus "shape-shifters." How can an amoeba capture a fast-moving organism? As an amoeba moves, its cytoplasm doesn't just move but also changes state, from a more liquid state to a more solid state and back again, allowing the amoeba to send out pseudopodia in different directions very quickly. These fast-moving pseudopods can capture even fast-swimming prey such as ciliates **(Figure 23.23).**

Amoebas reproduce only asexually, via binary fission. In unfavourable environmental conditions, some amoebas can form a cyst, essentially by rolling up and secreting a protective membrane. They survive as cysts until favourable conditions return.

Slime Moulds. After a very wet spring in 1973, residents of Dallas, Texas, were alarmed to see large, yellow blobs that resembled scrambled eggs *crawling* on their lawns. People thought it was an alien invasion. Luckily, a local biologist was able to prevent mass panic by identifying the blobs as slime moulds, unusual heterotrophic protists. Slime moulds exist for part of their lives as individuals that move by amoeboid motion but then come together in a coordinated

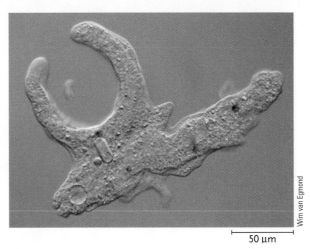

Figure 23.23
An amoeba capturing prey with pseudopods.

mass—essentially, a large amoeba—that ultimately differentiates into a stalked structure called a **fruiting body**, in which spores are formed.

There are two major evolutionary lineages of slime moulds: the **cellular slime moulds** and the plasmodial slime moulds, which differ in cellular organization. Both types of slime moulds have been of great interest to scientists because of their ability to differentiate into fruiting bodies with stalks and spore-bearing structures. This differentiation is much simpler than the complex developmental pathways of other eukaryotes, providing a unique opportunity to study cell differentiation at its most fundamental level. Slime moulds also respond to stimuli in their environment, moving away from bright light and toward food. We have learned a great deal about eukaryotic signalling pathways, cell differentiation, and cell movement from studies of slime moulds.

Slime moulds live on moist, rotting plant material such as decaying leaves and bark. The cells engulf particles of dead organic matter, along with bacteria, yeasts, and other microorganisms, and digest them internally. They can be a range of colours: brown, yellow, green, red, and even violet or blue.

These organisms exist primarily as individual cells, either separately or as a coordinated mass. Among the 70 or so species of cellular slime moulds, *Dictyostelium discoideum* is best known. Its life cycle begins when a haploid spore lands in a suitably moist environment containing decaying organic matter **(Figure 23.24, p. 514).** The spore germinates into an amoeboid cell that grows and divides mitotically into separate haploid cells as long as the food source lasts. When the food supply dwindles, some of the cells release a chemical signal in pulses; in response, the amoebas move together and form a sausage-shaped mass that crawls in coordinated fashion like a slug. Some "slugs," although not much more than a millimetre in length, contain more than 100 000 individual

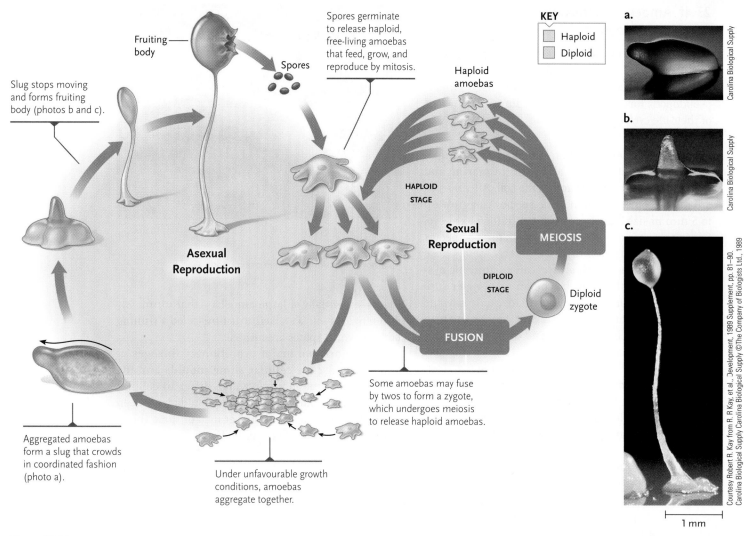

Figure 23.24

Life cycle of the cellular slime mould *Dictyostelium discoideum*. The light micrographs show **(a)** a migrating slug, **(b)** an early stage in fruiting body formation, and **(c)** a mature fruiting body.

cells. At some point, the "slug" stops moving and differentiates into a stalked fruiting body, with some cells becoming spores, whereas others form the stalk. The cells that form the stalk die in the process, essentially sacrificing themselves so that a stalk can form. Why is formation of a stalk so crucial? Raising the spore-forming cells higher up in the air improves the likelihood that spores will be carried away by air currents and dispersed farther away from the parent. Because the cells forming the "slug" and fruiting body are all products of mitosis, this is asexual reproduction.

Cellular slime moulds also reproduce sexually: two haploid cells fuse to form a diploid zygote (also shown in Figure 26.16) that enters a dormant stage. Eventually, the zygote undergoes meiosis, producing four haploid cells that may multiply inside the spore by mitosis. When conditions are favourable, the spore wall breaks down, releasing the cells. These grow and divide into separate amoeboid cells.

Plasmodial Slime Moulds. **Plasmodial slime moulds** exist primarily as a multinucleate **plasmodium**, in which individual nuclei are suspended in a common cytoplasm surrounded by a single plasma membrane. (This is not to be confused with *Plasmodium*, the genus of apicomplexans that causes malaria.) There are about 500 known species of plasmodial slime moulds. The plasmodium **(Figure 23.25a)** flows and feeds by phagocytosis like a single huge amoeba—a single cell that contains thousands to millions or even billions of diploid nuclei surrounded by a single plasma membrane. The plasmodium, which may range in size from a few centimetres to more than a metre in diameter, moves typically in thick, branching strands connected by thin sheets. The movements occur by cytoplasmic streaming, driven by actin microfilaments and myosin. These plasmodia are what the people in Dallas thought were aliens invading; after a period of heavy rain, plasmodia will sometimes crawl

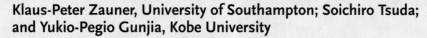

Klaus-Peter Zauner, University of Southampton; Soichiro Tsuda; and Yukio-Pegio Gunjia, Kobe University

Robots controlled by slime moulds? Far from being a bizarre science fiction story, slime moulds may be the future of robotics, as demonstrated in research carried out by Klaus-Peter Zauner (University of Southampton, UK) and his collaborators at Kobe University in Japan, Soichiro Tsuda and Yukio-Pegio Gunjia. Zauner and colleagues grew *Physarum polycephalum* in a six-pointed star shape on an electrical circuit and connected the circuit to a six-legged robot with a computer interface. Each point of the *Physarum* plasmodium star corresponded to one leg of the robot **(Figure 1).** When

Figure 1
A slime mould (image on screen) is able to direct the movement of a robot (in the foreground).

light was shone on certain parts of the robot, sensors mounted on the robot detected the light and illuminated the corresponding part of the plasmodium, which responded by moving away from the light, sending the robot scuttling into dark corners. One goal of Zauner's research in molecular computing is to incorporate this biological control right into the robot. Harnessing the capacity of living organisms to sense and respond to complex environments would give robots greater autonomy than is possible with control by computer programs.

out of the woods to appear on lawns or the mulch of flowerbeds.

At some point, often in response to unfavourable environmental conditions, fruiting bodies form on the plasmodium. At the tips of the fruiting bodies, nuclei become enclosed in separate cells. These cells undergo meiosis, forming haploid, resistant spores that are released from the fruiting bodies and carried by water or wind **(Figure 23.25b).** If they reach a favourable environment, the spores germinate to form gametes that fuse to form a diploid zygote. The zygote nucleus then divides repeatedly without an accompanying division of the cytoplasm, forming many diploid nuclei suspended in the common cytoplasm of a new plasmodium.

Plasmodial slime moulds are particularly useful in research because they become large enough to provide ample material for biochemical and molecular analyses. Actin and myosin extracted from *Physarum polycephalum,* for example, have been much used

in studies of actin-based motility. A further advantage of plasmodial slime moulds is that the many nuclei of a plasmodium usually replicate and pass through mitosis in synchrony, making them useful in research that tracks the changes that take place in the cell cycle. More recently, slime moulds have been used in robotics research, as outlined in *People Behind Biology.*

23.4g Archaeplastida Include the Red and Green Algae and Land Plants

The Archaeplastida group consists of the red and green algae, which are protists, and the land plants (the *Viridaeplantae,* or "true plants"), which comprise the kingdom Plantae. These three groups of photoautotrophs share a common evolutionary origin. Here we describe the two types of algae; we discuss land plants and how they evolved from green algae in Chapter 25.

a.

b.

Figure 23.25
(a) Plasmodium of slime mould. **(b)** Fruiting bodies of slime mould.

a. Filamentous red alga

b. Sheetlike red alga

© Wim van Egmond/Visuals Unlimited

Douglas Faulkner/Sally Faulkner Collection

Figure 23.26
Red algae. **(a)** *Antithamnion plumula,* showing the filamentous and branched body form most common among red algae. **(b)** A sheetlike red alga growing on a tropical reef.

Rhodophyta: The Red Algae. Nearly all of the 4000 known species of red algae, which are also known as the Rhodophyta (*rhodon* = rose), are small marine seaweeds **(Figure 23.26).** Fewer than 200 species are found in freshwater lakes and streams or in soils. If you have had sushi, then you have eaten red algae: *Porphyra* is harvested for use as the *nori* wrapped around fish and rice.

Rhodophyte cell walls contain cellulose and mucilaginous pectins that give red algae a slippery texture. These pectins are widely used in industry and science. Extracted **agar** is used as a culture medium in the laboratory and as a setting agent for jellies and desserts. **Carrageenan** is used to thicken and stabilize paints, dairy products such as ice cream, and many other emulsions.

Some species secrete calcium carbonate into their cell walls; these coralline algae are important in building coral reefs—in some places, they play a bigger role in reef building than do corals.

Red algae are typically multicellular organisms, with diverse morphologies, although many have plantlike bodies composed of stalks bearing leaflike blades. Although most are free-living autotrophs, some are parasites that attach to other algae or plants.

Although most red algae are reddish in colour, some are greenish purple or black. The colour differences are produced by accessory pigments, *phycobilins,* which mask the green colour of their chlorophylls. Phycobilins absorb the shorter wavelengths of light (green and blue-green light) that penetrate to the ocean depths, allowing red algae to grow at deeper levels than any other algae. Some red algae live at depths up to 260 m if the water is clear enough to transmit light to these levels.

Red algae have complex reproductive cycles involving alternation between diploid sporophytes and haploid gametophytes. No flagellated cells occur in the red algae; instead, gametes are released into the water to be brought together by random collisions in currents.

Chlorophyta: The Green Algae. The green algae or Chlorophyta (*chloros* = green) carry out photosynthesis using the same pigments as plants, whereas other photosynthetic protists contain pigment combinations that are very different from those of land plants. This shared pigment composition is one line of evidence that one lineage of green algae was the ancestor of land plants. With at least 16 000 species, green algae show more diversity than any other algal group. They also have very diverse morphologies, including single-celled, colonial, and multicellular species **(Figure 23.27;** see also Figure 23.1d). Multicellular forms have a range of morphologies, including filamentous, tubular, and leaflike forms. Most green algae are microscopic, but some range upward to the size of small seaweeds.

Most green algae live in freshwater aquatic habitats, but some are marine, whereas others live on rocks, soil surfaces, or tree bark, or even in snow. Other organisms rely on green algae to photosynthesize for them by forming symbiotic relationships. For example, lichens are symbioses between green algae and fungi (see Chapter 24), and many animals, such as the sea slugs described in Chapter 3, contain green algal chloroplasts, or entire green algae, as symbionts in their cells.

Life cycles among the green algae are as diverse as their body forms. Many can reproduce either sexually or asexually, and some alternate between haploid and diploid generations. Gametes in different species may be undifferentiated flagellated cells or differentiated as a flagellated sperm cell and a nonmotile egg cell. Most common is a life cycle with a multicellular haploid phase and a single-celled diploid phase **(Figure 23.28).**

Among all the algae, the green algae are the most closely related to land plants, based on molecular, biochemical, and morphological data. Evidence of this close relationship includes not only the shared photosynthetic pigments, but also the use of starch as storage reserve, and the same cell wall composition.

a. Single-celled green alga

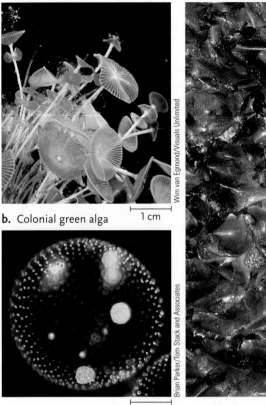

Wim van Egmond/Visuals Unlimited

b. Colonial green alga

1 cm

Brian Parker/Tom Stack and Associates

200 μm

c. Multicellular green alga

Manfrage Kage/Peter Arnold, Inc.

Figure 23.27

Green algae. **(a)** A single-celled green alga, *Acetabularia*, which grows in marine environments. Each individual in the cluster is a large single cell with a rootlike base, stalk, and cap. **(b)** A colonial green alga, *Volvox*. Each green dot in the spherical wall of the colony is a potentially independent, flagellated cell. Daughter colonies can be seen within the parent colony. **(c)** A multicellular green alga, *Ulva*, common to shallow seas around the world.

Which green alga might have been the ancestor of modern land plants? The evidence points to a group known as the **charophytes** as being most similar to the algal ancestors of land plants. This does not mean that modern-day charophytes are the ancestors of land plants but rather that the two groups share a common ancestor. Charophytes, including *Chara* **(Figure 23.29, p. 518)**, *Spirogyra, Nitella,* and *Coleochaete,* live in freshwater ponds and lakes. Their ribosomal RNA and chloroplast DNA sequences are more closely related to plant sequences than those of any other green alga. We discuss the evolution of land plants from an algal ancestor more thoroughly in Chapter 25.

23.4h Opisthokonts Include the Choanoflagellates, Which May Be the Ancestors of Animals

Opisthokonts (*opistho* = posterior; *kontos* = flagellum) are named for the single, posterior flagellum found at some stage in the life cycle of these organisms. This

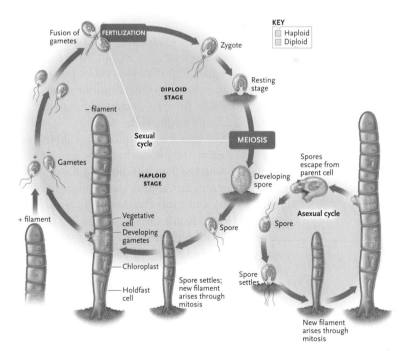

Figure 23.28

The life cycle of the green alga *Ulothrix*, in which the haploid stage is multicellular and the diploid stage is a single cell, the zygote. "+" and "−" are morphologically identical mating types ("sexes") of the alga.

Figure 23.30
A choanoflagellate.

Reproductive structures

Dr. John Clayton, National Institute of Water and Atmospheric Research, New Zealand

Figure 23.29
The charophyte *Chara*, representative of a group of green algae that may have given rise to the plant kingdom.

diverse group includes the choanoflagellates, protists thought to be the ancestors of fungi and animals.

Choanoflagellata (*choanos* = collar) are named for the collar surrounding the flagellum that the protist uses to feed and, in some species, to swim **(Figure 23.30)**. The collar resembles an upside-down lampshade and is made up of small, fingerlike projections (microvilli) of the plasma membrane. As the flagellum moves water through the collar, these projections engulf bacteria and particles of organic matter in the water.

About 150 species of choanoflagellates live in either marine or freshwater habitats. Some species are mobile, with the flagellum pushing the cells along (in the same way that animal sperm are propelled by their flagella), but most choanoflagellates are *sessile* (attached by a stalk to a surface). A number of species are colonial with a cluster of cells on a single stalk; these colonial species are of great interest to biologists studying the evolution of multicellularity in animals.

Why are choanoflagellates thought to be the ancestor of animals? Both molecular and morphological data indicate that a choanoflagellate type of protist gave rise to animals: for example, there are many morphological similarities between choanoflagellates and the collar cells (choanocytes) of sponges as well as the cells that act as excretory organisms in flatworms and rotifers (see Chapter 26). Comparisons of nucleic acid sequences done to date also support the hypothesis

that choanoflagellates are the closest living relatives to animals. Molecular data also indicate that a choanoflagellate-like organism was also likely the ancestor of the fungi (see Ch. 24).

STUDY BREAK

1. For each of the protist groups listed below, indicate the cell structure that characterizes the group: apicomplexans, dinoflagellates, discicristates, radiolarians.
2. Which groups of protists contain amoeboid forms?
3. What is the major difference between cellular slime moulds and plasmodial slime moulds?

23.5 Some Protist Groups Arose from Primary Endosymbiosis and Others from Secondary Endosymbiosis

We have encountered chloroplasts in a number of eukaryotic organisms in this chapter: red and green algae, euglenoids, dinoflagellates, heterokonts, chlorarachniophytes, and land plants. How did these chloroplasts evolve? Unlike the endosymbiotic event that gave rise to mitochondria, endosymbiosis involving photoautotrophs happened more than once, resulting in the formation of a wide range of photosynthetic eukaryotes.

The chloroplasts of the Archaeplastida—the red algae, green algae, and land plants—result from evolutionary divergence of the photosynthetic eukaryotes formed via a single primary endosymbiotic event (as shown in the top part of **Figure 23.31**) that happened about 1 billion years ago. In **primary endosymbiosis**, a eukaryotic cell engulfed a photosynthetic cyanobacterium but did not digest it. Organisms that originated from this event have chloroplasts with two membranes, one from the plasma membrane of the engulfing eukaryote and the other from the plasma membrane of the cyanobacterium.

This primary endosymbiotic event, which produced the first eukaryotic photoautorophs, was followed by at least three **secondary endosymbiosis** events, each time involving different heterotrophic

Figure 23.31

The origin and distribution of plastids among the eukaryotes by primary and secondary endosymbiosis.

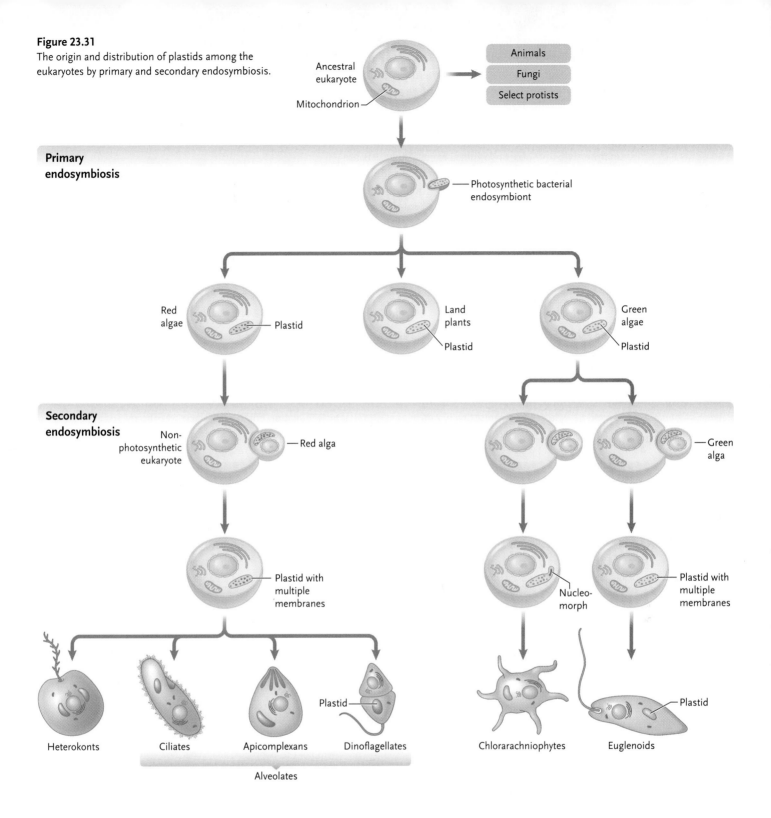

eukaryotes engulfing a photosynthetic eukaryote, producing new evolutionary lineages (see Figure 23.31). In one of these events, red algal ancestors were engulfed. Over evolutionary time, these became the chloroplasts of the heterokonts and the dinoflagellates. From the same photosynthetic ancestor, loss of chloroplast functions occurred in the lineage of the Apicomplexa, which have a remnant plastid.

In an independent endosymbiotic event, a nonphotosynthetic eukaryote engulfed a green algal ancestor. Subsequent evolution in this case produced the euglenoids. In yet another event, a similar endosymbiosis involving a green alga led to the chlorarachniophytes. In these protists, the chloroplast is still contained within the remnants of the original symbiont cell.

Organisms that formed via secondary endosymbiosis have chloroplasts surrounded by additional membranes acquired from the new host. For example, chlorarachniophytes have **plastids** with four membranes (see Figure 23.31). The new membranes correspond to the plasma membrane of the engulfed phototroph and the food vacuole membrane of the host. In chlorarachniophytes, a remant or vestigial nucleus (a nucleomorph) of the engulfed cell is present between the inner two and outer two membranes. Biologists are sequencing the genomes of the chlorarachniophyte's nucleus, chloroplast, and vestigial nucleus to learn more about the early endosymbiosis event that generated these organisms.

In sum, the protists are a highly diverse and ecologically important group of organisms. Their complex evolutionary relationships, which have long been a subject of contention, are now being revised as new information is discovered, including more complete genome sequences. A deeper understanding of protists is also contributing to a better understanding of their recent descendants, the fungi, plants, and animals. We turn to these descendants in the next four chapters, beginning with the fungi.

STUDY BREAK

In primary endosymbiosis, a nonphotosynthetic eukaryotic cell engulfed a photosynthetic cyanobacterium. How many membranes surround the chloroplast that evolved?

UNANSWERED QUESTIONS

What was the first eukaryote?

Since prokaryotes precede eukaryotes in the fossil record, we assume that eukaryotes arose after prokaryotes. The first eukaryote would have been some sort of protist—a single-celled organism with a nucleus and some rudimentary organelles, perhaps even a half-tamed mitochondrion. One approach to identifying which of the surviving protists is the most ancient has been to infer evolutionary trees from gene sequence data. To determine the earliest branching eukaryote, these trees need to include the prokaryotes. But herein lies the problem—prokaryotes are very distant, evolutionarily speaking, from even the simplest eukaryotes, and the mathematical models used to construct evolutionary trees are not yet up to the job. Initially, these models suggested that some protist parasites, like the excavates *Giardia* and *Trichomonas*, might be the most ancient eukaryotes, and this idea fit nicely with the fact that these protists lacked mitochondria. Indeed, for a time it was thought that the excavates might actually have diverged from the eukaryotic branch of life before the establishment of mitochondria. Nowadays, we know that *Giardia* and *Trichomonas* did initially have mitochondria. The latest research shows that they even have a tiny relic of the mitochondrion, although exactly what it does in these oxygen-shunning parasites remains to be figured out. Thus, trees depicting *Giardia* and *Trichomonas* at the base of the great expansion of eukaryotic life must be viewed with some caution—these protists might be the surviving representatives of the earliest cells with a nucleus, but they might not be. We simply need better methods for identifying what the first eukaryotes were like.

How many times did plastids arise by endosymbioses?

For many years, researchers thought that the green algae, plants, and red algae were the only organisms to have primary endosymbiosis–derived plastids. However, a second, independent primary endosymbiosis was recently discovered in which a shelled amoeba captured and partially domesticated a cyanobacterium. This organism, known as *Paulinella*, is a vital window into the process by which autotrophic eukaryotes first arose some 600 million years ago. *Paulinella* has tamed the cyanobacterium sufficiently to have it divide and segregate in coordination with host cell division, but the endosymbiont is still very much a cyanobacterium and has undergone little of the modification and streamlining we see in the red or green algal plastids.

After a primary endosymbiosis was established, the second chapter in plastid acquisition could take place. Secondary endosymbiosis involves a eukaryotic host engulfing and retaining a eukaryotic alga. Essentially, secondary endosymbiosis can convert a heterotrophic organism into an autotroph by hijacking a photosynthetic cell and putting it to work as a solar-powered food factory. Secondary endosymbiosis results in plastids with three or four membranes, and we know that it occurred at least three times—once for the euglenoids, once for the chlorarachniophytes, and once for the chromalveolates (a proposed grouping of heterokonts and alveolates). We can even tell what kind of endosymbiont was involved by the biochemistry and genetic makeup of the plastid: a green alga for euglenoids and chlorarachniophytes and a red alga for chromalveolates. The number of secondary endosymbioses is hotly debated, largely because not all protistologists support the existence of chromalveolates. Some contend that there were multiple, independent enslavements of different red algae to produce the dinoflagellates, heterokonts, and apicomplexans. Understanding these events is crucial to confirming or refuting the proposed chromalveolate "supergroup."

A nice example of secondary endosymbiosis in action was recently discovered by Japanese scientists who found a flagellate, *Hatena*, with a green algal endosymbiont. *Hatena* hasn't yet assumed control of endosymbiont division and has to get new symbionts each time it divides, so it appears to be at a very early stage in establishing a relationship. We also want to know how secondary endosymbioses proceed because they have been a major driver in eukaryotic evolution. The heterokonts, for instance, are the most important ocean phytoplankton and are key to ocean productivity and global carbon cycling. Knowing exactly how they got to be autotrophs in the first place is fundamental to understanding the world we live in.

Dr. Geoff McFadden is a professor of botany at the University of Melbourne. He studies the early evolution of eukaryotes, especially the origin and evolution of plastids and mitochondria. You can learn more about his research by visiting http://homepage.mac.com/fad1/McFaddenLab.html.

Review

Go to CENGAGENOW™ at http://hed.nelson.com/ to access quizzing, animations, exercises, articles, and personalized homework help.

23.1 Evolution of Protists Involved Endosymbiosis

- As eukaryotes, protists contain organelles including mitochondria and, sometimes, chloroplasts. Mitochondria evolved once via primary endosymbiosis, the engulfing of a free-living prokaryote that became an organelle over evolutionary time. Some photosynthetic protists were formed via primary endosymbiosis involving a photosynthetic prokaryote; others arose via more complex endosymbiotic events (see Section 23.5).

23.2 What Is a Protist? Characteristics of Protists

- Protists are eukaryotes that differ from fungi in having motile stages in their life cycles and cellulose cell walls. Unlike plants, they lack roots, stems, and leaves and do not retain embryos in parental tissue. Unlike animals, protists are often unicellular; they lack collagen, nerve cells, and an internal digestive tract.

23.3 Protists' Diversity Is Reflected in Their Metabolism, Reproduction, Structure, and Habitat

- Protists are aerobic organisms that live as autotrophs or as heterotrophs or by a combination of both nutritional modes. Some are symbionts living in or among the cells of other organisms.
- Protists live in aquatic or moist terrestrial habitats or as parasites within animals. They may be single-celled, colonial, or multicellular organisms, and they range in size from microscopic to some of Earth's largest organisms.
- Some protists are the most complex single cells known because of the wide variety of cytoplasmic structures they have; most are able to move by means of flagella, cilia, or pseudopodia.
- Reproduction may be asexual by mitotic divisions or sexual, involving meiosis and the union of gametes in fertilization.

23.4 The Protist Groups

- Excavates, exemplified by the Diplomonadida and Parabasala, are flagellated, single cells that lack "typical" mitochondria but often have organelles derived from mitochondria.
- Discicristates are almost all single-celled, autotrophic, and/or heterotrophic protists that swim using flagella.
- Alveolates include ciliates, which swim using cilia and have complex cytoplasmic structures, including both micronuclei and macronuclei; apicomplexans, nonmotile parasites of animals; and dinoflagellates, which have two flagella that propel them in a "whirling" motion and are primarily marine organisms. Many alveolates are photosynthetic.
- Heterokonts include diatoms, photosynthetic single-celled organisms covered by a glassy silica shell; golden algae, photosynthetic, mostly colonial forms; brown algae, primarily multicellular marine forms that include large seaweeds; and the funguslike Oomycota, which often grow as masses of microscopic filaments and live as saprophytes or parasites, secreting enzymes that digest organic matter in their surroundings. Most heterokonts have flagella only on reproductive cells.
- Cercozoa are amoebas with filamentous pseudopods supported by internal cellular structures. Many produce hard outer shells. Radiolarians are primarily marine organisms that secrete a glassy internal skeleton. Foraminifera are marine, single-celled organisms that form chambered, spiral shells containing calcium. Both groups engulf prey that adhere to thin extensions of their cells. Chlorarachniophytes engulf food using their pseudopodia.
- Amoebozoa includes most amoebas and two types of slime moulds, cellular (which move as individual cells) and plasmodial (which move as large masses of nuclei sharing a common cytoplasm). Amoebas in this group are heterotrophs abundant in marine and freshwater environments and in the soil. They move by extending pseudopodia.
- Archaeplastida include the red and green algae, as well as the land plants that comprise the kingdom Plantae. Red algae are typically multicellular, primarily photosynthetic organisms of marine environments with complex life cycles. The green algae are single-celled, colonial, and multicellular species that live primarily in freshwater habitats and carry out photosynthesis by mechanisms similar to those of plants.
- Opisthokonts are a broad group of eukaryotes that includes the choanoflagellates, which have a single flagellum surrounded by a collar of fingerlike membrane projections. A choanoflagellate type of protist was likely the ancestor of animals.
- Several groups of protists, as well as land plants, contain chloroplasts, which arose via endosymbiosis events. In a primary endosymbiosis event, a eukaryotic cell engulfed a cyanobacterium, which became an organelle, the chloroplast. Evolutionary divergence from this ancestral phototrophic organism produced the red algae, green algae, and land plants. Other photosynthetic protists were produced by secondary endosymbiosis, in which a nonphotosynthetic eukaryote engulfed a photosynthetic eukaryote.

Questions

Self-Test Questions

1. Freely beating flagella buried in a fold of cytoplasm moving through viscous fluids of humans and commonly found as an infective agent in university health centres describes a member of
   a. Ciliophora.
   b. Discicristates.
   c. Diplomonadida.
   d. Parabasala.
   e. Alveolates.

2. The protist group Diplomonadida is characterized by
   a. a mouthlike gullet and a hairlike surface. *Paramecium* is an example.
   b. flagella and a lack of mitochondria. *Giardia* is an example.
   c. nonmotility, parasitism, and sporelike infective stages. *Toxoplasma* is an example.
   d. switching between autotrophic and heterotrophic life styles. *Euglena* is an example.
   e. large protein deposits. Movement is by two flagella, which are part of an undulating membrane. *Trypanosoma* is an example.

3. The greatest contributors to protist fossil deposits are
   a. Oomycota.
   b. Chrysophyta.
   c. Bacillariophyta.
   d. Sporophyta.
   e. Alveolates.

4. The group with the distinguishing characteristic of gas-filled bladders and a cell wall composed of alginic acid is
   a. Chrysophyta.
   b. Phaeophyta.
   c. Oomycota.
   d. Bacillariophyta.
   e. none of the above.

5. *Plasmodium* is transmitted to humans by the bite of a mosquito (*Anopheles*) and engages in a life cycle with infective spores, gametes, and cysts. This infective protist belongs to the group
   a. Apicomplexa.
   b. Heterokonts.
   c. Dinoflagellata.
   d. Oomycota.
   e. Ciliophora.

6. The latest stage for evolving the double membrane seen in modern-day algal chloroplasts is thought to be the combining of
   a. two ancestral nonphotosynthetic prokaryotes.
   b. two ancestral photosynthetic prokaryotes.
   c. a nonphotosynthetic eukaryote with a photosynthetic eukaryote.
   d. a photosynthetic prokaryote with a nonphotosynthetic eukaryote.
   e. mitochondria with an already established plastid.

Questions for Discussion

1. We have seen that, as a group, protists use three kinds of motility: flagella, cilia, and amoeboid movement. Cells in your body use these same three forms of motility. Name an example of cells that use each form.

2. Photosynthetic protists (sometimes referred to as "algae") are often thought of as single-celled plants. Why is it not correct to consider them as plants? What features differentiate these protists from plants? Would it be correct to consider the protists known as "protozoa" as single-celled animals? Explain why or why not.

3. Why is it harder to treat human diseases caused by protists, such as *Giardia*, than diseases caused by bacteria?

4. Many protists are able to produce cysts or other resting stages in their life cycle. What is the advantage of producing these resting structures?

The mushroom-forming fungus *Inocybe fastigiata*, a forest-dwelling species that commonly lives in close association with conifers and hardwood trees.

Fritz Polking/Peter Arnold, Inc.

24 Fungi

WHY IT MATTERS

If you were asked what the first crop on Earth was and which organisms grew it, you would probably think of corn, wheat, or some other crop plant grown by humans. But you'd be wrong—the first domesticated crop was a fungus, and the first farmers were a certain group of ants over 50 million years ago, whereas humans did not start farming until about 10 000 years ago. Researchers have used molecular data combined with fossil evidence to determine when ants first domesticated their fungal crop. Today, these leaf-cutter ants (Tribe Attini) of Central and South America **(Figure 24.1a, p. 524)** still grow certain fungi in gardens. Just as humans do, the ants plant their crop of fungus, fertilize it, weed it, and then feed on it. The ants harvest leaves, flowers, and other plant parts and carry these back to their nests, where the fungal gardens are grown **(Figure 24.1b, p. 524)**.

The ants plant small pieces of the plant material in the garden, placing bits of the fungus on each piece. They fertilize the garden with their excrement and graze on the fungal filaments. In fact, although the ants collect a wide range of plant matter, they never eat any of it directly—their sole food source is the fungus. When a

Figure 24.1

(a) Leaf-cutter ants.
(b) Fungal garden of
leaf-cutter ants.

a.

Tim Flach/Stone/Getty Images

b.

Alex Wild

queen ant leaves her birth nest to start a new nest, she carries a bit of fungus in her mouth and uses it to start a garden in the new nest. The ants' habitat contains ample supplies of other foods, so why have these ants developed this complex and rather bizarre lifestyle? What benefit do they gain by devoting their lives to looking after a fungus? The answer lies in the ability of the fungus to unlock the nutrients tied up in plant tissue. Cellulose is the most abundant organic molecule on earth, but most organisms cannot get at the carbon it contains as they lack the enzymes needed to break apart the bonds in this molecule. Fungi are among the few organisms that can digest cellulose, so by forming a partnership with fungi, these ants gain access to a continuous source of carbon. In return, the fungus gains a secure habitat in which it doesn't have to compete with other organisms for a food source. Recent research has revealed that this ancient **symbiosis** is more complex than previously known (see *People Behind Biology*).

Although we often associate fungi with decay and decomposition, many fungi, such as those cultivated by leaf-cutter ants, instead live by forming symbiotic associations with other organisms. The vast majority of plants obtain soil minerals via a symbiotic relationship with soil fungi. Humans also have harnessed the metabolic activities of certain fungi to obtain substances ranging from flavourful cheeses and wine to bread and therapeutic drugs such as penicillin and the immunosuppressant cyclosporine. And, as you know from previous chapters, species such as the yeast *Saccharomyces cerevisiae* and the mould *Neurospora crassa* have long been pivotal model organisms in studies of DNA structure and function and in the development of genetic engineering methods. On the other hand, fungi collectively are the single greatest cause of plant diseases, and many species cause disease in humans and other animals. Some even produce carcinogenic toxins.

Evidence suggests that fungi were present on land at least 500 million years ago and possibly much earlier. Their presence on land was likely crucial for the successful colonization of land by plants, which

relied on symbiotic associations with the fungi to obtain nutrients from the nutrient-poor soils of early land environments. In the course of the intervening millennia, evolution equipped fungi with a remarkable ability to break down a wide range of compounds, ranging from living and dead organisms and animal wastes to groceries, clothing, paper, and wood—even photographic film. Along with heterotrophic bacteria, they have become Earth's premier decomposers **(Figure 24.2)**. Despite their profound impact on ecosystems and other life forms, most of us have only a passing acquaintance with the fungi—perhaps limited to the mushrooms on our pizza or the invisible but annoying types that cause skin infections, such as athlete's foot. This chapter provides you with an overview of fungal biology. We begin with the features that set fungi apart from all other organisms and discuss the diversity of fungi existing today before revisiting associations between fungi and other organisms.

Robert C. Simpson/Nature Stock

Figure 24.2

Example of a wood decay fungus: sulphur shelf fungus (*Polyporus*).

Cameron Currie, University of Wisconsin-Madison

Discovery has been defined as "seeing what everyone else has seen and thinking what no one else has thought." Even though ant-fungal mutualism has been studied since 1874, in 1999 a graduate student at the University of Toronto, Cameron Currie, discovered a whole new dimension to this mutualism. For years, researchers studying this symbiosis had wondered how the ants kept their gardens free of competing fungi. The conditions created by the ants are ideal for many other fungi besides the garden fungus, and, as you know, fungal spores are everywhere—yet the ant gardens are pure monocultures of a single fungus. What prevents other fungi from invading the gardens? Biologists had thought that the ants kept other fungi out simply by weeding the gardens, removing all traces of invading fungi, and so keeping fungal competitors at bay. But Currie discovered that there is a third symbiont at work, and this organism keeps out other fungi. Currie noticed that ants had a whitish substance on their **abdomens**; other researchers had previously noticed this crust as well but assumed it was just part of the ant's exoskeleton **(Figure 1a).** When Currie took a closer look, he discovered that the crust was actually a bacterium of the genus *Pseudonocardia*; these bacteria are actinomycetes, which are known to produce antibiotics (e.g., streptomycin). On further exploration, Currie found that this bacterium produced an antibiotic that specifically and completely inhibited growth of a parasitic fungus, *Escovopsis*, which is the greatest threat to the gardens. If *Escovopsis* isn't stopped, it will overgrow the desirable fungus and take over the garden. This groundbreaking research, demonstrating that mutualisms do not necessarily involve just two species, was done while Currie was still a student. Since finishing his Ph.D., Currie has gone on to show that the ants' bodies have changed over evolutionary time to create and maintain a favourable environment for their bacteria. The bacteria live in specialized crevices on the ant's body that are associated with glands; secretions from these glands provide nutrients for the bacteria **(Figure 1b, c).** So not only did ants invent agriculture long before humans, they also used microbes to produce antibiotics, long before we thought of doing so. An interesting aspect of antibiotic use by the ants is that even though the parasitic fungus has been exposed to the antibiotic produced by the bacterium for a very long time, it has not become resistant to the antibiotic. Perhaps we can learn something from the ants about preventing antibiotic resistance, which has rendered many of the antibiotics we rely on ineffective (you read about antibiotic resistance in Chapter 21).

Figure 1
(a) Leaf-cutter ant showing bacterial "crust." **(b)** crypts (white spots) on ant's body house bacteria; **(c)** Crypt on the body of a leaf-cutter ant. From Cameron R. Currie, Michael Poulsen, John Mendenhall, Jacobus J. Boomsma, Johan Billen, "Coevolved crypts and exocrine glands support mutualistic bacteria in fungus-growing ants", Science, Vol. 311, 6 January 2006, pp. 81–83. Reprinted with permission from AAAS.

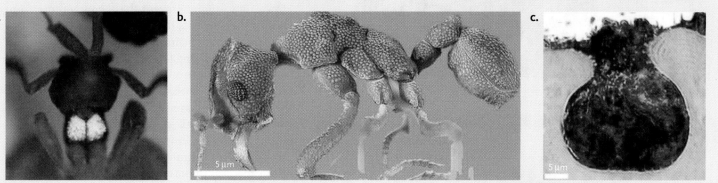

a.   b.   c.

24.1 What Is a Fungus? General Characteristics of Fungi

We begin our survey of fungi by examining the features that distinguish fungi from other forms of life, how fungi obtain nutrients, and adaptations for reproduction and growth that enable fungi to spread far and wide through the environment.

Fungi are heterotrophic eukaryotes that obtain carbon by breaking down organic molecules synthesized by other organisms. Although all fungi are heterotrophs, fungi can be divided into two broad groups based on how they obtain carbon. If a fungus obtains carbon from nonliving material, it is a **saprotroph.** Fungi that decompose dead plant and animal tissues, for example, are saprotrophs. If a fungus obtains carbon from living organisms, it is a **symbiont.** Symbiosis is the living together of two (or sometimes more) organisms for extended periods; symbiotic relationships range along a continuum from **parasitism,** in which one organism benefits at the expense of the other, to **mutualism,** in which both organisms benefit. Although we often think of fungi as decomposers, fully half of all identified fungi live as symbionts with another organism.

Regardless of their nutrient source, fungi feed by **absorptive nutrition:** they secrete enzymes into their environment, breaking down large molecules into smaller molecules that can then be absorbed into their cells. This mode of nutrition means that fungi cannot be stationary as they would then deplete all of the food in their immediate environment. Instead, fungi have evolved the ability to proliferate quickly through their environment, digesting nutrients as they grow. How can fungi proliferate so quickly? Although some fungi are unicellular, most are composed of **hyphae** ("web"; singular = hypha) **(Figure 24.3a),** fine filaments that spread through whatever substrate the fungus is growing in—soil, decomposing wood, your skin—forming a network or **mycelium (Figure 24.3b, c).** Hyphae are essentially tubes of cytoplasm surrounded by cell walls made of **chitin**, a polysaccharide also found in the exoskeletons of insects and other arthropods.

Hyphae grow only at their tips, but because a single mycelium contains many, many tips, the entire mycelium grows outward very quickly. Together, this **apical growth** and absorptive nutrition account for much of the success of fungi. As the hyphal tips extend, they exert a mechanical force, allowing them to push through their substrate, releasing enzymes and absorbing nutrients as they go. Fungal species differ in the particular digestive enzymes they synthesize, so a substrate that is a suitable food source for one species may be unavailable to another. Although there are exceptions, fungi typically thrive only in moist environments, where they can directly absorb water, dissolved ions, simple sugars, amino acids, and other small molecules. When some of a mycelium's hyphal filaments contact a source of food, growth is channelled in the direction of the food source.

Nutrients are absorbed at the porous tips of hyphae; small atoms and molecules pass readily through these tips, and then transport mechanisms move them through the underlying plasma membrane. Some hyphae have regular cross-walls or **septa** ("fence" or "wall"; singular = septum), whereas others lack septa and are effectively one large cell **(Figure 24.4).** But even septate hyphae should be thought of as interconnected compartments rather than separate cells as all septa have pores that allow cytoplasm and, in some fungi, even nuclei and other large organelles to flow through the mycelium. By a mechanism called *cytoplasmic streaming*, nutrients obtained by one part of a mycelium can be translocated to other nonabsorptive regions, such as reproductive structures.

When a fungus releases enzymes into its substrate, it faces competition from bacteria and other organisms for the nutrients that are now available. How can a fungus prevent these competitors from stealing the nutrients that it has just expended energy and resources to obtain? Many fungi produce antibacterial compounds and toxins that inhibit the growth of competing organisms. Many of these compounds are **secondary metabolites**, which are not required for day-to-day survival but are beneficial to the fungus. As we will see, many of these compounds are not only important in the life of a fungus but also benefit organisms associated with the fungus. Many are also of commercial or medical importance to humans; for example, the antibiotic penicillin is a secondary metabolite produced by species of *Penicillium*.

Figure 24.3
(a) Micrograph of fungal hyphae.
(b) Sketch of the mycelium of a mushroom-forming fungus, which consists of branching septate hyphae.
(c) Mycelium on leaf litter.

a. Fungal hyphae

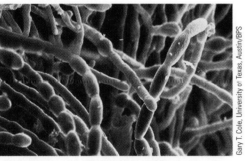

Gary T. Cole, University of Texas, Austin/BPS

b. Multicellular fungus

—Mycelium—

c. Mycelium on leaf litter

Dr. George Knaphus

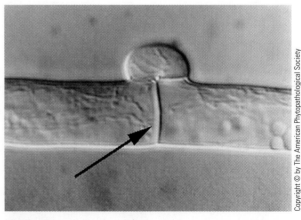

Copyright © by The American Phytopathological Society

Figure 24.4
Septum in fungal hypha (the arrow is pointing to the septum between two hyphal compartments).

Fungi reproduce by spores, and this spore production can be amazingly prolific, with some species of fungi producing billions of spores per day (**Figure 24.5**). These spores are microscopic, featherlight, and able to survive in the environment for extended periods after they are released. Reproducing via such spores allows fungi to be opportunists, germinating only when favourable conditions exist and quickly exploiting food sources that occur unpredictably in the environment. Releasing vast numbers of spores, as some fungi do, improves the odds that the spores will germinate and produce a new individual.

Spores can be produced asexually or sexually; some fungi produce both asexual and sexual spores at different stages of their lives. Sexual reproduction in fungi is quite complex. In all organisms, sexual reproduction involves three stages: the fusion of two haploid cells (**plasmogamy**), bringing together their two nuclei in one common cytoplasm; this cytoplasmic fusion is usually quickly followed by nuclear fusion (**karyogamy**) in most organisms; nuclear fusion is followed by meiosis to produce genetically distinct haploid cells. As we will see, fungi are unique in that these events can be separated in time for durations ranging from seconds to many years.

Figure 24.5
Spores galore! Spore production by fungal fruiting bodies. Some fruiting bodies can release billions of spores per day.

STUDY BREAK

1. What physical features distinguish fungi from other organisms?
2. How do fungi reduce competition for resources?
3. By what means do fungi reproduce? Why is this mode of reproduction advantageous?

24.2 Evolution and Diversity of Fungi

24.2a Fungi Were Present on Earth by at Least 500 Million Years Ago

For many years, fungi were classified as plants because the earliest classification schemes had only two kingdoms, plants and animals. Fungi, like plants, have cell walls and did not move as animals did, so they were grouped with plants. As biologists learned more about the distinctive characteristics of fungi, however, it became clear that fungi should be treated as a separate kingdom. The discovery of chitin in fungal cells and recent comparisons of DNA and RNA sequences all indicate that fungi and animals are more closely related to each other than they are to other eukaryotes. The close biochemical relationship between fungi and animals may explain why fungal infections are typically so resistant to treatment and why it has proven rather difficult to develop drugs that kill fungi without damaging their human or other animal hosts.

Analysis of the sequences of several genes suggests that the lineages leading to animals and fungi may have diverged around 965 million years ago. What were the first fungi like? We do not know for certain: phylogenetic studies indicate that fungi first arose from a single-celled, flagellated protist similar to choanoflagellates (see Ch. 23)—the sort of organism that does not fossilize well. Although traces of what may be fossil fungi exist in rock formations nearly 1 billion years old, the oldest fossils that we can confidently assign to the modern **kingdom Fungi** appear in rock strata laid down about 500 million years ago.

24.2b Once They Appeared, Fungi Radiated into Several Major Lineages

Most likely, the first fungi were aquatic. When other kinds of organisms began to colonize land, they may well have brought fungi along with them. For example, researchers have discovered what appear to be mycorrhizas—symbiotic associations of a fungus and a plant—in fossils of some of the earliest known land plants. The final section of this chapter examines mycorrhizas more fully.

Over time, fungi diverged into the strikingly diverse lineages that we consider in the rest of this section **(Table 24.1)**. Today, there are over 60 000 described species of fungi, with at least 1.6 million more that have not yet been described.

As the lineages diversified, different adaptations associated with reproduction arose. For example, you'll notice that the structures in which sexual spores are formed and mechanisms by which spores are dispersed become larger and more elaborate over evolutionary time. Traditionally, therefore, biologists have classified fungi primarily by the distinctive structures produced in sexual reproduction. These features are still useful indicators of the phylogenetic standing of a fungus, but the powerful tools of molecular analysis are bringing many revisions to our understanding of the evolutionary journey of fungi.

The evolutionary origins and lineages of fungi have been obscure ever since biologists began puzzling over the characteristics of this group. With the advent of molecular techniques for research, these topics have become extremely active and exciting areas of **biological research** that may shed light on fundamental events in the evolution of all eukaryotes. Not surprisingly, when so much new information is coming to light, biologists hold a wide range of views on how various groups arose and may be related. Currently, we recognize five phyla of fungi, known formally as the Chytridiomycota, Zygomycota, Glomeromycota, Ascomycota, and Basidiomycota **(Figure 24.6)**. However, we know now that two of these phyla, the chytridiomycota and the zygomycota, are not monophyletic (i.e., they are taxa that do not contain only an ancestor and all of its descendants; see Chapter 19), so the classification scheme presented in Figure 24.4 will soon change to reflect this new information. Why do classifications of organisms change so often? Bear in mind that classification schemes such as those presented here are hypotheses that explain our best understanding of evolutionary relationships among organisms at any one time; like any other hypotheses, classification schemes are open to revision as we find out more about the organisms. Even through fungal classification will change greatly over the next few years, we summarize the major phyla recognized today as a way of illustrating the diversity of this group of organisms.

Table 24.1 — Summary of Fungal Phyla

Phylum	Body Type	Key Feature
Chytridiomycota (chytrids)	One to several cells	Motile spores propelled by flagella; usually asexual
Zygomycota (zygomycetes)	Hyphal	Sexual stage in which a resistant zygospore forms for later germination
Glomeromycota (glomero-mycetes)	Hyphal	Hyphae associated with plant roots, forming arbuscular mycorrhizae
Ascomycota (ascomycetes)	Hyphal	Sexual spores produced in sacs called asci
Basidiomycota (basidiomycetes)	Hyphal	Sexual spores (basidiospores) form in basidia of a prominent fruiting body (basidiocarp)

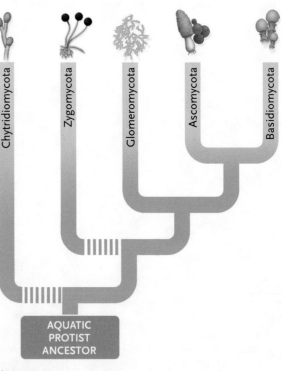

Figure 24.6

A phylogeny of fungi. This scheme represents a widely accepted view of the general relationships between major groups of fungi, but it may well be revised as new molecular findings provide more information. The dashed lines indicate that two groups, the chytrids and the zygomycetes, are probably paraphyletic—they include subgroups that are not all descended from a single ancestor.

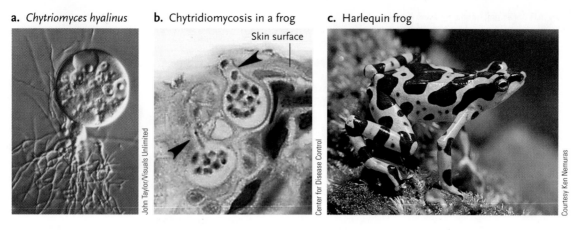

a. *Chytriomyces hyalinus*　　**b.** Chytridiomycosis in a frog　　**c.** Harlequin frog

Skin surface

John Taylor/Visuals Unlimited

Center for Disease Control

Courtesy Ken Nemuras

Figure 24.7
Chytrids. **(a)** *Chytriomyces hyalinus*, one of the few chytrids that reproduce sexually. **(b)** Chytridiomycosis, a fungal infection, shown here in the skin of a frog. The two arrows point to flask-shaped cells of the parasitic chytrid *Batrachochytrium dendrobatis*, which has devastated populations of harlequin frogs **(c)**.

Phylum Chytridiomycota The Chytridiomycota are likely the most ancient group of fungi as they retain several traits characteristic of an aquatic lifestyle. For example, chytrids (as they are commonly called) are the only fungi that produce flagellated, motile spores **(Figure 24.7a);** these spores use chemotaxis (movement in response to a chemical gradient) to locate suitable substrates. Chytrids live in soil or freshwater habitats, wherever there is at least a film of water through which their motile spores can swim.

Most chytrids are saprotrophs, organisms that obtain nutrients by breaking down dead organic matter, although some are symbionts in the gut of cattle and other herbivores, where they break down cellulose to provide carbon for their hosts, and still others are parasites of animals, plants, algae, or other fungi. These tiny fungi also cause a disease, chytridiomycosis, that is one cause of the decline in amphibian species worldwide. Globally, at least 43% of all amphibian species are declining in population, and nearly 33% are threatened with extinction. Although many factors contribute to amphibian decline, including habitat loss, fragmentation, and increasing levels of environmental pollutants, chytridiomycosis has been linked to the decline of amphibian populations in Australia, New Zealand, central and South America, and parts of Europe. This disease has wiped out an estimated two-thirds of the species of harlequin frogs (*Atelopus*) in the American tropics **(Figure 24.7b).** The epidemic has correlated with the rising average temperature in the frogs' habitats, an increase credited to global warming. Studies show that the warmer environment provides optimal growing temperatures for the chytrid pathogen. How does infection by a chytrid kill these animals? We don't yet fully understand why chytridiomycosis is so lethal. The fungus colonizes the skin of these animals **(Figure 24.7c)** and may release toxins that are absorbed through the animal's skin, or, given that amphibians take up water and breathe through their skin, the fungus may directly affect water uptake and respiration.

Although most chytrids are unicellular, some live as chains of cells and have rhizoids that anchor the

fungus to its substrate and that may also absorb nutrients from the substrate. The vegetative stage of most chytrids is haploid; asexual reproduction involves the formation of a **sporangium**, in which motile spores are formed. A few chytrids reproduce sexually, via male and female gametes that fuse, to form a diploid zygote. This cell may form a mycelium that gives rise to sporangia, or it may directly give rise to either asexual or sexual spores.

Zygomycota This group of fungi includes the moulds on fruit and bread familiar to many of us and takes its name from the structure formed in sexual reproduction, the **zygospore (Figure 24.8, p. 530).** Many zygomycetes are saprotrophs that live in soil, feeding on organic matter. Their metabolic activities release mineral nutrients in forms that plant roots can take up. Some zygomycetes are parasites of insects (and even other zygomycetes), and some wreak havoc on human food supplies, spoiling stored grains, bread, fruits, and vegetables **(Figure 24.9, p. 530).** Others, however, have become major players in commercial enterprises, where they are used in manufacturing products that range from industrial pigments to pharmaceuticals, such as production of steroids (e.g., anti-inflammatory drugs). Zygomycetes are also used in the production of fermented foods such as tempeh.

Most zygomycetes consist of a haploid mycelium that lacks regular septa, although some groups have septa, and in others, septa form to wall off reproductive structures and aging regions of the mycelium. Sexual reproduction occurs when mycelia of different **mating types** (known as + and − types, rather than male and female) produce specialized hyphae that grow toward each other and form sex organs **(gametangia)** at their tips (see Figure 24.8, steps 1 and 2). How do the gametangia find each other? Pheromones secreted by each mycelium stimulate the development of sexual structures in the complementary strain and cause gametangia to grow toward each other. The gametangia fuse, forming a thick-walled spore, a **zygospore** (see Figure 24.8, step 3), which can remain dormant for months or years, allowing the

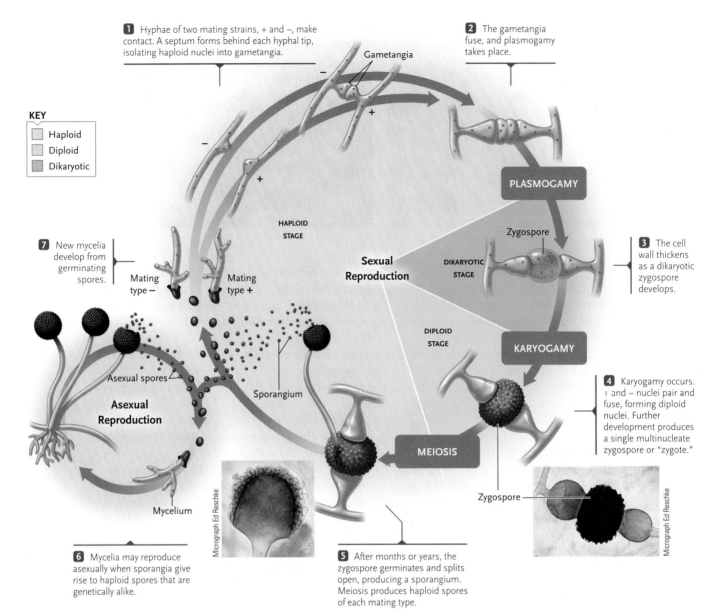

1 Hyphae of two mating strains, + and −, make contact. A septum forms behind each hyphal tip, isolating haploid nuclei into gametangia.

2 The gametangia fuse, and plasmogamy takes place.

Gametangia

PLASMOGAMY

Zygospore

3 The cell wall thickens as a dikaryotic zygospore develops.

HAPLOID STAGE

Sexual Reproduction

DIKARYOTIC STAGE

7 New mycelia develop from germinating spores.

Mating type −

Mating type +

DIPLOID STAGE

KARYOGAMY

4 Karyogamy occurs. + and − nuclei pair and fuse, forming diploid nuclei. Further development produces a single multinucleate zygospore or "zygote."

Asexual spores

Sporangium

Asexual Reproduction

MEIOSIS

Zygospore

Micrograph Ed Reschke

Mycelium

Micrograph Ed Reschke

6 Mycelia may reproduce asexually when sporangia give rise to haploid spores that are genetically alike.

5 After months or years, the zygospore germinates and splits open, producing a sporangium. Meiosis produces haploid spores of each mating type.

KEY

Haploid
Diploid
Dikaryotic

Figure 24.8

Life cycle of the bread mould *Rhizopus stolonifer*, a zygomycete. Asexual reproduction is common, but different mating types (+ and −) also reproduce sexually. In both cases, haploid spores are formed and give rise to new mycelia.

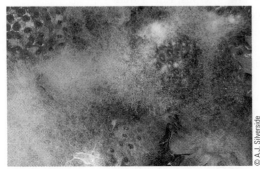

© A.J. Silverside

Figure 24.9

Zygomycete fungus growing on strawberries.

zygomycete to survive unfavourable environmental conditions. Eventually, meiosis occurs in the zygospore, forming a sporangium that will produce haploid spores (see Figure 24.8, step 5). Note that meiosis does not always produce gametes! We often tend to characterize meiosis as the formation of gametes, probably because we are so familiar with how sexual reproduction occurs in humans and other animals. But in many organisms, such as fungi and plants, meiosis results in the formation of haploid spores.

Like other fungi, however, zygomycetes also reproduce asexually, as shown in steps 6 and 7

of Figure 24.8. When a haploid spore lands on a favourable substrate, it germinates and gives rise to a branching mycelium. Some of the hyphae grow upward, and saclike sporangia form at the tips of these aerial hyphae. Inside the sporangia, the asexual cycle comes full circle as new haploid spores arise through mitosis and are released.

The black bread mould *Rhizopus stolonifer* may produce so many charcoal-coloured sporangia in asexual reproduction **(Figure 24.10a)** that mouldy bread looks black. The spores released are lightweight, dry, and readily wafted away by air currents. In fact, winds have dispersed *R. stolonifer* spores just about everywhere on Earth, including the Arctic. Another zygomycete, *Pilobolus* **(Figure 24.10b)**, forcefully spews its sporangia away from the dung in which it grows. A grazing animal may eat a sporangium on a blade of grass; the spores then pass through the animal's gut unharmed and begin the life cycle again in a new dung pile.

a. Sporangia of *Rhizopus stolonifer*

J. D. Cunningham/Visuals Unlimited

b. Sporangia (dark sacs) of *Pilobolus*

500 μm

Figure 24.10

Two of the numerous strategies for spore dispersal by zygomycetes. **(a)** The sporangia of *Rhizopus stolonifer*, shown here on a slice of bread, release powdery spores that are easily dispersed by air currents. **(b)** In *Pilobolus*, the spores are contained in a sporangium (the dark sac) at the end of a stalked structure. When incoming rays of sunlight strike a light-sensitive portion of the stalk, turgor pressure (pressure against a cell wall due to the movement of water into the cell) inside a vacuole in the swollen portion becomes so great that the entire sporangium may be ejected outward as far as 2 m—a remarkable feat given that the stalk is only 5 to 10 mm tall.

Glomeromycota Until recently, fungi in the phylum Glomeromycota were classified as zygomycetes based on morphological similarities such as the lack of regular septa. However, these fungi are quite dissimilar from zygomycetes in many ways—for example, sexual reproduction is unknown in this group of fungi, with spores usually forming asexually simply by walling off a section of a hypha **(Figure 24.11)**—causing many researchers to question the inclusion of these fungi in the phylum Zygomycota. Recent evidence from molecular studies resulted in these fungi being placed in their own phylum.

The 160 known members of this phylum are all specialized to form **mycorrhizas**, or symbiotic associations with plant roots. This group of fungi has a tremendous ecological importance as they collectively make up roughly half of the fungi in soil and form

mycorrhizas with many land plants, including most major crop species, such as wheat and maize. Mycelia of these fungi colonize the roots of host plants and also proliferate in the soil around the plants. Inside the roots, hyphae penetrate through cell walls and branch repeatedly to form **arbuscules** ("little trees") (see Figure 24.11). The branches of each arbuscule are enfolded by the cell's plasma membrane, forming an interface with a large surface area through which nutrients are exchanged between the plant and the fungus. Some glomeromycetes also form vesicles inside roots, which store nutrients and can also act as spores. The fungus obtains sugars from the plant and in return provides the plant with a steady supply of dissolved minerals that it has obtained from the surrounding soil. We take a closer look at mycorrhizas in Section 24.3.

Ascomycota The phylum Ascomycota takes its name from the saclike structures (**asci**; singular, ascus) in which spores are formed in sexual reproduction. These asci are often enclosed in a fruiting body

a. Arbuscules (black) in leek root colonized by arbuscular mycorrhizal fungus

b. Arbuscule

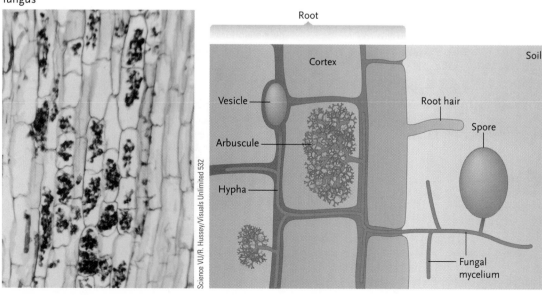

Science VU/R. Hussey/Visuals Unlimited 532

Root

Cortex

Soil

Vesicle

Arbuscule

Hypha

Root hair

Spore

Fungal mycelium

Figure 24.11

Glomeromycete fungus forming a mycorrhiza. **(a)** In this instance, the roots of leeks are growing in association with the glomeromycete fungus *Glomus versiforme* (longitudinal section). Notice the arbuscules that have formed as fungal hyphae branch after entering the root **(b)**.

a. Ascocarp

Ascospore
(sexual
spore)

Ascus

Spore-bearing
hypha of this
ascocarp

b. Asci

© North Carolina State University, Department of Plant Pathology

c. Asci within ascocarp

© Michael Wood/mykob.com

d. Morel

© Fred Stevens/mykob.com

Figure 24.12

A few of the ascomycetes, or sac fungi. The examples shown are species that form multicellular fruiting bodies as reproductive structures. **(a)** A cup-shaped ascocarp, composed of tightly interwoven hyphae. The spore-producing asci occur inside the cup. **(b)** Asci on the inner surface of an ascocarp. **(c)** Scarlet cup fungus (*Sarcoscypha*).**(d)** A true morel (*Morchella esculenta*), a prized edible fungus.

(ascocarp) **(Figure 24.12a, b, c).** Ascomycetes are much more numerous than chytrids, zygomycetes, or glomeromycetes, with more than 30 000 identified species.

Some ascomycetes are very useful to humans. One species, the orange bread mould *Neurospora crassa,* has been important in genetic research, including the elucidation of the one gene–one enzyme hypothesis (see Chapter 13). *Saccharomyces cerevisiae,* which produces the ethanol in alcoholic beverages and the carbon dioxide that leavens bread, is also a model organism used in genetic research. By one estimate, it has been the subject of more genetic experiments than any other eukaryotic microorganism. This multifaceted phylum also includes gourmet delicacies such

as truffles (*Tuber melanosporum*) and the succulent morel *Morchella esculenta* **(Figure 24.12d).**

Many ascomycetes are saprotrophs, playing a key role in the breakdown of cellulose and other polymers. Ascomycetes are also common in symbiotic associations, forming mycorrhizas and lichens (see Section 24.3). A few ascomycetes prey on various agricultural insect pests—some are even carnivores that trap their prey in nooses **(Figure 24.13a)**—and thus have potential for use as "biological pesticides."

However, other ascomycetes are devastating plant pathogens, including the blue-stain fungi that are associated with mountain pine beetles and contribute to the death of beetle-infested trees **(Figure 24.13b;** see also Chapter 3). Several ascomycetes can be serious pathogens of humans. The yeast *Candida albicans* **(Figure 24.14)** infects mucous membranes, especially of the vagina and mouth, causing a condition called thrush. Another yeast, *Pneumocystis carinii,* causes virulent pneumonia in AIDS patients and other immunocompromised people.

a. A trapping ascomycete

N. Allin and G.L Barron

b. Stump of pine tree infected with blue-stain fungus

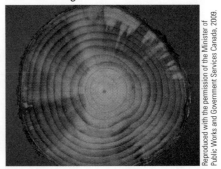

Reproduced with the permission of the Minister of Public Works and Government Services Canada, 2009.

Figure 24.13

(a) Nematode-trapping fungus. Hyphae of this ascomycete (*Arthobotrys*) form nooselike rings. When a prey organism enters the loop, rapid changes in ion concentration draw water into the loop by osmosis. The increased turgour pressure causes the noose to tighten, trapping its prey. Enzymes produced by the fungus then break down the nematode's tissues. **(b)** Stump of a pine tree infected with blue-stain fungus; the fungus grows into the tree's water-conducting tissue, blocking the flow of water.

Yeast cells

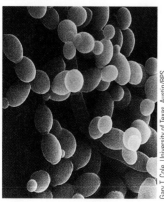

Gary T. Cole, University of Texas, Austin/BPS

Figure 24.14
Candida albicans, the cause of yeast infections of the mouth and vagina.

Claviceps purpurea, a parasite on rye and other grains, causes ergotism, a disease marked by vomiting, hallucinations, convulsions, and, in severe cases, gangrene and even death. It has even been suggested that this fungus was the cause of the Salem witch hunts of seventeenth century New England, as discussed in *Molecule Behind Biology*. Other ascomycetes cause nuisance infections, such as athlete's foot and ringworm.

Most ascomycetes grow as haploid mycelia with regular septa; large pores in the septa allow organelles, including nuclei, to move with cytoplasm through the mycelium. Some ascomycetes are **yeasts** or filamentous fungi with a yeast stage; a yeast is a unicellular growth form that reproduces asexually by **budding** or binary fission (see Figure 24.14). Sexual reproduction generally involves fusion of hyphae from mycelia of + and − mating types **(Figure 24.15)**. The cytoplasm of the two hyphae fuses, but fusion of the nuclei is delayed, resulting in the formation of **dikaryotic hyphae** that contain two separate nuclei and thus are

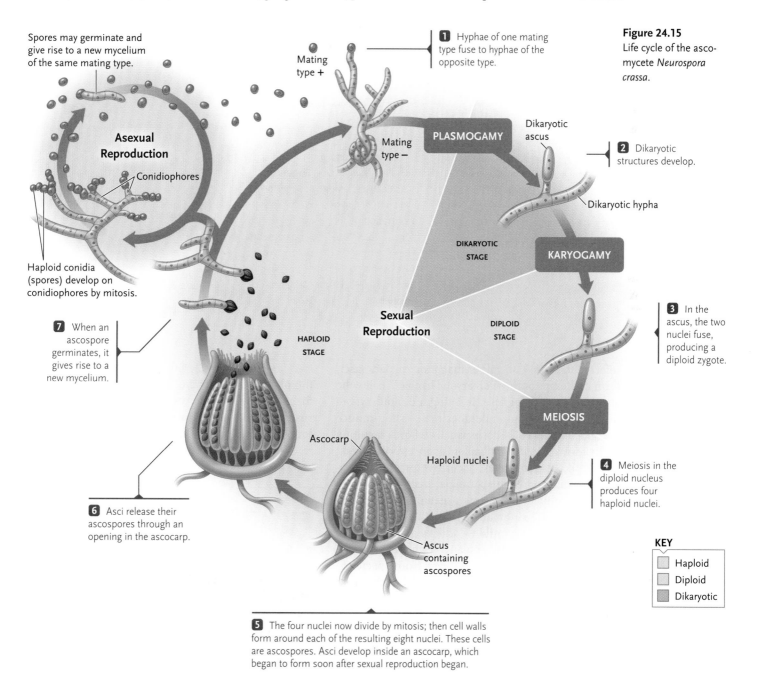

Figure 24.15
Life cycle of the ascomycete *Neurospora crassa*.

Spores may germinate and give rise to a new mycelium of the same mating type.

Mating type +

1 Hyphae of one mating type fuse to hyphae of the opposite type.

Asexual Reproduction

Conidiophores

Mating type −

PLASMOGAMY

Dikaryotic ascus

2 Dikaryotic structures develop.

Dikaryotic hypha

Haploid conidia (spores) develop on conidiophores by mitosis.

DIKARYOTIC STAGE

KARYOGAMY

Sexual Reproduction

DIPLOID STAGE

3 In the ascus, the two nuclei fuse, producing a diploid zygote.

7 When an ascospore germinates, it gives rise to a new mycelium.

HAPLOID STAGE

MEIOSIS

Haploid nuclei

4 Meiosis in the diploid nucleus produces four haploid nuclei.

Ascocarp

6 Asci release their ascospores through an opening in the ascocarp.

Ascus containing ascospores

KEY

- Haploid
- Diploid
- Dikaryotic

5 The four nuclei now divide by mitosis; then cell walls form around each of the resulting eight nuclei. These cells are ascospores. Asci develop inside an ascocarp, which began to form soon after sexual reproduction began.

Lysergic Acid

Was a fungus responsible for the Salem witch trials? In Salem, Massachusetts, in the 1700s, several women were tried and found guilty of witchcraft. Their accusers were young women who had been experiencing bizarre symptoms: hallucinations, convulsions, a sensation of "prickling" of the skin, and even paralysis. Further evidence of witchcraft was the fact that cattle and other animals also suffered these symptoms. What was the real cause of these symptoms? Were they an example of mass hysteria? Or is there a biological explanation?

The symptoms reported by the "bewitched" girls match those of someone who has eaten flour made from wheat infected by the ascomycete fungus *Claviceps purpurea*. Ascospores of this fungus germinate when they land on the flower of a grass plant, such as wheat. The fungus grows quickly and, by the end of the growing season, forms a tough mass of hyphae known as a **sclerotium** in the seed head of the grass **(Figure 1)**. If the seed head isn't harvested, the sclerotia will fall to the ground, where they remain over winter. In the spring, the sclerotia will germinate, producing numerous asci borne on stalks. However, if the fungus has infected a commercial grain crop, such as wheat, sclerotia

are easily harvested along with the plants' seed heads and often end up being ground into flour along with the grain. In medieval times, if the weather favoured development of the fungus, up to 30% of some grain harvests were evidently not grain but sclerotia!

Figure 1
Sclerotium of *Claviceps purpurea* in a grass seed head.

Sclerotia produce many alkaloids, including lysergic acid **(Figure 2),** which causes a range of symptoms, including hallucinations, convulsions, a sensation of ants crawling over the body, limb distortions, and dementia. These symptoms match those of the supposedly "bewitched" people of Salem in 1692. Further support for ergotism being the cause of the

bewitching is the fact that most of the victims were adolescents, who are most suspectible to the effects of ergot alkaloids. Furthermore, the fact that cattle and other domestic animals would also have eaten infected grain and also presented the same symptoms as the "victims" suggests that ergot, not mass hysteria, was involved. Lysergic acid was purified in 1943 by a chemist (Albert Hoffman) to produce the psychoactive drug LSD. Researchers hoped that this drug would be useful psychotherapy, but its negative effects outweighed the benefits, and this line of research was dropped. However, other ergot alkaloids offer promise as treatment for migraine headaches.

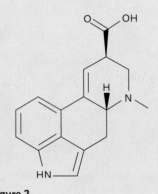

Figure 2
Structure of lysergic acid.

---

referred to as "$n + n$" rather than n or $2n$. Sacs (asci) form at the tips of these dikaryotic hyphae; inside the asci, the two nuclei fuse, forming a diploid zygote nucleus, which then undergoes meiosis to produce four haploid nuclei. Mitosis usually follows, resulting in the formation of eight haploid spores (**ascospores**).

Unlike zygomycetes, ascomycetes do not produce asexual spores in sporangia. Instead, modified hyphae produce numerous asexual spores called **conidia** ("dust"; singular, *conidium*), such as those seen when powdery mildew attacks grasses, roses, and other common garden plants **(Figure 24.16a).** The mode of conidial production varies from species to species, with some ascomycetes producing chains of conidia, whereas in others, the conidia are produced on a hypha in a series of "bubbles," rather like a string of detachable beads **(Figure 24.16b).** Either way, conidia are formed and released much more quickly than zygomycete spores.

Basidiomycota The 24 000 or so species of fungi in the phylum Basidiomycota include the mushroom-forming species, bracket fungi, stinkhorns, smuts, rusts, and puffballs **(Figure 24.17).** The common name for this group is club fungi, due to the club-shaped

Figure 24.16
(a) Powdery mildew on leaves. **(b)** Conidia produced in asexual reproduction by ascomycete fungi.

a. Coral fungus

b. Shelf fungus

c. White-egg bird's nest fungus

d. Fly agaric mushroom

e. Scarlet hood

Figure 24.17

Examples of basidiomycetes, or club fungi. **(a)** The light red coral fungus *Ramaria*. **(b)** The shelf fungus *Polyporus*. **(c)** The white-egg bird's nest fungus *Crucibulum laeve*. Each tiny "egg" contains spores. Raindrops splashing into the "nest" can cause "eggs" to be ejected, thereby spreading spores into the surrounding environment. **(d)** The fly agaric mushroom *Amanita muscaria*, which causes hallucinations. **(e)** The scarlet hood *Hygrophorus*.

cells (**basidia**; singular, basidium) in which sexual spores are produced.

Many basidiomycetes produce enzymes for digesting cellulose and lignin and are important decomposers of woody plant debris. Very few organisms can degrade lignin due to its very complex, irregular structure **(Figure 24.18, p. 536)**. The ability to degrade lignin also enables some basidiomycetes to break down complex organic compounds such as DDT, PCBs, and other persistent environmental pollutants that are structurally similar to lignin. Bioremediation of contaminated sites by these fungi is a very active research area.

A surprising number of basidiomycetes, including the prized edible oyster mushrooms (*Pleurotus ostreatus*), also can trap and consume small animals such as rotifers and nematodes by secreting paralyzing toxins or gluey substances that immobilize the prey, in a manner similar to that shown earlier for ascomycetes (see Figure 24.13). As is the case for insectivorous plants, such as the Venus flytrap (*Dionaea muscipula*), discussed in Chapter 47, this adaptation gives the fungus access to a rich source of molecular nitrogen, an essential nutrient that often is scarce in terrestrial habitats. For example, the wood that is the substrate for many basidiomycetes is high in carbon but low in

nitrogen; many wood-decay fungi have been found to be carnivorous, obtaining supplemental nitrogen from various invertebrates.

Some basidiomycetes form mycorrhizas with the roots of forest trees, as discussed later in this chapter. Recent research has shown that these mycorrhizas can be drawn into associations with achlorophyllous plants (plants that lack chlorophyll and so cannot carry out photosynthesis), which thus obtain nutrients from the trees via shared mycorrhizal fungi. Other basidiomycetes, the rusts and smuts, are parasites that cause serious diseases in wheat, rice, and other plants. Still others produce millions of dollars worth of the common edible button mushroom (*Agaricus bisporus*) sold in grocery stores. *Amanita muscaria* (see Figure 24.17d) has been used in the religious rituals of ancient societies in Central America, Russia, and India. Other species of this genus, including the death cap mushroom *Amanita phalloides*, produce deadly toxins. The *A. phalloides* toxin, called α-amanitin, halts gene transcription, and hence protein synthesis, by inhibiting the activity of RNA polymerase. Within 8 to 24 hours of ingesting as little as 5 mg of the mushroom, vomiting and diarrhea begin. Later, kidney and liver cells start to degenerate; without intensive

Figure 24.18
Structure of lignin.

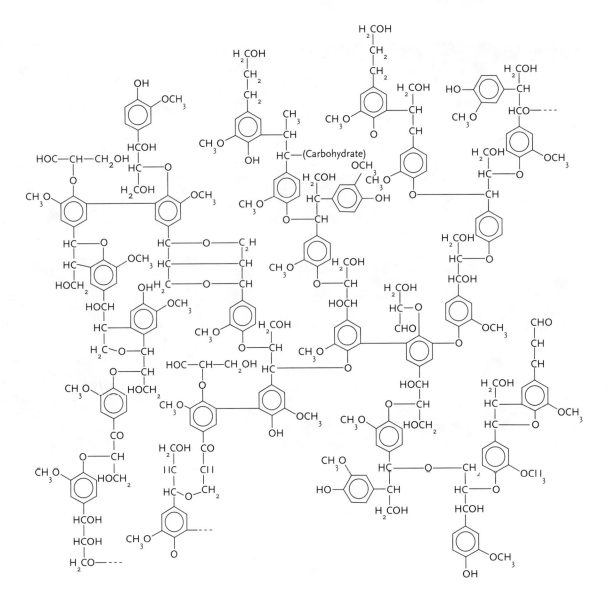

medical care, death can follow within a few days. You can read more about the effect of amanitin on gene expression in Chapter 14.

Most basidiomycetes are mycelial, although some grow as yeasts. The mycelium of many basidiomycetes contains two different, separate nuclei as a result of fusion between two different haploid mycelia and is termed a **dikaryon** ($n + n$) **(Figure 24.19)**. A dikaryotic mycelium is formed following fusion of the two haploid mycelia when both types of nuclei divide and migrate through the mycelium such that each hyphal compartment contains two dissimilar nuclei.

Basidiomycete fungi can grow for most of their lives as dikaryon mycelia—a major departure from an ascomycete's short-lived dikaryotic stage. After an extensive mycelium develops, favourable environmental conditions trigger the formation of fruiting bodies (**basidiocarps**), in which basidia develop. A basidiocarp consists of tight clusters of hyphae; the feeding mycelium is buried in the substrate. The shelflike bracket fungi visible on trees are basidiocarps, as are the structures we call mushrooms and toadstools. Each mushroom is a

short-lived reproductive body consisting of a stalk and a cap; basidia develop on "gills," the sheets of tissue on the underside of the cap. Inside each basidium, the two nuclei fuse; meiosis follows, resulting in the formation of four haploid **basidiospores** on the outside of the basidium (see Figure 24.19). Why does the fungus expend energy and resources on such elaborate spore dispersal structures? A layer of still air occurs just above the ground (and any other surface); by elevating the basidia above this layer, the fungus increases the likelihood that its spores will be carried away by the wind.

The prolonged dikaryon stage in basidiomycetes allows them many more opportunities for producing sexual spores than in ascomycetes, in which the dikaryon state is short-lived. Basidia can produce huge numbers of spores—some species can produce 100 million spores *per hour* during reproductive periods, day after day! Basidiomycete mycelia can live for many years and spread over large areas. The largest organism on Earth could be the mycelium of a single individual of the basidiomycete *Armillaria ostoyae*, which spreads over 8.9 km² of land in eastern Oregon. This organism

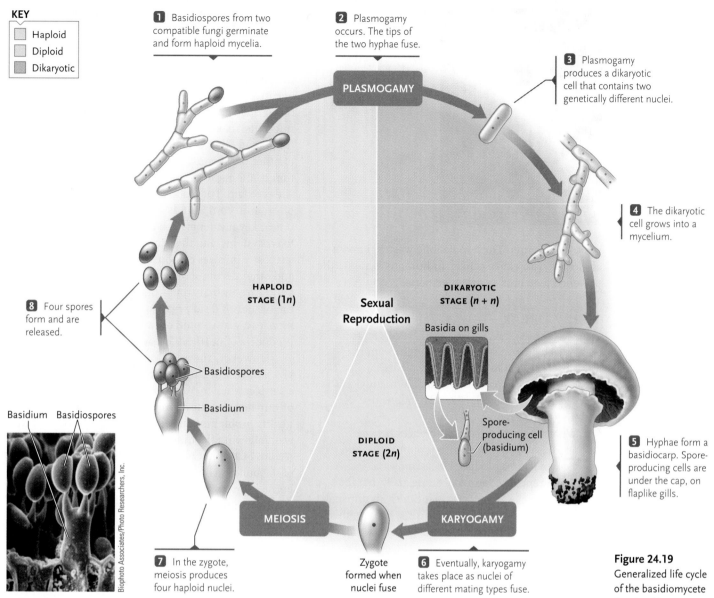

KEY
Haploid
Diploid
Dikaryotic

1 Basidiospores from two compatible fungi germinate and form haploid mycelia.

2 Plasmogamy occurs. The tips of the two hyphae fuse.

PLASMOGAMY

3 Plasmogamy produces a dikaryotic cell that contains two genetically different nuclei.

4 The dikaryotic cell grows into a mycelium.

HAPLOID STAGE (1*n*)

DIKARYOTIC STAGE (*n* + *n*)

Sexual Reproduction

Basidia on gills

8 Four spores form and are released.

Basidiospores

Basidium

Spore-producing cell (basidium)

DIPLOID STAGE (2*n*)

5 Hyphae form a basidiocarp. Spore-producing cells are under the cap, on flaplike gills.

Basidium Basidiospores

Biophoto Associates/Photo Researchers, Inc.

MEIOSIS

KARYOGAMY

7 In the zygote, meiosis produces four haploid nuclei.

Zygote formed when nuclei fuse

6 Eventually, karyogamy takes place as nuclei of different mating types fuse.

Figure 24.19
Generalized life cycle of the basidiomycete *Agaricus bisporus*, a species known commonly as the button mushroom. During the dikaryotic stage, cells contain two genetically different nuclei, shown here in different colours. Inset: Micrograph showing basidia and basidiospores.

weighs at least 150 tonnes and is likely at least 2400 years old, making it not only the largest but also one of the heaviest and oldest organisms on earth.

As for ascomycetes, asexual reproduction in basidiomycetes involves formation of conidia or budding, in yeast forms such as *Cryptococcus neoformans*, which causes a form of meningitis in humans.

Deuteromycota In the past, when biologists isolated fungi and tried to grow them in the lab, they found that many species did not produce a sexual stage. Since fungal classification traditionally relied on features produced in sexual reproduction, these fungi could not be placed in any of the phyla described above. Instead, researchers grouped them together in an artificial group called the Deuteromycota (also known as Fungi Imperfecti, or the "imperfect fungi"—imperfect meaning that a sexual stage is absent). This group is not a true phylum but serves as a "holding pen" for

fungal species that cannot yet be identified. With the development of molecular sequencing techniques, we have been able to identify many fungi classified as deuteromycetes and place them in the proper phylum. Others, however, defy classification—some of these fungi may not have any sexual stage or perhaps do not form sexual structures when cultured in the lab. When researchers discover a sexual phase for a conidial fungus, or when molecular studies establish a clear relationship to a sexual species, the conidial fungus is reassigned to the appropriate phylum. Thus far, some have been classified as basidiomycetes, but most conidial fungi have turned out to be ascomycetes.

Well-known examples of deuteromycetes are *Penicillium* and *Aspergillus*. Certain species of *Penicillium* **(Figure 24.20, p. 538)** are the source of the penicillin family of antibiotics, whereas others produce the aroma and distinctive flavours of Camembert and Roquefort cheeses. Strains of *Aspergillus* grow in damp

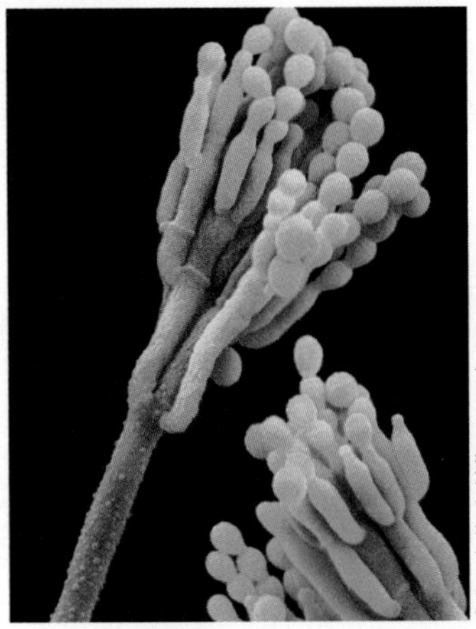

Figure 24.20
Conidia of *Penicillium*. Note the rows of conidia (asexual spores) atop the elongate cells that produce them.

grain or peanuts. Their metabolic wastes, known as aflatoxins, can cause cancer in humans who eat the poisoned food over an extended period.

STUDY BREAK

1. What evidence is there that fungi are more closely related to animals than plants?
2. Name the five phyla of the kingdom Fungi and describe the reproductive adaptations that distinguish each one.
3. What are the two main differences between asexual spores produced by zygomycetes and asexual spores produced by ascomycetes?
4. Fungi reproduce sexually or asexually, but for many species, the life cycle includes an unusual stage not seen in other organisms. What is this genetic condition, and what is its role in the life cycle?

24.3 Fungal Lifestyles

As mentioned earlier, fungi can be categorized as saprotrophs or symbionts, depending on whether they obtain nutrients from living organisms or from dead organic matter. It is important to remember that the categories of "saptrotoph" and "symbiont" are "boxes" that we have created to classify fungi, but fungi are very versatile organisms, and many fungi are capable of acting as both symbionts and saprotrophs at different times or under different conditions. Most people are more familiar with the role of fungi as saprotrophs (decomposers) rather than as symbionts, so in this section, we take a brief look at saprotrophy and then spend more time looking at fungal symbioses.

24.3a Fungi as Saprotrophs

With their adaptations for efficient extracellular digestion, fungi are masters of the decay so vital to terrestrial ecosystems (see Figure 24.2). For instance, in a single autumn, one elm tree can shed 200 kg of withered leaves! Without the metabolic activities of saprotrophic fungi and other decomposers such as bacteria and other organisms (e.g., earthworms), natural communities would rapidly become buried in their own detritus. Even worse, without decomposers to break down this detritus, the soil would become depleted of nutrients, making further plant growth impossible. As fungi (and other decomposers) digest the dead tissues of other organisms, they also make a major contribution to the recycling of chemical elements those tissues contain. For instance, over time, the degradation of organic compounds by saprotrophic fungi helps return key nutrients such as nitrogen and phosphorus to ecosystems. But the prime example of this recycling virtuosity involves carbon. The respiring cells of fungi and other decomposers give off carbon dioxide, liberating carbon that would otherwise remain locked in the tissues of dead organisms. Each year, this activity recycles a vast amount of carbon to plants, the primary producers of nearly all ecosystems on Earth.

However, there is a downside to the impressive enzymatic abilities of saprotrophic fungi: for example, when they decompose materials that are part of our houses, they can cause major economic and health problems. Fungi growing on wood and drywall following flooding or water damage to a building **(Figure 24.21a)** not only weaken the structural integrity of the building but also can be health hazards. The airborne spores of these fungi act as allergens, and some can also cause more serious health problems—for example, some fungi can colonize and grow in sinus cavities. Another example is dry rot, which causes millions of dollars in damage to buildings in Europe, Asia, and Australia **(Figure 24.21b)**. Dry rot is notorious not only because it causes widespread and costly damage but also because the fungus responsible, *Serpula lacrymans*, seems to have the mysterious ability to break down dry wood completely, which should not be possible—as described above, wood decay usually happens once wood becomes wet. Does this fungus really have the amazing ability to break down dry wood? In fact, this fungus is as dependent on water for growth as any other, but it can form specialized mycelial cords, which very efficiently transport water and nutrients over long distances through concrete, bricks, and other unfavourable substrates until the fungus at last finds wood. Then the mycelial cords release water into the substrate, allowing the fungus to spread through the wood and begin the process of decay.

24.3b Fungi as Symbionts

Many fungi are partners in mutually beneficial interactions with animals or photosynthetic organisms; some of these associations shaped the evolution of life on earth and still play major roles in the functioning of ecosystems today. Chapter 46 discusses the general

a.

U.S. Environmental Protection Agency

b.

DIY Doctor

Figure 24.21
(a) Mould growth following flooding.
(b) Dry rot (*Serpula lacrymans*).

features of symbiotic associations more fully; here we are interested in some examples of the symbioses fungi form with other organisms.

Lichens Are Associations Between a Fungus and One or More Photosynthetic Organisms A **lichen** is a compound organism formed by an association between a fungus, an ascomycete or sometimes a basidiomycete, and a green alga and/or a cyanobacterium. Lichens may grow as crusts on rocks, bark, or soil; as flattened leaflike forms; or as radially symmetrical cups, treelike structures, or hairlike strands **(Figure 24.22)**. Lichens have vital ecological roles and important human uses. Lichens secrete acids that eat away at rock, breaking it down and converting it to soil that can support plants.

Many animals, such as caribou (*Rangifer tarandus*), rely on lichens for their winter forage. Some environmental chemists monitor air pollution by monitoring lichens, most of which cannot grow in heavily polluted air. Humans use lichens as sources of dyes and perfumes, as well as medicines. Lichen chemicals are currently being explored as a source of natural pesticides.

The fungus (called the **mycobiont**) makes up most of the body (**thallus**) of the lichen, with the photosynthetic partner (**photobiont**) usually confined to a thin layer inside the lichen thallus (see **Figure 24.22a**). Some lichens have a green algal photobiont inside the thallus and a cyanobacterial photobiont contained in "pockets" on or in the thallus. Because lichens are composite organisms, it may seem odd to talk of

a. Thallus cross section

Soredium
(cells of mycobiont
and of photobiont)

Cortex (outer layer
of mycobiont)

Photobionts

Medulla (inner
layer of loosely
woven hyphae)

Cortex

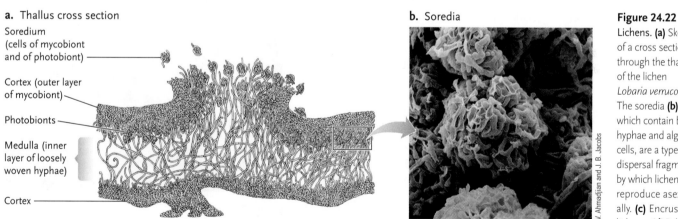

b. Soredia

V. Ahmadjian and J. B. Jacobs

c. Encrusting lichens

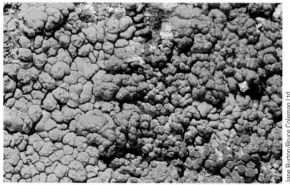

Jane Burton/Bruce Coleman Ltd.

d. Branching lichen

Eye of Science/Science Photo Library/Photo
Researchers, Inc.

Figure 24.22
Lichens. **(a)** Sketch of a cross section through the thallus of the lichen *Lobaria verrucosa*. The soredia **(b)**, which contain both hyphae and algal cells, are a type of dispersal fragment by which lichens reproduce asexually. **(c)** Encrusting lichens. **(d)** *Peltigera*, a flattened, leaf-like lichen.

lichen "species," but biologists do give lichens binomial names, based on the mycobiont. More than 13 500 different lichen species are recognized, each a unique combination of a particular species of fungus and one or more species of photobiont. As you might expect for a compound organism made up of two (or even three) organisms, reproduction can be complicated: it is not enough for each organism to reproduce itself because formation of a new lichen requires that both partners be dispersed and end up together. Many lichens reproduce asexually, by specialized fragments such as the **soredia** (singular, soredium), shown in Figure 24.22. Each soredium consists of photobiont cells wrapped in hypae; the soredia can be dispersed by water, wind, or passing animals.

Inside the thallus, specialized hyphae wrap around and sometimes penetrate photobiont cells, which become the fungus' sole source of carbon. Often the mycobiont absorbs up to 80% of the carbohydrates produced by the photobiont. Benefits for the photobiont are less clear-cut, in part because the drain on nutrients hampers its growth and because the mycobiont often controls reproduction of the photobiont. In one view, many and possibly most lichens are parasitic symbioses, with the fungus enslaving the photobiont. On the other hand, although it is relatively rare to find a lichen photobiont species living independently in the same conditions under which the lichen survives, it may eke out an enduring existence as part of a lichen; some lichens have been dated as being more than 4000 years old! Studies have also revealed that at least some green algae clearly benefit from the relationship. Such algae are sensitive to desiccation and intense ultraviolet radiation. Sheltered by the lichen's fungal tissues, a green alga can thrive in locales where alone it would perish. Clearly, we still have much to learn about the physiological interactions between lichen partners.

Lichens often live in harsh, dry microenvironments, including on bare rock and wind-whipped tree trunks. Some lichens actually live *inside* rocks (see *Life on the Edge*). Unlike plants, lichens do not control water loss from their tissues; instead, their water status reflects that of their environment, and some lichens may dry out and rewet several times a day. Lichens are very slow growing, even though the photobiont may have photosynthetic rates comparable to those of free-living species. What happens to all of the carbohydrates made in photosynthesis if they are not used to fuel growth? The mycobiont takes much of the carbohydrate made by the photobiont and uses it to synthesize secondary metabolites and other compounds that allow the lichen to survive repeated wet–dry cycles and extreme temperatures common in their habitats. These compounds give lichens their vibrant colours and may also inhibit grazing on lichens by slugs and other invertebrates. The mycobiont uses other lichen chemicals to control the photobiont; some chemicals regulate photobiont reproduction, whereas others cause photobiont cells to "leak" carbohydrates to the mycobiont.

Mycorrhizas Are Symbiotic Associations Between Fungi and Plant Roots You might have learned in previous courses that plant roots are responsible for taking up soil nutrients. For most plants, however, this is not true: the roots of most plants are colonized by mycorrhizal fungi, which have mycelia that extend out into the soil far beyond the root zone of the plant and which take up most of the nutrients used by the plant **(Figure 24.23)**. Mycorrhizas, or "fungus roots," are mutualistic symbioses between certain soil-dwelling fungi and plant roots. Mycorrhizal plants greatly enhance the uptake of various nutrients, especially phosphorus and nitrogen, from soil (as discussed in Chapter 41) because the fungal mycelium has a tremendous surface area for

a. Lodgepole pine

Prof. D. J. Read, University of Sheffield

b. Mycorrhiza

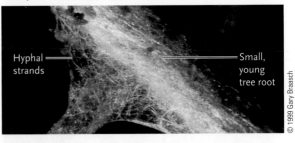

Hyphal strands   Small, young tree root

© 1999 Gary Braasch

Figure 24.23

Ectomycorrhizas. **(a)** Lodgepole pine, *Pinus contorta*, seedling, longitudinal section. Notice the extent of the mycorrhiza compared with the above-ground portion of the seedling, which is only about 4 cm tall. **(b)** Mycorrhiza of a hemlock tree.

absorbing mineral ions from a large volume of the surrounding soil.

As well, some mycorrhizal fungi can access sources of nutrients that are not available to plants: for example, certain basidiomycete fungi can penetrate directly into rocks and extract nutrients, which are then transported to their plant hosts. Other mycorrhizal associations involve the carnivorous basidiomycetes described above, which can obtain nitrogen by trapping and killing soil invertebrates and then transferring nitrogen from their prey to their host plants. By forming partnerships with these fungi, mycorrhizal plants gain access to nutrient sources that nonmycorrhizal plants do not. In exchange for soil nutrients, the plants provide the mycorrhizal fungi with sugars produced through photosynthesis. Mycorrhizas are generally mutualisms, representing a "win–win" situation for the partners. For plants that inhabit soils poor in mineral ions, such as in **tropical rain forests**, mycorrhizal associations are crucial for survival. Likewise, in temperate forests, species of spruce, oak, pine, and some other trees die unless mycorrhizal fungi are present **(Figure 24.24)**. There are at least seven different types of mycorrhizas, but the most common types are ectomycorrhizas and arbuscular mycorrhizas.

Arbuscular mycorrhizas are the oldest and most abundant type of mycorrhiza, formed by glomeromycete fungi and a wide range of plants, including nonseed plants and most flowering plants. In this type of mycorrhiza, fungal hyphae penetrate the cells of the root, forming arbuscules as described above (see Figure 24.11). Fossils show that arbuscular mycorrhizas were common among ancient land plants, and some biologists have speculated that they might have been crucial for the colonization of land by plants by enhancing the transport of water and minerals to the plants.

Ectomycorrhizas evolved more recently and involve basidiomycetes and some ascomycetes. In these mycorrhizas, fungal hyphae form a sheath or mantle around a root (see Figure 24.20) and also grow between, but not inside, the root cells of their plant hosts. Ectomycorrhizal associations are very common with trees, such as the conifers of Canada's **boreal forest** and coastal rain forests. The extensive root system of a single mature pine may be studded with ectomycorrhizas involving dozens of fungal species. The musky-flavoured truffles (*Tuber melanosporum*) prized by gourmets are ascomycetes that form ectomycorrhizal associations with oak trees (*Quercus* spp.).

For plants, the benefits of being mycorrhizal extend beyond enhanced uptake of soil nutrients. In some cases, mycorrhizal fungi enhance a plant's

Figure 24.24

Effect of mycorrhizal fungi on plant growth. The six-month-old juniper seedlings on the left were grown in sterilized low-phosphorus soil inoculated with a mycorrhizal fungus. The seedlings on the right were grown under the same conditions but without the fungus.

F. B. Reeves

defences against pathogens, and nutrients can be transferred among mycorrhizal plants via shared mycorrhizal fungal hyphae. Mycorrhizal fungi may, in fact, play a major role in shaping plant communities and ecosystems.

Endophytes Are Fungi Living in the Above-Ground Tissues of Plants Just as the roots of many plants are colonized by fungi, so too are leaves and shoots **(Figure 24.25)**. Although some of these fungi are pathogens, many others are evidently peacefully coexisting with their plant hosts.

Biologists have known about the presence of these leaf endophytes for some time, but recent discoveries have revealed a startling diversity of these fungi, sometimes within a single plant. Samples of plants from temperate regions have been revealed to have tens of different species of endophytes in a single plant, but tropical plants are truly impressive, with several reports of hundreds of different types of endophytes being isolated from a single plant. Most of these endophytes have not yet been identified to species as researchers have not yet observed sexual stages, so it is difficult to know how many species of endophytes are really living in these tropical plants. A bigger question is what are these endophytes doing in these leaves? Are they mutualists, like mycorrhizal fungi? In many cases, we simply don't know enough about the interaction between the fungus and its host to answer these questions, but in some cases, the fungi do benefit their plant hosts by producing toxins that deter herbivores. Synthesis of toxins and other secondary metabolites has made these endophytes of great potential importance to humans. For example, the anticancer drug taxol (sold under the tradename Taxol) was originally isolated from the bark of the Pacific yew tree (*Taxus brevifolia*). Production of taxol from this source was limited since the tree is quite rare and makes only a small amount of taxol. However, researchers later discovered that a fungal endophyte living in the needles of the Pacific yew also makes taxol—as do other endophytes living in completely different tree species. Evidence indicates that taxol inhibits the growth of other fungi, so these endophytes may be producing it to protect themselves. Unlike the yew trees that were the original source of taxol, these endophytic fungi can be grown very easily in the lab, so we may be able to produce large amounts of this promising anticancer drug very easily. What other sources of medicines are out there, hiding inside plants? The possibility of finding new antibiotics and medicinal compounds makes saving rain forests even more urgent as not only the trees are disappearing but the endophytes inside them as well.

Even though fungi are not closely related to plants in an evolutionary sense, you can see that relationships between fungi and plants play important roles in the lives of both types of organisms. Many saprotrophic and parasitic fungi depend on plants or their products as a source of carbon. Plants rely on fungi for nutrients, either directly, through mycorrhizal relationships, or indirectly, through the role of fungi as decomposers. The very first land plants likely relied on mycorrhizal associations to survive in the new harsh environments they faced. In the next chapter, we look at how land plants evolved and diversified.

STUDY BREAK

1. Describe the difference between a saprotroph and a symbiont.
2. What is a lichen? Explain how each partner contributes to the whole organism.
3. What benefit does a plant derive from being mycorrhizal?
4. What are the two most common types of mycorrhizas? How do they differ?
5. What is an endophyte? Why is their relationship with their plant hosts of interest to medical researchers?

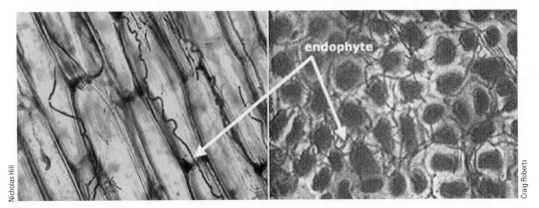

Nicholas Hill

Craig Roberts

Figure 24.25
Leaf endophytes growing inside plant leaves.

How is hyphal tip growth maintained?

In this chapter, we learned that fungi grow only at the tips of their hyphae. This pattern of growth requires that a fungus establishes and maintains polarized growth of hyphae, that is, that one end of a hypha is the tip, and growth occurs only at this end of a hypha. We know that both actin filaments and microtubules (components of the cytoskeleton, the matrix of protein fibres and tubes that maintains the shape and organization of eukaryotic cells; see Chapter 2) play a major role in the establishment and maintenance of polar growth in hyphae. In particular, microtubules (hollow tubes made of protein that can change length very quickly) are required for rapid tip growth of hyphae. Microtubules run the length of a hypha, and their ends extend into the hyphal tip; molecular motors (motor proteins; see Chapter 2) carry organelles and growth supplies along these microtubule "tracks" to the hyphal tip. In a surprise twist, it was recently found that the motors are involved in organizing the microtubules—this relationship is analogous to a train being involved in building its own railway. How do the motors organize the microtubules? We do not yet understand how these motor proteins regulate the stability and turnover of the microtubule system. Answering this question will not only give us a better understanding of fungal growth—which has practical implications, such as aiding in the development of fungicides for plant pathogenic fungi or enhancing growth of economically useful fungi—but will also clarify the role of cytoskeleton and motors in other eukaryotic cells.

How do fungi communicate with potential symbiotic partners?

For all of the symbiotic associations we have investigated in this chapter—mycorrhizas, endophytes, lichens—we still don't know how a fungus determines that it has the "right" partner. Establishment of these symbioses, especially mycorrhizas, requires coordinated development, which means the partners must be communicating with each other. Despite the ecological importance of these associations, we know very little about the signals through which the partners talk to each other. For mycorrhizas and other plant–microbe associations, we do know that secondary metabolites produced by the plant and exuded from the roots can act as branching factors, which stimulate branching of mycorrhizal hyphae near the roots, and may also induce expression of fungal genes necessary for establishment of the symbiosis. But the identity of which metabolite sends which signal and at what point in the establishment of a mycorrhiza is still unknown. In two recent studies, researchers in Japan and France identified a strigolactone as the active component of the branching factor. The strigolactone acts as a "metabolic switch," activating mitochondria and thus ramping up the respiration rate of fungus, providing the energy needed for increased branching. Other types of plant secondary metabolites known as flavonoids may also be involved in communication between a mycorrhizal fungus and its plant partner; flavonoids are known to be important signalling molecules in symbiosis between legumes and nitrogen-fixing bacteria (you will read more about this symbiosis in Chapter 41).

Do strigolactones play other roles in the development of mycorrhizas? For example, are they involved in the formation of arbuscules (see Figure 24.11), which involves prolific hyphal branching? Is the plant stimulated to produce strigolactones or other signalling molecules by the presence of the "right" mycorrhizal fungus? Many questions remain to be answered about how fungi communicate with plants and other symbiotic partners.

Review

Go to CENGAGENOW™ at http://hed.nelson.com/ to access quizzing, animations, exercises, articles, and personalized homework help.

24.1 What Is a Fungus? General Characteristics of Fungi

- Fungi can occur as single-celled yeasts or as multicellular filamentous organisms.

- A fungal mycelium consists of filamentous hyphae that grow throughout the substrate on which the fungus feeds (see Figure 24.3). A cell wall of chitin surrounds the plasma membrane, and in most species, septa partition the hyphae into cell-like compartments. Pores in septa permit cytoplasm and sometimes organelles to move between hyphal cells.

- Fungi gain nutrients by extracellular digestion and absorption at hyphal tips. Saprotrophic species feed on nonliving organic matter and are key decomposers contributing to the recycling of carbon and other nutrients in ecosystems. Many fungi are symbionts, obtaining nutrients from organic matter of living hosts; these symbioses range from parasitism, in which the fungus benefits at the expense of its host, to mutualism, in which both the fungus and its host benefit.

- All fungi reproduce via spores generated either asexually or sexually (see Figure 24.4). Some types also may reproduce asexually by budding or fragmentation of the parent body. Sexual reproduction usually has two stages. First, in plasmogamy, the cytoplasm of two haploid cells fuses, producing a cell that contains a haploid nucleus from each parent. In karyogamy, the nuclei fuse and form a diploid zygote; this stage is delayed in some phyla, resulting in a prolonged dikaryon ($n + n$) condition. Meiosis then generates haploid spores.

24.2 Evolution and Diversity of Fungi

- Fungi have traditionally been classified mainly on the basis of the structures formed in sexual reproduction. When a sexual phase cannot be detected, or is absent from the life cycle, the specimen is assigned to an informal grouping, the Deutero-mycete fungi. Currently, five main phyla of fungi are recognized (see Figure 24.6):

- Chytridomycetes are the only fungi that produce motile, flagellated spores. Many are parasites, including the species responsible for chytridomycosis, a disease contributing to the worldwide decline in amphibian populations (see Figure 24.7).

- Zygomycetes have aseptate hyphae. Asexual reproduction involves production of spores by sporangia. Sexual reproduction occurs by way of hyphae that occur in + and − mating types; haploid nuclei in the hyphae function as gametes. Further development produces the zygospore, which may remain dormant for a time. When the zygospore breaks dormancy, it produces a stalked sporangium containing haploid spores of each mating type, which are released (see Figure 24.8).

- Glomeromycetes form arbuscular mycorrhizas, the most widespread type of mycorrhiza (see Figure 24.11). They reproduce asexually, by way of spores formed from hyphae.

- Ascomycetes reproduce both asexually, via chains of haploid asexual spores called conidia, and sexually, via production of haploid ascospores in saclike cells called asci. In the most complex species, asci are produced in reproductive bodies called ascocarps (see Figure 24.12).

- Most Basidiomycete species reproduce only sexually. Club-shaped basidia develop on a basidiocarp (the fruiting body or mushroom) and bear sexual spores on their surface. When dispersed, these basidiospores may germinate and give rise to a haploid mycelium (see Figure 24.19).

24.3 Fungal Lifestyles

- All fungi are heterotrophs but can obtain carbon by degrading dead organic matter (as saptrotrophs) or from living hosts (as symbionts). The two lifestyles are not mutually exclusive, with many fungi—such as the mycorrhizal fungi that also prey on invertebrates—combining these two modes of nutrition.

- Some basidiomycete fungi form a mutualistic symbiosis with leaf-cutter ants (see Figure 1 and Figure 2, *People Behind Biology*); the ants raise the fungi, which is the sole crop on which they feed. Recently, it was discovered that there is another partner in this ancient symbiosis, an actinomycete bacterium that lives on the ants' bodies and contributes to keeping parasitic fungi out of their fungal gardens.

- Many ascomycetes and a few basidiomycetes enter into symbioses with green algae and/or cyanobacteria to produce a compound organism known as a lichen. Fungal hyphae form the bulk of the lichen body (thallus); the hyphae entwine the algal cells that supply the lichen's carbohydrates, most of which are absorbed by the fungus (see Figure 24.22).

- Fungi in the Glomeromycota, Ascomycota, and Basidiomycota form symbiotic associations known as mycorrhizas with plant roots. Hyphae of mycorrhizal fungi proliferate in the soil beyond plant roots and make mineral ions and, in some cases, organic forms of nutrients available to the plant. Some mycorrhizal associations also increase plant defences against pathogens. In turn, the fungus obtains carbohydrates and possibly other growth-enhancing substances from the plant (see Figures 24.14 and 24.25).

- Endophytic fungi occur in the above-ground parts of many plants (see Figure 24.22); this type of plant–fungus symbiosis is not as well understood as are mycorrhizas, but at least some endophytic fungi are known to produce toxins that deter herbivores.

Questions

Self-Test Questions

1. A trait common to all fungi is
   a. reproduction via spores.
   b. parasitism.
   c. septate hyphae.
   d. a dikaryotic phase inside a zygospore.
   e. plasmogamy when an ascogonium fuses with an antheridium.

2. The chief characteristic(s) used to classify fungi into the major fungal phyla is/are
   a. nutritional dependence on nonliving organic matter.
   b. recycling of nutrients in terrestrial ecosystems.
   c. adaptations for obtaining water.
   d. features of reproduction.
   e. cell wall metabolism.

3. At lunch, you eat a mushroom, some truffles, a little Camembert cheese, and a bit of mouldy bread. This meal includes fungi from all the following groups *except*
   a. Basidiomycota.
   b. Ascomycota.
   c. Deuteromycetes.
   d. Glomeromycota.
   e. Zygomycota.

4. Which of the following fungal reproductive structures is diploid?
   a. Basidiocarp
   b. Ascospore
   c. Conidium
   d. Gametangium
   e. Zygospore

5. A mushroom is
   a. the food-absorbing region of an ascomycete.
   b. the food-absorbing region of a basidiomycete.
   c. a reproductive structure formed only by basidiomycetes.
   d. a specialized form of mycelium not constructed of hyphae.
   e. a collection of saclike cells called asci.

6. A zygomycete is characterized by
   a. septate hyphae.
   b. mostly sexual reproduction.
   c. + and − mating strains.
   d. the tendency to form mycorrhizal associations with plant roots.
   e. a life cycle in which karyogamy does not occur.

7. Which of the following best describes a lichen? It is
   a. a fungus that breaks down rock to provide nutrients for an alga.
   b. the last organisms(s) to colonize bare rocks and convert them to soil.
   c. an organism that spends part of the life cycle as a photosymbiont and part as a mycobiont.
   d. an association between a basidiomycete and an ascomycete.
   e. an association between a green alga and a fungus.

Questions for Discussion

1. A mycologist wants to classify a specimen that appears to be a new species of fungus. To begin the classification process, what kinds of information on structures and/or functions must the researcher obtain to assign the fungus to one of the major fungal groups?

2. In a natural setting—a pile of horse manure in a field, for example—the sequence in which various fungi appear illustrates ecological succession, the replacement of one species by another in a community. The earliest fungi are the most efficient opportunists because they can form and disperse spores most rapidly. In what order would you expect representatives from each phylum of fungi to appear on the manure pile? Why?

3. As the text noted, conifers and some other types of plants cannot grow properly if their roots do not form associations with fungi. These associations provide the plant with minerals such as nitrogen and phosphate and in return fungi receive carbohydrates synthesized by the plant. In some instances, however, the plant receives proportionately more nutrients than the fungus does. Would you still classify such associations as mutualisms?

4. What evidence would you look for to determine whether the association between a plant and an endophyte was mutualistic?

5. Why is it more difficult to develop drugs against fungal infections of humans than bacterial infections?

Monotropa uniflora, a heterotrophic plant that lacks chlorophyll.

© Peter F. Zika/Visuals Unlimited

25 Plants

WHY IT MATTERS

You are out for a walk in a forest near your home; you are busy thinking about other things and so are not paying close attention to the plants that you're walking by—they are just a pleasing green background for your walk. Suddenly, your eye is caught by a small, glaringly white plant, like the one shown in the photo above—at least you think it's a plant. But aren't all plants green? How can there be a completely white plant?

What you have found is a plant known as ghost flower or Indian pipe (*Monotropa uniflora*), an achlorophyllous plant that does not produce chlorophyll and so cannot photosynthesize. Achlorophyllous plants like this are not photoautotrophs like most plants but instead are heterotrophs, living on organic carbon obtained from other plants. How do they get this carbon? They feed on neighbouring trees through shared root-colonizing fungi (mycorrhizal fungi; see Chapter 24).

What features could you look for to determine whether this *Monotropa* is a plant? What characteristics set plants apart from other organisms? And how did plants evolve? In this chapter, we investigate these questions and look at the adaptations to terrestrial life that have made plants so successful. And they are very successful organisms: they can thrive in habitats where no animal can survive for long and are able to grow much larger and live much longer than do animals. Together with photosynthetic bacteria and protists, plant tissues provide the nutritional foundation for nearly all communities of life. Humans also use plants as sources of medicinal drugs, wood for building, fibres used in paper and clothing, and a wealth of other products. The partnership between humans and plants goes back at least 9000 years, when we first domesticated cereal plants for crops.

Despite the long history between plants and humans, there is still much about their biology that we don't understand and many questions that remain to be answered.

We start by considering the defining characteristics of plants and then look at the evolution of plants and their adaptations to life on land; we conclude by looking at the diversity of land plants.

25.1 Defining Characteristics of Land Plants

Land plants are eukaryotes; as we learned from the *Monotropa* example, not all are capable of photosynthesizing, but almost all plants are photoautotrophs. Like animals, they are all multicellular, but if you'd taken a piece of tissue from the *Monotropa* and looked at it under the microscope, you'd see that, unlike animal cells, the cells have walls, which are made of cellulose. All plants are sessile or stationary (not able to move around); no terrestrial animals are sessile, although some aquatic ones are. Plants also have a very different life cycle from animals, known as an **alternation of generations** life cycle.

For sexually reproducing organisms, meiosis in diploid cells produces haploid (n) cells (see Chapter 10). In animals, the cells produced by meiosis are gametes—sperm or eggs—but in plants (and fungi), meiosis gives rise to **spores**, which can give rise to a new haploid individual asexually, without mating.

In most animals, the diploid stage dominates the life cycle, with single-celled gametes as the only haploid stage, which is short-lived: fusion of gametes produces a new diploid stage (some animals, e.g., social insects such as bees and wasps, have a different life cycle). In other organisms, such as many green algae, the haploid stage dominates the life cycle; the haploid alga spends much of its life producing and releasing gametes into the surrounding water. The single-celled zygote is the only diploid stage and divides by meiosis to produce spores that give rise to the haploid stage again.

In contrast, land plants have two multicellular stages in their life cycles, one diploid and one haploid **(Figure 25.1)**. The diploid generation produces spores and is called a **sporophyte** ("*phyte* = plant,"

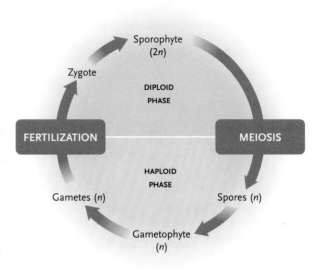

Figure 25.1

Overview of the alternation of generations, the basic pattern of the plant life cycle. The relative dominance of haploid and diploid phases is different for different plant groups.

hence "spore-producing plant"). The haploid generation produces gametes and is called a **gametophyte** ("gamete-producing plant"). The haploid phase of the plant life cycle begins in specialized cells of the sporophyte, where haploid spores are produced by meiosis. When a spore germinates, it divides by mitosis to produce a multicellular haploid gametophyte. A gametophyte's function is to nourish and protect the forthcoming sporophyte generation. Each generation gives rise to the other—hence the name *alternation of generations* for this life cycle.

The final defining feature of land plants is that the embryo (new sporophyte generation) is retained inside gametophyte tissue. The reason for retention of embryos in parental tissue and for the rather complex life cycle will become clearer after we've looked at the evolution of plants and their transition onto land.

STUDY BREAK

1. What features of land plants differentiate them from other eukaryotes, for example, from fungi? From animals?
2. What is an alternation of generations life cycle? How does this differ from the life cycle of most animals?
3. What does meiosis produce in plants?

25.2 The Transition to Life on Land

Ages ago, along the shores of the ancient ocean, the only sound was the rhythmic muffled crash of waves breaking in the distance. There were no birds or other animals, no plants with leaves rustling in the breeze. In the preceding eons, oxygen-producing photosynthetic cells had come into being and had gradually changed the atmosphere. Solar radiation had converted much of the oxygen into a dense ozone layer—a shield against lethal doses of ultraviolet radiation, which had kept early organisms below the water's surface. Now, they could populate the land.

Cyanobacteria were probably the first to adapt to intertidal zones and then to spread into shallow, coastal streams. Later, green algae and fungi made the same journey. Around 480 million years ago, one group of green algae, living near the water's edge, or perhaps in a moist terrestrial environment, became the ancestors of modern plants. Several lines of evidence indicate that these algae were charophytes (a group discussed in Chapter 23): both groups have cellulose cell walls, they store energy captured during photosynthesis as starch, and their light-absorbing pigments include both chlorophyll *a* and chlorophyll *b*. Molecular data also support the relationship between the charophytes and land plants. Like other green algae, the charophyte lineage that produced the ancestor of land plants arose in water and has aquatic descendants today **(Figure 25.2)**. Yet because terrestrial environments pose very different challenges than aquatic environments, evolution in land plants produced a range of adaptations crucial to survival on dry land.

The algal ancestors of plants probably invaded land about 450 million years ago (mya). We say "probably" because the fossil record is sketchy in pinpointing when the first truly terrestrial plants appeared, and many important stages in evolution are not represented in the fossil record. Even in more recent deposits, the most common finds of possible plant parts are microscopic bits and pieces; easily identifiable parts such as leaves, stems, roots, and reproductive parts seldom occur together, and even if they do, it can be difficult to determine whether the fossilized bits all belong to the same individual. Whole plants are extremely rare. Adding to the challenge, some chemical and structural adaptations to life on land arose independently in several plant lineages. Despite these problems, botanists have been able to gain insight into several innovations and overall trends in plant evolution.

While the ancestors of land plants were making the transition to a fully terrestrial life, some remarkable adaptive changes unfolded. Eons of natural selection sorted out solutions to fundamental problems, among them avoiding desiccation, physically supporting the plant body in air, obtaining nutrients from soil, and reproducing sexually in environments where water would not be available for dispersal of eggs and sperm. With time, plants evolved features that not only addressed these problems but also provided access to a wide range of terrestrial environments. Those ecological opportunities opened the way for a dramatic radiation of varied plant species—and for the survival of plant-dependent organisms such as ourselves. Today the **kingdom Plantae** encompasses more than 300 000 living species, organized in this textbook into 10 phyla. These modern plants range from mosses, horsetails, and ferns, to conifers and flowering plants **(Figure 25.3, p. 550)**.

25.2a Early Biochemical and Structural Adaptations Enhanced Plant Survival on Land

The greatest challenge plants had to overcome to survive on land was how to survive in the dry terrestrial conditions. Unlike most modern-day plants, the earliest land plants lacked a waterproof **cuticle** (a outer waxy layer that prevents water loss from plant tissues) and specialized tissues to transport water from the soil through the plant body. These limitations restricted these early plants to moist habitats and made it necessary for them to stay small and grow close to the ground so that they could obtain water via diffusion. Like modern-day mosses, these plants were **poikilohydric** (*poikilo* = variable; *hydric* = relating to water), meaning that they have little control over their internal water content. Instead, their water content fluctuates with moisture levels in their environment: as their habitat dries out, so do their tissues, and their metabolic activities virtually cease. When external moisture levels rise, they quickly rehydrate and become metabolically active. How are poikilohydric plants able to survive prolonged dehydration that would be lethal to most plants? This question is explored further in *Life on the Edge*. Later-evolving plants were able to regulate water content and restrict water loss because they had cuticles covering their outer surfaces **(Figure 25.4a, p. 550)**, as well as **stomata** (singular, stoma; *stoma* = mouth), pores in the cuticle-covered surfaces **(Figure 25.4b)** that open and

Figure 25.2

Chara, a stonewort. This representative of the charophyte lineage is known commonly as a stonewort due to the calcium carbonate that accumulates on its surface.

© Courtesy Microbial Culture Collection, National Institute for Environmental Studies, Japan

a. Mosses growing on rocks

Craig Wood/Visuals Unlimited

b. A jack pine

Michael P. Gadomski/Photo Researchers, Inc.

c. An orchid

© Don Enright/iStockPhoto

Figure 25.3
Representatives of the kingdom Plantae. **(a)** Mosses growing on rocks. Mosses evolved relatively soon after plants made the transition to land. **(b)** A jack pine (*Pinus banksiana*). This species and other conifers belonging to the phylum Coniferophyta represent the gymnosperms. **(c)** An orchid, *Calypso bulbosa*, a showy example of a flowering plant.

close to regulate water loss (and are the main route for carbon dioxide to enter leaves; see Chapter 29). These plants also had specialized water-transport tissues, described further in the next section.

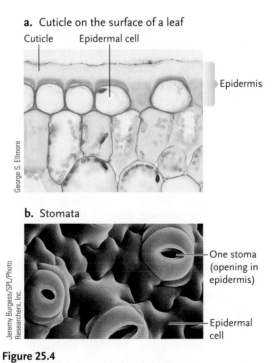

a. Cuticle on the surface of a leaf

Cuticle   Epidermal cell

Epidermis

George S. Ellmore

b. Stomata

Jeremy Burgess/SPL/Photo Researchers, Inc.

One stoma (opening in epidermis)

Epidermal cell

Figure 25.4
Adaptations for limiting water loss. **(a)** A waxy cuticle, which covers the epidermis of land plants and helps reduce water loss. **(b)** Surface view of stomata in the epidermis (surface layer of cells) of a leaf. Stomata allow carbon dioxide to enter plant tissues and oxygen and water to leave.

25.2b Symbiotic Associations with Fungi Were Likely Required for Evolution of Land Plants

The ancestor of land plants was not the first organism to colonize terrestrial habitats; certain bacteria, protists, and fungi had been present since the late Proterozoic (around 540 mya). Almost all modern-day plants form symbiotic associations, known as mycorrhizas, with certain soil fungi (see Chapter 24). In these associations, the fungus colonizes the plant's roots and grows prolifically in the soil beyond the root system **(Figure 25.5)**. Both partners generally benefit by a two-way exchange of nutrients: the plant provides the fun-gus with carbon, and the fungus increases the plant's supply of soil nutrients, which it is able to obtain much more efficiently than do the plant's own roots. Such mutually beneficial relationships may have been essential to the evolution of land plants and to their success in terrestrial habitats (see *People Behind Biology*).

25.2c Vascular Tissue Was an Innovation for Transporting Substances within a Large Plant Body

As mentioned above, the earliest land plants did not have specialized water-conducting tissue. Growing low to the ground helped them stay moist but was not very effective in capturing light; since all early land plants were low growing, there would have been intense competition for light. If any plant were able to grow taller than its neighbours, it would have had a major advantage. But how could a plant support upright growth against the force of gravity? Plants require strengthening tissue to grow upright. And growing up and away from the ground surface also requires an internal water circulation system since diffusion is not effective over larger differences. Both

Prof. D. J. Read, University of Sheffield

Figure 25.5
Mycorrhizal fungus colonizing plant root and soil around the root.

Kris Pirozynski, Biosystematics Research Institute of Agriculture Canada; David Malloch, Professor Emeritus, University of Toronto

If almost all land plants today are dependent to some extent on mutually beneficial relationships with mycorrhizal fungi, would the first land plants have been any different? The hypothesis that mutualisms with fungi were required for the evolution of land plants was first put forward in 1975 by two researchers at the Biosystematics Research Institute of Agriculture Canada and has since received strong support from both fossil and molecular data.

In their 1975 paper outlining their hypothesis, Kris Pirozynski and David Malloch pointed out that associations with fungi would have helped the earliest land plants avoid starvation: early soils would not have been as fertile as most modern-day soils, and nutrients would certainly not have been as abundant as in the aquatic environments in which the algal ancestor of land plants lived. Fungi are very adept at proliferating in their substrates and foraging for nutrients, which they take

up via extracellular enzymatic digestion (see Chapter 24). The earliest plants did not have roots, so forming a partnership with fungi would greatly have enhanced their uptake of nutrients. The fungi might also have protected the roots of its plant partner from root pathogens, as do modern-day mycorrhizal fungi.

Pirozynski and Malloch's hypothesis has since received strong support from both the fossil record and molecular data.

---

challenges were solved by the evolution of **xylem**, specialized tissue that transports water through the plant body and is made up of cells whose walls are reinforced with **lignin**, a tough complex polymer that strengthens the cell wall and allows for upright growth (see *Molecule Behind Biology*).

Xylem is one type of **vascular tissue** (*vas* = duct or vessel). Plants with this tissue (and the other type of vascular tissue, **phloem**, which conducts sugars through the plant body) are known as **vascular plants**. Chapter 29 explains how xylem and phloem perform these key internal transport functions.

Ferns, conifers, and flowering plants—most of the plants you are familiar with—are vascular

plants. Supported by lignin and with a well-developed vascular system, the body of a plant can grow very large. Extreme examples are the giant redwood trees of the northern California coast, some of which are more than 90 m tall. By contrast, nonvascular plants lack lignin, have very simple internal transport systems or none at all, and are generally small **(Table 25.1)**.

Vascular plants also have **apical meristems**, regions of constantly dividing cells near the tips of shoots and roots that produce all tissues of the plant body. Meristem tissue is the foundation for a vascular plant's extensively branching stem and root systems and is a central topic of Chapter 28.

Table 25.1   **Trends in Plant Evolution**

Traits derived from algal ancestor: cell walls with cellulose, energy stored in starch, two forms of chlorophyll (a and b)

Bryophytes	Ferns and Their Relatives	Gymnosperms	Angiosperms	Functions in Land Plants
Cuticle	→		→	Protection against water loss, pathogens
Stomata	→		→	Regulation of water loss and gas exchange (CO_2 in, O_2 out)
Nonvascular →	Vascular →		→	Internal tubes that transport water, nutrients
	Lignin →		→	Mechanical support for vertical growth
	Apical meristem →		→	Branching shoot system
	Roots, stems, leaves →		→	Enhanced uptake, transport of nutrients, and enhanced photosynthesis
Haploid phase dominant →	Diploid phase dominant →		→	Genetic diversity
One spore type (homospory) →	homospory in most but heterospory (two spore types) in some →	heterospory →	→	Promotion of genetic diversity
Motile sperm →		Nonmotile sperm →	→	Protection of gametes within parent body
Seedless →		Seeds →	→	Protection of embryo

Coniferyl Alcohol, a Building Block of Lignin

How is lignin formed, and how did it first evolve? Lignin is a polymer of several different monomers, including coniferyl alcohol **(Figure 1)**. These molecules are synthesized from the amino acid phenylalanine in a series of reactions in the cytoplasm. The monomers are then transported through the cell membrane, where polymerization happens. We still do not fully understand how lignin is formed

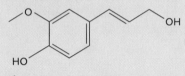

Figure 1
Coniferyl alcohol, one of the monomers of lignin.

from monomers, but we do know that oxidative enzymes are involved in polymerization; thus, oxygen is required for the process. Lignin is thought to have evolved due to the high oxygen levels in the atmosphere around 430 million years ago, which would have favoured the polymerization reaction.

Lignin is very difficult to degrade, with only a few fungi and bacteria able to break it down (see Chapter 24). Its accumulation in plant tissues would have meant that dead vascular plants, especially if large, would have decomposed more slowly than the earlier land plants, contributing to the formation of coal, one of today's fossil fuels. The forests of the Carboniferous period were dominated by large vascular

seedless plants, which were abundant in lignin. When these plants died and fell to the ground, they became buried in anaerobic sediments; even those that were not buried in such sediments would have been fairly slow to decompose due to their lignin content. Over geologic time, these buried remains became compressed and fossilized; today they form much of the world's coal reserves. This is why coal is called a "fossil fuel" and the Carboniferous period is called the Coal Age. Characterized by a moist climate over much of the planet and by the dominance of seedless vascular plants, the Carboniferous period continued for 150 million years, ending when climate patterns changed during the Paleozoic era.

25.2d Root and Shoot Systems Were Adaptations for Nutrition and Support

The body of a nonvascular plant is not differentiated into true roots and stems—structures that are fundamental adaptations for absorbing nutrients from soil and for support of an erect plant body. The evolution of sturdy stems—the basis of an aerial *shoot system*—went hand in hand with the capacity to synthesize lignin. To become large, land plants also require a means of anchoring aerial parts in the soil, as well as effective strategies for obtaining soil nutrients. **Roots**—anchoring structures that also absorb water and nutrients in association with mycorrhizal fungi—were the eventual solution to these problems. The earliest fossils showing clear evidence of roots are from vascular plants, although the exact timing of this change is uncertain. The first unquestioned fossils of a vascular plant, a small plant called *Cooksonia* **(Figure 25.6)**, were found in deposits that date to about 420 mya. *Cooksonia* fossils have been unearthed in various locales, but, frustratingly, none have ever included the lower portion of the plant—only its leafless, branching upper stems.

Figure 25.6
Fossil of one of the earliest vascular plants, *Cooksonia*, which dates to about 420 mya. *Cooksonia* was small, and as this image shows, its stems lacked leaves and probably were less than 3 cm long. The cup-shaped structures at the top of the stems produced reproductive spores.

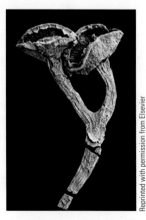

Reprinted with permission from Elsevier

Cooksonia probably was supported physically only by a **rhizome**—a horizontal, modified stem that can penetrate a substrate and anchor the plant. At some point, however, ancestral forms of vascular plants did come to have true roots. Ultimately, vascular plants developed specialized **root systems**, which generally consist of underground, cylindrical absorptive structures with a large surface area that favours the rapid uptake of soil water and dissolved mineral ions.

Above ground, the simple stems of early land plants also became more specialized, evolving into **shoot systems** in vascular plants. Shoot systems have stems and leaves that arise from apical meristems and that function in the absorption of light energy from the sun and carbon dioxide from the air. Stems grew larger and branched extensively after the evolution of lignin. The mechanical strength of lignified tissues almost certainly provided plants with several adaptive advantages. For instance, a strong, internal scaffold could support upright stems bearing leaves and other photosynthetic structures and so help increase the surface area for intercepting sunlight. Also, reproductive structures borne on aerial stems might serve as platforms for more efficient launching of spores from the parent plant.

Structures we think of as "leaves" arose several times during plant evolution. In general, leaves represent modifications of stems, and **Figure 25.7** illustrates the basic steps of two main evolutionary pathways. In at least one early group of plants, the club mosses described in Section 25.4, leaflike parts evolved as outgrowths of the plant's main vertical axis (see Figure 25.7a). In other groups, leaves arose when small,

a. Leaf development as an offshoot of the main vertical axis

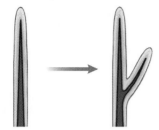

b. Development of leaves in a branching pattern

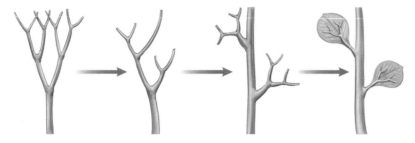

Figure 25.7

Evolution of leaves. **(a)** One type of early leaflike structure may have evolved as offshoots of the plant's main vertical axis; there was only one vein (transport vessel) in each leaf. Today, the seedless vascular plants known as lycophytes (club mosses) have this type of leaf. **(b)** In other groups of seedless vascular plants, leaves arose in a series of steps that began when the main stem evolved a branching growth pattern. Small side branches then fanned out and photosynthetic tissue filled the space between them, becoming the leaf blade. With time, the small branches became modified into veins.

neighbouring stem branches became joined by thin, weblike tissue containing cells that had chloroplasts (see Figure 25.7b).

Other land plant adaptations were related to the demands of reproduction in a dry environment. As described in more detail shortly, these adaptations included multicellular chambers that protect developing gametes and a dependent, multicellular embryo that is sheltered inside the tissues of a parent plant.

25.2e In the Plant Life Cycle, the Diploid Phase Became Dominant

As early plants moved into drier habitats, their life cycles also were modified considerably. As plants evolved on land, the haploid gametophyte phase became physically smaller and less complex and had a shorter life span, whereas the opposite occurred with the diploid sporophyte phase. In mosses and other nonvascular plants, the sporophyte is a little larger and long-lived than in green algae, and in vascular plants, the sporophyte clearly is larger and more complex and lives much longer than the gametophyte **(Figure 25.8).** When you look at a pine tree, for example, you see a large, long-lived sporophyte. The sporophyte generation begins after fertilization, when the zygote divides by mitosis to produce a multicellular diploid organism. Its body will eventually develop capsules called **sporangia** (*angium* = vessel or chamber," hence, "spore-producing chambers"; singular, sporangium), which produce spores by meiosis.

Why did the diploid phase become dominant over evolutionary time? Many botanists hypothesize that the trend toward "diploid dominance" reflects the advantage of being diploid in land environments; if there is only one copy of DNA, as in a haploid plant, and if a deleterious mutation occurs or if the DNA is damaged (e.g., by ultraviolet radiation, which is a greater problem on land than in aquatic habitats), the consequences could well be fatal. In contrast, the sporophyte phase of that plant is diploid and so has a

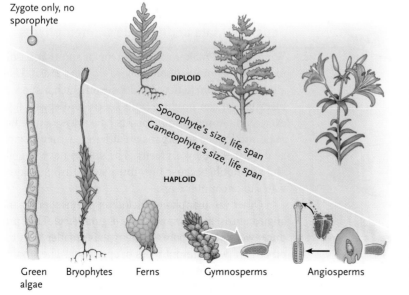

Zygote only, no sporophyte

DIPLOID

Sporophyte's size, life span

Gametophyte's size, life span

HAPLOID

Green algae   Bryophytes   Ferns   Gymnosperms   Angiosperms

Figure 25.8

Evolutionary trend from dominance of the gametophyte (haploid) generation to dominance of the sporophyte (diploid) generation, represented here by existing species ranging from a green alga (*Ulothrix*) to a flowering plant. This trend developed as early plants were colonizing habitats on land. In general, the sporophytes of vascular plants are larger and more complex than those of bryophytes, and their gametophytes are reduced in size and complexity. In this diagram, the fern represents seedless vascular plants.

Poikilohydric Plants

Most land plants, including our major crops, are killed if they dry out to the point of equilibrium with the water content of the air around them; this point is all too clearly illustrated by the terrible famines in Africa and other regions of the world that result from drought. But some plants are able to survive drying out to 10% absolute water content or less for months, and even years, in some cases **(Figure 1)**.

Figure 1
Desiccation-tolerant plant shown in a dehydrated state and following rewetting.

With kind permission from Springer Science + Business Media: Planta, "Molecular cloning of abscisic acid-modulated genes which are induced during desiccation of the resurrection plant", volume 181, April 1, 1990, pp. 27–34, Dorothea Bartels, figure: An illustration of the remarkable ability for extreme vegetative desiccation tolerance in an angiosperm species.

This ability is widespread among bryophytes but much less common in vascular plants: only about 50 species of seedless vascular plants have this ability in their sporophyte stage, along with about 300 species of angiosperms. Most of these desiccation-tolerant vascular plants, known as resurrection plants, live on rock outcrops in regions of southern Africa and Australia that receive only seasonal and sporadic rainfall. As far as we know, no gymnosperms have this ability.

How does dehydration kill a plant? Cellular water maintains membrane structure as well as the shapes of macromolecules such as enzymes and other proteins. Dehydration thus results in lethal changes to both membrane structure and macromolecular shape. A cell's metabolism also relies on water; as a cell dries out, metabolism first decreases and then ceases altogether. How do poikilohydric plants survive these changes that kill all other plants? We don't understand all of the mechanisms at play, but we do know that part of the answer is accumulation of sugars (e.g., sucrose) in cells.

These sugars and certain proteins replace the water in membranes and around macromolecules, preventing lethal changes in conformation. The high sugar content also converts the cytoplasm from its normal consistency to a thick, slow-moving liquid known as glass, immobilizing the cytoplasm. The cells are able to survive in a dehydrated state with metabolism slowed to a state of dormancy or "suspended animation." The cell walls of desiccation-tolerant plants are also more flexible, able to fold as the cell dries, allowing the entire cell to contract as it dries out.

These mechanisms come at a cost to the plant, limiting their growth and reproduction. We don't yet understand how tolerance restricts growth; once we have a better understanding of this relationship, might we be able to uncouple tolerance from slow growth and develop drought-tolerant plants with a higher productivity? This very active area of research clearly has practical applications in maintaining our food supply in the face of droughts and climate change.

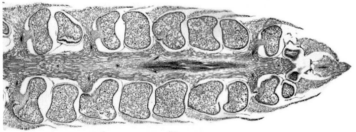

Lycopodium

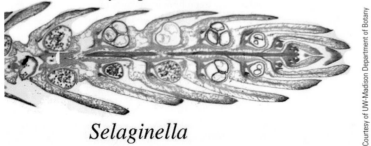

Selaginella

Courtesy of UW-Madison Department of Botany

Figure 25.9
Comparison of **(a)** homospory and **(b)** heterospory.

"backup" copy of the DNA that can continue to function normally even if one strand is damaged.

25.2f Some Vascular Plants Evolved Separate Male and Female Gametophytes

When a plant makes only one type of spore, it is said to be **homosporous** ("same spore") **(Figure 25.9a)**. Usually, a gametophyte that develops from such a spore is bisexual—it can produce both sperm and eggs. However, some homosporous plants have ways to produce male and female sex organs on different gametophytes, as described below in ferns. The sperm have flagella and are motile because they must swim through liquid water to encounter eggs.

Other vascular plants, including gymnosperms and angiosperms, are **heterosporous (Figure 25.9b).** They produce two types of spores—one type is smaller than the other—in two different types of sporangia. The smaller spores are **microspores**, which develop into male gametophytes, and the larger **megaspores** will develop into female gametophytes. Heterospory and the development of gametophytes inside spore walls are important steps in the evolution of the seed, as we will see further on.

As you will read in a later section, the evolution of seeds and related innovations, such as pollen grains and pollination, helped spark the rapid diversification of plants in the Devonian period, 408 to 360 mya. In fact, so many new fossils appear in Devonian rocks that paleobotanists—scientists who specialize in the study of fossil plants—have thus far been unable to determine which fossil lineages gave rise to the modern plant phyla. Clearly, however, as each major lineage came into being, its characteristic adaptations included major modifications of existing structures and functions (Figure 25.10).

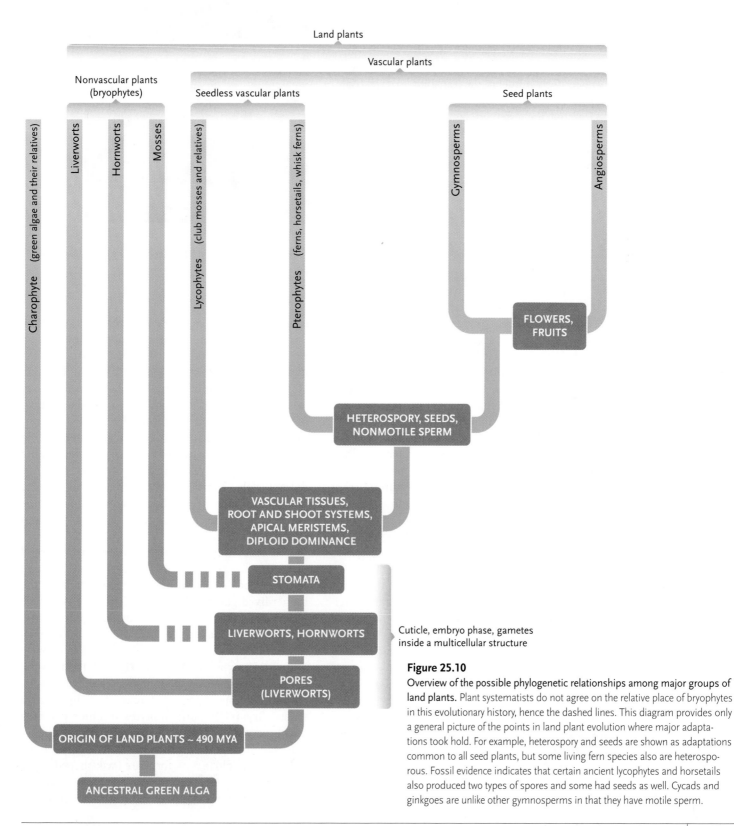

Figure 25.10

Overview of the possible phylogenetic relationships among major groups of land plants. Plant systematists do not agree on the relative place of bryophytes in this evolutionary history, hence the dashed lines. This diagram provides only a general picture of the points in land plant evolution where major adaptations took hold. For example, heterospory and seeds are shown as adaptations common to all seed plants, but some living fern species also are heterosporous. Fossil evidence indicates that certain ancient lycophytes and horsetails also produced two types of spores and some had seeds as well. Cycads and ginkgoes are unlike other gymnosperms in that they have motile sperm.

The next sections fill out this general picture, beginning with the plants that are the living representatives of the earliest land plants.

STUDY BREAK

1. What features do land plants share with their closest living relatives, the charophyte algae? What features differentiate the two groups?
2. How did mycorrhizal fungi fulfill the role we associate with roots in early land plants?
3. How did plant adaptations such as a root system, a shoot system, and a vascular system collectively influence the transition to terrestrial life?
4. Describe the difference between homospory and heterospory and explain how heterospory paved the way for other reproductive adaptations in land plants.

25.3 Bryophytes: Nonvascular Land Plants

The **bryophytes** (*bryon* = moss)—liverworts, hornworts, and mosses—are important both ecologically and economically. As colonizers of bare land, their small bodies trap particles of organic and inorganic matter, helping to build soil on bare rock and stabilizing soil surfaces with a biological crust in harsh places such as coastal dunes, inland deserts, and embankments created by road construction. In **arctic tundras**, bryophytes constitute as much as half of the biomass, and they are crucial components of the food web that supports animals in that ecosystem. People have long used *Sphagnum* and other absorbent "peat" mosses (which typically grow in bogs) for everything from primitive diapers and filtering whiskey to increasing the water-holding capacity of garden soil. Peat moss also has found use as a fuel; each day, the Rhode generating station in Ireland, one of several in that nation, burns 2000 tonnes of peat to produce electricity.

Bryophytes have a curious combination of traits that allow them to bridge aquatic and land environments. Because bryophytes lack vascular tissue and are poikilohydric, it is not surprising that they are small and commonly grow on wet sites along creek banks (see Figure 25.3a); in bogs, swamps, or the dense shade of damp forests; and on moist tree trunks or rooftops. However, some mosses live in very dry environments, such as alpine and arctic tundra **(Figure 25.11)**. Being poikilohydric enables them to live in such seemingly inhospitable habitats (see *Life on the Edge*).

Bryophytes retain many of the features of their algal ancestors: they produce flagellated sperm that

b.

Figure 25.11
Bryophytes of arid habitats: **(a)** moss growing on exposed rock; **(b)** mosses and other plants in alpine tundra.

must swim through water to reach eggs and lack a complex vascular system (although some have a primitive type of conducting tissue). Bryophytes have parts that are rootlike, stemlike, and leaflike. However, the "roots" are **rhizoids** that serve only to anchor the plant to its substrate and do not take up any water or nutrients from the substrate. Bryophyte "stems" and "leaves" are not considered to be true stems and leaves like those of vascular plants because they lack vascular tissue and because they did not evolve from the same structures as vascular plant stems and leaves did. (Said another way, stems and leaves are not homologous in bryophytes and vascular plants.)

In other ways, bryophytes are clearly adapted to land. Along with their leaflike, stemlike, and fibrous, rootlike organs, the sporophytes (but not the longer-lived gametophytes) of some species have a water-conserving cuticle and stomata. And, as is true of all plants, the life cycle has both multicellular gametophyte and sporophyte phases, although the sporophyte is tiny and lives only a short time. **Figure 25.12** shows the green, leafy gametophyte of a moss plant, with miniscule diploid sporophytes attached to it by slender stalks. Bryophyte gametophytes produce gametes sheltered within a layer of protective cells called a **gametangium** (plural, gametangia). The gametangia in which bryophyte eggs form are flask-shaped structures called **archegonia** (*archi* = first; *gonos* = seed). Flagellated sperm form in rounded gametangia called

a. Moss gametophyte with attached sporophytes

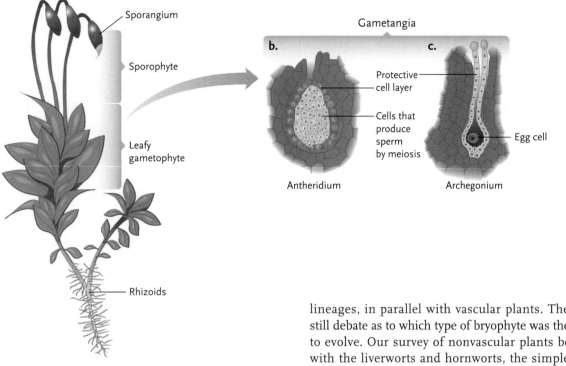

Sporangium

Sporophyte

Leafy gametophyte

Rhizoids

Gametangia

b.

Protective cell layer

Cells that produce sperm by meiosis

Antheridium

c.

Egg cell

Archegonium

Figure 25.12
Multicellular structures enclosing plant gametes, a bryophyte innovation. **(a)** The gametophyte and sporophyte phases of the moss *Mnium*. In this species, the gametangia are embedded in tissue of the gametophyte. In some other bryophytes, the gametangia are attached on the gametophyte's surface. The two types of moss gametangia are the **(b)** antheridium, containing cells from which sperm arise, and the **(c)** archegonium, containing an egg cell. The zygote that results from fertilization of an egg cell gives rise to a sporophyte.

antheridia (*antheros* = flowerlike; singular, antheridium). The sperm swim through a film of water to the archegonia and fertilize eggs. Each fertilized egg gives rise to a diploid embryo sporophyte, which stays attached to the gametophyte and produces spores—and the cycle repeats.

Despite these similarities with more complex plants, bryophytes are unique in several ways. Unlike vascular plants, the gametophyte is much larger and longer-lived than the sporophyte and is photosynthetic, whereas the comparatively tiny sporophyte remains attached to the gametophyte and depends on the gametophyte for much of its nutrition.

Bryophytes are not a monophyletic group (i.e., they did not all evolve from a common ancestor); instead, the various bryophytes evolved as separate lineages, in parallel with vascular plants. There is still debate as to which type of bryophyte was the first to evolve. Our survey of nonvascular plants begins with the liverworts and hornworts, the simplest of the group, and concludes with mosses—plants that not only are more familiar to most of us but whose structure and physiology more closely resemble those of vascular plants.

25.3a Liverworts May Have Been the First Land Plants

Liverworts make up the phylum **Hepatophyta**, so called because early herbalists thought that these small plants were shaped like the lobes of the human liver (*hepat* = liver; *wort* = herb). The resemblance might be a little vague to modern eyes: many of the 6000 species of liverworts consist of a flat, branching, ribbonlike plate of tissue closely pressed against damp soil **(Figure 25.13a)**. This simple body, called a **thallus** (plural, thalli), is the gametophyte generation.

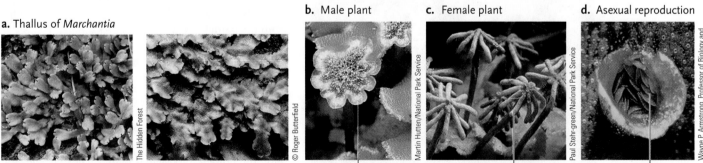

a. Thallus of *Marchantia*

The Hidden Forest

© Roger Butterfield

b. Male plant

Male gametophyte

Martin Hutten/National Park Service

c. Female plant

Female gametophyte

Paul Stehr-green/National Park Service

d. Asexual reproduction

Gemmae

Wayne P. Armstrong, Professor of Biology and Botany, Palomar College, San Francisco, CA

Figure 25.13
The bryophyte *Marchantia*; **(a)** thallus of *Marchantia*, the only liverwort to produce **(b)** male and **(c)** female gametophytes on separate plants. *Marchantia* also reproduces sexually by way of **(d)** gemmae, multicellular vegetative bodies that develop in tiny cups on the plant body. Gemmae can grow into new plants when splashing raindrops transport them to suitable sites.

Threadlike rhizoids anchor the gametophytes to their substrate. None have true stomata, the openings that regulate gas exchange in most other land plants, although some species do have pores. They lack some features present in the other two groups of bryophytes; this evidence, together with molecular data, suggests that liverworts were probably the first land plants.

We will look at one genus, *Marchantia* (see Figure 25.13), as an example of liverwort reproduction. Separate male and female gametophytes produce sexual organs (antheridia and archegonia) on tall stalks **(Figure 25.13b, c)**. The motile sperm released from antheridia swim through surface water to reach the eggs inside archegonia. After fertilization, a small, diploid sporophyte develops inside the archegonium, matures there, and produces haploid spores by meiosis. During meiosis, sex chromosomes segregate, so some spores have the male genotype and others the female genotype. As in other liverworts, the spores develop inside jacketed sporangia that split open to release the spores. A spore that is carried by air currents to a suitable location germinates and gives rise to a haploid gametophyte, which is either male or female. *Marchantia* also can reproduce asexually by way of **gemmae** (*gem* = bud; singular, gemma), small cell masses that form in cuplike growths on a thallus **(Figure 25.13d)**. Gemmae can grow into new thalli when rainwater splashes them out of the cups and onto an appropriately moist substrate.

25.3b Hornworts Have Both Plantlike and Algalike Features

Roughly 100 species of hornworts make up the phylum **Anthocerophyta**. Like some liverworts, a hornwort gametophyte has a flat thallus, but the sporangium of the sporophyte phase is long and pointed, like a horn **(Figure 25.14)**, and splits into two or three ribbonlike

Figure 25.14

The hornwort *Anthoceros*. The base of each long, slender sporophyte is embedded into the flattened, leafy gametophyte.

sections when it releases spores. Sexual reproduction occurs in basically the same way as in liverworts, and hornworts also reproduce asexually by fragmentation as pieces of a thallus break off and develop into new individuals.

25.3c Mosses Most Closely Resemble Vascular Plants

Chances are that you have seen, touched, or sat on at least some of the approximately 10 000 species of mosses, and the use of the name **Bryophyta** for this phylum underscores the fact that mosses are the best-known bryophytes, forming tufts or carpets of vegetation on the surface of rocks, soil, or bark.

The moss life cycle, diagrammed in **Figure 25.15**, begins when a haploid (*n*) spore lands on a wet soil surface. After the spore germinates, it elongates and branches into a filamentous web of tissue called a **protonema** ("first thread"), which can become dense enough to colour the surface of soil, rocks, or bark visibly green. After several weeks of growth, the budlike cell masses on a protoncma develop into leafy, green gametophytes anchored by rhizoids. A single protonema can be extremely prolific, producing bud after bud, thus giving rise to a dense clone of genetically identical gametophytes. Leafy mosses also may reproduce asexually by gemmae produced at the surface of rhizoids and on aboveground parts.

Antheridia and archegonia are produced at the tips of male and female gametophytes, respectively. Propelled by flagella, sperm released from antheridia swim through a film of dew or rainwater and down a channel in the neck of the archegonium, attracted by a chemical gradient secreted by each egg. Fertilization produces the new sporophyte generation inside the archegonium, in the form of diploid zygotes that develop into small, mature sporophytes, each consisting of a sporangium on a stalk. Moss sporophytes may eventually develop chloroplasts and nourish themselves photosynthetically, but initially they depend on the gametophytes for food. Even after a moss sporophyte begins photosynthesis, it still must obtain water, carbohydrates, and some other nutrients from the gametophyte.

Certain moss gametophytes are structurally complex, with features similar to those of higher plants. For example, some species have a central strand of primitive conducting tissue. One kind of tissue is made up of elongated, thin-walled, dead and empty cells that conduct water. In a few mosses, the water-conducting cells are surrounded by sugar-conducting tissue resembling the phloem of vascular plants. These tissues did not give rise to the xylem and phloem of vascular plants, however.

In the next section, we turn to the vascular plants, which have specialized tissues that can transport

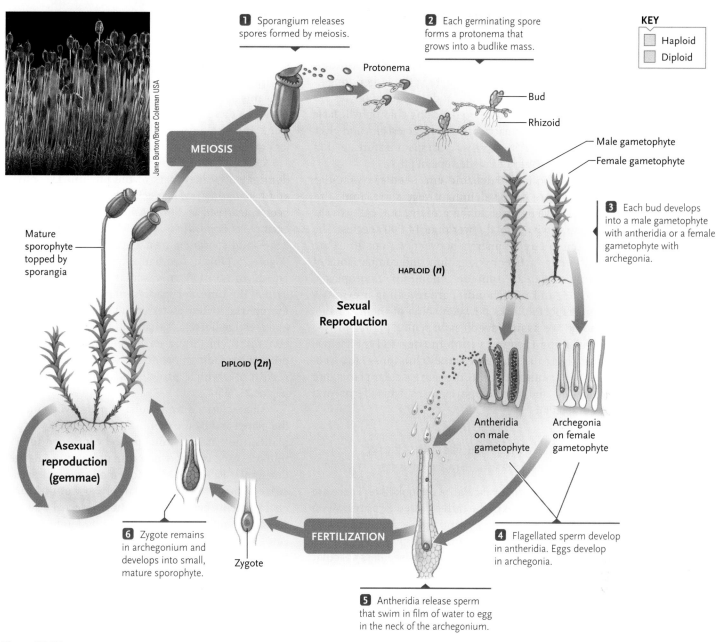

1 Sporangium releases spores formed by meiosis.

2 Each germinating spore forms a protonema that grows into a budlike mass.

Protonema

Bud

Rhizoid

KEY

Haploid
Diploid

Male gametophyte

Female gametophyte

MEIOSIS

3 Each bud develops into a male gametophyte with antheridia or a female gametophyte with archegonia.

HAPLOID (*n*)

Mature sporophyte topped by sporangia

Sexual Reproduction

DIPLOID (2*n*)

Asexual reproduction (gemmae)

Antheridia on male gametophyte

Archegonia on female gametophyte

6 Zygote remains in archegonium and develops into small, mature sporophyte.

Zygote

FERTILIZATION

4 Flagellated sperm develop in antheridia. Eggs develop in archegonia.

5 Antheridia release sperm that swim in film of water to egg in the neck of the archegonium.

Jane Burton/Bruce Coleman USA

Figure 25.15
Life cycle of the moss *Polytrichum*.

water, minerals, and sugars. Without the capacity to move these substances efficiently throughout the plant body, large sporophytes could not have survived on land. Unlike bryophytes, modern vascular plants are monophyletic—all groups are descended from a common ancestor.

STUDY BREAK

1. Give some examples of bryophyte features that bridge aquatic and terrestrial environments.
2. How do specific aspects of a moss plant's anatomy resemble those of vascular plants?

25.4 Seedless Vascular Plants

The first vascular plants, which did not produce seeds, were the dominant plants on Earth for almost 200 million years, until seed plants became abundant. The fossil record shows that seedless vascular plants were well established by the late Silurian, about 428 mya, and they flourished until the end of the Carboniferous, about 250 mya. Some living seedless vascular plants have certain bryophyte-like traits, whereas others have some characteristics of seed plants. On the one hand, like bryophytes, seedless vascular plants disperse themselves by releasing spores, and they have swimming sperm that require free water to reach eggs. On the other hand, as in seed plants, the sporophyte of a seedless vascular plant becomes independent of the gametophyte at a certain point in its development and has well-developed vascular tissues (xylem and phloem). Also, the sporophyte is the larger, longer-lived stage of the life cycle and the gametophytes are very small, with some even lacking chlorophyll. **Table 25.2, p. 573** summarizes these characteristics and gives an overview of seedless vascular plant features within the larger context of modern plant phyla.

In the late Paleozoic era, seedless vascular plants were Earth's dominant vegetation. Some lineages have endured to the present, but, collectively, these survivors total fewer than 14 000 species. The taxonomic relationships between various lines are still under active investigation, and comparisons of gene sequences from the genomes in chloroplasts, nuclei, and mitochondria are revealing previously unsuspected links between some of them. In this book, we assign seedless vascular plants to two phyla, the Lycophyta (club mosses and their close relatives; the common name "club moss" for lycophytes is misleading, as they are vascular plants, not mosses) and the **Pterophyta** (ferns, whisk ferns, and horsetails).

25.4a Early Seedless Vascular Plants Flourished in Moist Environments

What did the first vascular plant look like? There are no living relatives of the earliest vascular plants, so we rely on fossil data to answer this question. The extinct genus *Cooksonia* (see Figure 25.6) probably was one of the earliest ancestors of modern seedless vascular plants. Like other members of its extinct phylum, *Cooksonia* was small, rootless, and leafless, but its simple stems had a central core of xylem, an arrangement seen in many existing vascular plants. Mudflats and swamps of the damp Devonian period were dominated by plants such as *Cooksonia* and *Rhynia* **(Figure 25.16)**. Although these and other now-extinct phyla came and went, ancestral forms of both modern phyla of seedless vascular plants appeared.

Carboniferous forests were swampy places dominated by members of the phylum **Lycophyta**, and fascinating fossil specimens of this group have been unearthed in North America and Europe. One example is *Lepidodendron*, which had broad, straplike leaves and sporangia near the ends of the branches **(Figure 25.17b)**. It also had xylem and other tissues typical of all modern vascular plants. Also abundant at the time were representatives of the phylum **Pterophyta**, including ferns and giants such as *Calamites*—huge horsetails that could have a trunk diameter of 30 cm. Some early seed plants also were present, including now-extinct fernlike plants, called seed ferns, which bore seeds at the tips of leaves **(Figure 25.16b)**.

Characterized by a moist climate over much of the planet and by the dominance of seedless vascular plants, the Carboniferous period continued for 150 million years, ending when climate patterns changed during the Paleozoic era. Most modern seedless vascular plants are confined largely to wet or humid environments because they require external water for reproduction. However, some are poikilohydric and can survive in a dehydrated state for long periods of time (see *Life on the Edge*).

Figure 25.16

Rhynia, an early seedless vascular plant. **(a)** Fossil-based reconstruction of the entire plant, about 30 cm tall. **(b)** Cross section of the stem, approximately 3 mm in diameter. This fossil was embedded in chert approximately 400 million years ago. Still visible in it are traces of the transport tissues xylem and phloem, along with other specialized tissues.

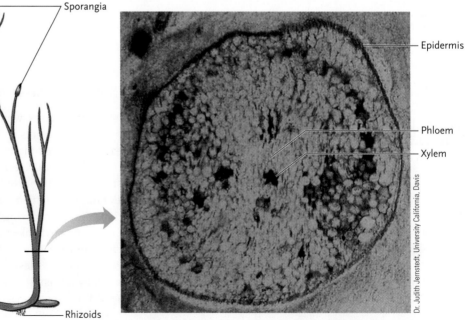

a. *Rhynia*

Sporangia

Upright stems

Rhizome

Rhizoids

b. *Rhynia* stem in cross section

Epidermis

Phloem

Xylem

Dr. Judith Jernstedt, University California, Davis

a. The lycophyte tree *(Lepidodendron)*   **b.** Artist's depiction of a Coal Age forest

Stem of a giant
lycophyte
(Lepidodendron)

Seed fern *(Medullosa)*; probably
related to the progymnosperms,
which may have been among the
earliest seed-bearing plants

Stem of a giant
horsetail *(Calamites)*

Field Museum of Natural History, Chicago

Figure 25.17

Reconstruction of the lycophyte tree *(Lepidodendron)* and its environment. **(a)** Fossil evidence suggests that *Lepidodendron* grew to be about 35 m tall with a trunk 1 m in diameter. **(b)** Artist's depiction of a Coal Age forest.

25.4b Modern Lycophytes Are Small and Have Simple Vascular Tissues

Lycophytes were highly diverse 350 mya, when some tree-sized forms inhabited lush swamp forests. Today, however, such giants are no more. The most familiar of the 1000 or so living species of lycophytes are club mosses (e.g., species of *Lycopodium* and *Selaginella*), which grow on forest floors **(Figure 25.18).** Club moss sporophytes have upright or horizontal stems that contain xylem and bear small green leaves and roots. Sporangia are clustered at the bases of specialized leaves, called **sporophylls** (*phyll* = leaf; thus, sporophyll = "spore-bearing leaf"). Sporophylls are clustered into a **cone** or **strobilus** (plural = strobili) at the tips of stems. Most lycophytes are homosporous, but some are heterosporous, producing two types of spores that will in turn produce separate male and female gametophytes.

Lycopodium sporophyte

Strobilus

© Ed Reschke/Peter Arnold, Inc.

Figure 25.18

Lycophytes. *Lycopodium* sporophyte, showing the conelike strobili in which spores are produced.

25.4c Ferns, Whisk Ferns, Horsetails, and Their Relatives Make Up the Diverse Phylum Pterophyta

Second in size only to the flowering plants, the phylum Pterophyta (*pteron* = wing) contains a large and diverse group of vascular plants—the 13 000 or so species of ferns, whisk ferns, and horsetails. Most ferns, including some that are popular houseplants, are native to tropical and temperate regions. Some floating species are less than 1 cm across, whereas some tropical tree ferns grow to 25 m tall. Other species are adapted to life in arctic and **alpine tundras**, salty mangrove swamps, and semi-arid deserts.

Features of Ferns. The familiar plant body of a fern is the sporophyte phase **(Figure 25.19, p. 562),** which produces an aboveground clump of leaves. Young leaves are tightly coiled, and as they emerge above the soil, these "fiddleheads" (so named because they resemble the scrolled pegheads of violins) unroll

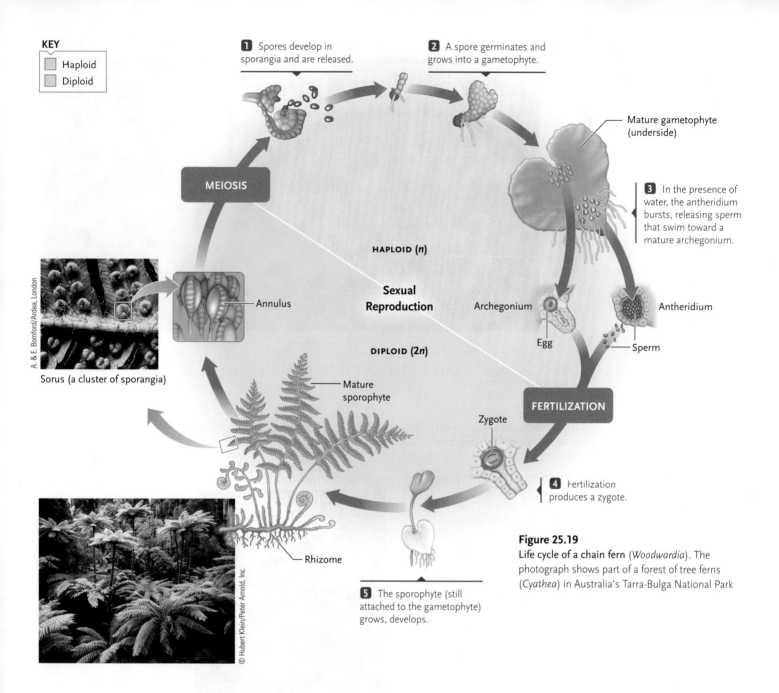

KEY
Haploid
Diploid

1 Spores develop in sporangia and are released.

2 A spore germinates and grows into a gametophyte.

Mature gametophyte (underside)

MEIOSIS

3 In the presence of water, the antheridium bursts, releasing sperm that swim toward a mature archegonium.

HAPLOID (*n*)

Sexual Reproduction

Archegonium

Antheridium

Egg

Sperm

DIPLOID (2*n*)

Annulus

A. & E. Bomford/Ardea, London

Sorus (a cluster of sporangia)

FERTILIZATION

Mature sporophyte

Zygote

4 Fertilization produces a zygote.

Figure 25.19

Life cycle of a chain fern (*Woodwardia*). The photograph shows part of a forest of tree ferns (*Cyathea*) in Australia's Tarra-Bulga National Park

Rhizome

© Hubert Klein/Peter Arnold, Inc.

5 The sporophyte (still attached to the gametophyte) grows, develops.

and expand. The fiddleheads of some species are edible when cooked, tasting similar to fresh asparagus, but be sure you have collected the right type of fiddlehead—some species contain a carcinogen.

Sporangia are produced on the lower surface or margins of leaves. Often several sporangia are clustered into a rust-coloured **sorus** ("heap"; plural, sori) (see Figure 25.18). Spores released from sporangia develop into gametophytes, which are typically small, heart-shaped plants anchored to the soil by rhizoids. Antheridia and archegonia develop on the underside of gametophytes, where moisture is trapped. Inside an antheridium is a globular packet of haploid cells, each of which develops into a helical sperm with many flagella. When water is present, the antheridium bursts, releasing the sperm. If mature archegonia are nearby, the sperm swim toward them, drawn by a chemical

attractant that diffuses from the neck of the archegonium, which is open when free water is present.

In some ferns, antheridia and archegonia are produced on a single bisexual gametophyte. In other ferns, the first spores to germinate develop into bisexual gametophytes, which produce a chemical (antheridiogen) that diffuses through the substrate and causes all later-germinating spores to develop into male gametophytes. What is the advantage of producing a few bisexual gametophytes followed by many male gametophytes? If a bisexual gametophyte is surrounded by several male gametophytes that developed from other spores, it is more likely that eggs will be fertilized by sperm from one of the male gametophytes rather than by its own sperm, thus increasing the genetic diversity of the resulting zygote.

An embryo is retained on and nourished by the gametophyte for the first part of its life but soon develops into a young sporophyte larger than the gametophyte, with its own green leaf and root system. Once the sporophyte is nutritionally independent, the parent gametophyte degenerates and dies.

Features of Whisk Ferns. The whisk ferns and their relatives are represented by only 2 genera, with about 10 species in total; we look at just one genus, *Psilotum* (pronounced si-lo'-tum) **(Figure 25.20)**. Whisk ferns grow in tropical and subtropical regions, often as epiphytes.

The sporophytes of *Psilotum* resemble the extinct vascular plants in that they lack true roots and leaves. Instead, small, leaflike scales adorn an upright, green, branching stem, which arises from a horizontal rhizome system anchored by rhizoids. Symbiotic fungi colonize the rhizoids, increasing the plant's uptake of soil nutrients (read more about these mycorrhizal fungi in Chapter 24). The stem is photosynthetic and bears sporangia above the small scales. Gametophytes of *Psilotum* are nonphotosynthetic and live underground **(Figure 25.21)**; like the sporophyte, they obtain nutrients via symbioses with mycorrhizal fungi.

Features of Horsetails. The ancient relatives of modern-day horsetails included treelike forms taller than a two-storey building. Only 15 species in a single genus, *Equisetum,* have survived to the present **(Figure 25.22)**. Horsetails grow in moist soil along streams and in disturbed habitats, such as roadsides and beds of railway tracks. Their sporophytes typically have underground rhizomes and roots that anchor the rhizome to the soil. Small, scalelike leaves are arranged in whorls about a photosynthetic stem that is stiff and gritty because horsetails accumulate silica in their tissues. Pioneers used them to scrub out pots and pans—hence their other common name, "scouring rushes."

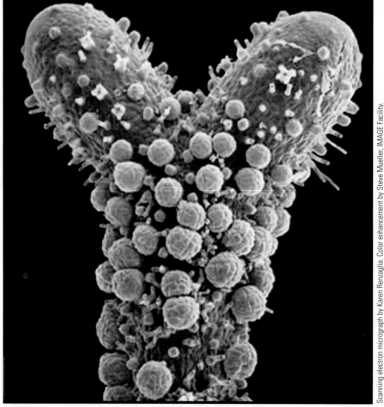

Scanning electron micrograph by Karen Renzaglia. Color enhancement by Steve Mueller. IMAGE Facility.

├─── 0.5 mm ───┤

Figure 25.21
Scanning electron micrograph image of the subterranean gametophyte of *Psilotum.* Antheridia have been coloured blue, and the smaller archegonia have been coloured pink.

a. Sporophyte stem   **b.** Sporangia

Strobilus, an aggregation of sporangia and sporophylls at the tip of the horsetail sporophyte

© Kratz/Zefa/CORBIS

c. Each petal-shaped sporangium of a strobilus contains spores that are formed by meiosis.

William Ferguson   W. H. Hodges

Figure 25.22
A species of *Equisetum,* the horsetails. **(a)** Vegetative stem. **(b)** Strobili, which bear sporangia. **(c)** Close-up of sporangium and associated structures on a strobilus.

Kingsley R. Stern

Figure 25.20
Sporophytes of a whisk fern (*Psilotum*), a seedless vascular plant. Three-lobed sporangia occur at the ends of stubby branchlets; inside the sporangia, meiosis gives rise to haploid spores.

As in lycophytes, *Equisetum* sporangia are borne in strobili. Haploid spores germinate within a few days to produce gametophytes, which are free-living plants about the size of a small pea.

25.4d Some Seedless Vascular Plants Are Heterosporous

Most seedless vascular plants are homosporous, but some (e.g., some lycophytes and some ferns) are heterosporous, producing microspores and megaspores in separate sporangia (see Figure 25.8). Both types of spores are usually shed from sporangia and germinate on the ground some distance from the parent plant. In many heterosporous plants, the gametophytes produced by the spores develop inside the spore wall; this **endosporous** development provides increased protection for the gametes and, later, for the developing embryo. The microspore gives rise to a male gametophyte, which produces motile sperm. At maturity, the microspore wall will rupture, releasing the sperm, which swim to the female gametophyte; water is thus still required for fertilization in these plants. The megaspore produces a female gametophyte inside the spore wall; archegonia of this gametophyte produce eggs as in other seedless plants.

STUDY BREAK

1. Compare the lycophyte and bryophyte life cycles with respect to the sizes and longevity of gametophyte and sporophyte phases.
2. How does the life cycle of a horsetail differ from that of a fern?

25.5 Gymnosperms: The First Seed Plants

Gymnosperms are the conifers and their relatives. The earliest fossils identified as gymnosperms are found in Devonian rocks. By the Carboniferous, when nonvascular plants were dominant, many lines of gymnosperms, including conifers, had also evolved. These radiated during the Permian period; the Mesozoic era that followed, 248 to 65 mya, was the age not only of the dinosaurs but of the gymnosperms as well.

The evolution of gymnosperms marked sweeping changes in plant structures related to reproduction. The evolution of gymnosperms included important reproductive adaptations—pollen and pollination, the ovule, and the seed. The fossil record has not revealed the sequence in which these changes arose, but all of them contributed to the radiation of gymnosperms into land environments.

As a prelude to our survey of modern gymnosperms, we begin by considering some of these innovations.

25.5a Major Reproductive Adaptations Occurred as Gymnosperms Evolved

The word *gymnosperm* is derived from the Greek *gymnos,* meaning naked, and *sperma,* meaning seed. As this name indicates, gymnosperms produce seeds that are exposed, not enclosed in fruit as are the seeds of other seed plants.

Ovules: Increased Protection for Female Gametophyte and Egg. How did seeds first arise? Think about the heterosporous plants described in the previous section and picture two steps that would lead us toward the development of a seed. In the first step, spores are not shed from the plant but instead are retained inside sporangia on the sporophyte. In the second step, the number of megaspores is reduced to just one per sporangium (i.e., four megaspores are produced by meiosis, but only one survives). These two steps result in retention of a single megaspore inside a megasporangium on a plant **(Figure 25.23).** As in all land plants, the megaspore will give rise to a female gametophyte; because this is a heterosporous plant, the gametophyte will develop inside the megaspore wall and inside the megasporangium. Physically connected to the sporophyte and surrounded by protective layers, a female gametophyte no longer faces the same risks of predation or environmental assault that can threaten a free-living gametophyte.

This new structure, of an egg developing inside a gametophyte that is retained not only inside the spore wall but also inside megasporangial tissue, is an **ovule.** When fertilized, an ovule becomes a **seed:** the

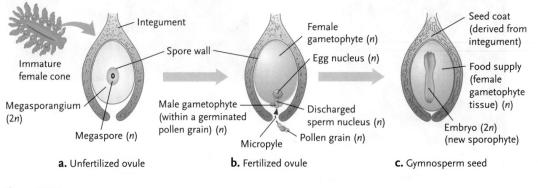

a. Unfertilized ovule   **b.** Fertilized ovule   **c.** Gymnosperm seed

Figure 25.23
Structure of an ovule.

fertilized egg will produce an embryo surrounded by nutritive tissue, all encased in sporangial tissue that has become a seed coat.

When you look at Figure 25.23, you can see that the megasporangium is surrounded by extra layers of sporophyte tissue, which would add additional protection for gametes and embryos, but this tissue, along with that of the megasporangium, has also created a problem: how can sperm get to the egg now that the gametophyte is enclosed inside these layers of tissue? The solution is similar to that of internal fertilization in animals: there needs to be a male structure that can penetrate through sporophyte tissue and release sperm inside the female gametophyte. In the next section, we look at the male gametophyte in seed plants.

Pollen: Eliminating the Need for Water in Reproduction. As for megaspores, the microspores of gymnosperms (and other seed plants) are not dispersed. Instead, they are retained inside microsporangia and are enveloped in additional layers of sporophyte tissue. As in other heterosporous plants, each microspore produces a male gametophyte, which develops inside the microspore wall. This male gametophyte is very small relative to those of nonseed plants—it is made of only a few cells—and is called a **pollen grain**. Pollen grains are transferred to female reproductive parts via air currents or on the bodies of animal pollinators; this transfer is known as **pollination**. When the pollen grain lands on female tissue, the pollen grain germinates to produce a **pollen tube (Figure 25.24),** a cell that grows through female gametophyte tissue by invasive growth and carries the nonmotile sperm to the egg.

Pollen and pollination were enormously important adaptations for gymnosperms because the shift to non-swimming sperm, along with a means for delivering them to female gametes, meant that reproduction no longer required liquid water. The only gymnosperms that have retained swimming sperm are the cycads and ginkgoes described shortly, which have relatively few living species and are restricted to just a few native habitats.

Seeds: Protecting and Nourishing Plant Embryos. As described above, a seed is the structure that forms when an ovule matures, after a pollen grain reaches it and a sperm fertilizes the egg. Seeds consist of three basic parts: (1) the embryo sporophyte, (2) tissues around it containing nutrients that nourish the embryo until it becomes established as a plantlet with leaves and roots, and (3) a tough, protective outer seed coat **(Figure 25.25).** This complex structure makes seeds ideal packages for sheltering an embryo from drought, cold, or other adverse conditions. As a result, seed plants enjoy a tremendous survival advantage over species that simply release spores to the environment. Encased in a seed, the embryo also can be transported far from its parent, as when ocean currents carry coconut seeds ("coconuts" protected in large, buoyant fruits) hundreds of kilometres across the sea. As discussed in Chapter 30, some plant embryos housed in seeds can remain dormant for months or years before environmental conditions finally prompt them to germinate and grow.

25.5b Modern Gymnosperms Include Conifers and a Few Other Groups Represented by Relatively Few Species That Tend to Be Restricted to Certain Climates

Today there are about 800 gymnosperm species. The sporophytes of nearly all are large trees or shrubs, although a few are woody vines.

Economically, gymnosperms, particularly conifers, are vital to human societies. They are sources of lumber, paper pulp, turpentine, and resins, among other products. They also have huge ecological importance. Their habitats range from tropical forests to deserts, but gymnosperms are most dominant in the cool-temperate zones of the Northern and Southern Hemispheres. They flourish in poor soils, where flowering plants don't compete as well. In Canada, for example, gymnosperms make up most of the boreal forests that cover about one-third of the country's landmass. Our survey of gymnosperms begins with the conifers and then we will look at the cycads, ginkgoes, and gnetophytes—the latter two groups are remnants of lineages that have all but vanished from the modern scene.

Conifers Are the Most Common Gymnosperms. About 80% of all living gymnosperm species are members of one phylum, the **Coniferophyta,** or conifers ("cone-bearers") such as pines, spruces, and firs. Coniferous trees and shrubs are longer-lived, and anatomically and

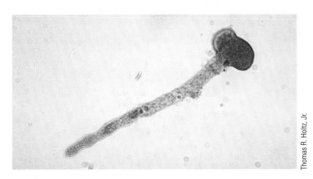

Figure 25.24
Pollen tube growth.

Thomas R. Holtz, Jr.

Seed coat

Embryo sporophyte

Nutritive tissue

Seed

Figure 25.25
Generalized view of the seed of a pine, a gymnosperm.

morphologically more complex, than any sporophyte phase we have discussed so far. Characteristically, they form woody cones, and most have needlelike leaves that are adapted to dry environments. For instance, needles have a thick cuticle, sunken stomata, and a fibrous epidermis, all traits that reduce the loss of water vapour.

Pines and many other gymnosperms produce resins, a mix of organic compounds that are by-products of metabolism. Resin accumulates and flows in long resin ducts through the wood, inhibiting the activity of wood-boring insects and certain microbes. Pine resin extracts are the raw material of turpentine and (minus the volatile terpenes), the sticky rosin used to treat violin bows. Fossil resin is known as amber and is commonly used in jewellery; often amber contains fossilized insects or even small animals.

We know a great deal about the pine life cycle (**Figure 25.26**), so it is a convenient model for gymnosperms.

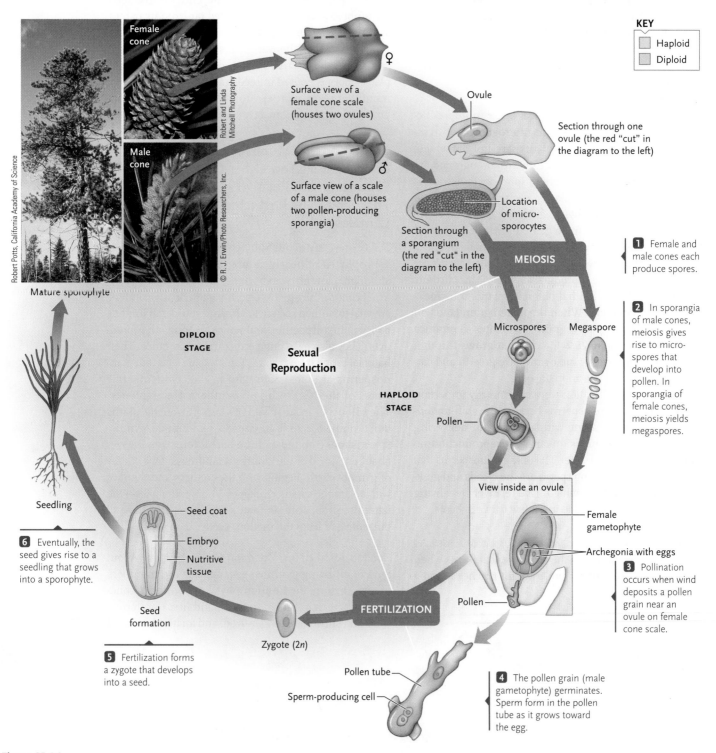

Figure 25.26

Life cycle of a representative conifer, a ponderosa pine (*Pinus ponderosa*). Pines are the dominant conifers in the Northern Hemisphere, and their large sporophytes provide a heavily exploited source of wood.

Male cones are relatively small and delicate (about 1 cm long) and are borne on the lower branches. Each cone consists of many sporophylls with two microsporangia on their undersides. Inside the microsporangia, **micro-spores** are produced by meiosis. Each microspore then undergoes mitosis to develop into a winged pollen grain—an immature male gametophyte. At this stage, the pollen grain consists of four cells, two that will degenerate and two that will function later in reproduction.

Young female cones develop higher in the tree, at the tips of upper branches. Ovules are produced on modified sporophylls. Inside each ovule, four megaspores are produced by meiosis, but only one survives to develop into a megagametophyte. This female gametophyte develops slowly, becoming mature only when pollination is under way; in a pine, this process takes well over a year. The mature female gametophyte is a small oval mass of cells with several archegonia at one end, each containing an egg.

Each spring, air currents release vast numbers of pollen grains from male cones—by some estimates, billions may be released from a single pine tree. The extravagant numbers ensure that at least some pollen grains will land on female cones. The process is not as random as it might seem: studies have shown that the contours of female cones create air currents that can favour the "delivery" of pollen grains near the cone scales. After pollination, the two remaining cells of the pollen grain divide, one producing sperm by mitosis, the other producing the pollen tube that grows toward the developing gametophyte. When a pollen tube reaches an egg, the stage is set for fertilization, the formation of a zygote, and early development of the plant embryo. Often fertilization occurs months to a year after pollination. Once an embryo forms, a pine seed—which, recall, includes the embryo, female gametophyte tissue, and seed coat—eventually is shed from the cone. The seed coat protects the embryo from drying out, and the female gametophyte tissue serves as its food reserve. This tissue makes up the bulk of a "pine nut."

Cycads Are Restricted to Warmer Climates. During the Mesozoic era, the **Cycadophyta** (*kykas* = palm), or cycads, flourished along with the dinosaurs. About 185 species have survived to the present, but they are confined to the tropics and subtropics.

At first glance, you might mistake a cycad for a small palm tree **(Figure 25.27)**. Some cycads have massive cones that bear either pollen or ovules. Air currents or crawling insects transfer pollen from male plants to the developing gametophyte on female plants. Poisonous alkaloids that may help deter insect predators occur in various cycad tissues. In tropical Asia, some people consume cycad seeds and flour made from cycad trunks, but only after rinsing away

Figure 25.27
The cycad *Zamia* showing a large, terminal female cone and fernlike leaves.

the toxic compounds. Much in demand from fanciers of unusual plants, cycads in some countries are uprooted and sold in what amounts to a black-market trade—greatly diminishing their numbers in the wild.

Ginkgoes Are Limited to a Single Living Species The phylum **Ginkgophyta** has only one living species, the ginkgo (or maidenhair) tree (*Ginkgo biloba*), which grows wild today only in warm-temperate forests of central China. Ginkgo trees are large, diffusely branching trees with characteristic fan-shaped leaves **(Figure 25.28)** that turn a brilliant yellow in autumn. Nursery-propagated male trees often are planted in cities because they are resistant to insects, disease, and air pollutants. The female trees are equally pollution resistant, but gardeners shy away from them because their seeds produce a foul odour that only a ginkgo could love. The

Figure 25.28
Ginkgo biloba. **(a)** A ginkgo tree. **(b)** A fossilized ginkgo leaf compared with a leaf from a living tree. The fossil formed at the Cretaceous–Tertiary boundary. Even though 65 million years have passed, the leaf structure has not changed much. **(c)** Pollen-bearing cones and **(d)** fleshy-coated seeds of the *Ginkgo*.

a. Ginkgo tree **b.** Fossil and modern ginkgo leaves

c. Male cone **d.** Ginkgo seeds

leaves and seeds have been used in traditional Chinese medicine for centuries. The extract of the leaves is one of the most intensely investigated herbal medicines; although studies have not found any conclusive evidence for claims that the extract improves memory, there is some evidence that it does assist in blood flow and so may be effective in treatment of circulatory disorders.

Gnetophytes Include Simple Seed Plants with Intriguing Features. The phylum Gnetophyta contains three genera—*Gnetum, Ephedra,* and *Welwitschia*—that together include about 70 species. Moist, tropical regions are home to about 30 species of *Gnetum,* which includes both trees and leathery-leafed vines (lianas). About 35 species of *Ephedra* grow in desert regions of the world **(Figure 25.29a–c).**

Of all the gymnosperms, *Welwitschia* is the most bizarre. This seed-producing plant grows in the hot deserts of southwest Africa. The bulk of the plant is a deep-reaching taproot. The only exposed part is a woody, disk-shaped stem that bears cone-shaped strobili and leaves. The plant never produces more than two strap-shaped leaves, which split lengthwise repeatedly as the plant grows older, producing a rather scraggly pile **(Figure 25.29d).**

a. *Ephedra* plant

b. *Ephedra* male cone

c. *Ephedra* female cone

William Ferguson

Edward S. Ross

Robert & Linda Mitchell Photography

d. *Welwitschia* plant with female cones

© Fletcher and Baylis/Photo Researchers, Inc.

Figure 25.29

Gnetophytes. **(a)** Sporophyte of *Ephedra,* with close-ups of **(b)** its pollen-bearing cones and **(c)** seed-bearing cone, which develop on separate plants. **(d)** Sporophyte of *Welwitschia mirabilis,* with seed-bearing cones.

25.6 Angiosperms: Flowering Plants

Of all plant phyla, the flowering plants, or **angiosperms,** are the most successful today. At least 260 000 species are known **(Figure 25.30,** shows a few examples), and botanists regularly discover new ones in previously unexplored regions of the tropics. The word *angiosperm* is derived from the Greek *angeion* ("vessel") and *sperma* ("seed"). The "vessel" refers to the modified sporophyll, called a *carpel,* which surrounds and protects the ovules. Carpels are located in the centre of **flowers,** reproductive structures that are a defining feature of angiosperms. Another defining feature is the **fruit**—botanically speaking, a structure that helps protect and disperse seeds.

In addition to having flowers and fruits, angiosperms are the most ecologically diverse plants on Earth, growing on dry land and in wetlands, freshwater, and the seas. Angiosperms range in size from tiny duckweeds that are about 1 mm long to towering *Eucalyptus* trees more than 100 m tall.

25.6a The Fossil Record Provides Little Information about the Origin of Flowering Plants

The evolutionary origin of angiosperms has confounded plant biologists for well over a hundred years. Charles Darwin called it the "abominable mystery" because flowering plants appear suddenly in the fossil record, without a fossil sequence that links them to any other plant groups. As with gymnosperms, attempts to reconstruct the earliest flowering plant lineages have produced several conflicting classifications and family trees. Some paleobotanists hypothesize that flowering plants arose in the Jurassic period; others propose that they evolved in the Triassic from now-extinct gymnosperms or from seed ferns. However, progress in this area does not rely solely on fossil evidence; molecular data can be used to test hypotheses, and the combination of molecular, morphological, and fossil evidence offers great promise (see *Unanswered Questions*).

a. Flowering plants in a desert

b. Alpine angiosperms

c. Triticale, a grass

d. The carnivorous plant Venus flytrap

Figure 25.30

Flowering plants. Diverse photosynthetic species are adapted to nearly all environments, ranging from **(a)** deserts to **(b)** snowlines of high mountains. **(c)** Triticale, a hybrid grain derived from parental stocks of wheat (*Triticum*) and rye (*Secale*), is one example of the various grasses used by humans. **(d)** The carnivorous plant Venus flytrap (*Dionaea muscipula*) grows in nitrogen-poor soils and traps insects as an additional source of nitrogen.

The fossil record has yet to reveal obvious transitional organisms between flowering plants and either gymnosperms or seedless vascular plants. As the Mesozoic era ended and the modern Cenozoic era began, great extinctions occurred among both plant and animal kingdoms. Gymnosperms declined, and dinosaurs disappeared. Flowering plants, mammals, and social insects flourished, radiating into new environments. Today we live in what has been called "the age of flowering plants."

25.6b Angiosperms Are Subdivided into Several Groups, Including Monocots and Eudicots

Angiosperms are assigned to the phylum **Anthophyta**, a name that derives from the Greek *anthos,* meaning flower. The great majority of angiosperms are classified either as monocots or eudicots, which are differentiated on the basis of morphological features such as the number of flower parts and the pattern of vascular tissue in stems and leaves. The two groups also differ in terms of the morphology of their embryos: **monocot** embryos have a single seed leaf called a cotyledon, whereas **eudicots** ("true dicots") generally have two cotyledons **(Figure 25.31, p. 570)**.

Botanists currently recognize several other groups of plants in addition to eudicots and monocots, but figuring out the appropriate classification for and relationships among these other groups is an ongoing challenge and an extremely active area of plant research. In this chapter, we focus only on monocots and eudicots.

There are at least 60 000 species of monocots, including 10 000 grasses and 20 000 orchids. **Figure 25.32a, p. 570** gives some idea of the variety of living monocots, which include grasses, palms, lilies, and orchids. The world's major crop plants (wheat, corn, rice, rye, sugarcane, and barley) are all monocots and are all domesticated grasses. Eudicots are even more diverse, with nearly 200 000 species **(Figure 25.32b).** They include flowering shrubs and trees, most non-woody (herbaceous) plants, and cacti. **Figure 25.33, p. 571** shows the life cycle of a lily, a monocot. The life cycle of a typical eudicot is described in detail in the next unit, which focuses on the structure and function of flowering plants.

Figure 25.31
Comparison of monocots and dicots.

a.

b.

c.

d.

e.

f.

g.

h.

a. Representative monocots

Wheat (*Triticum*)

Trillium (*Trillium*)

Western wood lily
(*Lilium philadelphicum*)

b. Representative eudicots

Wild rose (*Rosa acicularis*)

Twinflower (*Linnaea borealis*)

Claret cup cactus
(*Echinocereus triglochidratus*)

Figure 25.32

Examples of monocots and eudicots: **(a)** representative monocots: wheat (*Triticum*); trillium (*Trillium*), and Western wood lily (*Lilium philadelphicum*; **(b)** representative eudicots: wild rose (*Rosa acicularis*); twinflower (*Linnaea borealis*); cherry (*Prunus*); cactus (*Echinocereus triglochidiatus*).

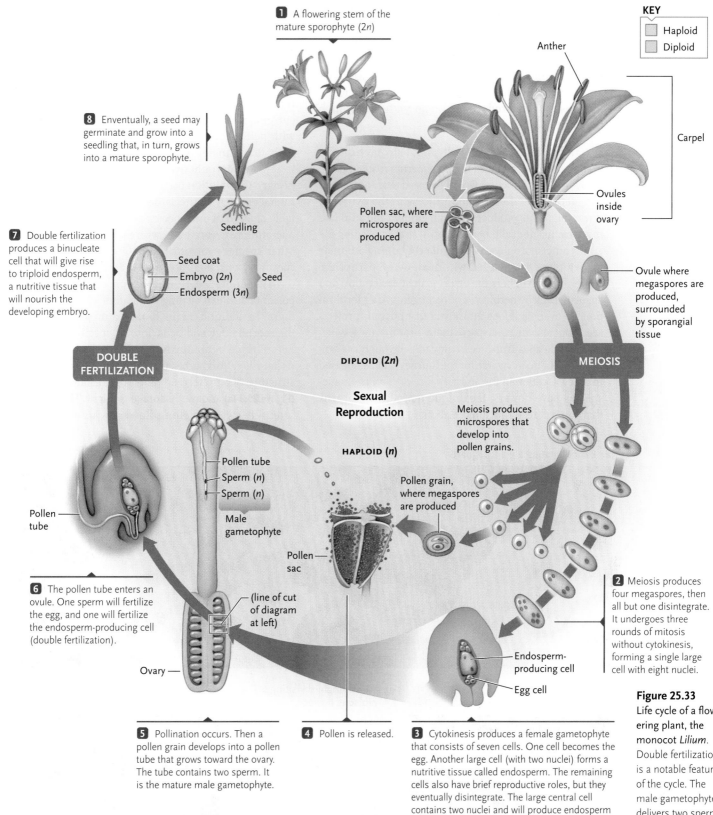

1 A flowering stem of the mature sporophyte (2n)

KEY
Haploid
Diploid

Anther

Carpel

8 Enventually, a seed may germinate and grow into a seedling that, in turn, grows into a mature sporophyte.

Seedling

Pollen sac, where microspores are produced

Ovules inside ovary

7 Double fertilization produces a binucleate cell that will give rise to triploid endosperm, a nutritive tissue that will nourish the developing embryo.

Seed coat
Embryo (2n)   Seed
Endosperm (3n)

Ovule where megaspores are produced, surrounded by sporangial tissue

DOUBLE FERTILIZATION

DIPLOID (2n)

MEIOSIS

Sexual Reproduction

Meiosis produces microspores that develop into pollen grains.

HAPLOID (n)

Pollen tube
Sperm (n)
Sperm (n)

Pollen grain, where megaspores are produced

Male gametophyte

Pollen tube

Pollen sac

6 The pollen tube enters an ovule. One sperm will fertilize the egg, and one will fertilize the endosperm-producing cell (double fertilization).

(line of cut of diagram at left)

2 Meiosis produces four megaspores, then all but one disintegrate. It undergoes three rounds of mitosis without cytokinesis, forming a single large cell with eight nuclei.

Ovary

Endosperm-producing cell

Egg cell

Figure 25.33
Life cycle of a flowering plant, the monocot *Lilium*. Double fertilization is a notable feature of the cycle. The male gametophyte delivers two sperm to an ovule. One sperm fertilizes the egg, forming the embryo, and the other fertilizes the endosperm-producing cell, which nourishes the embryo.

5 Pollination occurs. Then a pollen grain develops into a pollen tube that grows toward the ovary. The tube contains two sperm. It is the mature male gametophyte.

4 Pollen is released.

3 Cytokinesis produces a female gametophyte that consists of seven cells. One cell becomes the egg. Another large cell (with two nuclei) forms a nutritive tissue called endosperm. The remaining cells also have brief reproductive roles, but they eventually disintegrate. The large central cell contains two nuclei and will produce endosperm after fertilization.

25.6c Many Factors Contributed to the Adaptive Success of Angiosperms

Flowering plants likely originated about 140 mya. It took only about 40 million years—a short span in geologic time—for angiosperms to eclipse gymnosperms as the prevailing form of plant life on land. Several factors fuelled this adaptive success. As with other seed plants, the large, diploid sporophyte phase dominates a flowering plant's life cycle, and the sporophyte retains and nourishes the much smaller gametophytes. But flowering plants also show some evolutionary innovations not seen in gymnosperms.

More Efficient Transport of Water and Nutrients. Where gymnosperms have only one type of water-conducting cell in their xylem, angiosperms have an additional, more specialized type of cell that moves water more rapidly from roots to shoots. Also, modifications in angiosperm phloem tissue allow it to more efficiently transport sugars produced in photosynthesis through the plant body.

Enhanced Nutrition and Physical Protection for Embryos. Other changes in angiosperms made it more likely that reproduction would succeed. For example, a two-step double-fertilization process in the ovules of flowering plants produces both an embryo and a unique nutritive tissue (called endosperm) that nourishes the embryonic sporophyte. The ovule containing a female gametophyte is enclosed within an ovary, part of the carpel, which shelters the ovule against desiccation and against attack by herbivores or pathogens. After fertilization, an ovary develops into a fruit that not only protects seeds but also helps disperse them—for instance, when an animal eats a fruit, seeds may pass through the animal's gut none the worse for the journey and be released in a new location in the animal's feces. Above all, angiosperms have flowers, the unique reproductive organs that you will read much more about in the next unit.

25.6d Angiosperms Coevolved with Animal Pollinators

The evolutionary success of angiosperms is due not only to the adaptations just described but also to the efficient mechanisms of transferring pollen to female reproductive parts. Whereas a conifer depends on air currents to disperse its pollen, angiosperms coevolved with pollinators—insects, bats, birds, and other animals that transfer pollen from male floral structures to female reproductive parts (often while obtaining nectar). **Coevolution** occurs when two or more species interact closely in the same ecological setting. A heritable change in one species affects selection pressure operating between them, with the result being that the other species evolves as well. Over time, plants have coevolved with their pollinating animals.

In general, a flower's reproductive parts are positioned so that visiting pollinators will brush against them. In addition, many floral features correlate with the morphology and behaviour of specific pollinators. For example, reproductive parts may be located above nectar-filled floral tubes the same length as the feeding structure of a preferred pollinator. Nectar-sipping bats **(Figure 25.34a)** and moths forage by night. They pollinate intensely sweet-smelling flowers with white or pale

a. Bat pollinating a giant saguaro

Merlin D. Tuttle, Bat Conservation International

b. Hawkmoth pollinating an orchid

Photo by Marcel Lecoufle

c. Hummingbird visiting a hibiscus flower

Robert A. Tyrrell

d. Bee-attracting pattern of a marsh marigold

Visible light   UV light

Thomas Eisner/Cornell University

Figure 25.34

Coevolution of flowering plants and animal pollinators. The colours and configurations of some flowers, and the production of nectar or odours, have coevolved with specific animal pollinators. **(a)** At night, nectar-feeding bats sip nectar from flowers of the giant saguaro cactus (*Carnegia gigantea*), transferring pollen from flower to flower in the process. **(b)** The hawkmoth *Xanthopan morgani praedicta* has a proboscis long enough to reach nectar at the base of the equally long floral spur of the orchid *Angraecum sesquipedale*. **(c)** A Bahama woodstar hummingbird (*Calliphlox evelynae*) sipping nectar from a hibiscus blossom (*Hibiscus*). The long, narrow bill of hummingbirds coevolved with long, narrow floral tubes. **(d)** Under ultraviolet light, the bee-attracting pattern of a gold-petalled marsh marigold becomes visible to human eyes.

petals that are more visible than coloured petals in the dark. Long, thin mouthparts of moths and butterflies reach nectar in narrow floral tubes or floral spurs. The Madagascar hawkmoth uncoils a mouthpart the same length—an astonishing 22 cm—as the narrow flower of the orchid it pollinates, *Angraecum sesquipedale* **(Figure 25.34b)**. Red and yellow flowers attract birds **(Figure 25.34c)**, which have good daytime vision but a poor sense of smell. Hence, bird-pollinated plants do not squander metabolic resources to make fragrances. By contrast, flowers of species that are pollinated by beetles or flies may smell like rotten meat, dung, or decaying matter. Daisies and other fragrant flowers with distinctive pat-terns, shapes, and red or orange components attract butterflies, which forage by day.

Bees see ultraviolet light and visit flowers with sweet odours and parts that appear to humans as yellow, blue, or purple **(Figure 25.34d)**. Produced by pigments that absorb ultraviolet light, the colours form patterns called "nectar guides" that attract bees—which may pick up or drop off pollen during the visit. Here, as in our other examples, flowers contribute to the reproductive success of plants that bear them.

In this chapter, we have introduced some of the strategies that plants use to meet challenges of life on Earth; they face the same challenges as

Table 25.2		Plant Phyla and Major Characteristics		
Phylum	Common Name	Number of Species	Common General Characteristics	
Bryophytes: nonvascular plants. Gametophyte dominant, free water required for fertilization, cuticle and stomata present in some.				
Hepatophyta	Liverworts	6000	Leafy or simple flattened thallus, rhizoids; spores in capsules. Moist, humid habitats.	
Anthocerophyta	Hornworts	100	Simple flattened thallus, rhizoids; hornlike sporangia. Moist, humid habitats.	
Bryophyta	Mosses	10 000	Feathery or cushiony thallus; some have hydroids; spores in capsules. Moist, humid habitats; colonizes bare rock, soil, or bark.	
Seedless vascular plants: sporophyte dominant, free water required for fertilization, cuticle and stomata present.				
Lycophyta	Club mosses	1000	Simple leaves, true roots; most species have sporangia on sporophylls. Mostly wet or shady habitats.	
Pterophyta	Ferns, whisk ferns, horsetails	13 000	*Ferns:* Finely divided leaves, sporangia often in sori. Habitats from wet to arid. *Whisk ferns:* Branching stem from rhizomes; sporangia on stem scales. Tropical to subtropical habitats. *Horsetails:* Hollow photosynthetic stem, scalelike leaves, sporangia in strobili. Swamps, disturbed habitats.	
Gymnosperms: vascular plants with "naked" seeds. Sporophyte dominant, fertilization by pollination, cuticle and stomata present.				
Cycadophyta	Cycads	185	Shrubby or treelike with palmlike leaves, pithy stems; male and female strobili on separate plants. Widespread distribution.	
Ginkgophyta	Ginkgo	1	Woody-stemmed tree, deciduous fan-shaped leaves. Male, female structures on separate plants. Temperate areas of China.	
Gnetophyta	Gnetophytes	70	Shrubs or woody vines; one has strappy leaves. Male and female strobili on separate plants. Limited to deserts, tropics.	
Coniferophyta	Conifers	550	Mostly evergreen, woody trees and shrubs with needlelike or scalelike leaves; male and female cones usually on same plant.	
Angiosperms: plants with flowers and seeds protected inside fruits. Sporophyte dominant, fertilization by pollination, cuticle and stomata present. Major groups: monocots, eudicots.				
Anthophyta	Flowering plants	268 500+ (including magnoliids, other basal angiosperms)	Wood and herbaceous plants. Nearly all land habitats, some aquatic.	
Monocots	Grasses, palms, lilies, orchids, and others	60 000	One cotyledon; parallel-veined leaves common; bundles of vascular tissue scattered in stem.	
Eudicots	Most fruit trees, roses, beans, potatoes, and others	200 000	Most species have two cotyledons; net-veined leaves common; central core of vascular tissue in stem.	

animals and other terrestrial organisms (attract a mate, reproduce, disperse offspring, survive unfavourable conditions) but have had to find ways to do all of these without being able to move around (they are sessile). Many of these topics are followed up in more detail in the chapters dealing with plant biology (Chapters 28 to 31).

The next two chapters introduce animals. As you read those chapters, look for similarities and differences in how they have addressed the challenges of life compared to plants.

STUDY BREAK

List at least three adaptations that have contributed to the evolutionary success of angiosperms as a group.

UNANSWERED QUESTIONS

Where did flowering plants come from?

Flowers are a unique feature of the angiosperms, yet botanists still understand little of their evolutionary origin. When flowering plants appear in the Cretaceous fossil record, they appear suddenly and diversify immediately, a situation Darwin famously referred to as an "abominable mystery." What did the first angiosperms and the first flower look like? And where did they arise?

As described in this chapter, recent molecular analyses have converged on *Amborella trichopoda* as the living representative of the most ancient lineage in the angiosperm family tree. This research has shed light on many questions. For example, *Amborella* flowers have some features considered evolutionarily primitive, such as petals and sepals that are not distinctly different in form. This observation supports the hypothesis that two other types of flower parts, the **calyx** and corolla, arose later in angiosperm evolution. But *Amborella* also has some features thought to have evolved much more recently, such as single-sex flowers that have either male or female reproductive parts (but never both). Should we be surprised to find both primitive and advanced traits in this ancient lineage? Not at all. *Amborella* has existed on Earth for millions of years, and its flowers may have evolved new features over that time.

The puzzle of where angiosperms came from and what the first flowering plants looked like has not been solved by fossil studies either. The fossil species *Archaefructus* might be the oldest known fossil flower. It consists of an elongated axis with what its discoverers described as stamens (male reproductive structures) toward the base, carpels (female reproductive structures) toward the apex, and no sepals and petals. This elongated flower is unlike the flowers of any modern angiosperm, and its structure suggests that the earliest flowers may have been very different from what we see today. However, some paleobotanists have reinterpreted the *Archaefructus* "flower" as an inflorescence (a flower cluster), with male flowers at the base and female flowers toward the apex. In addition, radiometric dating places *Archaefructus* in the early to mid-Cretaceous, a period from which other early angiosperm fossils are known. Thus, *Archaefructus* may not be the oldest flower, and the fossil specimen may represent a cluster of flowers instead of a single flower. This debate continues.

Botanists also disagree about the ancestors of angiosperms. Some gnetophytes—gymnosperms that include *Welwitschia* and *Ephedra* species (refer to Figure 25.28∂)—have features similar to those of angiosperms. Botanists long speculated that the two groups were closely related, with a common ancestor that had flowerlike features.

However, recent analyses based on DNA sequence data suggest that gnetophytes are not closely related to angiosperms after all. There are also fossil gymnosperm taxa with features that might be forerunners of carpels or other flower parts, but paleobotanists disagree on these interpretations as well. Thus, examinations of fossils and extant species have yet to resolve key questions about the evolution of angiosperms.

What, then, can molecular data tell us? Studies of the genetic mechanisms that guide the development of flower parts have provided a framework for understanding how genes control flower formation. This research has also given us insight into what kinds of molecular changes may have led to the evolution of flowers. For instance, certain genes that encode transcription factors required for the formation of reproductive organs in flowers are also found in gymnosperms. This finding is not surprising because gymnosperms also form male and female reproductive structures; the most logical hypothesis is that angiosperms retained the gymnosperm developmental program for these organs. Yet genes for other transcription factors active in flower formation are not found in gymnosperms. We know that transcription factors may turn on and off entire developmental pathways, such as those that cause undifferentiated tissue (called meristem tissue) to form a flower. One hypothesis is that in an ancient gymnosperm ancestor, duplications in a particular gene family gave rise to genes that, in turn, accumulated mutations, allowing them to perform new functions that resulted in the formation of the first flowers.

As much insight as these molecular studies give us into events that might have resulted in the evolution of flowers, they have not brought us any closer to understanding the fundamental question of where angiosperms arose. Additional fossil data may help provide the answer, but it is also possible that the earliest angiosperms, or their direct ancestors, lived in habitats where fossils do not readily form. Additional molecular data may deepen our understanding of how changes in genes produced the first flower. But molecular data based on contemporary species will not help decipher what the first angiosperm and the first flower looked like. Thus, it is possible that the abominable mystery will live on.

Amy Litt is director of plant genomics and Cullman curator at the New York Botanical Garden, where she also earned her Ph.D. Her main interests lie in the evolution of plant form and how changes in gene function during the course of plant evolution have produced novel plant forms and functions—particularly new flower and fruit morphologies. Learn more about her work at http://sciweb.nybg.org/science2/Profile_106.asp.

Review

Go to CENGAGENOW™ at http://hed.nelson.com/ to access quizzing, animations, exercises, articles, and personalized homework help.

25.1 Defining Characteristics of Land Plants

- Land plants are multicellular eukaryotes with cellulose cell walls. Most, but not all, are photoautotrophs. All have an alternation of generations life cycle, although which generation is dominant varies among groups of plants, and all retain embryos inside parental tissue.

25.2 The Transition to Life on Land

- Plants are thought to have evolved from charophyte green algae between 425 and 490 million years ago.

- Adaptations to terrestrial life in the earliest land plants include poikilohydry, multicellular chambers that protect developing gametes, and an embryo sheltered inside a parent plant.

- Other key evolutionary trends among land plants included symbiotic associations with fungi; the development of vascular tissues, root systems, and shoot systems; lignified stems and leaves equipped with stomata; increasing dominance by the diploid sporophyte generation; and a shift from homospory to heterospory.

- Gametophytes became reduced in size; male gametophytes (pollen) became specialized for dispersal without liquid water, and female gametophytes are increasingly protected inside sporophyte tissues.

25.3 Bryophytes: Nonvascular Land Plants

- Existing nonvascular land plants, or bryophytes, include the liverworts, hornworts, and mosses. Liverworts may have been the first land plants.

- Bryophytes produce flagellated sperm that swim through free water to reach eggs. They lack a vascular system, roots, stems, and leaves. The gametophyte phase is dominant.

25.4 Seedless Vascular Plants

- Existing seedless vascular land plants include the lycophytes (club mosses), whisk ferns, horsetails, and ferns. Like bryophytes, they release spores and have swimming sperm. Unlike bryophytes, they have well-developed vascular tissues. The sporophyte generation is dominant and independent of the gametophyte.

- Most seedless vascular plants are homosporous, but some are heterosporous.

25.5 Gymnosperms: The First Seed Plants

- Gymnosperms (conifers and their relatives), together with angiosperms (flowering plants), are the seed-bearing vascular plants. Reproductive innovations include pollination, the ovule, and the seed. Liquid water is not required for reproduction.

- During the Mesozoic, gymnosperms were the dominant land plants. Today conifers are the primary vegetation of forests at higher latitudes and elevations and have important economic uses as sources of lumber and other products.

25.6 Angiosperms: Flowering Plants

- Angiosperms (Anthophyta) have dominated the land for more than 100 million years and currently are the most diverse plant group.

- The angiosperm vascular system moves water and sugars through the plant body more efficiently than that of gymnosperms. Reproductive adaptations include a protective ovary around the ovule, endosperm, flowers that attract pollinators, and fruits that protect and disperse seeds.

Questions

Self-Test Questions

1. Which of the following is not an evolutionary trend among plants?
   a. developing vascular tissues
   b. becoming seedless
   c. having a dominant diploid generation
   d. producing nonmotile gametes
   e. producing two types of spores

2. As plants made the evolutionary transition to a terrestrial existence, they benefited from adaptations that
   a. increased the motility of their gametes on dry land.
   b. flattened the plant body to expose it to the sun.
   c. reduced the number and distribution of roots to prevent drying.
   d. provided mechanisms for gaining access to nutrients in soil.
   e. allowed stems and leaves to absorb water from the atmosphere.

3. Land plants no longer required water as a medium for reproduction with the evolution of
   a. fruits and roots.
   b. flowers and leaves.
   c. cell walls and rhizoids.
   d. lignified stems.
   e. seeds and pollen.

4. Which is the correct matching of phylum and plant group?
   a. Anthophyta: pines
   b. Bryophyta: gnetophytes
   c. Coniferophyta: angiosperms
   d. Hepatophyta: cycads
   e. Pterophyta: horsetails

5. A homeowner noticed moss growing between bricks on his patio. Closer examination revealed tiny brown stalks with cup-like tops emerging from green leaflets. These brown structures were
   a. the sporophyte generation.
   b. the gametophyte generation.
   c. elongated haploid reproductive cells.
   d. archegonia.
   e. antheridia.

6. Horsetails are most closely related to
   a. mosses and whisk ferns.
   b. liverworts and hornworts.
   c. cycads and ginkgoes.
   d. club mosses and ferns.
   e. gnetophytes and gymnosperms.

7. The evolution of true roots is first seen in
   a. liverworts.
   b. seedless vascular plants.
   c. mosses.
   d. flowering plants.
   e. conifers.

8. Based solely on numbers of species, the most successful plants today are
   a. angiosperms.
   b. ferns.
   c. gymnosperms.
   d. mosses.
   e. the bryophytes as a group.

Questions for Discussion

1. Working in the field, you discover a fossil of a previously undescribed plant species. The specimen is small and may not be complete; the parts you have do not include any floral organs. What sorts of observations would you need to classify the fossil as a seedless vascular plant with reasonable accuracy? What evidence would you need to distinguish between a fossil lycopod and a fern?

2. Compare the size, anatomical complexity, and degree of independence of a moss gametophyte, a fern gametophyte, a Douglas fir female gametophyte, and a dogwood female gametophyte. Which one is the most protected from the external environment? Which trends in plant evolution does your work on this question bring to mind?

3. How has the relative lack of fossil early angiosperms affected our understanding of this group?

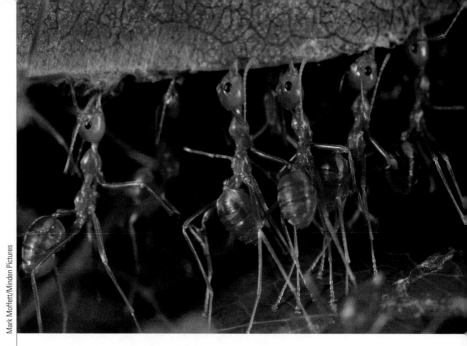

Workers of the weaver ant, *Oecophylla*, engaged in the construction of their nest, which is formed from living leaves, curled or folded to form an envelope held together by silk secreted by the larvae.

Mark Moffett/Minden Pictures

26 Protostomes

WHY IT MATTERS

During the early Cambrian, beginning about 540 million years ago, conditions were ripe for rapid development of the marine fauna and an explosion of new forms appeared, particularly in the warm and shallow seas bordering the continents. About 505 million years ago, a series of mud slides carried the animals that lived at the edge of a submarine cliff, the Cathedral Escarpment, over its edge, and buried them in fine silt. That mud and its contained fossils formed shale, a sedimentary rock that has layers that are easily split. During continent and mountain building, the shale beds, now known as the Burgess Shale, came to lie in the Canadian Rocky Mountains of eastern British Columbia in what is now Yoho National Park.

Charles Walcott, an American palaeontologist working in the Burgess Shale area in 1909, located a rich bed of very strange fossils that were exquisitely preserved, including the soft parts. Reconstructions have revealed not only familiar trilobites and sponges but also many truly bizarre animals **(Figure 26.1, p. 578).** For example, *Opabinia* was about as long as a tube of lipstick and had five eyes on its head and a single anterior grasping organ, which was probably used to catch prey. The smaller *Hallucigenia* had seven pairs of hard spines on its

Opabinia

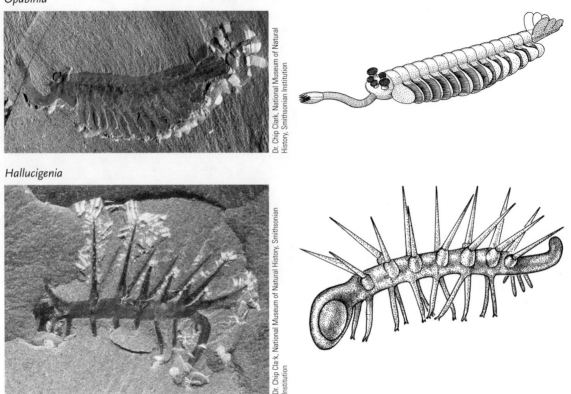

Hallucigenia

Figure 26.1

Animals of the Burgess Shale. *Opabinia* had five eyes and a grasping organ on its head. *Hallucigenia* had seven pairs of spines and soft protuberances.

back and what appear to be seven pairs of softer ventral protuberances that probably functioned for locomotion. Some organisms look like early chordates, but many do not resemble any living animals and may represent phyla that have never been described.

The Burgess Shale and other similar sites provide us with a snapshot of some of the animals that inhabited the coastal waters at the time of the "Cambrian Explosion." Most of the bizarre forms did not survive the extinctions that were to come. Without those extinctions, some of the forms might have survived to found lineages completely different from those living today.

In this chapter, we introduce the general characteristics of animals and a phylogenetic hypothesis about their evolutionary history and classification. We also survey the major invertebrate phyla belonging to one lineage, the Protostomia. In Chapter 19, we defined the various levels used in the Linnaen system of classifying animals. In Chapter 27, we examine the other major animal lineage, the Deuterostomia, which includes the phylum Chordata and their nearest invertebrate relatives.

26.1 What Is an Animal?

Biologists recognize the kingdom Animalia as a monophyletic group that is easily distinguished from the other kingdoms.

26.1a All Animals Share Certain Structural and Behavioural Characteristics

Animals are eukaryotic, multicellular organisms. The cell membranes of adjacent animal cells are in direct contact. This is different from plants and fungi, which have cell walls around the cells. Animal cells may be organized into different morphological types to reflect their role in the functioning of the animal as a single unit.

All animals are **heterotrophs**: they depend on other life forms for their food, either by eating them directly or living in a parasitic association with them. They use oxygen to metabolize their food through aerobic respiration, and most store excess energy as glycogen, oil, or fat.

All animals are **motile** (able to move from place to place) at some time in their lives. Most familiar animals are motile as adults. However, in some species, such as mussels and barnacles, only the young are motile; they eventually settle down as **sessile** (unable to move from one place to another) adults. All animals are able to perceive and respond to information about the environment in which they live.

Animals reproduce either asexually or sexually; in many groups, they switch from one mode to the other. Sexually reproducing species produce haploid **gametes** (eggs and sperm) that fuse to form diploid **zygotes** (fertilized eggs). For many invertebrates, development to the adult involves one or more **larval forms.** This

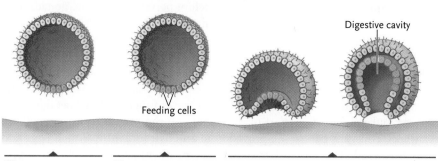

Feeding cells

Digestive cavity

Figure 26.2
Animal origins. Many biologists believe that animals arose from a colonial, flagellated protist in which cells became specialized for specific functions and a developmental reorganization produced two cell layers. The cell movements illustrated here are similar to those that occur during the development of many animals, as described in Chapter 48.

1 Colonial flagellated protist with unspecialized cells

2 Certain cells became specialized for feeding and other functions.

3 A developmental reorganization produced a two-layered animal with a sac-within-a-sac body plan.

pattern of development, in which a species can exist during development in two or more distinct forms, is referred to as **polymorphic development**. This developmental strategy is important for the success of many of the invertebrate groups.

26.1b The Animal Lineage Probably Arose from a Colonial Choanoflagellate Ancestor

Most biologists agree that the common ancestor of all animals was probably a colonial, flagellated protist that lived at least 700 million years ago, during the Precambrian. It may have resembled the minute, sessile choanoflagellates (see Chapter 23) that live in both freshwater and marine habitats today. The German embryologist Ernst Haeckel proposed a colonial, flagellated ancestor in 1874, suggesting that it was a hollow, ball-shaped organism with unspecialized cells. Its cells became specialized for particular functions, and a developmental reorganization produced a double-layered, sac-within-a-sac body plan **(Figure 26.2)**. The embryology of many living animals roughly parallels this hypothetical evolutionary transformation (see Chapter 39). He included this hypothetical organism among what he called the Metazoa (*meta* = more developed; *zoon* = animal) to distinguish them from the protozoa.

STUDY BREAK

1. What characteristics distinguish animals from plants?
2. What early steps may have led to the first metazoans?

26.2 Key Innovations in Animal Evolution

Once established, the animal lineage diversified quickly into an amazing array of body plans. Biologists have used several key morphological innovations to unravel the evolutionary relationships of the major animal groups.

26.2a Tissues and Tissue Layers Appeared Early in Animal Evolution

In most Metazoans, the process of development gives rise to two or three layers that eventually form **tissues**, groups of similar differentiated cells that are specialized for particular functions.

In most metazoans, embryonic tissues form as either two or three concentric **germ layers** (see Chapter 39). The innermost layer, the **endoderm**, eventually develops into the lining of the gut (digestive system) and, in some animals, respiratory organs. The outermost layer, the **ectoderm**, forms the external covering and nervous system. Between the two, the **mesoderm** forms the muscles of the body wall and most other structures between the gut and the external covering. Some animals have a **diploblastic** body plan that includes only two embryonic layers, endoderm and ectoderm, but most are **triploblastic**, having all three germ layers.

26.2b Most Animals Exhibit Either Radial or Bilateral Symmetry

The most obvious feature of an animal's body plan is its shape **(Figure 26.3)**. Most animals are **symmetrical**; in other words, their bodies can be divided by a

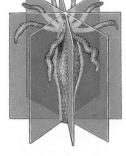
Radial symmetry

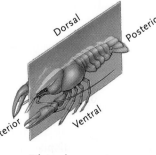
Dorsal
Posterior
Anterior
Ventral
Bilateral symmetry

Figure 26.3
Patterns of body symmetry. Most animals have either radial or bilateral symmetry.

plane into mirror-image halves. By contrast, most sponges have irregular shapes and are therefore **asymmetrical.**

All other phyla exhibit one of two body symmetry patterns (see Figure 26.3). The Radiata includes two phyla, Cnidaria (hydras, jellyfishes, and sea anemones) and Ctenophora (comb jellies), that have **radial symmetry.** Their body parts are arranged regularly around a central axis, like the spokes on a wheel. Thus, any cut down the long axis of a radially symmetrical animal divides it into matching halves.

All other metazoan phyla fall within the Bilateria, animals that have **bilateral symmetry.** In other words, they have left and right sides that are mirror images of each other on either side of the body's midline. Bilaterally symmetrical animals also have front (**anterior**) and back (**posterior**) ends, as well as upper (**dorsal**) and lower (**ventral**) surfaces. As they move through the environment, the anterior end encounters food, shelter, or enemies first. In bilaterally symmetrical animals, natural selection favoured **cephalization,** the development of an anterior head where sensory organs and nerve tissue are concentrated.

26.2c Many Animals Have Body Cavities That Surround Their Internal Organs

The body plans of many bilaterally symmetrical animals include a body cavity that separates the gut from the muscles of the body wall. **Acoelomate** animals (*a* = without; *koiloma* = cavity), such as flatworms (phylum Platyhelminthes), do not have such a cavity; instead, a mass of cells, derived largely from mesoderm, packs the region between the gut and the body wall **(Figure 26.4a).**

Pseudocoelomate animals (*pseudo* = false), including the roundworms (phylum Nematoda) and wheel animals (phylum Rotifera), have a **pseudocoelom,** a fluid-filled space between the gut and the muscles of the body wall that has no mesodermal lining around the endoderm **(Figure 26.4b).** The muscles of the body wall, derived from mesoderm, form the outer lining of the pseudocoelom, and its inner lining is the gut, which has no muscles. Internal organs lie within the pseudocoelom and are bathed by its fluid.

Coelomate animals have a **coelom,** a fluid-filled body cavity completely lined by mesoderm. In vertebrates, this lining takes the form of the **peritoneum,** a thin tissue derived from mesoderm **(Figure 26.4c).** The inner and outer layers of the peritoneum connect, forming **mesenteries,** membranes that surround the internal organs and suspend them within the coelom. In some arthropods and molluscs, the coelom has been displaced by the development of a haemocoel, resulting from an open circulatory system. This can be envisaged as consisting of a single large blood vessel that has expanded to fill the coelom. In these animals, the coelom persists aound the gonads and, in some cases, the heart.

Biologists describe the body plan of pseudocoelomate and coelomate animals as a "tube-within-a-tube." The digestive system forms the inner tube, and the body wall forms the outer tube. The body cavity may serve a number of functions, such as the transport of nutrients and the products of metabolism, the provision of an environment in which eggs and sperm can develop, a **hydrostatic skeleton** that provides a basis for locomotion (see Chapter 36), and an appropriate environment for the functioning of internal organs.

26.2d Developmental Patterns Mark a Major Divergence in Animal Ancestry

Embryological evidence suggests that bilaterally symmetrical animals are divided into two lineages, the **protostomes** and the **deuterostomes,** that differ in several developmental characteristics **(Figure 26.5, p. 582).**

Shortly after fertilization, an egg undergoes a series of cell divisions called **cleavage.** The first two cell divisions divide a zygote as you might slice an apple, cutting it into four wedges from top to bottom. In some animals, subsequent cell divisions occur at oblique angles to the vertical axis of the embryo, ultimately producing a mass in which each cell at the top of the embryo lies in the groove between the pair of cells below it (see the left side of Figure 26.5a). This pattern is called **spiral cleavage.** It is generally characteristic of most protostomes, although cleavage patterns in arthropods and some other groups are highly specialized. In deuterostomes, by contrast, the third cell division is perpendicular to the vertical axis of the embryo, cutting each of the four cells near its midsection. The fourth cell division is vertical, producing a mass of cells that are stacked directly above and below one another (see the right side of Figure 26.5a). This pattern is called **radial cleavage.**

Protostomes and deuterostomes often differ in the timing of important developmental events. During cleavage, certain genes are activated at specific times, determining a cell's developmental path and ultimate fate. Many protostomes undergo **determinate cleavage:** each cell's developmental path is determined as the cell is produced. Thus, one cell isolated from a two- or four-cell protostome embryo cannot develop into a functional embryo or larva. By contrast, many deuterostomes have **indeterminate cleavage:** the developmental fates of cells are determined later. A cell isolated from a four-cell deuterostome embryo will develop into a functional embryo. In humans, the two cells produced by the first cleavage division sometimes separate and develop into identical twins.

As development proceeds, an opening on the surface of the embryo eventually connects the

a. In acoelomate animals, no body cavity separates the gut and body wall.

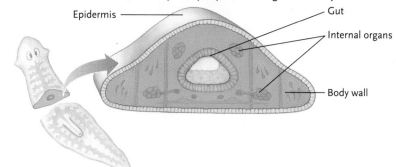

Epidermis

Gut

Internal organs

Body wall

Figure 26.4
Body plans of triploblastic animals. Derivatives of endoderm are yellow, those of mesoderm are red, and those of ectoderm are blue.

b. In pseudocoelomate animals, the pseudocoelom forms between the gut (a derivative of endoderm) and the body wall (a derivative of mesoderm).

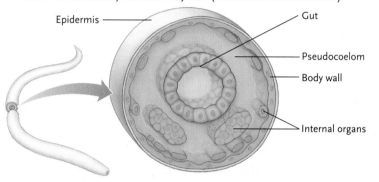

Epidermis

Gut

Pseudocoelom

Body wall

Internal organs

c. In coelomate animals, the coelom is completely lined by peritoneum (a derivative of mesoderm).

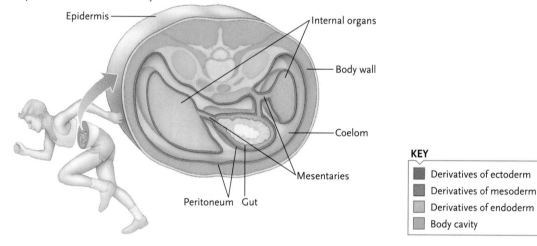

Epidermis

Internal organs

Body wall

Coelom

Mesentaries

Peritoneum   Gut

KEY

	Derivatives of ectoderm
	Derivatives of mesoderm
	Derivatives of endoderm
	Body cavity

developing gut, called the **archenteron**, to the outside environment. This opening is called the **blastopore** (see Figure 26.5b). Later in development, a second opening at the opposite end of the embryo transforms the pouchlike gut into a digestive tube (see Figure 26.5c). In protostomes (*proto* = first; *stoma* = mouth), the blastopore develops into the mouth and the second opening forms the anus. In deuterostomes (*deuteros* = second), the blastopore develops into the anus and the second opening becomes the mouth.

Protostomes and deuterostomes differ in the origin of mesoderm and the coelom (see Figure 26.5b).

In most protostomes, mesoderm originates from a few specific cells near the blastopore. As the mesoderm grows and develops, it splits into inner and outer layers. The space between the layers forms a **schizocoelom** (*schizo* = split). In deuterostomes, mesoderm forms from outpocketings of the archenteron. The space pinched off by the outpocketings forms an **enterocoelom** (*entero* = intestine).

Several other characteristics differ in protostomes and deuterostomes. For example, the nervous system of protostomes is positioned on the ventral side of the body, and their brain surrounds the opening of the

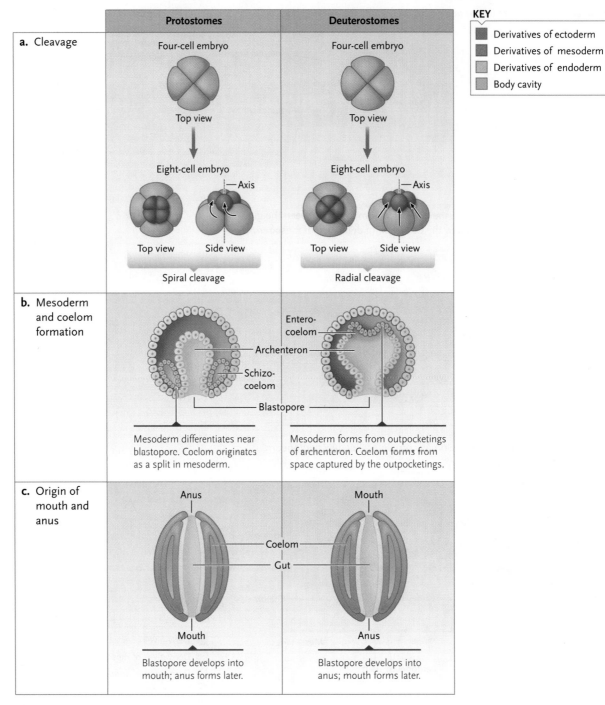

	Protostomes	Deuterostomes
a. Cleavage	Four-cell embryo Top view Eight-cell embryo Top view — Side view — Axis Spiral cleavage	Four-cell embryo Top view Eight-cell embryo Top view — Side view — Axis Radial cleavage
b. Mesoderm and coelom formation	Archenteron Schizo-coelom Blastopore Mesoderm differentiates near blastopore. Coelom originates as a split in mesoderm.	Entero-coelom Archenteron Blastopore Mesoderm forms from outpocketings of archenteron. Coelom forms from space captured by the outpocketings.
c. Origin of mouth and anus	Anus Coelom Gut Mouth Blastopore develops into mouth; anus forms later.	Mouth Coelom Gut Anus Blastopore develops into anus; mouth forms later.

KEY
- Derivatives of ectoderm
- Derivatives of mesoderm
- Derivatives of endoderm
- Body cavity

Figure 26.5

Protostomes and deuterostomes. The two lineages of coelomate animals differ in **(a)** cleavage patterns, **(b)** the origin of mesoderm and the coelom, and **(c)** the polarity of the digestive system.

digestive tract. By contrast, the nervous system and brain of deuterostomes lie on the dorsal side of the body.

26.2e Segmentation Divides the Bodies of Some Animals into Repeating Units

Some phyla in both the protostome and deuterostome lineages exhibit varying degrees of **segmentation**, the production of body parts as repeating units. During development, segmentation first arises in the mesoderm, the middle tissue layer that produces most of the body's bulk. In vertebrates, segmentation is obvious in the embryo, and in the adult there is evidence of segmentation in the vertebral column (backbone), ribs, and associated muscles, as well as the nervous system. Among invertebrates, segmentation is pronounced in annelids (earthworms and their relatives), where each segment, visible externally as a ring, has its own set of muscles, ganglion (collection of nerve cells), and excretory structures. Arthropods (insects and their relatives) are also segmented, although some segments may be specialized, bearing, for example, wings or reproductive structures.

The advantages of segmentation lie principally in movement, but to different degrees. In vertebrates, with their articulated backbone and each segment with its own muscles, segmentation permits the S-shaped side-to-side motion—think of fish or snakes. Annelids are capable of similar motion, but many of them live in burrows or tubes. The ability to expand segments by contracting muscles of adjacent segments assists this lifestyle. Arthropods, with their articulated stiffened cuticle to which their muscles are attached, gain significant leverage and strength (see Chapter 36). They have taken advantage of the existence of segmental appendages to assign special functions such as locomotion, reproduction, or gas exchange to particular appendages.

STUDY BREAK

1. What is a tissue, and what three primary tissue layers are present in the embryos of most animals? Explain the function of each layer.
2. What kind of symmetry does an earthworm have?
3. What is the function of the coelom, and what is the importance of the fluid?

26.3 An Overview of Animal Phylogeny and Classification

For many years, biologists used the morphological innovations and embryological patterns described above, together with evidence from the fossil record, to trace the phylogenetic history of animals (see Chapter 19). That evidence led to the construction of phylogenetic trees that were broadly accepted as reasonable hypotheses about the relatedness of various phyla. Thus, phyla with similar developmental and morphological patterns were regarded as sharing common ancestries. For example, annelids and arthropods, both schizocoelous, segmented coelomates, were seen as sharing a common ancestor, a view that was supported by the fossil record and by the existence of the Phylum Onychophora, which has some of the characteristics of both phyla. Increasingly, however, biologists are using molecular sequence data to reanalyze animal relationships.

26.3a Molecular Analyses Have Refined Our Understanding of Animal Phylogeny

Molecular analyses of animal relationships are often based on nucleotide sequences in small subunit ribosomal RNA and mitochondrial DNA, and, more recently, the sequences of specific genes. These analyses are used to construct molecular cladograms (see Chapter 19). **Figure 26.6, p. 584,** is a phylogenetic tree

developed from a number of cladograms based on molecular sequences. It represents, as do all such trees, a working hypothesis that explains the information that is now available.

The phylogenetic tree based on molecular characters includes the major lineages that biologists had defined using the morphological innovations and embryological characters described above. For example, molecular data confirm the distinctions between the Radiata and the Bilateria. They also confirm the separation of the deuterostome phyla from all others within the Bilateria.

The sponges are to some degree a special case. Because the way that the tissues are formed during embryology in the most primitive sponges differs from the other Metazoa, sponges have in the past been regarded as lacking "true" tissues and were placed in a separate subkingdom, the Parazoa, distinct from the remaining metazoans in the Eumetazoa. But the most recent molecular evidence includes them with the other Metazoa in a single monophyletic lineage. They do not form distinct nervous tissue, and that, together with absence of symmetry, separates them from all other Metazoans. However, molecular studies confirm that sponges and other Metazoa share a common ancestor.

Molecular phylogeny confirms the Protostomia and Deuterostomia as separate lineages within the Metazoa. Protostomia is, in turn, subdivided into two major lineages, the Lophotrochozoa and the Ecdysozoa, groupings that were not previously recognized. The name Lophotrochozoa (*lophos* = crest; *troch* = wheel; *zoa* = animals, plural of *zoon*) refers to both the "lophophore," a feeding structure found in three phyla (illustrated in Figure 26.15), and the "trochophore," a type of larva found in annelids and molluscs (illustrated in Figure 26.23). The name Ecdysozoa (*ekdero* = strip off the skin) refers to the cuticle that these species secrete and periodically replace; the shedding of the cuticle is called **ecdysis**.

26.3b Molecular Phylogeny Reveals Surprising Patterns in the Evolution of Key Morphological Innovations

Molecular phylogeny has forced biologists to reevaluate the evolution of several important morphological innovations. Traditional phylogenies based on morphology and embryology implied that the absence of a body cavity, the acoelomate condition, was ancestral and that the presence of a body cavity, the pseudocoelomate or coelomate condition, was derived. But the molecular tree provides a very different view. It suggests that the schizocoelomate condition is ancestral, having evolved in the common ancestor of the lineage. If that hypothesis is correct, then the acoelomate condition of flatworms may represent the evolutionary *loss* of the schizocoelom, *not* an ancestral condition. Similarly, the molecular tree hypothesizes that the pseudocoelom

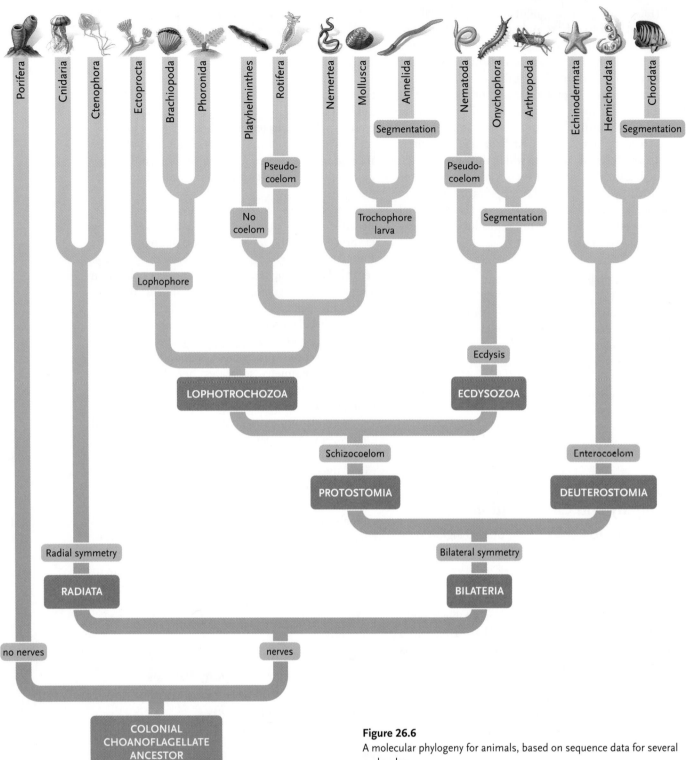

Figure 26.6
A molecular phylogeny for animals, based on sequence data for several molecules.

evolved independently in rotifers (Lophotrochozoa, phylum Rotifera) and in roundworms (Ecdysozoa, phylum Nematoda) as modifications of the ancestral schizocoelom.

Traditional phylogenies also suggested that the segmented body plan of several protostome phyla was inherited from a segmented common ancestor and that segmentation arose independently in the chordates by convergent evolution. The molecular tree, by contrast, suggests that segmentation evolved independently in

three lineages: segmented worms (Lophotrochozoa, phylum Annelida), arthropods and velvet worms (Ecdysozoa, phyla Arthropoda and Onychophora), and chordates (Deuterostomia, phylum Chordata).

The hypothesis based on molecular studies and represented in Figure 26.6 is the framework that we use for our consideration of the major invertebrate phyla. It is important to recognize, however, that phylogenetic trees are always provisional. In the future, new data may lead to revisions of the phylogeny.

Marty Snyderman/Planet Earth Pictures

Figure 26.7

Asymmetry in sponges. The shapes of sponges vary with their habitats. Those that occupy calm waters, such as this stinker vase sponge (*Ircinia campana*), may be lobed, tubular, cuplike, or vaselike.

STUDY BREAK

1. How is molecular analysis used in creating phylogenetic trees?
2. Describe the way molecular phylogeny has changed how biologists view the absence of the coelom.

26.4 Phylum Porifera

Sponges **(Figure 26.7)** are mostly marine, with a small number of species living in fresh water. They have no particular symmetry, are completely sessile as adults, and obtain their food by filtering it from the water. Sponges have been abundant since the Cambrian, and about 8000 living species are known. They range in size from 1 cm to 2 m.

Their body plan **(Figure 26.8)** is simple: sponges can be regarded as sacs with a cavity, the spongocoel, opening to the environment via an osteopore. There are two layers of organized cells. The cells on the outside of the sponge, the pinacocytes, form an epithelium. The inner layer of cells, lining the cavity, are **choanocytes**, each with a flagellum surrounded by microvilli. The two layers are separated by a gelatinous matrix, the mesohyl. The mesohyl contains archaeocytes, amoebalike cells that move throughout the mesohyl by typical amoeboid movement. The wall of the bag is perforated by a number of pores lined by porocytes, specialized derivatives of the pinacocytes.

Almost all sponges are filter feeders. The action of the choanocytes sets up a unidirectional current by which water enters the **spongocoel** through the porocytes and leaves via the osteopore. Flow rates can be adjusted by the porocytes, which are capable of contraction, suggesting communication among the cells in spite of the absence of nerves. Particles of food are captured by the choanocytes and passed to the mesohyl, where they are ingested and digested by the archaeocytes, which may also store reserves.

Some archaeocytes may become specialized to form extracellular rigid supporting structures that give shape to the sponge. These are microscopic rigid structures of various shapes (depending on the species) composed of a calcareous or siliceous (silicon) material. Collagen is also found in the mesohyl, as is a collagen-like protein, spongin. These are products of the

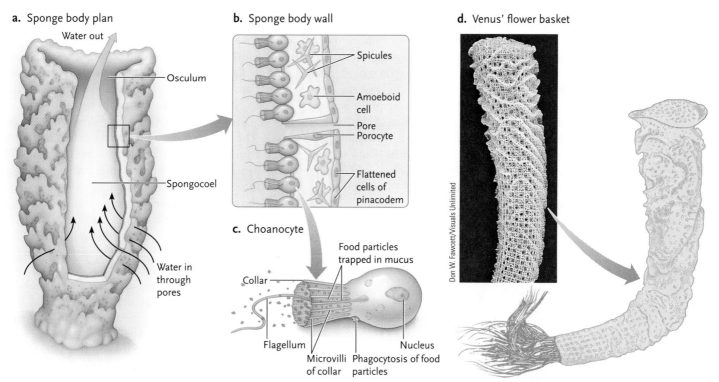

a. Sponge body plan

Water out

Osculum

Spongocoel

Water in through pores

b. Sponge body wall

Spicules

Amoeboid cell

Pore
Porocyte

Flattened cells of pinacodem

c. Choanocyte

Food particles trapped in mucus

Collar

Flagellum

Microvilli of collar

Phagocytosis of food particles

Nucleus

d. Venus' flower basket

Don W. Fawcett/Visuals Unlimited

Figure 26.8

The body plan of sponges. Most sponges have **(a)** simple body plans and **(b)** relatively few cell types. **(c)** Beating flagella on the choanocytes create a flow of water through incurrent pores, into the spongocoel, and out through the osculum. **(d)** Venus flower basket (*Euplectella* species), a marine sponge, has spicules of silica fused into a rigid framework.

archaeocytes. The archaeocytes are "totipotent"—like stem cells, they have the capacity to differentiate into any of the cell types, including eggs and sperm.

Most sponges are monoecious: individuals produce both sperm and eggs. Sperm are released into the spongocoel and then out into the environment; eggs (oocytes) remain in the mesohyl, where sperm from other sponges, drawn in with water, are captured by choanocytes and carried to oocytes. Early development occurs within the sponge and produces a ciliated larva that permits the distribution of the species within the habitat. The larvae are of various types: many are free swimming, whereas some use their cilia to crawl over the substrate. There is evidence that some larvae avoid light to select a location to settle, where they undergo **metamorphosis** (a reorganization of form) into sessile adults. Some sponges also reproduce asexually; small fragments break off an adult and grow into new sponges. Many species, particularly those in fresh water, also produce **gemmules**, clusters of cells with a resistant covering that allows them to survive unfavourable conditions. Gemmules germinate into new sponges when conditions improve.

Even with a very simple basic body plan, sponges have achieved remarkable diversity. Sponges formed very large reefs during the Mesozoic, and a modern reef, originating at the end of the last ice age, has been found off the west coast of Canada. It is being studied by Verena Tunnicliffes lab at the University of Victoria.

Many sponges serve as refuges for other species. Blue-green algae and cyanobacteria can be found in the mesohyl and, in some species, within the archaeocytes. A curious relationship with another species can be found in the Venus flower basket, *Euplectella aspergillum* (see Figure 26.8d). Male and female shrimp (*Spongicola* species) may enter the spongocoel when small, feed on material brought in by the sponge, and grow large enough that they are unable to leave. The pair of shrimp spend their entire lives in the prison formed by the elaborate basket of spicules.

One species, *Asbestopluma hypogea*, catches small arthropods that become entangled in hook-shaped spicules on the surface. The prey are then encased in filamentous structures and digested. Choanocytes are absent in this sponge.

STUDY BREAK

1. Do sponges exhibit symmetry? If so, what type?
2. How does a sponge gather food from its environment?

26.5 Metazoans with Radial Symmetry

Unlike sponges, the remaining metazoans have some form of symmetry and well-differentiated tissues, including nerves, that develop from distinct layers in the embryo. In this section, we describe metazoans with radial symmetry, a body plan that permits the detection of stimuli from all directions. This is an effective adaptation for life in open water.

Two phyla of soft-bodied organisms, Cnidaria and Ctenophora, have radial symmetry and nerves. Both phyla possess a **gastrovascular cavity** with a single opening, the mouth. Gas exchange and excretion can occur by diffusion because no cell is far from a body surface.

The radiate phyla have a diploblastic body plan with only inner and outer tissue layers, the **gastrodermis** (an endoderm derivative) and the **epidermis** (an ectoderm derivative), respectively. Most species also possess a gelatinous **mesoglea** (*meso* = middle; *glea* = glue) between the two layers. The mesoglea contains widely dispersed fibrous and amoeboid cells, recalling the organization of the mesohyl in sponges.

26.5a Phylum Cnidaria

Nearly all of the 8900 species in the phylum Cnidaria (*cnid* = stinging nettle, a plant with irritating hairs) live in the sea. Their body plan is organized around a saclike gastrovascular cavity and the mouth is ringed with tentacles, which push food into it. Cnidarians may be vase-shaped, upward-pointing **polyps** or bell-shaped, downward-pointing **medusae (Figure 26.9)**. Most polyps attach to a substrate at the *aboral* (opposite the mouth) end; medusae are unattached and float.

Cnidarians are the simplest animals that exhibit a division of labour among irreversibly specialized tissues (see Figure 26.9c) and that have nerve cells. The gastrodermis includes sensory receptor cells, gland cells, and phagocytic nutritive cells. Gland cells secrete enzymes for the **extracellular digestion** of food, which is then engulfed by nutritive cells and exposed to **intracellular digestion**. The epidermis includes sensory cells, contractile cells, and cells specialized for prey capture.

Cnidarians prey on crustaceans, fishes, and other animals. The epidermis includes unique cells, **cnidocytes**, each armed with a stinging **nematocyst (Figure 26.10)**. The nematocyst contains an encapsulated, coiled thread that is fired at prey or predators, sometimes releasing a toxin through its tip. Discharge of nematocysts may be triggered by touch, vibrations, or chemical stimuli. The toxin can paralyze small prey by disrupting nerve cell membranes. The painful stings of some jellyfishes and certain corals result from the discharge of nematocysts.

Cnidarians engage in directed movements by contracting specialized ectodermal cells that look like muscles. In medusae, the mesogleal jelly serves as a deformable skeleton against which contractile cells act. Rapid contractions narrow the bell, forcing out jets of water that propel the animal. Polyps use their water-filled gastrovascular cavity as a hydrostatic skeleton. When some cells contract, fluid within the chamber is shunted about, changing the body's shape and moving it in a particular direction.

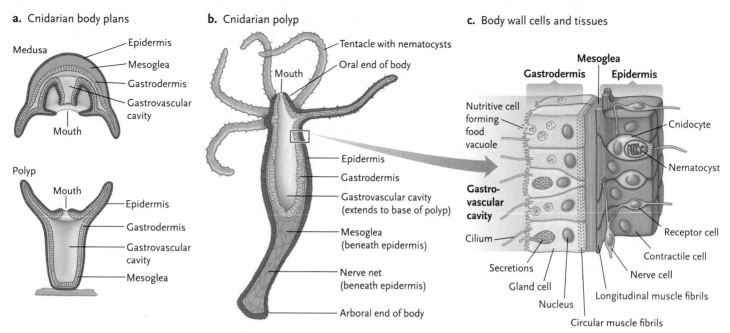

a. Cnidarian body plans

Medusa
- Epidermis
- Mesoglea
- Gastrodermis
- Gastrovascular cavity
- Mouth

Polyp
- Mouth
- Epidermis
- Gastrodermis
- Gastrovascular cavity
- Mesoglea

b. Cnidarian polyp

- Tentacle with nematocysts
- Oral end of body
- Mouth
- Epidermis
- Gastrodermis
- Gastrovascular cavity (extends to base of polyp)
- Mesoglea (beneath epidermis)
- Nerve net (beneath epidermis)
- Arboral end of body

c. Body wall cells and tissues

- Mesoglea
- Gastrodermis
- Epidermis
- Nutritive cell forming food vacuole
- Gastrovascular cavity
- Cilium
- Secretions
- Gland cell
- Nucleus
- Cnidocyte
- Nematocyst
- Receptor cell
- Contractile cell
- Nerve cell
- Longitudinal muscle fibrils
- Circular muscle fibrils

Figure 26.9

The cnidarian body plan. **(a)** Cnidarians exist as either polyps or medusae. **(b)** The body of both forms is organized around a gastrovascular cavity, which extends all the way to the aboral end of the animal. **(c)** The two tissue layers in the body wall, the gastrodermis and the epidermis, include a variety of cell types.

The **nerve net**, which threads through both tissue layers, is a simple nervous system that coordinates responses to stimuli (see Chapter 33). Although there is no recognizable "brain," there are control

a. *Hydra* consuming a crustacean

Kim Taylor/Bruce Coleman Ltd.

Kim Taylor/Bruce Coleman Ltd.

b. Cnidocytes

- Operculum (capsule's lid at cnidocyte's free surface)
- Trigger (modified cilium)
- Nematocyst coiled inside capsule
- Barbs

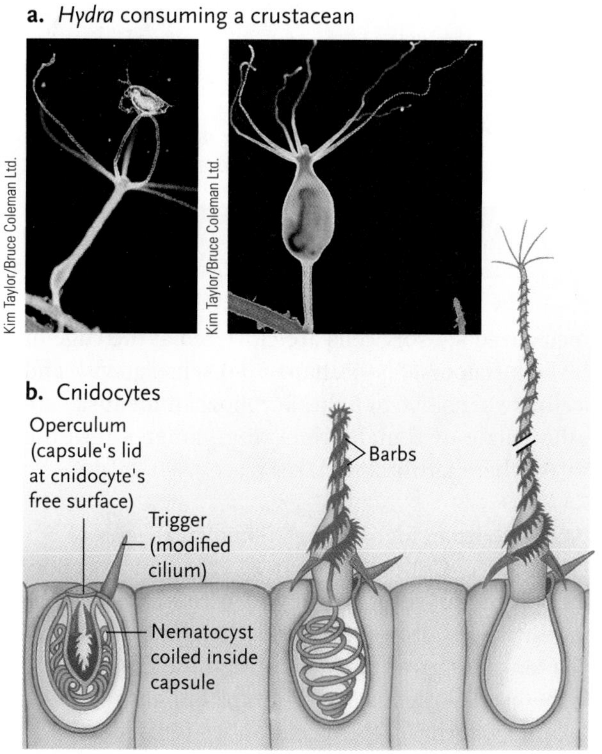

Figure 26.10

Predation by cnidarians. **(a)** A polyp of a freshwater *Hydra* captures a small crustacean with its tentacles and swallows it whole. **(b)** Cnidocytes, special cells on the tentacles, encapsulate nematocysts, which are discharged at prey.

and coordination centres, particularly in a ring of nerves encircling the mouth. In spite of its structural simplicity, the nerve net permits directed swimming movements so the animal can escape predators.

Many cnidarians exist in only the polyp or the medusa form, but some have a life cycle that alternates between them **(Figure 26.11, p. 588)**. In the alternating type, the polyp often produces new individuals asexually from buds that break free of the parent (see Chapter 40). The medusa is often the sexual stage, producing sperm and eggs, which are released into the water. Sexual reproduction results in a ciliated, nonfeeding larval stage, the planula, that eventually settles and undergoes metamorphosis into the polyp form. The four classes of Cnidaria differ in the form that predominates in the life cycle.

Class Hydrozoa. Most of the 2700 species in the class Hydrozoa have both polyp and medusa stages in their life cycles (see Figure 26.11). The polyps form sessile colonies that develop asexually from one individual. A colony can include thousands of polyps, which may be specialized for feeding, defence, or reproduction. They share food through their connected gastrovascular cavities. A few warm-water species secrete a calcareous skeleton and form large colonies. These hydrocorals are different from the anthozoans that form coral reefs (see Class Anthozoa, below).

Some pelagic hydrozoans have both polyp and medusoid forms present in the same colony, which functions as an individual organism. The majestic Portuguese man-of-war jellyfish, for example, has the medusoid bell modified to form a gas-filled sail.

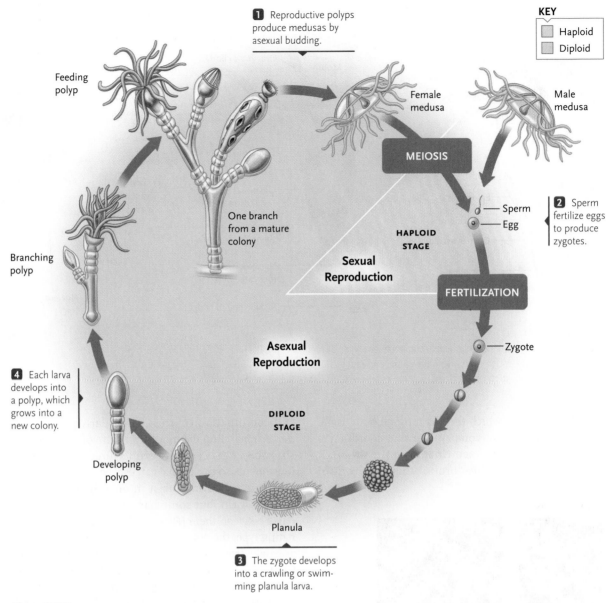

1 Reproductive polyps produce medusas by asexual budding.

KEY
☐ Haploid
☐ Diploid

Feeding polyp

Female medusa

Male medusa

MEIOSIS

One branch from a mature colony

Sperm

Egg

2 Sperm fertilize eggs to produce zygotes.

HAPLOID STAGE

Sexual Reproduction

Branching polyp

FERTILIZATION

Asexual Reproduction

Zygote

4 Each larva develops into a polyp, which grows into a new colony.

DIPLOID STAGE

Developing polyp

Planula

3 The zygote develops into a crawling or swimming planula larva.

Figure 26.11
Life cycle of *Obelia*. The life cycle of *Obelia*, a colonial hydrozoan, includes both polyp and medusa stages.

The hydroid form is represented by feeding and reproductive polyps dangling from the sail (see Chapter 46).

Unlike most Hydrozoa, freshwater species of *Hydra* (see Figure 26.10a) live as solitary polyps that attach temporarily to rocks, twigs, and leaves. Under favourable conditions, hydras reproduce by budding. Under adverse conditions, they produce eggs and sperm. Zygotes, formed by fertilization, are encapsulated in a protective coating but develop and grow when conditions improve. There is no larval stage; the eggs hatch into small *Hydra*.

Class Scyphozoa. The medusa stage predominates in the 200 species of the class Scyphozoa or jellyfish **(Figure 26.12a).** They range from 2 cm to more than 2 m in diameter. Nerve cells near the margin of the bell control their tentacles and coordinate the rhythmic activity of contractile cells, which move the animal. Specialized sensory cells are clustered at the edge of the bell: **statocysts** (see Chapter 34) sense gravity, and ocelli are sensitive to light. Scyphozoan medusae are either male or female, releasing gametes into the water, where fertilization takes place.

Class Cubozoa. Most of the 20 known species of box jellyfish, the Cubozoa **(Figure 26.12b),** exist as cube-shaped medusae only a few centimetres tall; the largest species grows to 25 cm in height. Nematocyst-rich tentacles grow in clusters from the four corners of the boxlike medusa, and groups of light receptors and image-forming eyes occur on the four sides of the bell. The eyes have lenses and retinas and are used in actively pursuing prey. Unlike the scyphozoan jellyfish, cubozoans are active swimmers. They eat small fish and invertebrates, immobilizing their prey with one of the deadliest toxins produced by animals.

a. Scyphozoan

© Michael Durham/Minden Pictures

b. Cubozoan

Anders Garm

Figure 26.12

Scyphozoans and cubozoans. **(a)** Most scyphozoans, like the sea nettle (*Chrysaora* species), live as floating medusae. Their tentacles trap prey, and the long oral arms transfer it to the mouth on the underside of the bell. **(b)** Cubozoans, unlike most jelly fish, are active swimmers and can change direction abruptly in their pursuit of prey. They have several light-sensitive organs, but only four of them, two of which are clearly visible here, form images.

Cubozoans live in tropical and subtropical coastal waters, where they sometimes pose a serious threat to swimmers: the nematocysts of some species can inflict considerable pain to, and may kill, humans.

Class Anthozoa. The Anthozoa includes 6000 species of corals and sea anemones **(Figure 26.13, p. 590).** Anthozoans exist only as polyps, which have a more complex structure than the Hydrozoa. A muscular pharynx leads into the gastrovascular cavity, and the body often consists of compartments partially separated by vertical membranes called septa. They reproduce by budding or **fission**. Most also reproduce sexually, producing eggs that develop into ciliated larvae. Corals (see Figure 26.13a) are always sessile and colonial. Their ciliated larvae settle and metamorphose into polyps that produce colonies by budding. Most species of corals build calcium carbonate skeletons that sometimes accumulate into gigantic underwater reefs. A coral reef usually contains more than one species of anthozoan. The energy needs of corals are partly fulfilled by the photosynthetic activity of symbiotic protists that live within the anthozoans. For this reason, corals are restricted to shallow water, where sunlight can penetrate.

Sea anemones (see Figure 26.13b), by contrast, are soft-bodied, solitary polyps, ranging from 1 to 10 cm in diameter. They occupy shallow coastal waters. Most species are sessile, but some move by crawling slowly or by using the gastrovascular cavity as a hydrostatic skeleton.

26.5b Phylum Ctenophora

The 100 species of comb jellies in the marine phylum Ctenophora (*ctenos* = comb; *phor* = to carry) also have radial symmetry, mesoglea, and feeding tentacles. However, they differ from Cnidaria in significant ways. They lack nematocysts, they expel some waste through anal pores at the other end of the body from the mouth, and certain tissues appear to be of mesodermal origin. These transparent and often luminescent (light producing) animals range in size from a few millimetres to 30 cm in diameter, with tentacles up to 1 m or more in length **(Figure 26.14, p. 590).**

Ctenophores move by beating cilia arranged on eight longitudinal plates that resemble combs. They are the largest animals to use cilia for locomotion, but they are feeble swimmers. Nerve cells coordinate the animals' movements, and a gravity-sensing statocyst helps them maintain an upright position. Most species have two tentacles with specialized cells that discharge sticky filaments to entrap small animals floating in the sea, particularly small crustaceans. The food-laden

a. Coral

b. Sea anemone escape behaviour

Tentacle of one polyp

Interconnected
skeletons of polyps
of a colonial coral

Christian DellaCorte

F. S. Westmorland

F. S. Westmorland

F. S. Westmorland

Figure 26.13
Anthozoans. **(a)** Many corals are colonial, and their polyps build a hard skeleton of calcium carbonate. The skeletons accumulate to form coral reefs in shallow tropical waters. **(b)** A sea anemone detaches from its substrate to escape from a predatory sea star.

tentacles are drawn across the mouth. Others lack tentacles and take large prey by a single gulp of the mouth. Some species that attack Cnidaria incorporate the nematocysts from the prey and use them in feeding (see Chapter 46). Ctenophores are hermaphroditic, producing gametes in cells that line the gastrovascular cavity. Eggs and sperm are expelled through the mouth or from special pores, and fertilization occurs in the open water.

STUDY BREAK

1. How do cnidarians capture, consume, and digest their prey?
2. Describe the differences between a polyp and a medusa.
3. Which group of cnidarians has only a polyp stage in its life cycle?
4. What do ctenophores eat, and how do they collect their food?

Figure 26.14
Ctenophores. The comb jelly *Pleurobrachia* collects microscopic prey on its two long sticky tentacles and then wipes the food-laden tentacles across its mouth.

© Norbert Wu/Minden Pictures

26.6 Lophotrochozoan Protostomes

The remaining organisms described in this chapter are in the group Bilateria because of their bilateral symmetry. They have a greater variety of tissues, some of which are developed into organ systems. Most of the phyla have a coelom or pseudocoelom. With bilateral symmetry and sensory organs that are concentrated at the anterior end of the body, most bilaterians can make directed movements in pursuit of food or mates or to escape danger. Organ systems can operate more efficiently than simple tissues. For example, animals that have a tubular digestive system surrounded by a space (the coelom) use muscular contractions of the digestive system to move ingested food past specialized epithelial cells that break it down and absorb the breakdown products.

Molecular analyses group eight of the Bilateria phyla into the Lophotrochozoa, one of the two main protostome lineages (see Figure 26.6).

26.6a Three Lophophorate Phyla Share a Distinctive Feeding Structure

Three small groups of mostly marine (a few are aquatic), coelomate animals, the phyla Brachiopoda, Ectoprocta, and Phoronida, possess a **lophophore**, a circular or U-shaped fold with one or two rows of hollow, ciliated tentacles surrounding the mouth **(Figure 26.15)**. Molecular sequence data and the lophophore suggest that these phyla share a common ancestry.

The coelomic cavity extends into the lophophore, which looks like a crown of tentacles at the anterior end of the animal. The lophophore is involved in the capture of food and serves as a site for gas exchange. Most lophophorates are sessile suspension-feeders as adults. Movement of cilia on the tentacles brings food-laden water toward the lophophore, where the tentacles capture small organisms and debris, and the cilia transport

a. Ectoprocta (*Plumatella repens*) **b.** Brachiopoda (*Terebraulina septentrionalis*)

c. Phoronida (*Phoronis*)

Figure 26.15

Lophophorate animals. Although the lophophorate animals differ markedly in appearance, they all use a lophophore to acquire food.

them to the mouth. The lophophorates have a complete digestive system, which is U-shaped in most species, with the anus lying outside the ring of tentacles.

Phylum Ectoprocta. The Ectoprocta (sometimes called Bryozoa or Polyzoa) are tiny colonial animals that occupy mainly marine habitats (see Figure 26.15a). They secrete a hard covering over their soft bodies. The lophophore is normally retracted into a chamber at the anterior end of the animal and extended when the animal feeds. Each colony, which may include more than a million individuals, is produced asexually by a single animal. Ectoproct colonies are permanently attached to solid substrates, where they form encrusting mats, bushy upright growths, or jellylike blobs. Sexual reproduction involves the production of eggs and sperm in the coelom. The sperm are shed through special pores. Fertilization may be internal or external, and the zygote gives rise to a ciliated larva that eventually settles and undergoes metamorphosis. Nearly 5000 living species are known, and about 50 of those live in fresh water.

Phylum Brachiopoda. The brachiopods, or lampshells, have two calcified shells that are secreted on the animal's dorsal and ventral sides (see Figure 26.15b). Most species attach to substrates with a stalk that protrudes through one of the shells. The lophophore is held within the two shells, and the animal feeds by opening its shell and drawing water over its tentacles. The animal has well-developed organs, such as a

heart that propels blood through a number of interconnected sinuses and specialized excretory organs. Eggs and sperm are produced in different individuals (dioecious), and fertilization is external. The zygote gives rise to a ciliated larva.

Phylum Phoronida. The 18 or so species of phoronid worms vary in length from a few millimetres to 25 cm (see Figure 26.15c). They usually build tubes of chitin, a polymer of N-acetylglucosamine (see *Molecule Behind Biology,* Chapter 36), in soft ocean sediments or on hard substrates and feed by protruding the lophophore from the top of the tube. Phoronids reproduce both sexually and by budding. The animals are monoecious (both eggs and sperm produced by one individual). A ciliated feeding larva is produced that settles, undergoes metamorphosis, secretes a tube, and develops into an adult.

26.6b Phylum Platyhelminthes

The 13 000 flatworm species in the phylum Platyhelminthes (*plat* = flat; *helminth* = worm) live in aquatic and moist terrestrial habitats. Some are parasitic. Like cnidarians, flatworms can swim or float in water, but they are also able to crawl over surfaces. They range from less than 1 mm to more than 20 m in length, and most are just a few millimetres thick. Free-living species eat live prey or decomposing carcasses, whereas parasitic species derive their nutrition from the tissues of living hosts.

Like the radiate phyla, flatworms are acoelomate, but they have a complex structural organization that reflects their triploblastic construction **(Figure 26.16, p. 592).** In those with a gut (some parasitic forms lack this organ), endoderm lines the digestive cavity with cells specialized for the chemical breakdown and absorption of ingested food. A single opening serves as both mouth and anus. Mesoderm, the middle tissue layer, produces muscles and reproductive organs. Ectoderm produces a ciliated epidermis, the nervous system, and the **flame cell** system, a simple excretory system (see Chapter 43). Flatworms lack circulatory or **respiratory systems**, but because all cells of their dorsoventrally (top-to-bottom) flattened bodies are near an interior or exterior surface, diffusion supplies them with nutrients and oxygen.

The flatworm nervous system includes two or more longitudinal ventral nerve cords interconnected

Digestive system

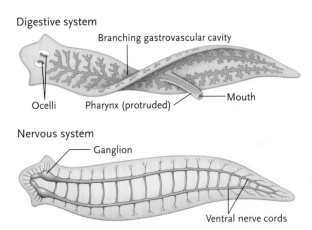

Branching gastrovascular cavity

Ocelli — Pharynx (protruded) — Mouth

Nervous system

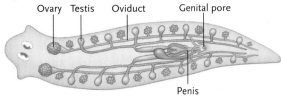

Ganglion

Ventral nerve cords

Reproductive system

Ovary — Testis — Oviduct — Genital pore

Penis

Excretory system

Flame cells

Figure 26.16

Flatworms. The phylum Platyhelminthes, exemplified by a freshwater planarian, have well-developed digestive, excretory, nervous, and reproductive systems. Because flatworms are acoelomate, their organ systems are embedded in a solid mass of tissue between the gut and the epidermis.

Figure 26.17

Turbellaria. A few turbellarians, such as *Pseudoceros dimidiatus*, are colourful marine worms.

© Cory Gray

by numerous smaller nerve fibres, like rungs on a ladder. An anterior **ganglion**, a concentration of nervous system tissue that serves as a primitive "brain," integrates their behaviour (see Chapter 33). Most free-living species have ocelli or "eye spots" that distinguish light from dark and chemoreceptor organs that sense chemical cues.

The phylum Platyhelminthes includes four classes, defined largely by their anatomical adaptations to free-living or parasitic habits. One class, Turbellaria, is free-living, whereas the remaining three classes are parasitic, obtaining their nutrition from the tissues of another animal, the host.

Class Turbellaria. Most free-living flatworms (class Turbellaria) live in the sea **(Figure 26.17)**, where they may be brightly coloured. The familiar planarians and a few others live in fresh water or on land and are drab. Turbellarians swim by undulating the body wall musculature or crawl across surfaces by using muscles and cilia to glide on mucus trails produced by the ventral epidermis. Some terrestrial turbellarians are relatively large and prey on other invertebrates. For example, *Microplana termitophaga* waits at the entrance to termite colonies in Africa and

entangles the prey in the slime that they produce. Other species may gang up on large snails.

The gastrovascular cavity in free-living flatworms is similar to that in cnidarians. Food is ingested and wastes are eliminated through a single opening, the mouth, located on the ventral surface. Most turbellarians acquire food with a muscular **pharynx** that connects the mouth to the digestive cavity (see Figure 26.16a). Chemicals secreted into the saclike cavity digest ingested items, after which cells throughout the gastrovascular surface engulf food particles and subject them to intracellular digestion. In some species, the digestive cavity is highly branched, increasing the surface area for digestion and absorption.

Nearly all turbellarians are hermaphroditic, with complex reproductive systems (see Figure 26.16c). When they mate, each partner functions simultaneously as a male and a female. The eggs of most species hatch directly into small worms, but ciliated larvae occur in a few marine turbellarians. Many free-living species also reproduce asexually by simply separating the anterior half of the animal from the posterior half. Both halves subsequently regenerate the missing parts.

Class Monogenea. Flukes (classes Trematoda and Monogenea) are **parasites** that obtain nutrients from host tissues. Monogenea flukes are ectoparasites that attach to the gills or skin of aquatic vertebrates. They have an anterior sucker surrounding the mouth and a more posterior sucker. The suckers may be equipped with hooks.

Reproduction occurs by internal fertilization. The eggs are released into water and hatch as ciliated larvae. The larvae attach to a new host and undergo metamorphosis.

Class Trematoda. Adult trematodes **(Figure 26.18)** are all internal parasites of vertebrates, but their development involves two or more host species in their life cycle. They are sometimes called digenean (two hosts) flukes. The host species in which sexual reproduction occurs is

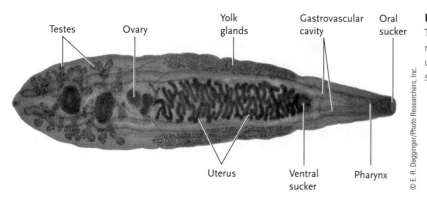

Testes Ovary Yolk glands Gastrovascular cavity Oral sucker

Uterus Ventral sucker Pharynx

© E. R. Degginger/Photo Researchers, Inc.

Figure 26.18

Trematoda. The hermaphroditic Chinese liver fluke (*Opisthorchis sinensis*) uses a well-developed reproductive system to produce thousands of eggs.

the primary host, and other hosts, usually invertebrates, are secondary hosts. Thus, the same individual will encounter very different environments during its life and may have two or more very different larval stages during development (see Polymorphic Development). Like the monogeneans, trematodes normally have two suckers, one of which is around the mouth. The unciliated epidermis is a syncytium (the cells are interconnected without separating membranes). Trematodes can be found in many vertebrates, including humans, where they may cause some serious diseases.

Class Cestoda. Tapeworms **(Figure 26.19)** are parasitic in the intestines of vertebrates, their primary host. They lack a mouth or digestive system and absorb nutrients from the host's intestinal contents across the syncytial epithelium. The anterior end is modified as a **scolex**, consisting of hooks and/or suckers that allow it to attach to the wall of the intestine. The remainder of the worm consists of a series of identical units, proglottids, each with its own reproductive system. **Proglottids** are generated just posterior to the scolex and become progressively more mature near the tail. The posterior, fully mature units break off or burst and are passed out with the feces. Worms may consist of only a few proglottids, but many species have 2000 to 3000, and such worms may be 10 m in length, occupying the entire length of the human small intestine.

Each proglottid contains a complete set of reproductive organs producing both sperm and eggs. Fertilization is internal and may involve a neighbouring worm, or the worm may be self-fertilizing. Each proglottid may contain as many as 50 000 eggs. Further development varies with the species, but, typically, the eggs must be eaten by an appropriate intermediate host, usually an arthropod, in which it undergoes development into a series of larval stages. The life cycle is completed when an appropriate primary host eats an infected intermediate host. For example, the adult tapeworm *Hymenolepis diminuta* lives in rat intestines. The eggs in rat feces are eaten by flour beetles, where larvae develop and form cysts. Rats become infected when they eat the beetles. Humans can also become infected by unwittingly consuming infected beetles that may live in dry breakfast cereals.

26.6c Phylum Rotifera

Most of the 1800 species in the pseudocoelomate phylum Rotifera (*rota* = wheel; *fera* = to bear) live in fresh water, and a few are marine **(Figure 26.20, p. 594)**. Most are less than 0.5 mm long, but a few range up to 3 mm. They exhibit *eutely*, a mode of development in which cell division ceases early and subsequent growth is by cell enlargement. In spite of their size, they have well-developed digestive, reproductive, excretory, and nervous systems. In some habitats, rotifers make up a large part of the zooplankton (tiny animals that float in open water). Some species, however, are attached to the substrate and move only a little. Others may form colonies, and some live in pitcher plants (see Chapter 47).

Rotifers use coordinated movements of cilia, arranged in a wheel-like **corona** around the head, to propel themselves in the environment. Cilia also bring food-laden water to their mouths. Ingested

a. Tapeworm **b.** Scolex

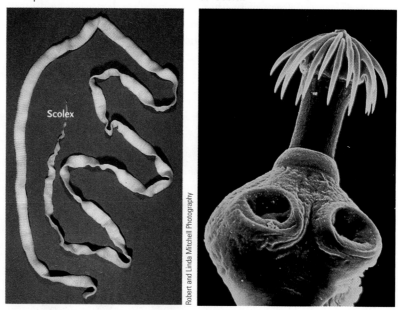

Scolex

Robert and Linda Mitchell Photography

Cath Ellis, University of Hull/SPL/Photo Researchers, Inc.

Figure 26.19

Cestoda. **(a)** Tapeworms have long bodies composed of a series of proglottids, each of which produces thousands of fertilized eggs. **(b)** The anterior end is a scolex with hooks and suckers that attach to the host's intestinal wall.

a. Rotifer body plan

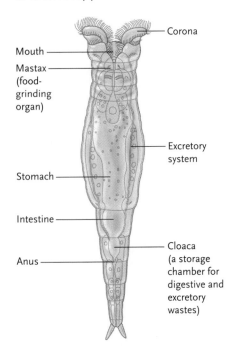

- Corona
- Mouth
- Mastax (food-grinding organ)
- Excretory system
- Stomach
- Intestine
- Cloaca (a storage chamber for digestive and excretory wastes)
- Anus

b. Rotifer laying eggs

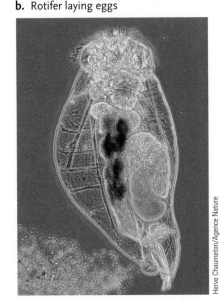

Herve Chaumeton/Agence Nature

Figure 26.20

Phylum Rotifera. **(a)** Despite their small size, rotifers such as *Philodina roseola* have complex body plans and organ systems. **(b)** This rotifer, another *Philodina* species, is laying eggs.

microorganisms are conveyed to the **mastax**, a toothed grinding organ, and then passed to the stomach and intestine. Rotifers have a **complete digestive tract**: food enters through the mouth, and undigested waste is voided through a separate anus.

The life history patterns of some rotifers are adapted to the ever-changing environments in small bodies of water. During most months, rotifer populations of these species include only females that reproduce by **parthenogenesis** (the development of unfertilized eggs; see Chapter 39). In this particular form of parthenogenesis, females produce diploid eggs by mitosis that develop into females. When environmental conditions deteriorate, females produce eggs by meiosis. If these eggs remain unfertilized,

they develop into haploid males that produce sperm. If the haploid eggs are fertilized, they produce diploid female zygotes. The fertilized eggs have durable shells and food reserves to survive drying or freezing.

26.6d Phylum Nemertea

The 650 species of ribbon worms or proboscis worms vary from less than 1 cm to 30 m in length **(Figure 26.21)**. Most species are marine, but a few occupy moist terrestrial habitats. The often brightly coloured ribbon worms have no obvious coelom and use a ciliated epidermis to glide over a film of secreted mucus. Ribbon worms have a complete digestive tract with a mouth and an anus. They have a circulatory system in which fluid flows through **circulatory vessels** that carry nutrients and oxygen to tissues and remove wastes. They have a muscular, mucus-covered proboscis, a tube that can be everted (turned inside out) through a separate pore to capture prey. The proboscis is housed within a chamber, the **rhynchocoel**, which is unique to this phylum (see Figure 26.21b).

Nemerteans are aggressive predators. The proboscis may have a barb that is used to impale the prey, or the proboscis may wrap around the prey in a form of stranglehold. Many nemerteans are burrowing animals, living in tubes that protect them from predators. The life cycle includes a microscopic ciliated larva.

a. Ribbon worm

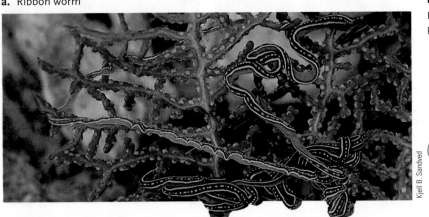

Kjell B. Sandved

b. Ribbon worm anatomy

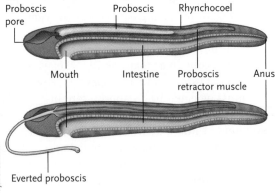

- Proboscis pore
- Proboscis
- Rhynchocoel
- Mouth
- Intestine
- Proboscis retractor muscle
- Anus
- Everted proboscis

Figure 26.21

(a) The flattened, elongated bodies of ribbon worms, such as genus *Lineus*, are often brightly coloured. **(b)** Ribbon worms have a complete digestive system and a specialized cavity, the rhynchocoel, that houses a protrusible proboscis.

Polymorphic Development

Most of the protostomes share a capacity for developmental polymorphism. During development from egg to adult, the organism may assume different morphologies. Most commonly, the immature form is referred to as a larva. In insects, for example, the caterpillar that hatches from the egg and that grows through a number of moults is a feeding stage very different from the adult butterfly, the distributive and reproductive stage. The transformation from larva to adult stage is accomplished by metamorphosis.

In other cases, particularly in sessile marine animals, the larval stage functions in distribution. Often this is an inconspicuous ciliated stage, such as the trochophore larva of molluscs and marine annelids (see Figure 26.23), that drifts with ocean currents. It settles to the ocean floor in response to some signal and metamorphoses into the form that will eventually become the adult. Some of the Cnidaria may have three distinct forms (see Figure 26.11). This capacity for assuming different forms during development is particularly important for two lifestyles, parasitism and social insects.

Populations of animals that live in other organisms are faced with a particular challenge. The environment in which they live, the host, is discontinuous in space: one host is not connected to another. It is also discontinuous in time: the host eventually dies. It is thus essential for a parasite to move from one part of this discontinuous environment to another if the parasite population is to survive. Moving to another host may involve a period as a free-living form or further development in an alternate host. During its life cycle, the parasite is thus obliged to experience two or more different environments. These different environments have favoured different developmental stages, often a series of morphologically distinct larvae. In the Chinese liver fluke (*Opisthorchis sinensis*), for example **(Figure 1),** the egg is eaten by a snail and hatches into a ciliated larva, the miracidium.

Almost immediately, metamorphosis occurs involving extensive reorganization

(continued on page 596)

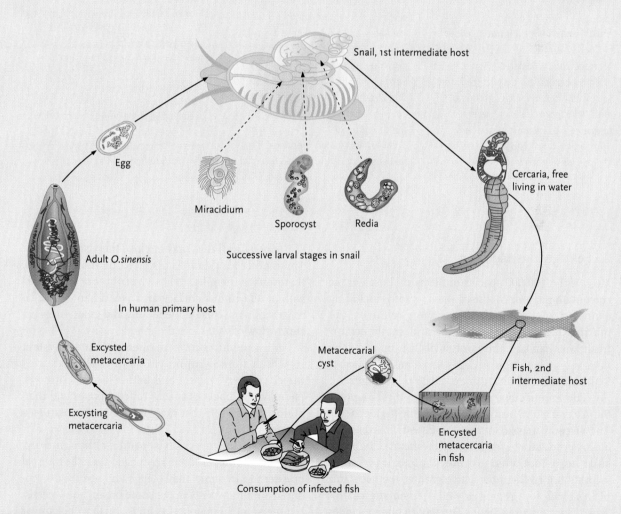

Figure 1

The life cycle of the liver fluke *Opisthorchis sinensis*. Humans become infected by eating raw fish, and the adult fluke lives in the liver and bile duct. Estimates of the number of persons infected range up to 30 000 000.

(continued from page 595)

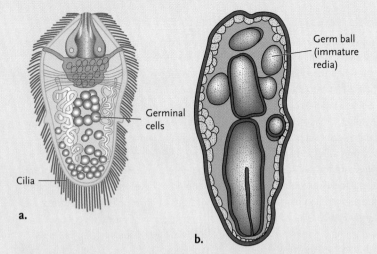

Germinal cells

Cilia

a.

b.

Germ ball (immature redia)

Entomological Society of America

Figure 2

The transformation of a miracidium **(a)** into a sporocyst **(b)**, involving the development of totipotent germ cells (stem cells) into germ balls that will form several copies of the next larval stage.

of the larva. This produces the sporocyst. Groups of embryonic cells, called "germ balls" **(Figure 2),** within the body cavity of the larva develop to produce additional larval stages, which are morphologically distinct from the sporocyst. In each stage, groups of embryonic germ balls are reserved to give rise to increased numbers of the next stage. The snail eventually releases enormous numbers of

another larval form, the free-swimming cercaria, that enters another intermediate host, a fish, where it forms a cyst in the muscle. This cyst will develop into the adult fluke if it is consumed by a human. The existence of populations of totipotent stem cells in flatworms has made possible the developmental polymorphism on which parasitism depends. The development of the cells is directed

into different pathways appropriate for each parasitic stage.

Developmental polymorphism is also a feature of social insects. Social insects live in colonies and are characterized by different castes (individuals that perform particular tasks on behalf of the entire colony), which usually differ in morphology. The difference among the castes is particularly pronounced in termites **(Figure 3).**

Figure 3

Termite castes. The queen termite in the centre of the photograph is surrounded by workers, called "pseudergates." One soldier, with an enlarged head and mandibles, is also visible. At each moult, depending on the conditions in the colony, a pseudergate may develop into another pseudergate, embark on development to a soldier, or develop into a winged supplementary reproductive caste that will leave the colony to found a new one.

26.6e Phylum Mollusca

Most of the 100 000 species of fleshy molluscs in the coelomate phylum Mollusca (*moll* = soft), including clams, snails, octopuses, and their relatives, are marine. However, many clams and snails occupy freshwater habitats, and some snails live on land. Molluscs vary in length from clams less than 1 mm across to the giant squids that can exceed 18 m in length.

The mollusc body is divided into three regions: the visceral mass, head–foot, and mantle **(Figure 26.22).** The **visceral mass** contains the digestive, excretory, and reproductive systems and the heart. The muscular **head–foot** often provides the major means of locomotion. In the more active groups, the head area of the head–foot region is well defined and carries sensory organs and a brain. The mouth often includes a toothed **radula**, which scrapes food into small particles or drills through the shells of prey.

Many molluscs are covered by a protective shell of calcium carbonate secreted by the **mantle**, a folding

of the body wall that may enclose the visceral mass. The mantle also defines a space, the **mantle cavity**, that houses the **gills**, delicate respiratory structures with an enormous surface area (see Chapter 42). In most molluscs, cilia on the mantle and gills generate a steady flow of water into the mantle cavity.

Most molluscs have an **open circulatory system** in which **hemolymph**, a bloodlike fluid, leaves the circulatory vessels and bathes tissues directly. Hemolymph pools in spaces called **sinuses** and then drains into vessels that carry it back to the heart (see Figure 26.25).

The sexes are usually separate, although many snails are hermaphroditic. Fertilization may be internal or external. In some snails, eggs and sperm are produced simultaneously in the same organ, an ovotestis. In others, the hermaphroditism is serial, with younger snails producing sperm and older individuals switching to egg production. Fertilization is often internal in these organisms, and in simultaneous hermaphrodites, there is a mutual exchange of sperm during

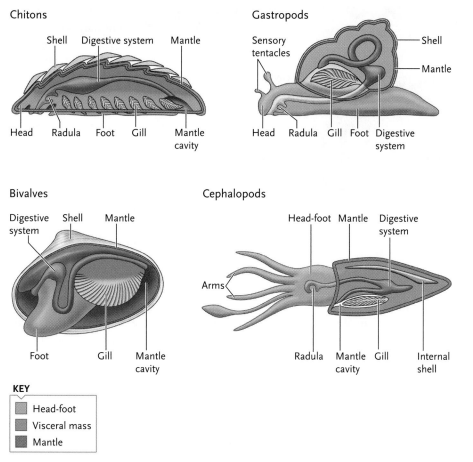

Figure 26.22

Molluscan body plans. The bilaterally symmetrical body plans of molluscs include a muscular head–foot, a visceral mass, and a mantle.

copulation. Sperm may be stored for long periods before being used. In some terrestrial snails, a calcium "love dart" may be fired into one of the partners preceding a mutual exchange of sperm. Dr. Ron Chase of McGill University has shown that mucus coating the dart makes it more likely that the shooter's sperm will be used to fertilize the eggs.

The zygotes of marine species often develop into free-swimming, ciliated **trochophore** larvae **(Figure 26.23)**, typical of both this phylum and the phylum Annelida, which we describe next. In some molluscs, the trochophore develops into a second larval stage, called a **veliger**, before metamorphosing into an adult. In some snails, the larval stage may occur only within the egg. Squids and octopuses have no larval stage, and eggs hatch into miniature replicas of the adult. Although members of the phylum share common characteristics, they have evolved an extraordinary diversity in form and lifestyle, ranging from sessile clams to the agile octopus capable of learned behaviour. The phylum includes seven classes. We examine the four most commonly encountered classes below.

Class Polyplacophora. The 600 species of chitons (Polyplacophora, from *poly* = many and *plak* = plate) are sedentary molluscs that graze on algae along rocky marine coasts. The oval, bilaterally symmetrical body has a dorsal shell divided into eight plates that allow it to conform to irregularly shaped surfaces **(Figure 26.24, p. 598)**. When a chiton is disturbed or exposed to strong wave action, the muscles of its broad foot maintain a tenacious grip, and the mantle's edge functions like a suction cup to hold fast to the substrate.

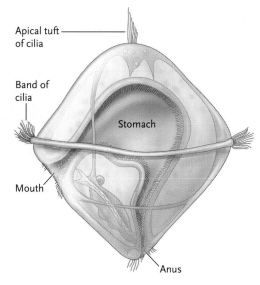

Figure 26.23

Trochophore larva. At the conclusion of their embryological development, both molluscs and annelids typically pass through a trochophore stage. The top-shaped trochophore larva has a band of cilia just anterior to its mouth.

Figure 26.24

Polyplacophora. Chitons live on rocky shores, where they use their foot and mantle to grip rocks and other hard substrates. This chiton (*Mopalia ciliata*) lives in Monterey Bay, California.

Class Gastropoda. Snails and slugs (Gastropoda, from *gaster* = belly and *pod* = foot) are the largest molluscan group, numbering 40 000 species **(Figure 26.25)**. The class exhibits a wide range of morphologies and lifestyles. Aquatic and marine species use gills to acquire oxygen, but in terrestrial species, a modified mantle cavity functions as an air-breathing lung. Some snails have the opening into the mantle cavity extended as a tubular siphon. Gastropods feed on algae, vascular plants, or animal prey. Some are scavengers, and a few are parasites.

The visceral mass of most snails is housed in a coiled or cone-shaped shell that is balanced above the rest of the body, much as you balance a backpack full of books (see **Figure 26.25a, b**). Most shelled species undergo **torsion** during development. Differential growth rates and muscle contractions twist the developing visceral mass and mantle a full 180° relative to the head and foot. These events begin in the larva before the shell is established and thus are not dictated by the coiling of the shell. Indeed, a snail that has undergone torsion to the right may exist in a left-handed shell. Among the many results of this developmental manoeuvre is the relocation of the mantle cavity to the anterior, allowing the head and foot to be withdrawn into the shell. In some snails, the posterior part of the foot carries an ovoid disk of protein fortified with calcium that can be used to close the entrance to the shell. This permits the snail to survive unfavourable conditions.

Some gastropods, including terrestrial slugs and colourful nudibranchs (sea slugs), are shell-less, a condition that leaves them somewhat vulnerable to predators (see **Figure 26.25c**). Some nudibranchs consume cnidarians and then transfer undischarged nematocysts to projections on their dorsal surface, where these "borrowed" stinging capsules provide protection (see Chapter 46).

Because many of its neurons are large and easily accessed and identifiable, the nudibranch *Aplysia* has been widely used to explore fundamental questions in neurobiology. For example, Dr. Wayne Sossin's lab at the Montreal Neurological Institute at McGill University is examining the biochemical and molecular basis of memory and learning in *Aplysia*.

The nervous and sensory systems of gastropods are well developed. Tentacles on the head include chemical and touch receptors; the eyes detect changes in light intensity but do not form images. The importance and relative sophistication of the nervous system is well illustrated by some limpets. *Patella vulgaris* is a gastropod with a conical shell **(Figure 26.26)** that lives on rocks in the intertidal zone. During low tide, it is exposed to the air and its foot and mucus secretion combine to fasten it closely to the rock. During development, the edges of its shell grow to conform to irregularities in the rock, increasing the protection against drying. As the rising tide covers the limpet, it moves

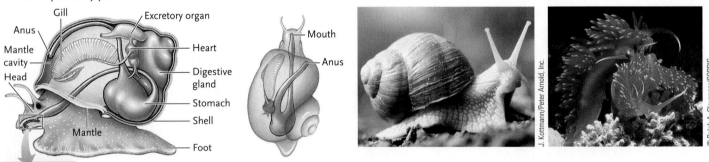

a. Gastropod body plan

Gill
Anus
Mantle cavity
Head
Mantle
Radula

Excretory organ
Heart
Digestive gland
Stomach
Shell
Foot

b. Terrestrial snail

Mouth
Anus

c. Marine nudibranchs

Figure 26.25

Gastropoda. **(a)** Most gastropods have a coiled shell that houses the visceral mass. A developmental process called torsion causes the digestive and excretory systems to eliminate wastes into the mantle cavity, near the animal's head. **(b)** The terrestrial snail (*Helix pomatia*) is a typical terrestrial gastropod. **(c)** Nudibranchs, like this pair of Spanish shawl nudibranchs (*Flabellina iodinea*), are shell-less marine snails. Photo: Herve Chaumeton/Agence Nature

Figure 26.26
The common limpet, *Patella vulgata*.

about, foraging and feeding on algae. About an hour before the falling tide would once again expose it to desiccation, it returns to its precise location so that it can seal itself against exposure to air. This involves not only precise navigation but also a sense of time attuned to the tides.

Class Bivalvia. The 8000 species of clams, scallops, oysters, and mussels (Bivalvia, from *bi* = two and *valv* = folding door) are restricted to aquatic habitats. They are enclosed within a pair of shells, hinged together dorsally by an elastic ligament. Contraction of the **adductor muscles** closes the shell and stretches the ligament. When the muscles relax, the stretched ligament opens the shell **(Figure 26.27)**. Although some bivalves are tiny, the giant clams of the South Pacific can be more than 1 m across and weigh 225 kg.

Adult mussels and oysters are sessile and permanently attached to hard substrates. However, many clams are mobile and use their muscular foot to burrow in sand or mud. Some bivalves, such as young scallops, swim by rhythmically clapping their valves together, forcing a current of water out of the mantle

cavity (see Figure 26.27b). The "scallops" that we eat are their well-developed adductor muscles.

Bivalves have a reduced head and lack a radula. Part of the mantle forms two tubes called *siphons* (see Figure 26.27c). Beating of cilia on the gills and mantle carries water into the mantle cavity through the **incurrent siphon** and out through the excurrent siphon. Incurrent water carries dissolved oxygen and particulate food to the gills, where oxygen is absorbed. Mucus strands on the gills trap food, which is then transported by cilia to *palps*, where final sorting takes place; acceptable bits are carried to the mouth. The excurrent water carries away metabolic wastes and feces.

Despite their sedentary existence, bivalves have moderately well-developed nervous systems: sensory organs that detect chemicals, touch, and light and statocysts to sense their orientation. When they encounter pollutants, many bivalves stop pumping water and close their shells. When confronted by a predator, some burrow into sediments or swim away.

Class Cephalopoda. The 600 species of octopuses, squids, and nautiluses constituting the class Cephalopoda (*cephal* = head; *pod* = foot) are active marine predators and include the fastest and most intelligent invertebrates **(Figure 26.28, p. 600).** They vary in length from a few centimetres to 18 m.

The cephalopod body has a fused head and foot. The head comprises the mouth and eyes. The ancestral "foot" forms a set of arms, which are equipped with suction pads, adhesive structures, or hooks. Cephalopods use their arms to capture prey and a pair of beaklike jaws to bite or crush it. Venomous secretions often speed the captive's death. Some species use their radula to drill through the shells of other molluscs.

Cephalopods have a highly modified shell. Octopuses have no remnant of a shell at all. In squids and

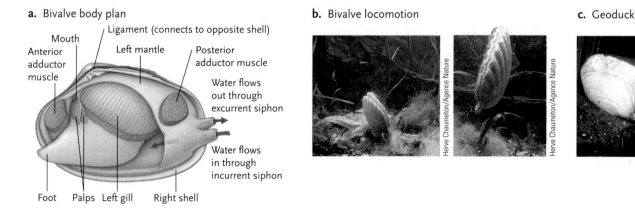

a. Bivalve body plan

Mouth
Ligament (connects to opposite shell)
Anterior adductor muscle
Left mantle
Posterior adductor muscle
Water flows out through excurrent siphon
Water flows in through incurrent siphon
Foot   Palps   Left gill   Right shell

b. Bivalve locomotion

c. Geoduck

Figure 26.27
Bivalvia. **(a)** Bivalves are enclosed in a hinged two-part shell. Part of the mantle forms a pair of water-transporting siphons. **(b)** When threatened by a predator (in this case, a sea star), some scallops clap their shells together rapidly, propelling the animal away from danger. **(c)** The geoduck (*Panope generosa*) is a clam with enormous muscular siphons.

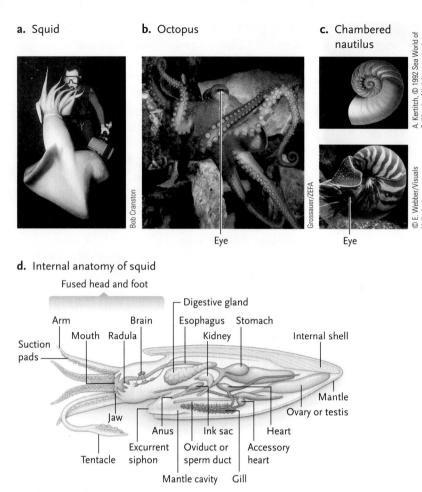

a. Squid

b. Octopus

c. Chambered nautilus

Eye

Eye

d. Internal anatomy of squid

Fused head and foot

Arm — Brain — Digestive gland — Esophagus — Stomach

Mouth — Radula — Kidney — Internal shell

Suction pads

Jaw

Tentacle

Anus

Excurrent siphon

Oviduct or sperm duct

Mantle cavity — Gill

Ink sac

Accessory heart

Heart

Ovary or testis

Mantle

Figure 26.28

Cephalopoda. **(a)** Squids, such as *Dosidicus gigas*, and **(b)** octopuses, such as *Octopus vulgaris*, are the most familiar cephalopods. **(c)** The chambered nautilus (*Nautilus macromphalus*) and its relatives retain an external shell. **(d)** Like other cephalopods, the squid body includes a fused head and foot; most organ systems are enclosed by the mantle.

Cephalopods are the only molluscs to have a **closed circulatory system**. The heart and accessory hearts speed the flow of hemolymph through blood vessels and gills, enhancing the uptake of oxygen and release of carbon dioxide.

Cephalopods have larger brains than other molluscs, and their brains are more complex than any other invertebrate. Giant nerve fibres connect the brain with the muscles of the mantle, enabling quick responses to food or danger (see Chapter 33).

The image-forming eyes of cephalopods, complete with lens and retina, are similar to those of vertebrates (see Chapter 34). The same basic plan for an eye has arisen independently in the cubozoan Cnidaria, the cephalopods, and the vertebrates, and represents an example of convergent evolution. Cephalopods are also highly intelligent. Octopuses, for example, learn to recognize objects with distinctive shapes or colours and can be trained to approach or avoid them.

Cephalopods have separate sexes and elaborate courtship rituals. Males store sperm within the mantle cavity and use a specialized tentacle to transfer packets of sperm into the female's mantle cavity, where fertilization occurs. The young hatch with an adult body form.

cuttlefishes, the shell is reduced to a stiff internal support. Only the chambered nautilus (see Figure 26.28c) and its relatives retain an external shell; spaces (chambers) in the shell regulate the animal's buoyancy. Species in the genus *Nautilus* are clearly cephalopods because the foot is modified in a way that is characteristic of that class. But they have retained an elegant, chambered shell, a body plan that is very successful, since essentially identical animals can be found among the Cambrian fossils.

Squids (see Figure 26.28a, d) move by a kind of jet propulsion. When muscles in the mantle relax, water enters the mantle cavity. When they contract, a jet of water is squeezed out through a funnel. By manipulating the position of the mantle and funnel, the animal can control the rate and direction of its locomotion. While escaping, many species simultaneously release a dark fluid ("ink") that obscures their direction of movement. Octopuses and squids are able to change colour rapidly by the migration of various pigments in special pigment cells called chromatophores. Many squids have light-emitting cells called photophores.

26.6f Phylum Annelida

The 15 000 species of segmented worms in the phylum Annelida (*annelis* = ring) occupy marine, freshwater, and moist terrestrial habitats. They range from a few millimetres to as much as 3 m in length. Terrestrial annelids eat organic debris, whereas aquatic species consume algae, microscopic organisms, detritus, or other animals. They have a complete digestive system, with the mouth at the front end and the anus at the rear.

The annelid body is highly segmented: the body wall muscles and some organs, including **respiratory surfaces**; parts of the nervous, circulatory, and excretory systems; and the coelom, are divided into similar repeating units **(Figure 26.29)**. Body segments are separated by transverse partitions called **septa** (singular, septum). The digestive system and major blood vessels are not segmented and run the length of the animal.

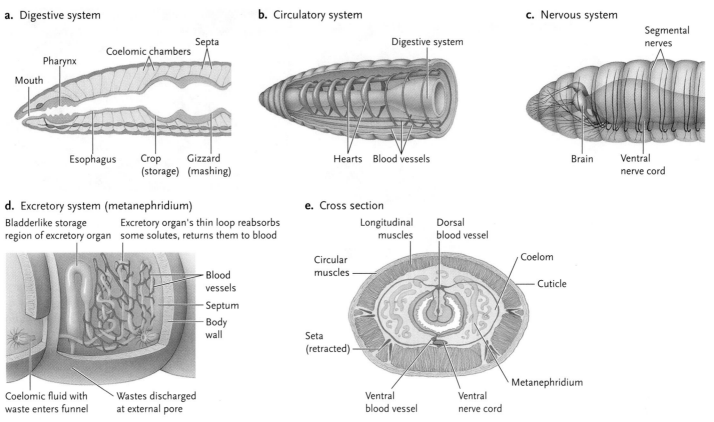

a. Digestive system

Mouth
Pharynx
Coelomic chambers
Septa
Esophagus
Crop (storage)
Gizzard (mashing)

b. Circulatory system

Digestive system
Hearts
Blood vessels

c. Nervous system

Segmental nerves
Brain
Ventral nerve cord

d. Excretory system (metanephridium)

Bladderlike storage region of excretory organ
Excretory organ's thin loop reabsorbs some solutes, returns them to blood
Blood vessels
Septum
Body wall
Coelomic fluid with waste enters funnel
Wastes discharged at external pore

e. Cross section

Longitudinal muscles
Dorsal blood vessel
Circular muscles
Coelom
Cuticle
Seta (retracted)
Ventral blood vessel
Ventral nerve cord
Metanephridium

Figure 26.29

Segmentation in the phylum Annelida. Although the digestive system **(a)**, the longitudinal blood vessels **(b)**, and the ventral nerve cord **(c)** form continuous structures, the coelom **(a)**, blood vessels **(b)**, nerves **(c)**, and excretory organs **(d)** appear as repeating structures in most segments. The body musculature **(e)** includes both circular and longitudinal layers that allow these animals to use the coelomic chambers as a hydrostatic skeleton.

The body wall muscles of annelids have both circular and longitudinal layers. Alternate contractions of these muscle groups allow annelids to make directed movements, using the coelom as a hydrostatic skeleton. The outer covering of annelids is a flexible cuticle that grows with the animal; it is not moulted. All annelids except leeches also have chitin-reinforced bristles, called **setae** (sometimes written *chaetae*; singular, seta), which protrude outward from the body wall. Setae anchor the worm against the substrate, providing traction.

Annelids have a closed circulatory system. The blood of most annelids contains haemoglobin or another oxygen-binding pigment. Oxygen diffusing across the cuticle may be picked up by capillaries in the skin to be transported to the tissues.

The excretory system is composed of paired **metanephridia** (singular, metanephridium) (see Figure 26.29d and Chapter 43), which usually occur in all body segments posterior to the head. The nervous system is well developed, with local control centres (ganglia) in every segment, a simple brain in the head, and sensory organs that detect chemicals, moisture, light, and touch.

Most freshwater and terrestrial annelids are hermaphroditic, and worms exchange sperm when they mate. Newly hatched worms have an adult morphology. Some terrestrial annelids also reproduce asexually by fragmenting and regenerating missing parts. Marine annelids usually have separate sexes and release gametes into the sea for fertilization. The zygotes develop into trochophore larvae that add segments, gradually assuming an adult form.

Annelids are divided into three classes.

Class Polychaeta. The 10 000 species of bristle worms (Polychaeta, from *poly* = many and *chaeta* = bristles) are primarily marine **(Figure 26.30, p. 602)**. Many live under rocks or in tubes constructed from mucus, calcium carbonate secretions, grains of sand, and small shell fragments. Their setae project from well-developed **parapodia** (singular parapodium = closely resembling a foot), fleshy lateral extensions of the body wall used for locomotion and gas exchange. Sense organs are concentrated on a well-developed head.

Many crawling or swimming polychaetes are predatory, using sharp jaws in a protrusible muscular

a. Feather duster worm

Kjell B. Sandved@sandved.com

b. Polychaete feeding structures

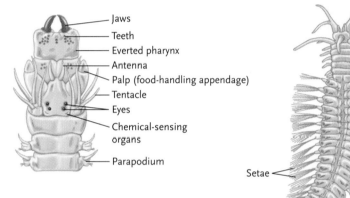

- Jaws
- Teeth
- Everted pharynx
- Antenna
- Palp (food-handling appendage)
- Tentacle
- Eyes
- Chemical-sensing organs
- Parapodium

c. Polychaete setae

Setae

Figure 26.30
Polychaeta. **(a)** The tube-dwelling feather duster worm (*Sabella melanostigma*) has mucus-covered tentacles that trap small food particles. **(b)** Some polychaetes, such as *Nereis*, actively seek food; when they encounter a suitable tidbit, they evert their pharynx, exposing sharp jaws that grab the prey and pull it into the digestive system. **(c)** Many marine polychaetes (such as *Proceraea cornuta*, shown here) have numerous setae, which they use for locomotion.

pharynx to grab small invertebrate prey. Other species graze on algae or scavenge organic matter. A few tube dwellers draw food-laden water into the tube by beating their parapodia; most others collect food by extending feathery, ciliated, mucus-coated tentacles.

Class Oligochaeta. Most of the 3500 species of oligochaete worms (*oligo* = few) are terrestrial **(Figure 26.31)**, but they are restricted to moist habitats because they quickly dehydrate in dry air or soil. They range in length from a few millimetres to more than 3 m. Terrestrial oligochaetes, the earthworms, are nocturnal, spending their days in burrows that they excavate. They are important scavengers, assisting in mixing and aerating soil and the conversion of plant and animal debris to nutrients useful to plants.

Duncan Mcewan/npl/Minden Pictures

Figure 26.31
Oligochaeta. Earthworms (genus *Lumbricus*) generally move across the ground surface at night.

Aquatic species live in mud or detritus at the bottom of lakes and rivers. Earthworms have complex organ systems (see Figure 26.29), and they sense light and touch at both ends of the body. In addition, they have moisture receptors, an important adaptation in organisms that must stay wet to allow gas exchange across the skin.

Class Hirudinea. Most of the 500 species of leeches (*hirudo* = leech) live in fresh water and suck the blood of vertebrates. These blood feeders have dorsoventrally flattened, tapered bodies with a sucker at each end. Although the body wall is segmented, the coelom is reduced and not partitioned. About a quarter of the known species are not blood feeders but prey on other invertebrates. Almost all of the leeches live in fresh water, but a few marine species are known. Some leeches are terrestrial, living in the moist tropics and feeding on warm-blooded vertebrates.

Blood-feeding leeches attach to the host with the posterior sucker and use their sharp jaws on the anterior sucker to make a small, often painless, triangular incision. A sucking apparatus draws blood from the prey, and a special secretion prevents the host's blood from coagulating. Leeches have a highly branched gut that allows them to consume huge blood meals **(Figure 26.32)**. For centuries, doctors used medicinal

Leech before feeding   Leech after feeding

J. A. L. Cooke/Oxford Scientific Films/Photolibrary.com

Figure 26.32
Hirudinea. Parasitic leeches consume huge blood meals, as shown by these before and after photos of a medicinal leech (*Hirudo medicinalis*). Because suitable hosts are often hard to locate, gorging allows a leech to take advantage of any host it finds.

Hydrothermal Vents

Hydrothermal vents on the sea bed, discovered in 1970, are equivalent to miniature undersea volcanoes. Superheated water emerges from them at temperatures up to 400°C, laden with sulphides **(Figure 1)**. The Endeavour Hot Vent Area, over 2000 m deep, lies 250 km off the coast of Vancouver Island. It has been explored by Verena Tunnicliffe at the University of Victoria and was declared a Marine Protected Area by the Canadian government in 2003. A range of invertebrates, particularly molluscs and annelids, flourish near the vents. Many of these species are new to science, and they are larger and more numerous than the fauna nearby. They experience at least brief exposure to temperatures as high as 50°C. More important, however, is the absence of sunlight, which deprives them of a source of food from plants, and the presence of sulphides. Sulphide is normally toxic, but associated with the vents are mats of bacteria that utilize sulphide for energy production and growth. The metazoans feed on these, and some of the invertebrates have symbiotic bacteria that rely on the sulphides.

Figure 1
A hot vent "smoker," surrounded by organisms specific to the environment. Inset "Tube worms," originally placed in a separate Phylum Vestimentifera. Molecular analysis places them among the annelids.

Canadian Scientific Submersible Facility

leeches (*Hirudo medicinalis*) to "bleed" patients; today, surgeons still use them to drain excess fluid from tissues after reconstructive surgery, reducing swelling until the patient's blood vessels regenerate and resume this function.

STUDY BREAK

1. What characteristic reveals the close evolutionary relationship of ectoprocts, brachiopods, and phoronid worms?
2. Describe the three regions of the mollusc body.
3. Which organ systems exhibit segmentation in most annelid worms?

26.7 Ecdysozoan Protostomes

The three phyla in the protostome group Ecdysozoa all have an external cuticle secreted by epidermal cells. The cuticle serves as protection from harsh environmental conditions and helps parasitic species resist host defences. It also permits these animals to change the nature of the covering, which is important if the life stages live in different environments. Although many of these animals live in aquatic or moist terrestrial habitats, a tough exoskeleton allows many, particularly the insects, to thrive on dry land.

26.7a Phylum Nematoda

Members of the phylum Nematoda (*nemata* = thread) are round worms, often tapered at each end. The numerous species of free-living worms are microscopic, reaching a size of at most a few millimetres. Some parasitic species, however, are larger **(Figure 26.33)**, and some are very large. The record is held by *Placentonema gigantissima*, a parasite of the placenta of the sperm whale: it may reach 9 m in length! Although superficially very similar in morphology, nematodes have achieved remarkable diversity. One species lives only in vinegar, and another is found in beer vats. In marine sediments, concentrations of a million or more worms per square metre have been reported.

Figure 26.33
Phylum Nematoda. Many roundworms are animal parasites, like these *Anguillicola crassus*, shown here inside the swim bladder of an eel.

© 2006 Alistair Dove/Image Quest Marine

A hectare of farm soil may contain a billion or more nematodes. A single rotting fruit on the ground will contain tens of thousands of worms. Many species are parasitic in plants and animals, and some cause serious diseases in humans. Although fewer than 20 000 species have been described, it is generally agreed that the number of living species is at least 100 000.

The nematode cuticle, often complex in structure, is composed of collagen-like proteins secreted by an epidermis that is often syncytial **(Figure 26.34)**. The cuticle is replaced four times during the life of the nematode, and in some cases, the characteristics of each of the cuticles differ. Moulting of the cuticle is not necessary for the worms to increase in size, and growth usually occurs between moults. *Ascaris lumbricoides*, a common intestinal parasite in humans, represents an extreme case, growing in length from about 6 mm after the final moult to an adult of more than 20 cm. Nematodes, like rotifers, exhibit eutely, having few or no cell divisions in somatic cells after hatching.

This characteristic, together with a transparent cuticle, has made *Caenorhabditis elegans*, which has fewer than 1000 cells, such a useful model for studying development. It eats bacteria such as *E. coli* and can be reared in the lab easily. Because the number of cells is so small, the developmental fate of each cell in the embryo has been documented using techniques such as microinjection or laser microsurgery. The genome is small and has been completely sequenced, yielding about 17 000 genes. *C. elegans* is widely used as a model to explore general questions in developmental biology. For example, Dr. David Bailey at Simon Fraser University in Vancouver uses *C. elegans* to ask questions such as how many of the genes are essential to normal development. He has determined which mutations are lethal and estimates that about 4000 to 5000 genes of the 17 000 are essential for development in *C. elegans*.

Growth in nematodes occurs by an increase in cell size, and in a large nematode such as *Ascaris*, a muscle cell may be more than a centimetre in length.

There are no cilia or flagella in nematodes; the spermatozoa move by amoeboid motion. A single layer of muscles forms part of the body wall. These muscles, like those of flatworms, do not receive nerves but make contact with the ventral, dorsal, or lateral nerve cords by long extensions of the muscle (see Figure 26.34).

The nervous system consists of dorsal, lateral, and particularly prominent ventral nerve cords, with a nerve ring surrounding the pharynx at the anterior. Nematodes respond to various chemicals, likely through sense organs located in pits at the anterior end. Some are sensitive to light, possibly through a general sensitivity of their nerves, but others have pigmented eye spots.

The gut of nematodes is a simple tube consisting of a single layer of epithelial cells. There are no muscles surrounding the gut, and food is propelled through the digestive system by a muscular pharynx. The pumping action of the pharynx is also responsible for maintaining pressure in the pseudocoelom. The resulting stiffness produces a hydrostatic skeleton. The cuticle has some elasticity, so that a contraction of muscles in the dorsal part of the worm results in an expansion on the ventral side. Alternate contraction and relaxation produces the dorsoventral wave that characterizes the movement of most nematodes.

The sexes of most nematodes are separate, and fertilization is internal. A few nematodes are hermaphroditic and may be self-fertilizing. Others may be parthenogenetic. Fertilized females, particularly those of parasitic species, produce huge numbers of eggs. The intestinal parasite *A. lumbricoides* may produce 200 000 eggs per day for about 10 months.

Nematodes are particularly successful as parasites and have invaded representatives of most other phyla. *A. lumbricoides* infects about a billion people, or about a sixth of the entire human population. Most wild vertebrates harbour one or more species of nematode parasites. The replaceable cuticle contributes to this success for it allows the worm to produce a different cuticle in each different environment that it encounters as it moves from a free-living form to a parasitic form or from one host to another.

26.7b Phylum Onychophora

The 65 living species of velvet worms (Onychophora, from *onux* = claw and *phor* = to bear) live under stones, logs, and forest litter in moist temperate and tropical habitats in the southern hemisphere. They range in size from 15 mm to 15 cm and feed on small invertebrates and plants. Living onychophorans are all terrestrial, but fossils are known from marine environments.

Onychophorans have a flexible cuticle, superficially segmented bodies, and numerous pairs of unjointed legs **(Figure 26.35)**. Like annelids, they have pairs of excretory organs in most segments. But unlike

Figure 26.34
Cross section of a typical nematode.

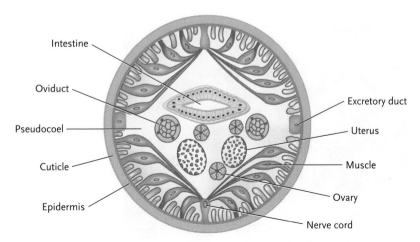

Intestine
Oviduct
Pseudocoel
Cuticle
Epidermis
Excretory duct
Uterus
Muscle
Ovary
Nerve cord

Figure 26.35

Phylum Onychophora. Members of the small phylum Onychophora, such as species in the genus *Dnycophor*, have segmented bodies and unjointed appendages.

annelids, no internal septa separate the segments; they have an open circulatory system, a specialized respiratory system similar to that of insects, and relatively large brains, jaws, and tiny claws on their feet. Many produce live young, which, in some species, are nourished within a uterus (see Chapter 40). The sexes are separate, and fertilization is internal.

Fossil onychophorans are known from the Cambrian (they are represented in the Burgess Shale), and the body plan has not changed much since then, suggesting that this highly specialized group of animals represented one of the successes in the experiments of the Cambrian speciation.

26.7c Phylum Arthropoda

If the Mesozoic was the age of the dinosaurs, we are living in the age of the arthropods (*arthros* = joint; *poda* = feet). About three-quarters of all living species of animals are arthropods, a phylum that includes insects, spiders, scorpions, crustaceans, centipedes, millipedes, and the extinct trilobites.

Arthropods have a segmented body encased in a rigid **exoskeleton.** This external covering is a complex of chitin (see *Molecule Behind Biology*) and glycoproteins. In some marine and freshwater groups, such as crabs and lobsters, the cuticle is hardened with calcium carbonate. In terrestrial forms, such as insects, a surface layer of wax provides protection from dehydration. The exoskeleton is thin and flexible at the joints between body segments and at the joints of appendages. Contractions of muscles attached to the exoskeleton move individual body parts like levers, allowing highly coordinated movements and patterns of locomotion.

Although the exoskeleton has obvious advantages, it is nonexpandable and could limit the growth of the animal. Arthropods periodically develop a new cuticle beneath the old one, which they shed in the complex process of ecdysis **(Figure 26.36).** The new cuticle is soft and usually pleated, allowing for expansion after ecdysis. After shedding the old cuticle, arthropods swell with water or air before the new one hardens. They are especially vulnerable to predators at these times.

Primitively, each segment had a pair of lateral appendages, often specialized for locomotion, gas exchange, eating, or reproduction. As arthropods evolved, however, body segments became grouped in various ways. Each region, along with its highly modified paired appendages, is specialized, and the structure and function of the regions vary greatly among groups.

The coelom of arthropods is greatly reduced, and another cavity, the **haemocoel**, is filled with bloodlike **haemolymph.** The heart pumps the haemolymph through an open circulatory system, bathing tissues directly.

Because the hardened cuticle does not permit the easy passage of O_2 and CO_2, arthropods have specialized mechanisms for gas exchange. Marine and freshwater species, such as crabs and lobsters, rely on diffusion across gills that are specialized appendages, usually assisted by currents established by the appendages. The terrestrial groups have developed unique respiratory systems (see Chapter 42).

Many arthropods are equipped with a highly organized central nervous system, touch receptors, chemical

Figure 26.36

Ecdysis in insects. Like all other arthropods, this cicada (*Graptopsalatsia nigrofusca*) sheds its old exoskeleton as it grows.

sensors, image-forming **compound eyes**, and, in some, hearing organs. These are described in Chapters 33 and 34.

The phylogeny of this huge and diverse phylum has been a difficult and disputed subject for many years. Hexapods, and specifically insects, have been regarded by some as most closely related to myriapods, based largely on shared anatomical characters such as Malpighian tubules for excretion and one pair of antennae. Others, however, relate insects more closely to Crustacea, based on other morphological characteristics such as similarities in mouthparts and walking appendages. Molecular studies, including analysis of mitochondrial DNA and *Hox* genes, support the view that hexapods and crustacea are paraphyletic (see Chapter 19 for a definition of paraphyletic) and that myriapods and chelicerates form a separate paraphyletic grouping. This is an active area in research, and other hypotheses may be developed.

We follow the traditional definition of five *subphyla*, partly because this classification adequately reflects arthropod diversity and partly because no alternative hypothesis has been widely adopted by experts.

Subphylum Trilobita. The trilobites (*tri* = three; *lob* = lobed), now extinct, were among the most numerous animals in the shallow Paleozoic seas. Most were ovoid, dorsoventrally flattened, and heavily armoured, with two deep longitudinal grooves that divided the body into one median and two lateral lobes **(Figure 26.37)**. The head included a pair of sensory antennae (singular, antenna) and compound eyes, and the segmented **thorax** and **abdomen** had pairs of identical appendages, each with two branches. The inner branch was used for locomotion, and the outer, consisting of a number of fine filaments, was used as a gill or in filter feeding.

The position of trilobites in the fossil record indicates that they were among the earliest arthropods. Thus, biologists are confident that their three

Figure 26.37
Subphylum Trilobita. Trilobites, such as the *Olenellus gilberti*, bore many pairs of relatively undifferentiated appendages.

body regions and unspecialized appendages represent ancestral traits in the phylum. Although there were numerous species, indicating a high degree of success, trilobites disappeared in the Permian mass extinction.

Subphylum Chelicerata. In spiders, ticks, mites, scorpions, and horseshoe crabs (subphylum Chelicerata, from *cheol* = claw and *cera* = horn), the first pair of appendages, the **chelicerae**, are fanglike structures used for biting prey. The second pair of appendages, the **pedipalps**, serve as grasping organs, sensory organs, or walking legs. All chelicerates have two major body regions, the **cephalothorax** (a fused head–thorax) and the abdomen. The group originated in shallow Paleozoic seas, but most living species are terrestrial. They vary in size from less than a millimetre to 20 cm; all are predators or parasites.

The 60 000 species of spiders, scorpions, mites, and ticks (class Arachnida) represent the vast majority of chelicerates **(Figure 26.38)**. Arachnids have four pairs of walking legs on the cephalothorax and highly modified chelicerae and pedipalps. In some spiders, males use their pedipalps to transfer packets of sperm to females. Scorpions use them (the "claws") to shred food and to grasp one another during courtship. Many predatory arachnids have excellent vision, provided by up to four pairs of simple eyes on the cephalothorax. Scorpions and some spiders also have unique pocketlike respiratory organs called **book lungs** (see Chapter 42), derived from abdominal appendages.

Like most other arachnids, spiders subsist on a liquid diet. They use their chelicerae to inject paralyzing poisons and digestive enzymes into prey and then suck up the partly digested tissues. Many spiders are economically important predators, helping to control insect pests. Only a few are a threat to humans. The toxin of a black widow (*Latrodectus mactans*) causes paralysis, and the toxin of the brown recluse (*Loxosceles reclusa*) destroys tissues around the site of the bite.

Although many spiders hunt actively, others capture prey on silken threads secreted by **spinnerets**, which are modified abdominal appendages. Some species weave the threads into complex, netlike webs. The silk is secreted as a liquid protein but quickly polymerizes. Spiders also use silk to make nests, to protect their egg masses, as a safety line when moving through the environment, and to wrap prey for later consumption. Spider silk is extremely tough, and the material from some spiders exceeds the tensile strength of steel. It is also highly elastic. These properties have led to proposals for its use in fabrics. A Canadian company has developed transgenic goats that produce spider silk in their milk.

Most mites are tiny, but they have a big impact. Some are serious agricultural pests that feed on plant sap. Others cause mange (patchy hair loss) or painful

a. Wolf spider

b. Spider anatomy

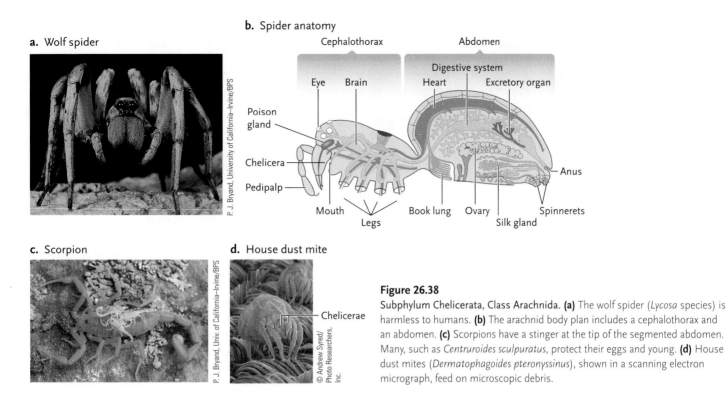

P. J. Bryand, University of California–Irvine/BPS

c. Scorpion

P. J. Bryand, Univ. of California–Irvine/BPS

d. House dust mite

— Chelicerae

© Andrew Syred/ Photo Researchers, Inc.

Figure 26.38
Subphylum Chelicerata, Class Arachnida. **(a)** The wolf spider (*Lycosa* species) is harmless to humans. **(b)** The arachnid body plan includes a cephalothorax and an abdomen. **(c)** Scorpions have a stinger at the tip of the segmented abdomen. Many, such as *Centruroides sculpuratus*, protect their eggs and young. **(d)** House dust mites (*Dermatophagoides pteronyssinus*), shown in a scanning electron micrograph, feed on microscopic debris.

and itchy welts on animals. House dust mites, which feed on the dried skin cast off by humans, cause allergic reactions in many people. Ticks, which are generally larger than mites, are blood feeders that often transmit pathogens, such as those causing Rocky Mountain spotted fever and Lyme disease.

The subphylum Chelicerata also includes five species of horseshoe crabs (class Merostomata), an ancient lineage that has not changed much over its 350 million–year history **(Figure 26.39)**. Horseshoe crabs are carnivorous bottom feeders in shallow coastal waters. Beneath their characteristic shell, they have one pair of chelicerae, a pair of pedipalps, four pairs of walking legs, and a set of paperlike gills, derived from ancestral walking legs. A component of horse-shoe crab blood is important to the pharmaceutical industry, where it is used to test for the presence of endotoxins resulting from bacterial contamination during manufacture.

Subphylum Crustacea. The 35 000 species of shrimps, lobsters, crabs, and their relatives in the subphylum Crustacea (*crusta* = shell) represent a lineage that emerged more than 500 million years ago **(Figure 26.40, p. 608)**. They are abundant in marine and freshwater habitats. A few species, such as sowbugs and pillbugs, live in moist, sheltered terrestrial environments. In many crustaceans, two and, in some cases, all three of the arthropod body regions (head, thorax, and abdomen) may be fused. Fusion of the head and thorax into a cephalothorax is a common pattern. In some, the exoskeleton forms a **carapace**, a protective covering that extends backward from the head. Crustaceans vary in size from water fleas less than 1 mm long to lobsters that can grow to 60 cm in length and weigh as much as 20 kg.

Crustaceans generally have five characteristic pairs of appendages on the head (see Figure 26.40c). Most have two pairs of sensory antennae and three pairs of mouthparts. The latter include one pair of **mandibles**, which move laterally to bite and chew, and two pairs of **maxillae** (singular, maxilla), which hold and manipulate food. Numerous paired appendages posterior to the mouthparts vary among groups. Ancestrally, crustacean appendages were divided into two branches at the base, but many living species have unbranched appendages.

Most crustaceans are active animals that exhibit complex movements during locomotion and in the

Jane Burton/Bruce Coleman Inc.

Figure 26.39
Marine chelicerates. Horseshoe crabs, such as *Limulus polyphemus*, are included in the Merostomata.

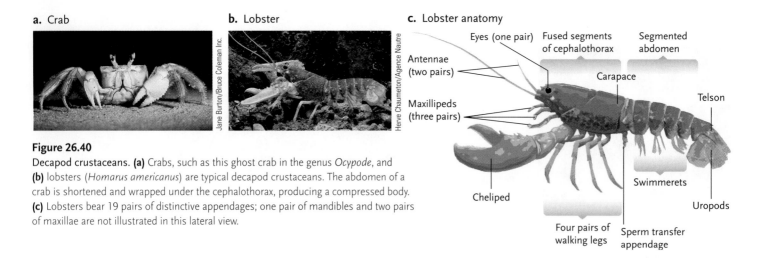

a. Crab

b. Lobster

c. Lobster anatomy

Eyes (one pair)
Fused segments of cephalothorax
Segmented abdomen
Antennae (two pairs)
Carapace
Telson
Maxillipeds (three pairs)
Cheliped
Swimmerets
Uropods
Four pairs of walking legs
Sperm transfer appendage

Figure 26.40

Decapod crustaceans. **(a)** Crabs, such as this ghost crab in the genus *Ocypode*, and **(b)** lobsters (*Homarus americanus*) are typical decapod crustaceans. The abdomen of a crab is shortened and wrapped under the cephalothorax, producing a compressed body. **(c)** Lobsters bear 19 pairs of distinctive appendages; one pair of mandibles and two pairs of maxillae are not illustrated in this lateral view.

performance of other behaviours. These activities are coordinated by elaborate sensory and nervous systems, including chemical and touch receptors in the antennae, compound eyes, statocysts on the head, and sensory hairs embedded in the exoskeleton throughout the body. The nervous system is similar to that in annelids, but the ganglia, particularly those forming the brain, are larger and more complex. Larger species have complex, feathery gills derived from appendages tucked beneath the carapace. Metabolic wastes such as ammonia are excreted by diffusion across the gills or, in larger species, by **antennal glands**, located in the head.

The sexes are typically separate, and courtship rituals are often complex. Eggs are usually brooded on the surface of the female's body or beneath the carapace. Many have free-swimming larvae that, after undergoing a series of moults, gradually assume an adult form.

The subphylum includes so many different body plans that it is usually divided into six classes with numerous subclasses and orders. The crabs, lobsters, and shrimps (class Malacostraca, order Decapoda, *deka* = 10 + *poda* = foot) number more than 10 000 species. The vast majority of decapods are marine, but a few shrimps, crabs, and crayfishes occupy freshwater habitats. Some crabs also live in moist terrestrial habitats, where they scavenge dead vegetation, clearing the forest floor of debris.

All decapods exhibit extreme specialization of their appendages. In the American lobster, for example, each of the 19 pairs of appendages is different (see Figure 26.40c). Behind the antennae, mandibles, and maxillae, the thoracic segments have three pairs of maxillipeds, which shred food and pass it up to the mouth, a pair of large chelipeds (pinching claws), and four pairs of walking legs. The

abdominal appendages include a pair specialized for sperm transfer (in males only), swimmerets for locomotion and for brooding eggs, and uropods, which, in combination with the telson (the tip of the abdomen), make a fan-shaped tail.

Representatives of several crustacean classes—fairy shrimps, amphipods, water fleas, ostracods, and copepods **(Figure 26.41)**—live as plankton in the upper waters of oceans and lakes. Most are only a few millimetres long but are present in huge numbers. They feed on microscopic algae or detritus and are themselves food for larger invertebrates, fishes, and some suspension-feeding marine mammals such as the baleen whales. Planktonic crustaceans are among the most abundant animals on Earth. The total biomass of a single species, *Euphausia superba*, is estimated at 500 000 000 tonnes, more than the total mass of humans.

Adult barnacles (class Maxillopoda, subclass Cirripedia, *cirrus* = curl of hair and *poda* = foot) are sessile marine crustaceans that live within a strong, calcified, cup-shaped shell **(Figure 26.42)**. Their free-swimming larvae attach permanently to substrates—rocks, wooden pilings, the hulls of ships, the shells of

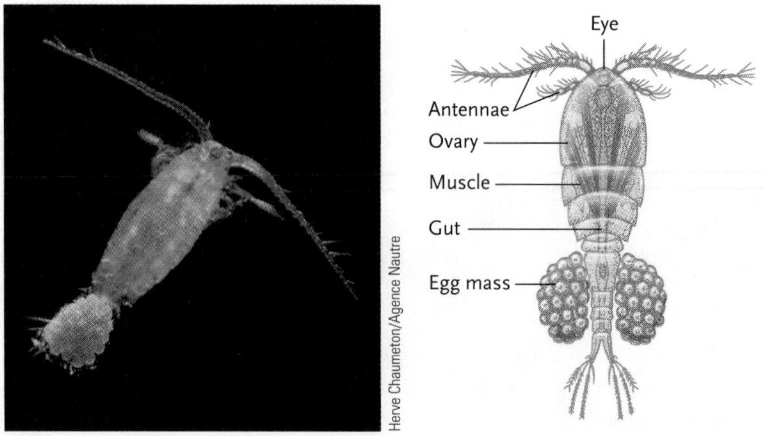

Eye
Antennae
Ovary
Muscle
Gut
Egg mass

Figure 26.41

Copepods. Tiny crustaceans, such as this copepod (*Calanus* species on the left, *Cyclops* species on the right), occur by the billions in freshwater and marine plankton.

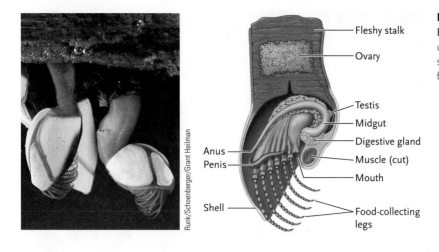

Figure 26.42

Barnacles. Gooseneck barnacles (*Lepas anatifera*) attach to the underside of floating debris. Like other barnacles, they open their shells and extend their feathery legs to collect particulate food from seawater.

Labels on figure: Fleshy stalk, Ovary, Testis, Midgut, Digestive gland, Muscle (cut), Mouth, Food-collecting legs, Anus, Penis, Shell

molluscs, and even the skin of whales—and secrete the shell, which is a modified exoskeleton. To feed, barnacles open the shell and extend six pairs of feathery legs. The beating legs capture microscopic plankton and transfer it to the mouth. Unlike most crustaceans, barnacles are hermaphroditic.

Subphylum Myriapoda. The 3000 species of centipedes (class Chilopoda) and 10 000 species of millipedes (class Diplopoda) are classified together in the subphylum Myriapoda (murias = 10 000; poda = foot). Myriapods have two body regions, a head and a segmented trunk **(Figure 26.43)**. The head bears one pair of antennae, and the trunk bears one (centipedes) or two (millipedes) pairs of walking legs on most of its many segments. Myriapods are terrestrial, and many species live under rocks or dead leaves. Centipedes are fast and voracious predators; they generally feed on invertebrates, but some eat small vertebrates. Although most species are less than 10 cm long, some

grow to 25 cm. The millipedes are slow but powerful herbivores or scavengers. The largest species attain a length of nearly 30 cm.

Subphylum Hexapoda. The subphylum Hexapoda (hex = six) includes the class Insecta, as well as some other smaller classes. In terms of sheer numbers and diversity, the approximately 1 000 000 species of insects are the most successful animals on Earth, occupying virtually every terrestrial and aquatic habitat. They were among the first animals to colonize terrestrial habitats, where most species still live. The oldest Hexapod fossils date from the Devonian, about 400 million years ago, and the first insect fossils appeared shortly after. Insects are generally small, ranging from 0.1 mm to 30 cm in length. The class is divided into about 30 orders **(Figure 26.44, p. 610)**.

The insect body plan always includes a head, a thorax, and an abdomen **(Figure 26.45, p. 611)**. The head is equipped with multiple mouthparts, a pair of compound eyes, and one pair of sensory antennae. The thorax has three pairs of walking legs and often one or two pairs of wings. Adult insects are the only invertebrates capable of flight. The origin of wings is uncertain. The traditional view holds that they are new structures arising as outgrowths of the body wall. However, on the basis of both fossil and molecular evidence, one of the foremost researchers in the field, Jarmila Kukalova-Peck of Carleton University in Ottawa, maintains that wings are derived from branches of a proximal (near the body) segment of the leg.

Insects exchange gases through a specialized **tracheal system** (see Chapter 42), a branching network of tubes that carries oxygen from small openings in the exoskeleton to individual cells throughout the body. Insects excrete nitrogenous wastes through

a.

b.

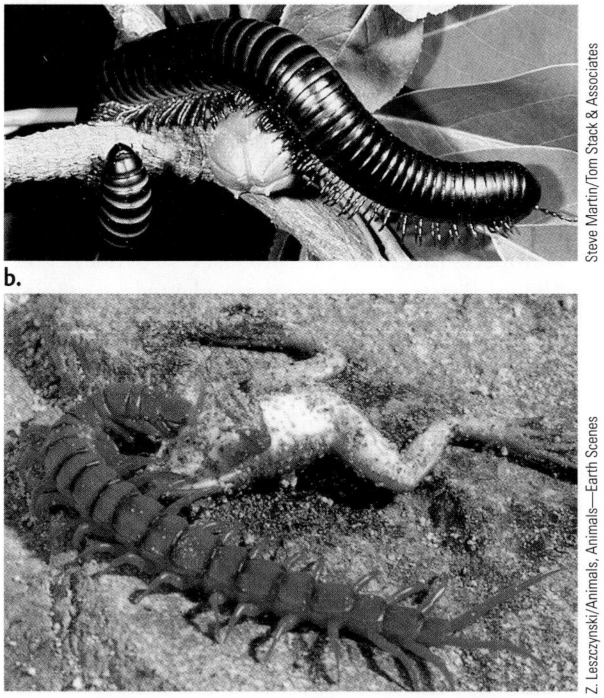

Figure 26.43

Millipedes and centipedes. (a) Millipedes, such as *Spirobolus* species, feed on living and decaying vegetation. They have two pairs of walking legs on most segments. **(b)** Like all centipedes, this Southeast Asian species (*Scolopendra subspinipes*), shown feeding on a small frog, is a voracious predator. Centipedes have one pair of walking legs per segment.

a. Silverfish (Thysanura, *Ctenolepisma longicaudata*) are primitive wingless insects.

b. Dragonflies, like the flame skimmer (Odonata, *Libellula saturata*), have aquatic larvae that are active predators; adults capture other insects in mid-air.

c. Male praying mantids (Mantodea, *Mantis religiosa*) are often eaten by the larger females during or immediately after mating.

d. This rhinoceros beetle (Coleoptera, *Dynastes granti*) is one of more than 250,000 beetle species that have been described.

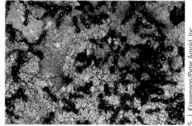

e. Fleas (Siphonoptera, *Hystrichopsylla dippiei*) have strong legs with an elastic ligament that allows these parasites to jump on and off their animal hosts.

f. Crane flies (Diptera, *Tipula* species) look like giant mosquitoes, but their mouthparts are not useful for biting other animals; the adults of most species live only a few days and do not feed at all.

g. The luna moth (Lepidoptera, *Actias luna*), like other butterflies and moths, has wings that are covered with colorful microscopic scales.

h. Like many other ant species, fire ants (Hymenoptera, *Solenopsis invicta*) live in large cooperative colonies. Fire ants— named for their painful sting—were introduced into southeastern North America, where they are now serious pests.

Figure 26.44
Insect diversity. Insects are grouped into about 30 orders, 8 of which are illustrated here.

specialized **Malpighian tubules** (see Chapter 43) that transport wastes to the digestive system for disposal with the feces. These two organ systems also appear in some of the terrestrial chelicerates. Since these are not paraphyletic with hexapods, this is another example of convergent evolution.

Insect sensory systems are diverse and complex. Besides a pair of image-forming compound eyes, many insects have light-sensing ocelli on their heads. Many also have hairs, sensitive to touch, on their antennae, legs, and other regions of the body. Chemical receptors are particularly common on the legs and feet, allowing the identification of food. Many groups of insects have sound receptors to detect predators and potential mates. The familiar chirping of crickets, for example, is a mating call emitted by males that may repel other males and attract females. The beetles of the family Lampyridae emit light signals from their abdomens to attract mates (see Chapter 33).

As a group, insects use an enormous variety of materials as food, and their mouthparts may be modified to reflect the nature of the food source **(Figure 26.46)**. The basic plan is reflected in a plant feeder such as a locust or a generalized feeder such as a cockroach. The *labrum* is an anterior flaplike extension of the front of the head that covers the mouthparts and has sensory structures. The mouthparts themselves

are modified appendages. The paired mandibles are chewing organs, and behind those are paired maxillae abundantly supplied with sense organs, particularly on its *palps* (jointed projections), which act to scoop the food. The most posterior is the *labium*, representing a fused pair of appendages, is well supplied with sensory structures and palps. This ancestral mandibulate pattern, with mouthparts representing three of the six segments that form the insect head, is modified in various ways to accommodate different modes of feeding. In some biting flies, such as mosquitoes, the mouthparts are piercing structures, with a narrow channel to suck up blood. In butterflies and moths, the mouthparts include a long proboscis to drink nectar. In houseflies, the mouthparts are adapted for sopping up food that has been moistened by its saliva.

Life on land requires internal fertilization (see Chapter 38). In insects, males may produce packets of sperm enclosed in spermatophores and insert them into the female ducts, or sperm transfer may be direct via a penis. Sperm are stored in the female until used to fertilize eggs at the time of egg laying. The eggs of most insects are covered with a waterproof shell before they are fertilized and have one or more minute pores to permit the entry of sperm.

Parthenogenesis occurs in a number of species. In aphids, not only are the females parthenogenetic at

External anatomy of a grasshopper

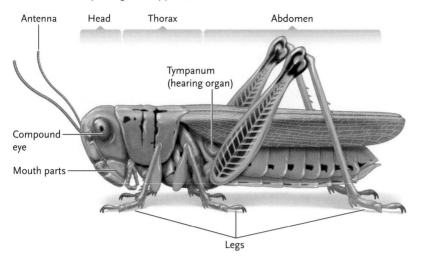

Internal anatomy of a female grasshopper

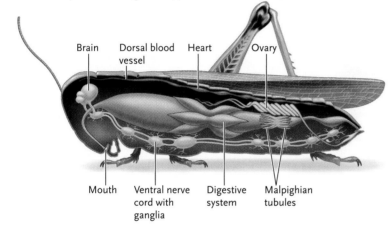

Figure 26.45
The insect body plan. Insects have a distinct head, thorax, and abdomen. Of all the internal organ systems, only the dorsal blood vessel, ventral nerve cord, and some muscles are strongly segmented.

times when food plants are abundant, they also produce live young, and development is so telescoped that embryos within the mother already have embryos within their ovaries. This results in an enormously rapid increase in population when conditions are favourable. Under less favourable conditions, normal sexual reproduction occurs. In a few species, parthenogenesis is the only mode of reproduction and males are unknown.

After it hatches from an egg, an insect passes through a series of developmental stages called **instars.** Several hormones control development and ecdysis, which marks the passage from one instar to the next. Insects exhibit one of three basic patterns of postembryonic development **(Figure 26.47, p. 612).** Primitive, wingless species (order Thysanura) simply grow and shed their exoskeleton, undergoing only minimal changes in morphology. Early instars lack scales on their cuticle, and the appearance of scales corresponds with reproductive maturity. Moulting cycles may continue after reproductive maturity.

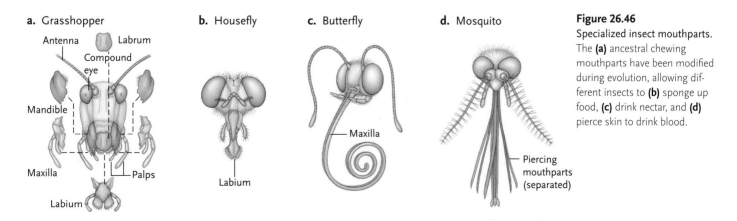

Figure 26.46
Specialized insect mouthparts. The **(a)** ancestral chewing mouthparts have been modified during evolution, allowing different insects to **(b)** sponge up food, **(c)** drink nectar, and **(d)** pierce skin to drink blood.

PEOPLE BEHIND BIOLOGY

V.B. Wigglesworth, Cambridge University

V.B. Wigglesworth was a British researcher who founded the subject of insect physiology. He had an active research career that spanned seven decades, from 1928 to 1991. He discovered the utility of the blood-sucking bug *Rhodnius prolixus* **(Figure 1)** for experimental work. Unfed, the insect remains in a state of suspended development. However, when it takes a blood meal, development to the next stage begins, and Wigglesworth used

this signal, together with clever surgical approaches **(Figure 2),** to establish the basic facts of the hormonal control of development in insects. Although he is perhaps best known for this work, he also established the basic facts of insect digestion, excretion and the operation of the Malpighian tubules, the operation of the tracheal system, and the properties of the cuticle. He used a keen sense of observation to identify appropriate

From: Plate II a opposite p.45 of the "Physiology of Insect Metamorphosis" by VB Wigglesworth. Cambridge University Press 1954

Figure 2
One of Wigglesworth's surgical procedures. The nymph on the right was decapitated within a day of feeding, before the hormones from the head governing moulting were secreted; therefore, it will not develop. The insect on the left was decapitated after the hormones were released and will develop normally. The two are joined so that their hemocoels are connected (a procedure called parabiosis). They will both initiate the formation of a new cuticle driven by hormones from the insect on the left.

experimental questions, and devised and carried out clever experimental approaches to answer the questions he investigated.

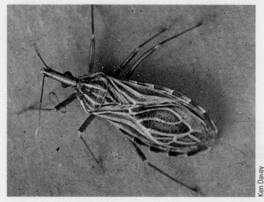

Ken Davey

Figure 1
The adult female of *Rhodnius prolixus.*

Figure 26.47
Patterns of postembryonic development in insects.

a. Limited metamorphosis

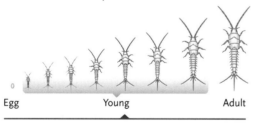

Egg   Young   Adult

Some wingless insects, like silverfish (order Thysanura), do not undergo a dramatic change in form as they grow.

b. Metamorphosis without a pupa

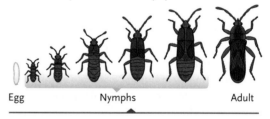

Egg   Nymphs   Adult

Some insects, such as the Order Hemiptera, undergo a metamorphosis that involves no major reorganisation in form apart from the development of wings.

c. Metamorphosis with a pupa

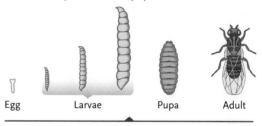

Egg   Larvae   Pupa   Adult

Fruit flies (order Diptera) and many other insects undergo a total reorganization of their internal and external anatomy when they pass through the pupal stage of the life cycle.

Other species undergo what is often called **incomplete metamorphosis.** They hatch from the egg as a nymph, which lacks functional wings. In many species, such as grasshoppers (order Orthoptera), the nymphs resemble the adults. In other insects, such as dragonflies (order Odonata), the aquatic nymphs are morphologically very different from the adults. Even in insects following this developmental pattern, the adult form differs by more than the abrupt development of the wings. The nature or colour of the cuticle may differ

Insect Juvenile Hormone

The juvenile hormone of insects is a family of hormones, each differing only slightly in structure **(Figure 1).** Its existence was first demonstrated by the English researcher V.B. Wigglesworth (see People Behind Biology) in 1948. Using surgical procedures, he showed that the corpus allatum, an endocrine organ just behind the brain, was the source of a factor governing metamorphosis. In the presence of the factor, the insect remained larval, and in its absence, metamorphosis occurred, leading to the adult insect. In the adult, the hormone governs egg production and other elements of reproduction. The precise structure of the first member of the family of molecules was not elucidated until 1967. Because juvenile hormone is an oil, it passes easily through the cuticle of insects **(Figure 2).** This raised the possibility that mimics of the hormone might be useful as insecticides. Since the hormone has no obvious counterpart in other animals, it was argued that insecticides

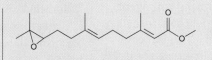

Figure 1
JH III, the most common of the family of molecules used as juvenile hormone in insects.

Ken Davey

Figure 2
Juvenile hormone passes easily through the cuticle. In this experiment, V.B. Wigglesworth applied the appropriate concentration of the hormone to a localized area on the dorsal surface of a last-stage larva of *Rhodnius prolixus* during the process of forming the adult cuticle. On the left, he applied the hormone to a single segment, and on the right, he applied it in the form of his initials. When the insects moulted to the adult, the new cuticle in the treated portions retained the characteristics of the larval cuticle, whereas the rest of the insect exhibited normal adult cuticle. This photo also shows that in some insects with "incomplete metamorphosis," the changes in morphology may be very great.

based on the hormone should be safe. Some compounds have emerged as useful pesticides and have been particularly useful in controlling mosquito larvae in water bodies and fleas on pets.

(see *Molecule Behind Biology*). The terminal segments are reorganized to produce the external genitalia. In general, however, the descendants of the cells present in the first instar produce these changes.

Most insects undergo **complete metamorphosis:** the larva that hatches from the egg differs greatly from the adult. Larvae and adults often occupy different habitats and consume different food. The larvae (caterpillars, grubs, or maggots) are often worm-shaped, with chewing mouthparts. They grow and moult several times, retaining their larval morphology. Before they transform into sexually mature adults, they spend a period of time as a sessile **pupa**. During this stage, most of the larval tissues are destroyed and replaced by groups of embryonic cells, called "disks," that have been in place since hatching. Although these cells are not obviously differentiated, their developmental fate is determined. Thus, there are antennal disks, eye disks, wing disks, and so on. The process is fundamentally different from that in insects with incomplete metamorphosis. In the latter, existing cells are reprogrammed at the last moult to produce the adult form, whereas in insects with

complete metamorphosis, entirely new cells, programmed during embryogenesis to produce adult tissues, are involved.

Moths, butterflies, beetles, wasps, and flies are examples of insects with complete metamorphosis. Their larval stages specialize in feeding and growth, whereas the adults are adapted for dispersal and reproduction. In some species, the adults never feed, relying on the energy stores accumulated during the larval stage. This mode of development has been highly successful. The four principal orders with a pupa—the Lepidoptera, Coleoptera, Hymenoptera, and Diptera—account for about two-thirds of all known species of animals.

The evolution of insects has been characterized by innovations in morphology, life cycle patterns, locomotion, feeding, and habitat use. Insects' well-developed nervous systems govern exceptionally complex patterns of behaviour, including parental care, a habit that reaches its zenith in the colonial social insects, the termites, ants, bees, and wasps (see *Polymorphic Development*). The factors that contribute to the insects' success also make them our most aggressive competitors. They destroy agricultural crops, stored food, wool, paper, and timber. They feed on blood from humans and domesticated animals, sometimes transmitting disease-causing pathogens such as malaria as they do so. Nevertheless, insects are essential members of terrestrial ecological communities. Many species pollinate flowering plants, including important crops. Many others attack or parasitize species that are harmful to human activities. Most insects are a primary source of food for other animals. Some make useful products, such as honey, shellac, beeswax, and silk, and many human cultures use them for food.

STUDY BREAK

1. What are the advantages of moulting in nematodes?
2. If an arthropod's rigid exoskeleton cannot be expanded, how does the animal grow?
3. How do the number of body regions differ among the four subphyla of living arthropods?
4. How do the life stages differ between insects that have incomplete metamorphosis and those that have complete metamorphosis?

UNANSWERED QUESTIONS

How many species of animals are there? Most scientists agree that we have only begun to document the diversity of life. A little over a million species of animals have been described so far, and the number increases every day, but estimates of the total differ widely. Some estimates, based on sampling from single trees in a tropical rain forest, place the number of insect species alone at between 5 and 10 million. Recently, more concerted international efforts to document the diversity of life have begun to emerge. For example, the Census of Marine Life is an international consortium dedicated to exploring marine diversity. Directed by Ron O'Dor, on leave from Dalhousie University, it coordinates the efforts from all of the major countries and regions of the world. One of the major tools for management of the enormous amount of data is the Barcode of Life, a concept originated by Paul Hebert at the University of Guelph in 2003 (see Chapter 3). This initiative has grown to a major international consortium involving more than 45 countries.

Review

Go to CENGAGENOW™ at http://hed.nelson.com/ to access quizzing, animations, exercises, articles, and personalized homework help.

26.1 What Is an Animal?

- Animals are eukaryotic, multicellular organisms that are differentiated from plants by heterotrophy, motility, and direct contact between adjacent cells.
- Animals probably arose in the Precambrian from a hollow sphere of colonial flagellates that reorganized as a double-layered sac-within-a-sac.

26.2 Key Innovations in Animal Evolution

- Tissues, groupings of identical cells specialized to perform specific functions, are organized into two or three tissue layers, ectoderm, endoderm, and, in those animals with three layers, mesoderm. In some sponges, the specialized cells may be capable of dedifferentiation.
- Some animals exhibit radial symmetry; most exhibit bilateral symmetry. Bilaterally symmetrical animals have left and right sides, dorsal and ventral sides, and anterior and posterior ends.
- Acoelomate animals have no body cavity. Pseudocoelomate animals have a body cavity between the derivatives of endoderm and of mesoderm. Coelomate animals have a body cavity that is entirely lined by derivatives of mesoderm. The cavities are filled with fluid that separates and protects the organs and in some cases functions as hydrostatic skeleton.

- Two lineages of animals differ in developmental patterns. Most protostomes exhibit spiral, determinate cleavage; the coelom (when present) is a schizocoelom; and the blastopore develops into the mouth. Deuterostomes have radial symmetry, indeterminate cleavage, an enterocoelom, and their blastopore becomes the anus.
- The development of many protostomes includes a larval stage. This polymorphic development allows sessile animals to be distributed, permits parasitic forms to exist in widely different environments, and avoids competition between the young and the adults.
- Four animal phyla exhibit segmentation.

26.3 An Overview of Animal Phylogeny and Classification

- Sequence analyses of highly conserved structures such as rRNA, mitochondrial DNA, and DNA coding for specific proteins can be compared in various species. The closer the similarity, the more closely related the species are assumed to be. Phylogenetic trees based on such data have confirmed some relationships based on developmental and morphological data and challenged others.
- The Radiata includes animals with two tissue layers and radial symmetry, and the Bilateria includes animals with three tissue layers and bilateral symmetry.

- Bilateria is further subdivided into Protostomia and Deuterostomia. The phylogeny based on molecular evidence divides the Protostomia into the Lophotrochozoa and the Ecdysozoa.
- Molecular phylogeny suggests that ancestral protostomes had a coelom and that acoelomate and pseudocoelomate conditions were derived from the coelomate.
- Segmentation arose independently in three lineages: the annelids, the Onychophora/Arthropoda, and the Chordata.

26.4 Phylum Porifera
- Sponges (phylum Porifera) are asymmetrical animals, many with limited integration of cells in their bodies.
- The body of many sponges is a water-filtering system with incurrent pores, a spongocoel, and an osculum, through which water exits the body. Flagellated choanocytes draw water into the body and capture particulate food.

26.5 Metazoans with Radial Symmetry
- The two major radiate phyla have two well-developed tissue layers with a gelatinous mesoglea between them. They lack organ systems but have well-developed nerve nets. All are aquatic or marine.
- The hydrozoans, jellyfishes, sea anemones, and corals (phylum Cnidaria) are predators that capture prey with tentacles and stinging nematocysts.
- The life cycles of cnidarians may include polyps, medusae, or both. Anthozoans lack a medusa stage, whereas in jellyfish (Scyphozoa and Cubozoa), medusae are prominent and hydroids may be absent, and both are present in Hydrozoa.
- The small, translucent comb jellies (phylum Ctenophora) use long, sticky tentacles to capture particulate food. They are weak swimmers that use rows of cilia for locomotion.

26.6 Lophotrochozoan Protostomes
- The taxon Lophotrochozoa includes eight phyla that share either a characteristic type of larva or a specialized feeding structure.
- Flatworms (phylum Platyhelminthes) are either free-living or parasitic. Free-living species have well-developed digestive, excretory, reproductive, and nervous systems. Parasitic flukes and tapeworms live within or upon animal hosts. They attach to hosts with suckers or hooks, and they produce numerous eggs. Some organ systems may be greatly reduced in parasitic species.
- The wheel animals (phylum Rotifera) are tiny and abundant inhabitants of freshwater and marine ecosystems. Movements of cilia in the corona control their locomotion and bring food to their mouths. Many are parthenogenetic.
- Three small phyla (Ectoprocta, Brachiopoda, and Phoronida) all use a lophophore to feed on particulate matter. Brachiopods live within a two-part shell; ectoprocts form flattened or branching colonies; and phoronids are small, usually tube-dwelling worms.
- The ribbon worms (phylum Nemertea) are elongate and often colourful animals with a proboscis housed in a unique structure, the rhynchocoel.

- Chitons, snails, clams, octopuses, and their relatives (phylum Mollusca) have fleshy bodies that are often enclosed in a hard shell. The molluscan body plan includes a head–foot, a visceral mass, and a mantle.
- Segmented worms (phylum Annelida) generally exhibit segmentation of the coelom and of the muscular, circulatory, excretory, respiratory, and nervous systems. Polychaetes have segmental appendages used in locomotion and gas exchange. Leeches have reduced segmentation.

26.7 Ecdysozoan Protostomes
- The taxon Ecdysozoa includes three phyla that periodically shed their cuticle.
- Roundworms (phylum Nematoda) feed on decaying organic matter or parasitize plants or animals. Locomotion depends on muscles contracting against a hydrostatic skeleton provided by a fluid-filled pseudocoel. Moulting is not essential for growth, but it permits changing the nature of the cuticle to accommodate different environments.
- The velvet worms (phylum Onychophora) have segmented bodies and unjointed legs. Some species bear live young, which develop in a uterus.
- The arthropods (phylum Arthropoda) are the most diverse animals on Earth. Their segmented bodies are often differentiated into distinct regions, and their jointed appendages are specialized for feeding, locomotion, or reproduction. They shed their firm, water-resistant exoskeleton to accommodate growth or when they begin a new stage of the life cycle. Arthropods have an open circulatory system, numerous sense organs that provide input to a complex nervous system, and, in some groups, highly specialized respiratory and excretory systems.
- Arthropods are divided into five subphyla. The extinct trilobites (subphylum Trilobita), with three-lobed bodies and relatively undifferentiated appendages, were abundant in Paleozoic seas.
- Spiders, ticks, mites, scorpions, and horseshoe crabs (subphylum Chelicerata) have a cephalothorax and an abdomen; two pairs of appendages on the head serve in feeding.
- Lobsters, crabs, and their relatives (subphylum Crustacea) have a carapace that covers the cephalothorax as well as highly modified appendages, including five pairs on the head.
- The centipedes and millipedes (subphylum Myriapoda) are largely terrestrial. They have a head and an elongate, segmented trunk.
- Insects and their relatives (subphylum Hexapoda) are also largely terrestrial. Insects have three body regions, three pairs of walking legs on the thorax, and a pair of antennae and three pairs of feeding appendages on the head.
- Most insects undergo metamorphosis. In incomplete metamorphosis, the cells of the nymph are reprogrammed to produce adult structures. In complete metamorphosis, an additional stage, the pupa, permits entirely new adult structures to replace larval cells.

Questions

Self-Test Questions

1. Which of the following characteristics is *not* typical of most animals?
   a. heterotrophic
   b. sessile
   c. radially symmetrical
   d. multicellular
   e. motile at some stage of life cycle

2. A body cavity that separates the digestive system from the body wall but is *not* completely lined with mesoderm is called a
   a. schizocoelom.
   b. mesentery.
   c. peritoneum.
   d. pseudocoelom.
   e. hydrostatic skeleton.

3. Which part of a mollusc secretes the shell?
   a. visceral mass
   b. radula
   c. trochophore
   d. head–foot
   e. mantle

4. Which of the following is not a result of polymorphic development?
   a. castes in social insects
   b. alternation of generations in Cnidaria
   c. the pupal stage in insects
   d. the adult octopus
   e. the trochophore larva

5. Ecdysis refers to a process in which
   a. bivalves use siphons to pass water across their gills.
   b. arthropods and nematodes shed their cuticles.
   c. cnidarians build skeletons of calcium carbonate.
   d. rotifers produce unfertilized eggs.
   e. squids escape from predators in a cloud of ink.

Questions for Discussion

1. Many invertebrate species are hermaphroditic. What selective advantages might this characteristic offer? In what kinds of environments might it be most useful?

2. In terms of numbers of species, insects are the dominant life form on Earth, but the individuals are also smaller in size than many other groups. What has contributed to their success, and why are they not larger?

3. The egg of the human parasite *A. lumbricoides* hatches in the small intestine. What experiments would you do to test whether this is a result of the egg shell being digested by the intestinal enzymes?

The molar tooth of a an extinct mammal *(Desmostylus)* was used to crush and grind marine plants. Paleontologists discovered that *Desmostylus* was more walrus- than seacowlike only when they found almost-complete skeletons. You may remember this as Figure 3.22c.

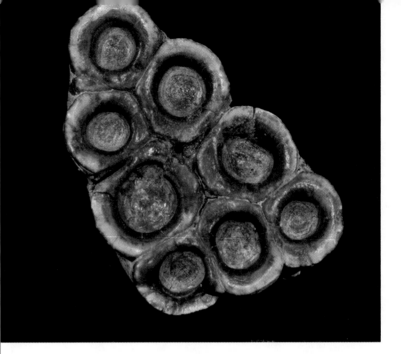

M. B. Fenton

27 Deuterostomes: Vertebrates and Their Closest Relatives

WHY IT MATTERS

Based on molecular evidence, Xenoturbellida was identified as a new phylum in November 2006. This new phylum is closely related to the Chordata (traditional phylogeny in **Figure 27.1a, p. 618**), which includes vertebrates, among them *Homo sapiens*. Specifically, a phylogenetic analysis of 170 nuclear proteins and 13 mitochondrial proteins was used to derive the phylogeny that placed Xenoturbellida among the Deuterostomes **(Figure 27.1b, p. 619)**. Look at some of the organisms **(Figure 27.2, p. 620)** arranged in the phylogeny.

Xenoturbellida (such as *Xenoturbella bocki*; see Figure 27.2f) was originally described in 1949. They are delicate, ciliated marine worms with simple body plans. They lack a gut wih two openings, organized gonads, excretory structures, and a coelom. The nervous system is a diffuse net with no brain. Until 2006, there were more questions than answers about their phylogenetic position, even to what phylum they should belong. At first, *X. bocki* was thought to be a turbellarian flatworm (Platyhelminthes), but it also was identified as a possible hemichordate or echinoderm (based on similarities in the nerve net). The details of *Xenoturbella*'s cilia are like those of hemichordates,

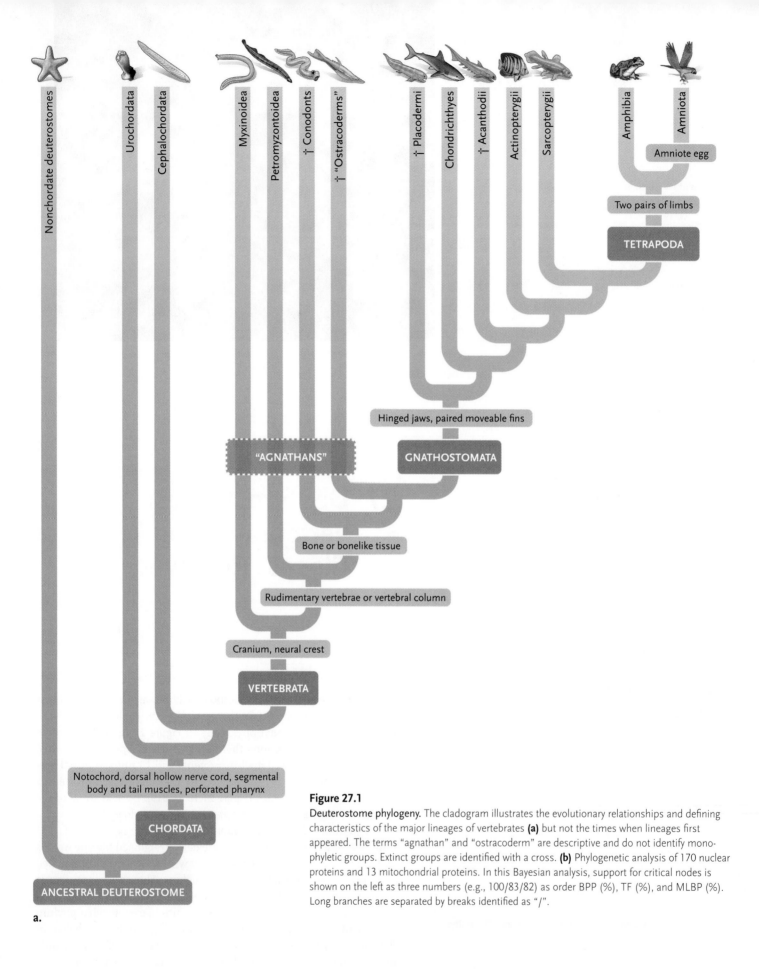

Figure 27.1

Deuterostome phylogeny. The cladogram illustrates the evolutionary relationships and defining characteristics of the major lineages of vertebrates **(a)** but not the times when lineages first appeared. The terms "agnathan" and "ostracoderm" are descriptive and do not identify monophyletic groups. Extinct groups are identified with a cross. **(b)** Phylogenetic analysis of 170 nuclear proteins and 13 mitochondrial proteins. In this Bayesian analysis, support for critical nodes is shown on the left as three numbers (e.g., 100/83/82) as order BPP (%), TF (%), and MLBP (%). Long branches are separated by breaks identified as "/".

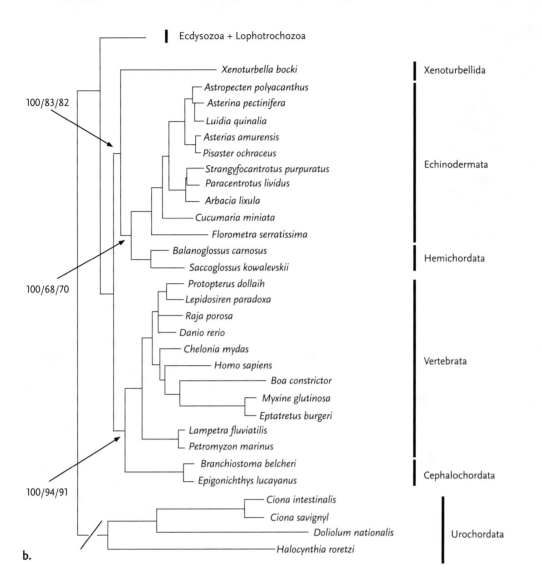

b.

which could indicate that it is really an acoelomorph flatworm.

In 1997, analysis of molecular phylogenetic data was used to place *Xenoturbella* in the Mollusca, specifically among the bivalves. This arrangement was supported by the discovery of bivalvelike eggs and larvae within specimens of *Xenoturbella*. In 1997, it was easy to believe the molecular argument.

How can molecular data be challenged? In 1998, an alternative explanation was offered: the mollusc genetic information appeared inside *Xenoturbella* because it eats molluscs. When the molluscan genetic information is ignored, *Xenoturbella* is clearly a deuterostome, most closely related to Echinodermata (see Figure 27.1).

Thus, making correct choices about classification (see Chapter 19) means looking beyond appearance and may also require careful consideration of molecular data.

27.1 Deuterostomes

Membership in the Deuterostomia (Greek, *deutero* = second; *stomia* = opening) is restricted to animals in which the anus develops from the blastopore and the mouth from a second opening. At first glance, deuterostome animals—such as echinoderms, chordates, and hemichordates, let alone *Xenoturbella*—are not obviously similar, reflecting modifications of their bodies that mask underlying developmental and genetic features.

STUDY BREAK

What is the difference between protostomes and deuterostomes?

27.2 Phylum Echinodermata

The phylum Echinodermata (*echino* = spiny; *derm* = skin) includes 6500 species of sea stars, sea urchins, sea cucumbers, brittle stars, and sea lilies. These slow-moving or sessile, bottom-dwelling animals are important herbivores and predators living in oceans from the shallow coastal waters to the oceans' depths. The phylum was diverse in the Paleozoic, but only a

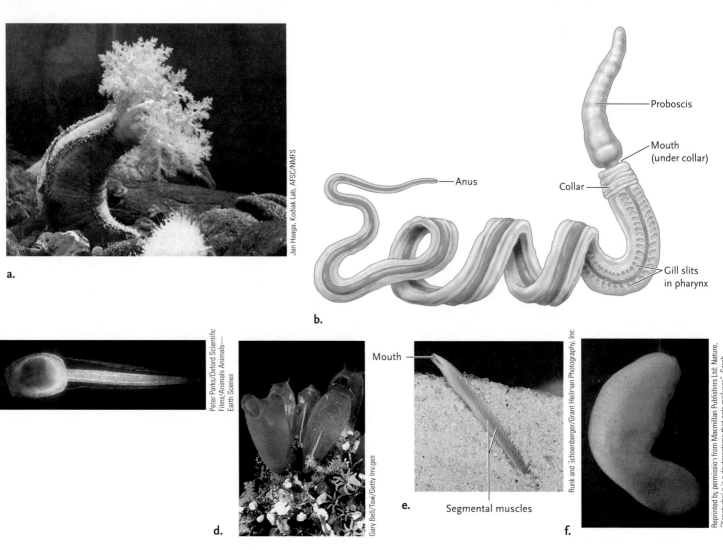

Labels on figure:
- Anus
- Proboscis
- Mouth (under collar)
- Collar
- Gill slits in pharynx
- Mouth
- Segmental muscles

Photo credits:
Jan Haaga. Kodiak Lab. AFSC/NMFS
Peter Parks/Oxford Scientific Films/Animals Animals—Earth Scenes
Gary Bell/Taxi/Getty Images
Runk and Schoenberger/Grant Heilman Photography, Inc.
Reprinted by permission from Macmillan Publishers Ltd: Nature, "Xenoturbella is a deuterostome that eats molluscs", Sarah J. Bourlat, Claus Nielsen, Anne E. Lockyer, D. Timothy J. Littlewood and Maximilian J. Telford, vol. 424, pp. 925-928, copyright (2003).

Figure 27.2

Deuterostomes. **(a)** Holothuroidea. A sea cucumber (*Cucumaraia miniata*) extends its tentacles, which are modified tube feet. **(b)** Phylum Hemichordata. Acorn worms draw food- and oxygen-laden water in through the mouth and expel it through gill slits in the anterior region of the trunk. **(c)** Urochordates. A tadpole-like tunicate larva will metamorphose into a sessile adult. **(d and e)** Cephalochordates. The unpigmented skin of an adult lancet (*Brachiostoma* species) reveals their segmented body wall muscles. **(f)** A *Xenoturbella bocki* does not look very similar to any of the other animals illustrated here.

remnant of that fauna remains. Echinoderms vary in size from less than 1 cm in diameter to more than 50 cm long. Adult echinoderms develop from bilaterally symmetrical, free-swimming larvae. As the larvae develop, they assume a secondary radial symmetry, often organized around five rays or "arms" **(Figure 27.3)**. Many echinoderms have an *oral surface*, with the mouth facing the substrate, and an *aboral surface* facing in the opposite direction. Virtually all echinoderms have an internal skeleton made of calcium-stiffened *ossicles* that develop from mesoderm. In some groups, fused ossicles form a rigid container called a *test*. In most, spines or bumps project from the ossicles.

The internal anatomy of echinoderms is unique among animals (see Figure 27.3). They have a well-defined coelom and a complete digestive system (see Figure 27.3e) but no excretory or respiratory systems,

and most have only a minimal circulatory system. In many, gases are exchanged and metabolic wastes eliminated through projections of the epidermis and peritoneum near the base of the spines. Given their radial symmetry, there is no head or central brain; the nervous system is organized around nerve cords that encircle the mouth and branch into the radii. Sensory cells are abundant in the skin.

Echinoderms move using a system of fluid-filled canals, the *water vascular system* (see Figure 27.3f). In a sea star, for example, water enters the system through the *madreporite*, a sievelike plate on the aboral surface. A short tube connects it to the *ring canal*, which surrounds the **esophagus**. The ring canal branches into five *radial canals* that extend into the arms. Each radial canal is connected to numerous *tube feet* that protrude through holes in the plates. Each tube foot has a mucus-covered, suckerlike tip and a small muscular

a. Asteroidea: This sea star (*Fromia milleporella*) lives in the intertidal zone.

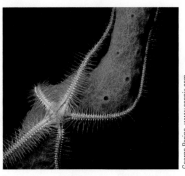

b. Ophiuroidea: A brittle star (*Ophiothrix swensonii*) perches on a coral branch.

c. Echinoidea: A sea urchin (*Strongylocentrotus purpuratus*) grazes on algae.

d. Crinoidea: A feather star (*Himerometra robustipinna*) feeds by catching small particles with its numerous arms

Figure 27.3

Echinoderm diversity. **(a)–(d)** Echinoderms exhibit secondary radial symmetry, usually organized as five rays around an oral–aboral axis. Internal anatomy of a sea star. The coelom **(e)** is well developed in echinoderms, as illustrated by this cutaway diagram of a sea star. The water vascular system **(f)**, unique in the animal kingdom, operates the tube feet. Tube feet **(g)** are responsible for locomotion. Note the pedicillariae on the upper surface of the star's arm.

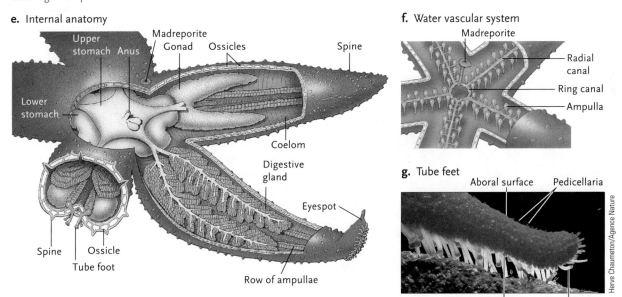

e. Internal anatomy

f. Water vascular system

g. Tube feet

bulb, the *ampulla*, that lies inside the body. When an ampulla contracts, fluid is forced into the tube foot, causing it to lengthen and attach to the substrate (see Figure 27.3g). The tube foot then contracts, pulling the animal along. As the tube foot shortens, water is forced back into the ampulla, and the tube foot releases its grip on the substrate. The tube foot can then take another step forward, reattaching to the substrate.

Although each tube foot has limited strength, the coordinated action of hundreds or even thousands of them is so strong that they can hold an echinoderm to a substrate even against strong wave action.

Echinoderms have separate sexes, and most reproduce by releasing gametes into the water. Radial cleavage is so clearly apparent in the transparent eggs of some sea urchins that they are commonly used to demonstrate cleavage in introductory biology laboratories. A few echinoderms reproduce asexually by splitting in half and regenerating the missing parts. Other echinoderms regenerate body parts lost to predators. Four-day-old sand dollars (*Dendraster excentricus*) asexually clone themselves in response to the odour of fish (in mucus), apparently a defensive response.

Echinoderms are divided into six groups, the most recently described (1986) being the sea daisies (Concentricycloidea). These small, medusa-shaped animals occupy sunken, waterlogged wood in the deep sea. Sunken ships often are important habitats for marine organisms. The five other groups, described below, are more diverse and better known.

27.2a Asteroidea: Starfish or Sea Stars

Sea stars live on rocky shorelines to depths of 10 000 m. Many are brightly coloured. The body consists of a central disk surrounded by 5 to 20 radiating "arms" (see Figure 27.3a), with the mouth centred on the oral surface. The ossicles of the endoskeleton are not fused, permitting flexibility of the arms and disk. **Pedicellariae** are small pincers at the base of short spines. They are used to remove debris that falls onto the animal's aboral (see Figure 27.3c). Many sea stars eat invertebrates and small fishes. Species that consume bivalve molluscs grasp the two valves with tube feet and slip their everted stomachs between the bivalve's shells **(Figure 27.4)**. The stomach secretes digestive enzymes that dissolve the mollusc's tissues. Some sea stars are destructive predators of corals, endangering many reefs.

Figure 27.4
Starfish feeding on a mussel. Even when the tide is out in the Queen Charlotte Islands, starfish hunt mussels.

M.B. Fenton

27.2b Ophiuroidea: Brittle Stars

The 2000 species of brittle stars and basket stars occupy roughly the same range of habitats as sea stars. Their bodies have a well-defined central disk and slender, elongated arms that are sometimes branched (see Figure 27.3b). Ophiuroids can crawl fairly swiftly across substrates by moving their arms in a coordinated fashion. As their common name implies, the arms are delicate and easily broken, an adaptation allowing them to escape from predators with only minor damage. Brittle stars feed on small prey, suspended plankton, or detritus that they extract from muddy deposits.

27.2c Echinoidea: Sea Urchins and Sand Dollars

The 950 species of sea urchins and sand dollars lack arms (see Figure 27.3c). Their ossicles are fused into solid tests that provide excellent protection but restrict flexibility. The test is spherical in sea urchins and flattened in sand dollars. These animals use tube feet in locomotion. Five rows of tube feet emerge through pores in the test. Most echinoids have movable spines, some with poison glands. A jab from some tropical species can cause a careless swimmer severe pain and inflammation. Echinoids graze on algae and other organisms that cling to surfaces. In the centre of an urchin's oral surface is a five-part nipping jaw that is controlled by powerful muscles. Some species damage kelp beds, disrupting the habitat of young lobsters and other crustaceans. Echinoid ovaries are a gourmet delicacy in many countries, making these animals a prized natural resource.

27.2d Holothuroidea: Sea Cucumbers

Sea cucumbers are elongated animals that lie on their sides on the ocean bottom (see Figure 27.2a) and number about 1500 species. Although they have five rows of tube feet, their endoskeleton is reduced to widely separated microscopic plates. The body, which is elongated along the oral–aboral axis, is soft and fleshy, with a tough, leathery covering. Modified tube feet form a ring of tentacles around the mouth. The central disk and mouth point upward rather than toward the substrate. Some species secrete a mucus net that traps plankton or other food particles. The net and tentacles are inserted into the mouth, where the net and trapped food are ingested. Other species extract food from bottom sediments. Many sea cucumbers exchange gases through an extensively branched *respiratory tree* arising from the rectum, the part of the digestive system just inside the anus at the aboral end of the animal. A well-developed circulatory system distributes oxygen and nutrients to tissues throughout the body.

Sea cucumbers actually are home for specialized symbiotic fish. *Carapus bermudensis*, the pearl fish, enters sea cucumbers' cloacal opening tail first. The cloaca is the chamber receiving urine, feces, and reproductive products. Pearl fish are members of a group that usually live in the tubes of other animals, including the cavities of bivalves. These fish have elongated, thin bodies. They have lost pelvic fins and scales, and the anal opening has moved forward to a position under the head. This adaptation ensures that the fish defecates outside the body of the sea cucumber. These fishes use olfactory cues to find the "correct" host.

27.2e Crinoidea: Sea Lilies and Feather Stars

The 600 living species of sea lilies and feather stars are the surviving remnants of a diverse and abundant fauna 500 million years ago (see Figure 27.3d). Most species occupy marine waters of medium depth. Between five and several hundred branched arms surround the disk that contains the mouth. New arms are added as a crinoid grows larger. The branches of the arms are covered with tiny, mucus-coated tube feet that trap suspended microscopic organisms. Sessile sea lilies have the central disk attached to a flexible stalk that can reach 1 m in length. By contrast, adult feather stars can swim or crawl weakly, attaching temporarily to substrates. The disks comprising sea lily stalks, called ossicles, are common fossils in many deposits **(Figure 27.5)**.

STUDY BREAK

1. What are echinoderms? How do adult echinoderms develop?
2. Use a table to compare an echinoderm and a human by system: (a) digestive, (b) excretory, (c) respiratory, (d) circulatory, and (e) nervous.
3. Using a sea star as an example, describe how echinoderms move.

27.3 Phylum Hemichordata

The 80 species of **acorn worms** comprising this phylum take their name from *hemi*, meaning half, and *chord*, referring to the phylum Chordata. Acorn worms are sedentary marine animals living in U-shaped tubes or burrows in coastal sand or mud. Their soft bodies range in length from 2 cm to 2 m and are organized into an anterior proboscis, a tentacled collar, and an elongate trunk (see Figure 27.2b). They use the muscular, mucus-coated proboscis to construct burrows and trap food particles. Acorn worms also have pairs of gill slits in the pharynx, the part of the digestive

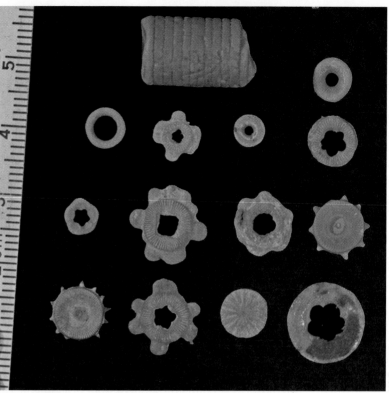

Figure 27.5
Fossil crinoid stems. Ossicles comprising the stems of crinoids are commonly fossilized. The individual ossicles are from the Devonian of Ontario. The section of complete stem is *Encrinus liliiformis* from the Triassic of Germany. Scale is in mm.

system just posterior to the mouth. Beating cilia create a flow of water, which enters the pharynx through the mouth and exits through the gill slits. As water passes through, suspended food particles are trapped and shunted into the digestive system, and gases are exchanged across the partitions between gill slits. The dorsal nerve cord, coupled with feeding and respiration, reflects a close evolutionary relationship between hemichordates and chordates.

STUDY BREAK

How do hemichordates feed?

27.4 Phylum Chordata

This phylum includes evolutionary lines of invertebrates, the Urochordata and Cephalochordata, as well as the more diverse line, the Vertebrata. A *notochord*, a *dorsal hollow nerve cord*, and *gill slits* (a perforated pharynx) are key morphological features distinguishing chordates from all other Deuterostomes. These features occur during at least some time in a chordate's life cycle. Chordates also have segmental muscles in the body wall and tail **(Figure 27.6, p. 624)**. Collectively, these structures enable higher levels of

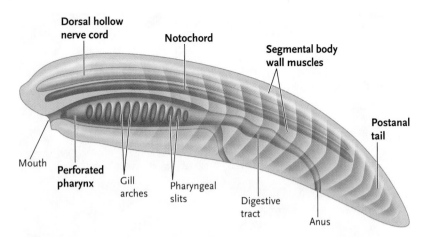

Figure 27.6
Diagnostic chordate characteristics. Chordates have a notochord, a dorsal hollow nerve cord, gill slits (a perforated pharynx), and a muscular postanal tail with segmental body wall and tail muscles.

Labels: Dorsal hollow nerve cord, Notochord, Segmental body wall muscles, Postanal tail, Mouth, Perforated pharynx, Gill arches, Pharyngeal slits, Digestive tract, Anus

activity and unique modes of aquatic locomotion, as well as more efficient feeding and oxygen acquisition.

Early in chordate embryonic development, the **notochord** (*noto* = back; *chord* = string), a flexible rod, develops from mesoderm dorsal to the developing digestive system. The notochord is constructed of fluid-filled cells surrounded by tough connective tissue. It supports the embryo from head to tail. The notochord is the skeleton of invertebrate chordates, serving as an anchor for body wall muscles. When these muscles contract, the notochord bends but does not shorten. Waves of contractions pass down one side of the animal and then down the other, sweeping the body and tail back and forth in a smooth and continuous movement. Thus, the chordate body swings left and right during locomotion, propelling the animal forward. The chordate tail, which is posterior to the anus, provides most of the propulsion in some aquatic species. Segmentation allows each muscle block to contract independently. Unlike the bodies of annelids and other nonchordate invertebrates, the chordate body does not shorten when the animal is moving. Remnants of the notochord persist as gelatinous disks between the vertebrae of some adult vertebrates.

The central nervous system of chordates is a hollow nerve cord on the dorsal side of the embryo (see Chapter 39). Most nonchordate invertebrates have ventral, solid nerve cords. In vertebrates, an anterior enlargement of the nerve cord forms the brain. In invertebrates, an anterior concentration of nervous system tissue is a *ganglion* and may be referred to as a "brain."

Gill slits mean that the chordate pharynx is perforated. The pharynx is the part of the digestive system just behind the mouth. **Gill slits** are paired openings originating as exit holes for water that carried particulate food into the mouth, allowing chordates to gather food by filtration. Invertebrate chordates also collect oxygen and release carbon dioxide across the walls of the pharynx. In fishes, gill arches have evolved as supporting structures between the slits in the pharynx. Invertebrate chordates and fishes retain a perforated

pharynx throughout their lives. In most air-breathing vertebrates, the slits are present only during embryonic development and in some larvae (see Chapter 34).

27.4a Subphylum Urochordata: Sea Squirts and Tunicates

The 2500 species of urochordates (*uro* = tail) float in surface waters or attach to substrates in shallow marine habitats. Sessile adults of many species secrete a gelatinous or leathery "tunic" around their bodies and squirt water through a siphon when disturbed. Adults can attain lengths of several centimetres (**Figure 27.7**; see also Figure 27.2c, d). In the most common group of sea squirts (Ascidiacea), swimming larvae have notochords, dorsal hollow nerve cords, and gill slits, features lacking in the sessile adults. Larvae eventually attach to substrates and transform into sessile adults. During metamorphosis, larvae lose most traces of the notochord, dorsal nerve cord, and tail, and their basket-like pharynx enlarges. In adults, beating cilia pull water into the pharynx through an *incurrent siphon*. A mucus net traps particulate food, which is carried with the mucus to the gut. Water passes through the pharyngeal slits, enters a chamber called the *atrium*, and is expelled through the **atrial siphon** along with digestive wastes and carbon dioxide. Oxygen is absorbed across the walls of the pharynx. In some urochordates, the larvae are neotenous (see Chapters 19 and 26), acquiring the ability to reproduce and remaining active throughout their life cycles.

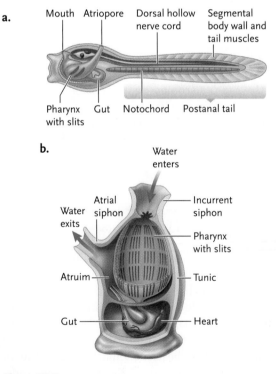

a.

Labels: Mouth, Atriopore, Dorsal hollow nerve cord, Segmental body wall and tail muscles, Pharynx with slits, Gut, Notochord, Postanal tail

b.

Labels: Water enters, Water exits, Atrial siphon, Incurrent siphon, Pharynx with slits, Atruim, Tunic, Gut, Heart

Figure 27.7
Diagrams of urochordates. The tadpole-like tunicate larva **(a)** metamorphoses into an adult, a sessile filter-feeder. **(b)** In the adult, the atriopore becomes the atrial siphon.

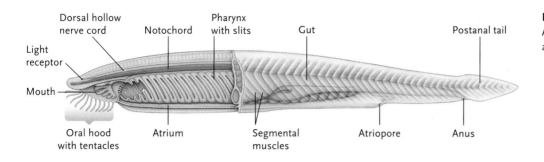

Figure 27.8
A drawing of the internal anatomy of an adult lancet (*Brachiostoma*).

Labels: Dorsal hollow nerve cord, Notochord, Pharynx with slits, Gut, Postanal tail, Light receptor, Mouth, Oral hood with tentacles, Atrium, Segmental muscles, Atriopore, Anus

27.4b Subphylum Cephalochordata: Lancelets

All 28 species of cephalochordates (*cephalo* = head) live in warm, shallow marine habitats, where they lie mostly buried in sand (see Figure 27.2e). Although generally sedentary, they have well-developed body wall muscles and a prominent notochord. Most species are included in the genus *Branchiostoma* (formerly *Amphioxus*). Lancelet bodies, which are 5 to 10 cm long, are pointed at both ends like the double-edged surgical tools for which they are named **(Figure 27.8)**. Adults have light receptors on the head as well as chemical sense organs on tentacles that grow from the *oral hood*. Lancelets use cilia to draw food-laden water through hundreds of pharyngeal slits; water flows into the **atrium** and is expelled through the **atriopore**. Most gas exchange occurs across the skin.

27.4c Subphylum Vertebrata: Vertebrates

Species in this subphylum have a distinct head (they are craniate), and most have a backbone (spine) made up of individual bony vertebrae (see Chapters 19 and 39). This internal skeletal feature provides structural support for muscles and protects the nervous system and other organs. In addition, the internal skeleton and attached muscles allow most vertebrates to move rapidly. Vertebrates are the only animals that have bone, a connective tissue in which cells secrete the mineralized matrix that surrounds them (see Chapter 36). One vertebrate lineage, cartilaginous fishes (class Chondrichthyes), may have lost its bone over evolutionary time. These animals, mostly sharks and rays, have skeletons of cartilage, a dense, flexible connective tissue that can be a developmental precursor of bone (see Chapters 36 and 39).

At the anterior end of the vertebral column, the head is usually protected by a bony **cranium** or skull. The backbone surrounds and protects the dorsal nerve cord, and the bony cranium surrounds the brain. The cranium, vertebral column, ribs, and sternum (breastbone) comprise the axial skeleton. Most vertebrates also have a **pectoral girdle** anteriorly and a **pelvic girdle** posteriorly that attach bones in the fins or limbs to the axial skeleton. The bones of the two girdles and the appendages constitute the appendicular skeleton.

Vertebrates have neural crest cells (see Chapter 39), a unique cell type distinct from endoderm, mesoderm, and ectoderm. Neural crest cells arise next to the developing nervous system but migrate throughout the body. Neural crest cells ultimately contribute to uniquely vertebrate structures such as parts of the cranium, teeth, sensory organs, cranial nerves, and the medulla (the interior part) of the adrenal glands.

The brains of vertebrates are larger and more complex than those of invertebrate chordates. Moreover, the vertebrate brain is divided into three regions, the forebrain, midbrain, and hindbrain, each govering distinct nervous system functions (see Chapter 33).

STUDY BREAK

1. List four morphological features distinguishing chordates from other deuterostomes.
2. Explain the purpose and structure of gill slits.
3. What are tunicates and lancelets? To which subphyla do they belong? What characteristics of swimming tunicate larvae are missing from the sessile adults?

27.5 The Origin and Diversification of Vertebrates

Biologists have used embryological, molecular, and fossil evidence to trace the origin of vertebrates and to chronicle the evolutionary diversification of the group to which humans belong. We suspect that vertebrates arose from a cephalochordate-like ancestor through duplication of genes that regulate development. Vertebrates appear to be more closely related to cephalochordates than to urochordates (see Figure 27.1). The change from cephalochordate-like creature to vertebrate was marked by the emergence of neural crest, bone, and other vertebrate traits. Biologists hypothesize that an increase in the number of genes that control the expression of other genes (homeotic) may have facilitated the development of more complex anatomy. (For more about homeotic genes, see Chapters 14 and 20.) When it comes to organization, there is no

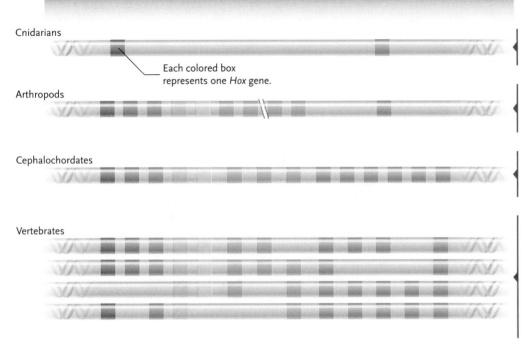

Each row of colored boxes represents one *Hox* gene complex.

Cnidarians

Each colored box represents one *Hox* gene.

a. Invertebrates with simple anatomy, such as cnidarians, have a single *Hox* gene complex that includes just a few *Hox* genes.

Arthropods

b. Invertebrates with more complicated anatomy, such as arthropods, have a single *Hox* gene complex, but with a larger number of *Hox* genes.

Cephalochordates

c. Invertebrate chordates, such as cephalochordates, also have a single *Hox* gene complex, but with even more *Hox* genes than are found in nonchordate invertebrates.

Vertebrates

d. Vertebrates, such as the laboratory mouse, have numerous *Hox* genes, arranged in two to seven *Hox* gene complexes. The additional *Hox* gene complexes are products of wholesale duplications of the ancestral *Hox* gene complex. The additional copies of *Hox* genes specify the development of uniquely vertebrate characteristics, such as the cranium, vertebral column, and neural crest cells.

Figure 27.9

Hox genes and the evolution of vertebrates. The *Hox* genes in different animals appear to be homologous, indicated here by their colour and position in the complex. Vertebrates have many more individual *Hox* genes than invertebrates, and the entire *Hox* gene complex was duplicated in the vertebrate lineage.

compelling reason to believe that "more complex" is superior to "simple."

Hox genes are homeotic genes that influence the three-dimensional shape of the animal and the locations of important structures such as eyes, wings, or legs, particularly along the head-to-tail axis of the body. *Hox* genes are arranged on chromosomes in a particular order, forming the *Hox* gene complex. Each gene in the complex governs the development of particular structures. Animal groups with the simplest structure, such as cnidarians, have two *Hox* genes. Those with more complex anatomy, such as insects, have 10. Chordates typically have up to 13 or 14. Lineages with many *Hox* genes generally have more complex anatomy than those with fewer *Hox* genes.

Molecular analyses reveal that the entire *Hox* gene complex was duplicated several times in the evolution of vertebrates, producing multiple copies of all the genes in the *Hox* complex **(Figure 27.9)**. The cephalochordate *Branchiostoma* has one *Hox* gene complex, whereas hagfish, the most ancestral living vertebrate, has two. All vertebrates with jaws have at least four sets of *Hox* genes, and some fishes have seven. Evolutionary biologists who study development hypothesize that the duplication of *Hox* genes and other tool-kit genes allowed the evolution of new structures. Although original copies of these genes maintained their ancestral functions, duplicate copies were available to assume *new* functions, leading to the development of novel structures, such as the vertebral column and jaws. These changes coincided with the adaptive radiation of vertebrates.

The oldest known vertebrate fossils are from the early Cambrian (about 550 million years ago) in China. Both *Myllokunmingia* and *Haikouichthys* were fish-shaped animals about 3 cm long **(Figures 27.10 and 27.11)**. In both species, the brain was surrounded by a cranium of fibrous connective tissue or cartilage. They also had segmental body wall muscles and fairly well-developed fins, but neither shows any evidence of bone.

The early vertebrates gave rise to numerous descendants (see Figure 27.1a), which varied greatly in anatomy, physiology, and ecology. New feeding mechanisms and locomotor structures were correlated with their success. Today, vertebrates occupy nearly every habitat on Earth and eat virtually all other organisms. Although biologists identify vertebrates from four key morphological innovations (cranium, vertebrae, bone, and neural crest cells), these structures did not evolve spontaneously. Important biological changes during the evolution of vertebrates included improved access to energy (food), which involved mobility and jaws, combined with effective aerobic metabolism (access to oxygen).

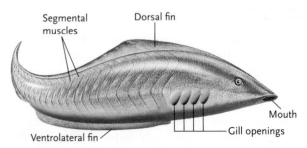

Segmental muscles   Dorsal fin

Mouth

Gill openings

Ventrolateral fin

Figure 27.10

Cambrian agnathan, *Haikouichthys*, was more like a hagfish than a lamprey but generally similar to an ammocoetes larva.

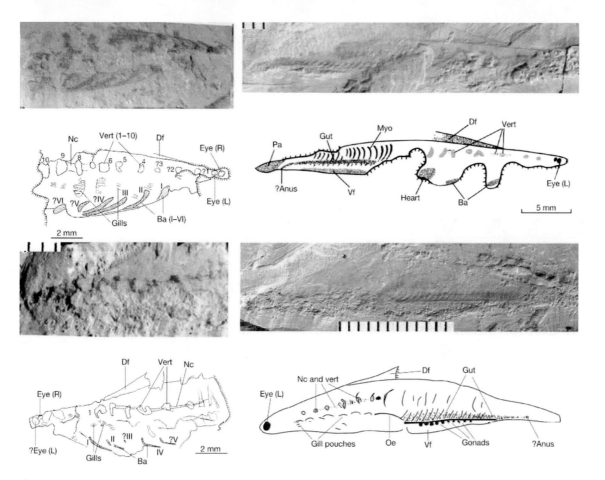

Figure 27.11

A diagram showing an early vertebrate. *Myllokunmingia* is one of the earliest vertebrates yet discovered. This species has no bones and was about 30 cm long. The labels identify features, some with abbreviations, including the following: Ap – anterior plates; Ba – branchial arches; Df – dorsal fin; Myo – myosepta; Nc – notochord; Nc and Vert – notochord with vertebral elements; Nos – nostril; Ns – nasal sacs; Oc – otic capsule; Oe – oesophagus; Pa – post anal tail; Vert – vertebral elements; Vf – ventral fin fold; L – left; R – right. Reprinted by permission from Macmillan Publishers Ltd: Nature, "A role for the immunological synapse in lineage commitment of CD4 lymphocytes", Roberto A. Maldonado, Darrell J. Irvine, Robert Schreiber and Laurie H. Glimcher, vol. 431, pp. 527-532, copyright (2004).

The earliest vertebrates lacked jaws (Agnatha, from *a* = not and *gnath* = jawed), but Agnatha is not a monophyletic group. Although most became extinct by the end of the Paleozoic, two ancestral lineages, Myxinoidea (hagfishes) and Petromyzontoidea (lampreys), survive today. All other vertebrates have movable jaws and form a monophyletic lineage **Gnathostomata** (*gnath* = jawed; *stoma* = mouth). The first jawed fishes, the Acanthodii and Placodermi, are now extinct, but several other lineages of jawed fishes are still abundant. Included are Chondrichthyes, fishes with cartilaginous skeletons (sharks, skates, chimaeras), and Teleostei (actinopterygians and sarcopterygians) with bony endoskeletons. Although all jawless vertebrates and most jawed fishes are restricted to aquatic habitats, mudskippers (*Periophthalmus* species) and climbing perch (*Anabas* species) regularly venture onto land. Many fish have developed lunglike structures for breathing atmospheric oxygen, but most use gills to extract dissolved oxygen from water. Lungs may be an ancestral trait in vertebrates.

Gnathostomata also includes the monophyletic lineage Tetrapoda (*tetra* = four; *pod* = foot), most of which use four limbs for locomotion. Many tetrapods are amphibious, semiterrestrial, or terrestrial, although some, such as sea turtles and porpoises, have secondarily returned to aquatic habitats. Adult tetrapods generally use lungs to breathe atmospheric oxygen. Within the Tetrapoda, one lineage, the Amphibia (such as frogs and salamanders), typically needs standing water to complete its life cycle. Another lineage, the Amniota, comprises animals with specialized eggs that can develop on land. Shortly after their appearance, amniotes diversified into three lineages, one ancestral to living mammals, another to living turtles, and a third to lizards, snakes, alligators, and birds.

STUDY BREAK

1. What is the advantage of a backbone?
2. What marked the change from a cephalochordate-like creature to a vertebrate?
3. What is a *Hox* gene, and how does it influence the diversity of vertebrates?

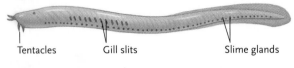

a. Living jawless fishes

Hagfish

Tentacles   Gill slits   Slime glands

Lamprey

Oral disk   Gill slits

b. Mouth of a lamprey

Heather Angel

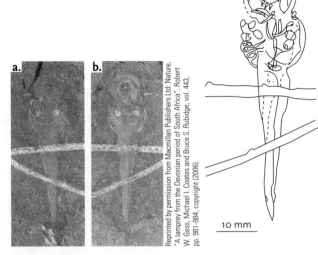

a.   b.

Reprinted by permission from Macmillan Publishers Ltd: Nature, "A lamprey from the Devonian period of South Africa", Robert W. Gess, Michael I. Coates and Bruce S. Rubidge, vol. 443, pp. 981-984, copyright (2006).

10 mm

Figure 27.12

Living agnathans. Two groups of jawless fishes, the hagfishes and the lampreys **(a)**, are shown as diagrams with a photograph of a lamprey **(b).** Also shown is the fossil and diagram of a Devonian lamprey from South Africa.

27.6 Agnathans: Hagfishes and Lampreys, Conodonts, and Ostracoderms

Lacking jaws, the earliest vertebrates used a muscular pharynx to suck water containing food particles into the mouth, and used gills both to acquire dissolved oxygen and to filter food from the water. The aganthans that flourished in the Paleozoic varied greatly in size and shape and possessed different combinations of vertebrate characters.

Lampreys and hagfishes, the two living groups of agnathans, have skeletons composed entirely of cartilage. Although as yet no fossilized lampreys or hagfishes have been found in early Paleozoic strata, the absence of bone in their living descendants suggests that they arose early in vertebrate history, before the evolution of bone. The first fossil lamprey is known from the Devonian of South Africa **(Figure 27.12).** Hagfishes and lampreys have a well-developed notochord but no true vertebrae or paired fins. Their skin lacks scales. Individuals grow to a maximum length of about 1 m (see Figure 27.12). Two possible phylogenies for hagfishes and other vertebrates are presented **(Figure 27.13),** but at this time, there are too few data to decide which is most likely to be correct.

The axial skeletons of the 60 living species of hagfishes include only a cranium and a notochord. No specialized structures surround the dorsal nerve cord. Hagfishes are marine scavengers that burrow in sediments on continental shelves. They feed on invertebrate prey and on dead or dying fishes. In response to

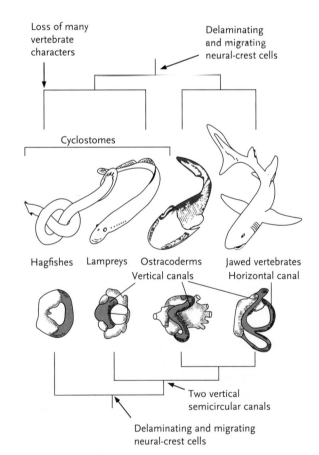

Loss of many vertebrate characters

Delaminating and migrating neural-crest cells

Cyclostomes

Hagfishes   Lampreys   Ostracoderms   Jawed vertebrates
                   Vertical canals   Horizontal canal

Two vertical semicircular canals

Delaminating and migrating neural-crest cells

Figure 27.13

Two alternatives for hagfishes. The top tree implies that they are vertebrates that have lost features and the bottom one that they are a sister group of all other vertebrates. One striking difference is the presence of one semicircular canal in hagfishes and at least two in all other vertebrates. The "truth" remains elusive.

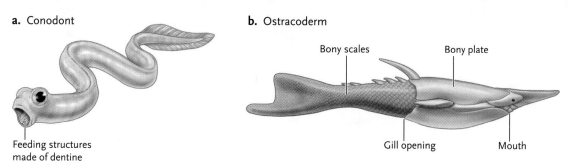

a. Conodont

b. Ostracoderm

Feeding structures made of dentine

Bony scales

Bony plate

Gill opening

Mouth

Figure 27.14

Extinct agnathans. **(a)** Conodonts were elaborate, soft-bodied animals with bonelike feeding structures in the mouth and pharynx. **(b)** *Pteropsis*, an ostracoderm, had large bony plates on its head and small body scales on the rest of its body. It was about 6 cm long.

predators, they secrete an immense quantity of sticky, noxious slime. When no longer threatened, a hagfish ties itself into a knot and wipes the slime from its body. The life cycle of a hagfish lacks a larval stage.

The 38 living species of lamprey have a more specialized axial skeleton than hagfishes do. Their notochord is surrounded by dorsally pointing cartilage that partially covers the nerve cord, perhaps representing an early stage in the evolution of the vertebral column. About half of the living lamprey species are parasitic as adults and use the sucking disk around their mouths to attach to the bodies of fish (or other prey), rasp a hole in the host's body, and ingest body fluids. In most species, sexually mature adults migrate from the ocean or a lake to the headwaters of a stream, where they reproduce and then die. The suspension-feeding ammocoetes larvae of lampreys resemble adult cephalochordates. They burrow into mud and develop for as long as seven years before metamorphosing and migrating to the sea or a lake to live as adults.

Conodonts and ostracoderms were early jawless vertebrates with bony structures. Conodonts are mysterious bonelike fossils, most less than 1 mm long, occurring in oceanic rocks from the early Paleozoic through the early Mesozoic. Called **conodont** elements, these abundant fossils were originally described as supporting structures of marine algae or feeding structures of ancient invertebrates. Recent analyses of their mineral composition reveal that they were made of dentine, a bonelike component of vertebrate teeth. In the 1980s and 1990s, fossils of intact conodont animals with these elements in place were discovered.

Now it is clear that conodonts were elongate, soft-bodied animals, 3 to 10 cm long. They had a notochord, a cranium, segmental body wall muscles, and large, movable eyes **(Figure 27.14a)**. The conodont elements at the front of the mouth were forward-pointing, hook-shaped structures (the original fossils) that apparently were used in the collection of food. Conodont elements in the pharynx were stouter, suitable for crushing food. Paleontologists now classify conodonts as vertebrates, the earliest ones with bonelike structures.

Ostracoderms (*ostrac* = shell; *derm* = skin) include an assortment of jawless fishes representing several evolutionary lines that lived from the Ordovician through the Devonian **(Figure 27.14b)**. Like their invertebrate chordate ancestors, ostracoderms probably used their pharynx to draw water with food particles into their mouths and used gills to filter food from water. The muscular pharynx was more efficient than that of agnathans that used currents generated by cilia. Greater flow rates allowed ostracoderms to collect food more rapidly and achieve larger body sizes. Although most ostracoderms were much smaller, some were 2 m long.

The skin of ostracoderms was heavily armoured with bony plates and scales. Although some had paired lateral extensions of their bony armour, they could not move them in the way living fishes move paired fins. Ostracoderms lacked a true vertebral column, but they had rudimentary support structures surrounding the nerve cord. Ostracoderms had other distinctly vertebrate-like characteristics. Their head shields indicate that their brains had the three regions (forebrain, midbrain, and hindbrain) typical of all later vertebrates (see Chapter 33).

STUDY BREAK

1. How did the earliest vertebrates feed without jaws?
2. Compare the hagfish and the lamprey based on their body structure, feeding habits, and life cycles.

27.7 Jawed Fishes: Jaws Expanded the Feeding Opportunities for Vertebrates

The first gnathostomes were jawed fishes. Jaws meant that they could eat more than just filtered food particles and take larger food items with higher energy content. The renowned anatomist and paleontologist A.S. Romer (see Chapter 19, *People Behind Biology*) described the evolution of jaws as "perhaps the greatest of all advances in vertebrate history." Hinged jaws allow vertebrates to grasp, kill, shred, and crush large food items. Some species also use their jaws for defence, for grooming, to construct nests, and to transport young.

Embryological evidence suggests that jaws evolved from paired gill arches in the pharynx of a jawless ancestor **(Figure 27.15, p. 630)**. One pair of ancestral **gill arches** formed bones in the upper and lower

Figure 27.15
The evolution of jaws.

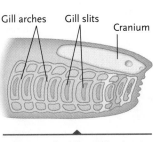

Gill arches Gill slits Cranium

a. Jaws evolved from gill arches in the pharynx of jawless fishes.

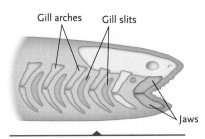

Gill arches Gill slits

Jaws

b. In early jawed fishes, the upper jaw was firmly attached to the cranium.

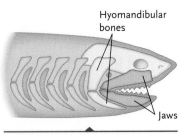

Hyomandibular bones

Jaws

c. In later jawed fishes, the jaws were supported by the hyomandibular bones, which were derived from a second pair of gill arches.

jaws, whereas a second pair was transformed into the **hyomandibular bones** that braced the jaws against the cranium. Nerves and muscles of the ancestral suspension-feeding pharynx control the movement and actions of jaws. Jawed fishes also had fins, first appearing as folds of skin and movable spines that stabilized locomotion and deterred predators. Movable fins appeared independently in several lineages, and by the Devonian, most jawed fishes had unpaired (dorsal, anal, and caudal) and paired (pectoral and pelvic) fins **(Figure 27.16)**.

In two early lineages of jawed fishes (Acanthodii and Placodermi), the upper jaw was firmly attached to the cranium. This meant an inflexible mouth that simply snapped open and shut. Acanthodians and placoderms had internal skeletons.

27.7a Class Acanthodii

The spiny "sharks" (*acanth* = spine) persisted from the late Ordovician through the Permian. Most of these sharklike fishes were less than 20 cm long, with small, light scales, streamlined bodies, well-developed eyes, large jaws, and numerous teeth **(Figure 27.17a)**. Although acanthodians were not true sharks, they probably were fast swimmers and efficient predators. Many of them lived in fresh water. Most had a row of ventral spines and fins with internal skeletal support on each side of the body. The anatomy of acanthodians suggests a close relationship to bony fishes of today.

27.7b Class Placodermi

The placoderms (*plac* = plate; *derm* = skin) appeared in the Silurian and diversified in the Devonian and Carboniferous but left no direct descendants. Some, such as *Dunkleosteus* species **(Figure 27.17b and c)**, reached

lengths of 10 m. The bodies of placoderms were covered with large, heavy plates of bone anteriorly and smaller scales posteriorly. Their jaws had sharp cutting edges but no separate teeth, and their paired fins had internal skeletons and powerful muscles.

27.7c Class Chondrichthyes

The cartilaginous fishes (*chondr* = cartilage; *ichthy* = fish) are represented today by about 850 living species of sharks, skates and rays, and chimeras. As the name implies, their skeletons are entirely cartilaginous. However, the absence of bone is a derived trait because

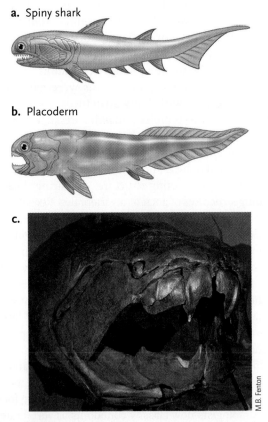

a. Spiny shark

b. Placoderm

c.

M.B. Fenton

Figure 27.17
Early gnathostomes. *Climatius*, an acanthodian **(a)** (spiny shark), was small, about 8 cm long. The placoderm **(b)** *Dunkleosteus* was gigantic, growing to 10 m in length. Although some acanthodians had teeth, placoderms had only sharp cutting edges. The 10 m long skull of a *Dunkleosteus* **(c)** demonstrates how impressive placoderms could be.

Figure 27.16
Fish fins. Most fishes have both paired and unpaired fins.

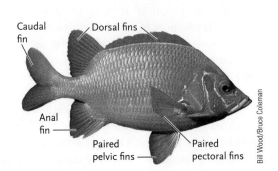

Caudal fin Dorsal fins

Anal fin

Paired pelvic fins Paired pectoral fins

Bill Wood/Bruce Coleman

a. Manta ray

c. Swell shark egg case

© Gido Braase/Deep Blue Productions

b. Galápagos shark

Jonathan Bird/Oceanic Research Group, Inc.

Alex Kerstitch/Visuals Unlimited

Figure 27.18

Chondricthyes. **(a)** Skates and rays, such as the manta ray (*Manta birostris*), as well as **(b)** sharks, such as the Galapagos shark (*Carcharhinus galapagensis*), are grouped in the Elasmobranchii. The eggs of many sharks **(c)** include a large yolk that nourishes the developing embryo.

all earlier fishes had bony armour or bony endoskeletons. Most living chondrichthyans are grouped into two subclasses, the **Elasmobranchii** (skates, rays, and sharks; **Figure 27.18**) and the **Holocephali** (chimeras). Most are marine predators. With about 40 living species, holocephalians are the only cartilaginous fishes with an operculum (gill cover).

Skates and rays are dorsoventrally flattened (see Figure 27.18a) and swim by undulating their enlarged pectoral fins. Most are bottom dwellers that often lie partly buried in sand. They eat hard-shelled invertebrates (see Chapter 26), which they crush with rows of flattened teeth (see Figure 27.18). The largest species, the manta ray (*Manta birostris*), measures 6 m across and eats plankton in the open ocean. Some rays have electric organs that stun prey with shocks of as much as 200 volts. There are species of freshwater skates and rays in some rivers in the tropics; for example, in the Mekong River basin, some *Himantura chaophraya* are 2 m across.

Sharks (see Figure 27.18b) are among the oceans' dominant predators. Flexible fins, lightweight skeletons, streamlined bodies, and the absence of heavy body armour allow most sharks to rapidly pursue prey. Their livers often contain **squalene**, an oil that is lighter than water, which increases their buoyancy. The great white shark (*Carcharodon carcharias*), the largest living predatory species of shark, can be 10 m long. At 18 m, the whale shark (*Rhincodon typus*) is the world's largest fish, and it eats only plankton. Sharks' teeth are designed for cutting. *Isisius plutodus*, the cookie-cutter shark, uses piercing teeth in its upper jaw to attach to a prey, biting with the lower jaw and its cutting teeth while rotating its body (see Figure 3.22h). The feeding process removes a disk of flesh from its prey. The combination of serrated teeth and flexible extensible jaws makes the effects of shark bites awesome.

Elasmobranchs have remarkable adaptations for acquiring and processing food. Their teeth develop in whorls under the fleshy parts of the mouth. New teeth migrate forward as old, worn teeth break free (**Figure 27.19, p. 632;** see also Figure 3.22h). In many sharks, the upper jaw is loosely attached to the cranium, and it swings down during feeding. As the jaws open, the mouth spreads widely, sucking in large, hard-to-digest chunks of prey, which are swallowed intact allowing hurried eating. Although the elasmobranch digestive system is short, it includes a corkscrew-shaped **spiral valve**, which slows the passage of material and increases the surface area available for digestion and absorption.

Elasmobranchs also have well-developed sensory systems. In addition to vision and olfaction, they use **electroreceptors** to detect weak electric currents produced by other animals. Their **lateral line system**, a row of tiny sensors in canals along both sides of the body, detects vibrations in water (see Figure 35.8). They use urea as a metabolite, meaning that their body fluids are more concentrated than sea water. Freshwater skates have much lower concentrations of urea in their blood than their saltwater relatives do.

Chondrichthyans have evolved numerous reproductive specializations. Males have a pair of organs, the **claspers**, on the pelvic fins, which help transfer sperm into the female's reproductive tract. Fertilization occurs internally. In many species, females produce yolky eggs with tough leathery shells (see Figure 27.18c). Others retain the eggs within the oviduct until the young hatch. A few species nourish young in utero (see Chapters 38 and 39).

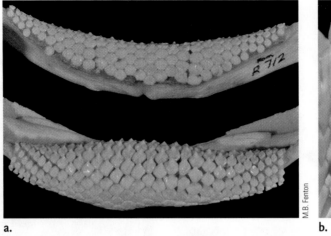

a.

b.

27.7d The Bony Fishes

In terms of diversity (numbers of species) and sheer numbers of individuals, fishes with bony endoskeletons (cranium, vertebral column with ribs, and bones supporting their movable fins) are the most successful of all vertebrates. The endoskeleton provides lightweight support compared with the bony armour of ostracoderms and placoderms, enhancing their locomotor efficiency. Some "bony" fish have cartilaginous skeletons, but they are not chondrichthyeans.

Bony fishes have numerous adaptations that increase swimming efficiency. The scales of most bony fishes are small, smooth, and lightweight, and their bodies are covered with a protective coat of mucus that retards bacterial growth and minimizes drag as water flows past the body.

Bony fishes first appeared in the Silurian and rapidly diversified into two lineages, Actinopterygii and Sarcopterygii. The ray-finned fishes (Actinopterygii, from *acti* = ray and *ptery* = fin) have fins supported by thin and flexible bony rays, whereas the fleshy-finned fishes (Sarcopterygii, from *sarco* = flesh) have fins supported by muscles and an internal bony skeleton. Ray-finned fishes are more diverse as measured by numbers of species and today vastly outnumber fleshy-finned fishes. The ~30 000 living species of bony fishes occupy nearly every aquatic habitat and represent more than 95% of living fish species. Adults range from 1 cm to more than 6 m in length. In the Yangtze River basin, *Pseuphurus glodius*, the Chinese paddlefish, can weigh up to 500 kg.

Class Actinopterygii. Sturgeons **(Figure 27.20a)** and paddlefishes, the most ancestral members of this group, are characterized by mostly cartilaginous skeletons. These large fishes live in rivers and lakes of the Northern Hemisphere. Sturgeons eat detritus and invertebrates, whereas paddlefish eat plankton. Gars **(Figure 27.20b)** and bowfins are remnants of a more recent radiation. They occur in the eastern half of North America, where they eat fish and other prey. Gars are protected from predators by a heavy coat of bony scales.

The subclass Teleosteii represents the latest radiation of Actinopterygii, one that produced a wide range of body forms **(Figure 27.21)**. Teleosts have an internal skeleton made almost entirely of bone. On either side of the head, the **operculum**, a flap of the body wall, covers a chamber that houses the gills. Sensory systems (see Chapter 34) generally include large eyes, a lateral line system, sound receptors, chemoreceptive nostrils, and taste buds.

Variations in jaw structure allow different teleosts to consume plankton, seaweed, invertebrates, or other vertebrates. Teleosts exhibit remarkable adaptations for feeding and locomotion. When some teleosts open their mouths, bones at the front of the jaws swing forward to create a circular opening. Folds of skin extend

a. Lake sturgeon　　　　　　　　　　**b.** Long-nosed gar

Figure 27.20

Ancestral actinopterygians (ray-finned bony fishes). Lake sturgeon (**a**, *Acipenser fulvescens*) and a long-nosed gar (**b**, *Lepidosteus sasteus*) are living representatives of early ray-finned fishes.

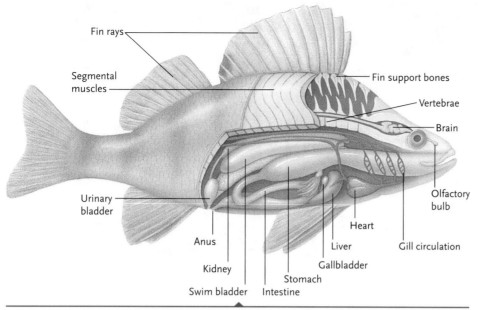

Fin rays

Segmental muscles

Fin support bones

Vertebrae

Brain

Olfactory bulb

Urinary bladder

Anus

Kidney

Swim bladder

Intestine

Stomach

Gallbladder

Liver

Heart

Gill circulation

a. Teleost internal anatomy

b. Sea horses, like the northern sea horse (*Hippocampus hudsonius*), use a prehensile tail to hold on to substrates; they are weak swimmers.

c. The long, flexible body of a spotted moray eel (*Gymnothorax moringa*) can wiggle through the nooks and crannies of a reef.

d. Flatfishes, like this European flounder (*Platichthys flesus*), lie on one side and leap at passing prey.

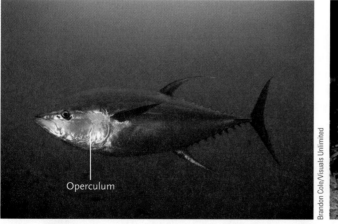

Operculum

e. Open ocean predators, like the yellowfin tuna (*Thunnus albacares*), have strong, torpedo-shaped bodies and powerful caudal fins.

f. Kissing Gouramis (*Helostoma temmincki*) extend their jaws into a tube that sucks food into the mouth.

Figure 27.21

Teleost diversity. Although all teleosts (bony fish) share similar internal features, their diverse shapes adapt them to different diets and types of swimming.

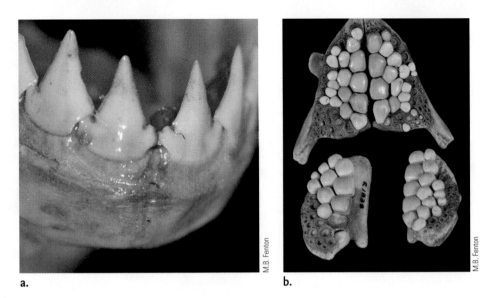

a.   b.

M.B. Fenton

Figure 27.22

Teleost teeth. Like Chrondricthyes, bony fish also have developed cutting **(a)** and crushing **(b)** teeth. The cutting teeth are those of a pirhana (*Sarrasalamus* species); the crushing teeth are from a black drum (*Pogones cromis*).

Figure 27.23

Sarcopterygians. The coelocanth (**a**, *Latimeria chalumnae*) is now one of two living species of lobe-finned fishes. The Australian lungfish (**b**, *Neoceratodus forsteri*) is one of six living lungfish species.

backward, forming a tube through which they suck food (see Figure 27.21f). Like Chondrichthyes, Actinopterygii exhibit great variation in tooth structure **(Figure 27.22)**. Species such as pirhanas (*Sarrasalamus*) are notorious for their bites. Other species have teeth specialized for crushing hard prey, such as bivalve molluscs. Whereas the pirhana's teeth are on the premaxilla, maxilla, and mandible (as they are in mammals and many other vertebrates), the crushing teeth of ray-finned fishes often occur on the bones of the pharynx.

In many modern ray-finned fishes, a gas-filled **swim bladder** serves as a hydrostatic organ that increases buoyancy (see Figure 27.21). The swim bladder is derived from an ancestral air-breathing lung that allowed early actinopterygians to gulp air, supplementing gill respiration in aquatic habitats, where dissolved oxygen concentration is low.

Many have symmetrical tail fins posterior to the vertebral column that provide power for locomotion. Their pectoral fins often lie high on the sides of the body, providing fine control over swimming. Some species use pectoral fins for acquiring food, for courtship, and for care of eggs and young. Some teleosts use pectoral fins for crawling on land (e.g., mudskippers, *Periophthalmus* species, climbing perch, *Anabas* species) or gliding in air (flying fish, family Exocoetidae).

Most marine species produce small eggs that hatch into larvae that live among the plankton. Eggs of freshwater teleosts are generally larger and hatch into tiny versions of the adults. Parents often care for their eggs and young, fanning oxygen-rich water over them, removing fungal growths, and protecting them from predators. Some freshwater species, such as guppies, give birth to live young (see Box 38.3).

Class Sacropterygii. The two groups of fleshy-finned fishes—lobe-finned fishes and lungfishes—are represented by only eight living species **(Figure 27.23)**. Although lobe-finned fishes were once thought to have been extinct for 65 million years, a living coelacanth (*Latimeria chalumnae*) was discovered in 1938 near the Comoros Islands, off the southeastern coast of Africa. A population of these metre-long fish live at depths of 70 to 600 m, feeding on fishes and squid. Remarkably, a second population of coelacanths was discovered in 1998, 10 000 km east of the Comoros, when a specimen

a. Coelacanth

Norbert Wu/Peter Arnold, Inc.

b. Australian lungfish

Werner Krutein/photovault.com

was found in an Indonesian fish market. Analyses of the DNA of the Indonesian specimen indicated that it is a distinct species (*Latimeria menadoensis*).

Lungfishes have changed relatively little over the last 200 million years. Six living species are distributed on southern continents. Australian lungfishes live in rivers and pools, using their lungs to supplement gill respiration when dissolved oxygen concentration is low. South American and African species live in swamps and use their lungs for breathing during the annual dry season, which they spend encased in a mucus-lined burrow in the dry mud. When the rains begin, water fills the burrow and the fishes awaken from dormancy. During their periods of dormancy, these fishes excrete urea.

STUDY BREAK

1. What did the evolution of jaws mean for fish?
2. What physiological characteristics make sharks dominant ocean predators?
3. What is the lateral line system? What does it do?

27.8 Early Tetrapods and Modern Amphibians

The fossil record suggests that tetrapods evolved in the late Devonian from a group of fleshy-finned fishes, the Osteolepiformes. Osteolepiforms and early tetrapods shared several derived characteristics. Both had infoldings of their tooth surfaces, a trait of unknown function. The shapes and positions of bones on the dorsal side of their crania and in their appendages were similar.

Some problems of moving onto land were identified earlier (see Chapter 3). During dry periods in swampy, late Devonian habitats, drying pools may have forced osteolepiform ancestors to move overland to adjacent pools that still had water. During these excursions, the fish may have found that land plants, worms, and arthropods provided abundant food, and oxygen was more readily available in air than in water (see Table 3.1). Furthermore, there may well have been fewer terrestrial predators at that time, but this interpretation is open to question.

Osteolepiforms **(Figure 27.24a)** usually had strong, stout fins that allowed them to crawl on mud. Crescent-shaped bones in their vertebral columns provided good support. Their nostrils lead to sensory pits housing olfactory (odour) receptors (see Chapter 34). They almost certainly had lungs, allowing them to breathe atmospheric oxygen. Like living lungfishes, they also could have excreted urea or uric acid rather than ammonium, which is toxic.

The earliest tetrapod with nearly complete skeletal data is the semiterrestrial, metre-long *Ichthyostega* **(Figure 27.24b)**. Compared with its fleshy-finned ancestors, *Ichthyostega* had a more robust vertebral column, sturdier limb girdles and appendages, a rib cage that protected its internal organs (including lungs), and a neck. Fishes lack necks because the pectoral girdle is fused to the cranium. In *Ichthyostega*, several vertebrae separated the pectoral girdle and the cranium, allowing the animal to move its head to scan the environment and capture food. *Ichthyostega* retained a fishlike lateral line system, caudal fin, and scaly body covering.

Life on land also required changes in sensory systems. In fishes, the body wall picks up sound vibrations and transfers them directly to sensory receptors. Sound waves are harder to detect in air. Early tetrapods evolved a **tympanum** (ear drum), a specialized membrane on either side of the head that is vibrated by airborne sounds. The tympanum connects to the **stapes**, a bone homologous to the hyomandibula, which had supported the jaws of fishes (see Figure 19.10). The stapes, in turn, transfers vibrations to the sensory cells of an inner ear.

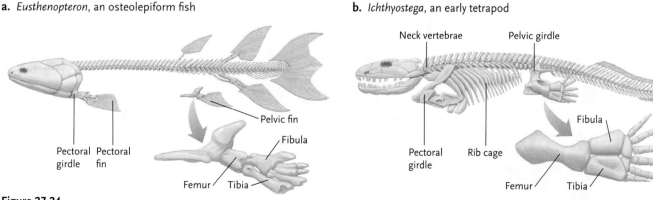

a. *Eusthenopteron*, an osteolepiform fish

b. *Ichthyostega*, an early tetrapod

Neck vertebrae · Pelvic girdle

Pectoral girdle · Rib cage

Fibula

Femur · Tibia

Pelvic fin

Fibula

Pectoral girdle · Pectoral fin

Femur · Tibia

Figure 27.24

Evolution of tetrapod limbs. The limb skeleton of osteolepiform fishes such as **(a)** *Eusthenopteron* is homologous to that of early tetrapods, such as **(b)** *Ichthyostega*. Although *Ichthyostega* retained many fishlike characteristics, its pectoral girdle was completely freed from the cranium, and it had a heavy rib cage. Fossils of its forefoot have not yet been discovered.

Figure 27.25
A fossil amphibian. This amphibian, *Eryops*, from the Texas Permian, was about 1.8 m long. It is classified as a rhachitomus labryrinthodont of the order Temnospondyli.

M.B. Fenton

27.8a Class Amphibia: Frogs and Toads, Salamanders, and Caecilians

Most of the 6000+ living species of amphibians (*amphi* = both; *bios* = life) are small, and their skeletons contain fewer bones than those of Paleozoic tetrapods such as *Ichthyostega*. All living amphibians are carnivorous as adults, but the aquatic larvae of some are herbivores. Fossil amphibians, such as *Eryops* **(Figure 27.25),** were quite large and predatory.

The thin, scaleless skin of most living amphibians is well supplied with blood vessels and can be a major site of gas exchange. Because some oxygen and carbon dioxide enter the body across a thin layer of water, most amphibians have moist skin, restricting them to aquatic or humid terrestrial habitats. Adults of some species also breathe using saclike lungs. The evolution of lungs was accompanied by modifications of the heart and circulatory system that increase the efficiency with which oxygen is delivered to body tissues (see Chapter 39). Some adult anurans have a waxy coating on their skin, making them as waterproof as lizards **(Figure 27.26).**

The life cycles of many amphibians include larval and adult stages. In frogs, larvae (tadpoles) hatch from fertilized eggs and eventually metamorphose into adults (see Chapter 39). The larvae of most frog species are aquatic, but adults may live their lives in water (be aquatic), move between land and water (be amphibious), and live entirely on land (be terrestrial). Some salamanders are pedomorphic (see Figure 20.19), which means that the larval stage attains sexual maturity without changing its form or moving to land. Some frogs and salamanders reproduce on land, omitting the larval stage altogether. In these speies, tiny adults emerge directly from fully developed eggs. However, the eggs of terrestrial breeders dry out quickly unless they are laid in moist places.

a.

Figure 27.26
Waterproof frogs. **(a)** *Chiromantis xerampelina* from southern Africa and **(b)** *Phyllomedusa sauvagii* from South America make their skin waterproof with a waxy secretion. These frogs are as waterproof as chameleons. They also excrete uric acid to further conserve water.

b.

M.B. Fenton and D. Kocinski

M.B. Fenton and D. Kocinski

a. A frog

b. A salamander

c. A caecelian

Stephen Dalton/Photo Researchers, Inc.

Bill M. Campbell, MD

Juan M. Renjifo/Animals Animals—Earth Scenes

Figure 27.27

Living amphibians. Anurans **(a),** such as the northern leopard frog (*Rana pipiens*), have compact bodies and long hind legs. Urodeles **(b),** such as the red-spotted newt (*Notophthalmus viridescens*), have an elongate body and four legs. Caecilians **(c),** such as *Caecelia nigricans* from Colombia, are legless burrowers.

Modern amphibians are represented by three lineages **(Figure 27.27),** but the evolutionary origin of frogs, salamanders, and caecilians has remained unresolved. The 2008 description of a small fossil from the Lower Permian of Texas suggests that frogs and salamanders share a relatively close common ancestor, whereas caecilians are distantly related to them.

Populations of practically all amphibians have declined rapidly in recent years. These declines are probably due to exposure to acid rain, high levels of ultraviolet B radiation, and fungal and parasitic infections. Another major factor in the decline of amphibians may be habitat splitting, the human-induced disconnection of habitats essential to the survival of amphibians. This aspect of **habitat fragmentation** (see Box 47.2) can cause adult amphibians to move across inhospitable habitat (roads, power line rights-of-way) to reach breeding habitats.

Anura. The 3700 species of frogs and toads (*an* = not; *ura* = tail) have short, compact bodies, and the adults lack tails. Their elongated hindlegs and webbed feet allow them to hop on land or to swim. A few species are adapted to dry habitats, encasing themselves in mucus cocoons to withstand periods of drought.

Urodela. The 400 species of salamanders (*uro* = tail; *del* = visible) have an elongate, tailed body and four legs. They walk by alternately contracting muscles on either side of the body, much the way fishes swim. Species in the most diverse group, the lungless salamanders, are fully terrestrial throughout their lives, using their skin and the lining of the throat for gas exchange.

Gymnophonia. The 200 species of caecilians (*gymno* = naked; *ophioneos* = snakelike) are legless, burrowing animals with wormlike bodies. They occupy tropical habitats throughout the world. Unlike other extant amphibians, caecilians have small bony scales embedded in their skin. Fertilization is internal, and females give birth to live young. In some species, the mother's skin produces a milklike substance for the young, which use specialized teeth to collect it from the mother's body (see Chapter 39).

STUDY BREAK

1. Present four lines of evidence suggesting that tetrapods arose from Osteolepiformes.
2. Why was the development of the tympanum important to life on land?
3. What characteristics allow amphibians to use their skin as a major site of gas exchange?

27.9 The Origin and Mesozoic Radiations of Amniotes

The amniote lineage arose during the Carboniferous, a time when seed plants and insects began to invade terrestrial habitats, providing additional food and cover for early terrestrial vertebrates. Amniotes take their name from the **amnion**, a fluid-filled sac that surrounds the embryo during development (see Chapter 39). Although the fossil record includes many skeletal remains of early amniotes, it provides little direct information about soft body parts and physiology. Three key features of living amniotes allow life on dry land and liberate them from reliance on standing water. The changes involve being waterproof and producing waterproof eggs.

- First, waterproof skin: keratin and lipids in the cells make skin relatively impermeable to water.
- Second, **amniote (amniotic) eggs** can survive and develop on dry land because they have four specialized membranes and a hard or leathery shell perforated by microscopic pores **(Figure 27.28)**. Amniote eggs are resistant to desiccation. The membranes protect the developing embryo and facilitate gas exchange and excretion. The shell mediates the exchange of air and water between the egg and its environment. Developing amniote embryos can excrete uric acid, which is stored in the allantois of the embryo, which will later become the bladder. Generous supplies of **yolk** in the egg are the developing embryo's main energy source, whereas **albumin** supplies nutrients and water. There is no larval stage, and hatchling amniotes are miniature versions of the adult. Amniote eggs are the ancestral condition, but they are circumvented in most mammals (and some reptiles; see Chapter 19).
- Third, some amniotes produce *urea* and/or *uric acid* as a waste product of nitrogen metabolism (see Chapter 44). Although ammonium is less expensive (metabolically) to produce, it is toxic and must be flushed away with water. Urea and uric acid are not toxic, so they can be stored or voided without risk while conserving water.

The abundance and diversity of fossils of amniotes indicate that they were extremely successful, quickly replacing many nonamniote species in terrestrial habitats. During the Carboniferous and Permian, amniotes produced three major radiations: synapsids, anapsids, and diapsids **(Figure 27.29)**, distinguishable by the numbers of bony arches in the temporal region of the skull (in addition to the openings for the eyes). The bony arches delimit fenestrae, openings in the skull that allow space for contraction (and expansion) of large and powerful jaw muscles.

Synapsids (Figure 27.30a, p. 640), a group of small predators, were the first offshoot from ancestral amniotes. Synapsids (*syn* = with; *apsid* = connection) had one temporal arch on each side of the head. They emerged late in the Permian, and mammals are their living descendants.

Anapsida (Figure 27.30b), the second lineage (*an* = not), had no temporal arches and no spaces on the sides of the skull. Turtles are living representatives of this group.

Diapsida (Figure 27.30c, d; *di* = two) comprise the third lineage and included most Mesozoic amniotes. Diapsids had two temporal arches, and their descendants include the dinosaurs, as well as extant lizards and snakes, crocodilians, and birds.

27.9a Extinct Diapsids

Early diapsids differentiated into two lineages, **Archosauromorpha** (*archo* = ruler + *sauro* = lizard + *morph* = form) and **Lepidosauromorpha** (*lepi* = scale), which differed in many skeletal characteristics. Archosaurs (archosauromorphs), or "ruling reptiles", include include crocodilians, pterosaurs, and dinosaurs. Crocodilians first appeared during the Triassic. They have bony armour and a laterally flattened tail, which is used to propel them through water. Pterosaurs, now extinct, were flying predators of the Jurassic and

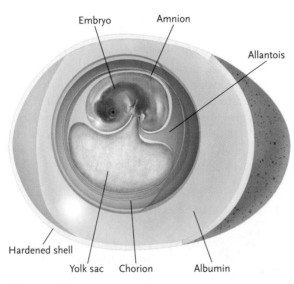

Embryo Amnion
Allantois
Hardened shell
Yolk sac Chorion Albumin

Figure 27.28
The amniote egg. A water-retaining egg with four specialized membranes surrounded by a hard or leathery shell allowed amniotes and their descendants to reproduce in dry environments.

Figure 27.29
Amniote ancestry. The early amniotes gave rise to three lineages (anapsids, synapsids, and diapsids) and numerous descendants. The lineages are distinguished by the number of bony arches in the temporal region of the skull (indicated on the small icons).

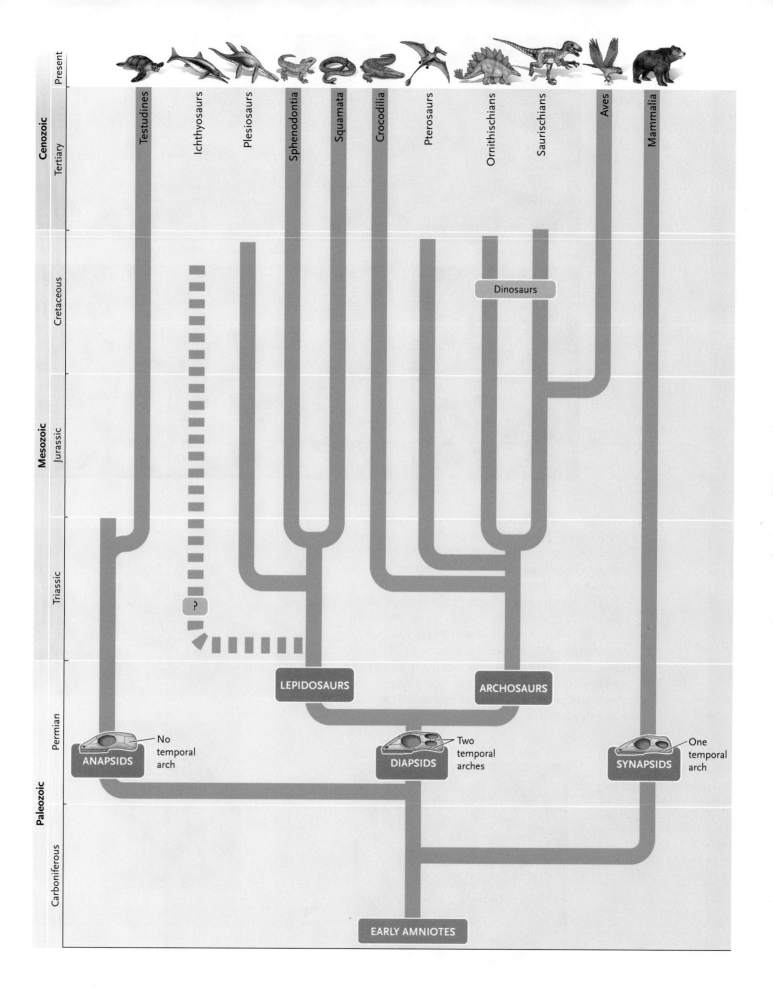

Figure 27.30
Skulls of reptiles. The anapsid condition **(a)** shown by a snapping turtle, the synapsid condition **(b)** shown by *Dimetrodon*, and the diapsid conditions shown by *Camarosaurus* **(c)** and Champosaurus **(d)**.

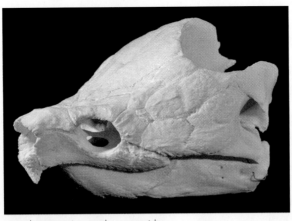
M.B. Fenton

a. is the snapping turtle - anapsid

M.B. Fenton

b. is *Dimetrodon* a synapsid

M.B. Fenton

c.

M.B. Fenton

d.

Cretaceous **(Figure 27.31)**. The smallest were sparrow-sized; the largest had wing spans of 11 m. Some evidence indicates that pterosaur wings attached to the side of their bodies at about the hips.

Two lineages of dinosaurs, "lizard-hipped" saurischians and "bird-hipped" ornithischians, proliferated in the Triassic and Jurassic **(Figure 27.32).** Saurischians included bipedal carnivores and quadrupedal herbivores. Some carnivorous saurischians **(Figure 27.33a)** were swift runners, and some had short forelimbs (e.g., *Tyrannosaurus rex*, which was 12 m long and stood 6 m high; **Figure 27.33b)**. One group of small carnivorous

M.B. Fenton

Figure 27.31
Rhamphorynchus meunsteri, a pterosaur with a wing span of about 1.7 m. Note the impressions of the wing membranes, the teeth, and the long tail. This species is known from the Upper Jurassic of Germany.

M.B. Fenton

M.B. Fenton

Figure 27.32
Ornithischian (top) and saurischian (bottom) dinosaurs differed in their pelvic structures. The ornithischian is a hadrasaur (duck-billed dinosaur), the saurischian an Albertosaurus. In each case, the acetabulum is the large elliptical area in the middle.

a.

b.

Figure 27.33

Saurischian dinosaurs. Whereas *Ornitholestes hermanii* stood less than 1 m at the shoulder, the fearsome *Tyrannosaurus rex* was about 12 m long. Both were carnivores.

saurischians, the deinonychsaurs, is ancestral to birds (see Figure 27.33a).

By the Cretaceous, some herbivorous saurischians **(Figures 27.34 and 27.35)** were gigantic, and many had long, flexible necks. *Apatosaurus* (previously known as *Brontosaurus*) was 25 m long and may have weighed 50 000 kg. The largely herbivorous ornithischian dinosaurs had large, chunky bodies. This lineage included armoured or plated dinosaurs (*Ankylosaurus* and *Stegosaurus*), duck-billed dinosaurs (*Hadrosaurus*), horned dinosaurs (*Styracosaurus*), and some with remarkably thick skulls (*Pachycephalosaurus*). Ornithischians were most abundant in the Jurassic and Cretaceous.

Lepidosaurs (Lepidosauromorpha) are the second major lineage of diapsids. This diverse group included

both marine and terrestrial animals. Fossil lepidosaurs include champsaurs (see Figure 27.30d), which were freshwater fish eaters, and the marine, fish-eating plesiosaurs, with long, paddlelike limbs they used like oars **(Figure 27.36. p. 642)**. Fossil lepidosaurs also included ichthyosaurs (see Figure 19.1), porpoise-like animals with laterally flattened tails. Like today's whales, ichthyosaurs were highly specialized for marine life and gave birth to live young. Squamates, the living lizards and snakes, is the third important group within this lineage. *Sphenodon*, the tuatara, is the last living genus of a once diverse group of lizard-like squamates.

a. *Lambosaurus*

b. *Stegosaurus*

a.

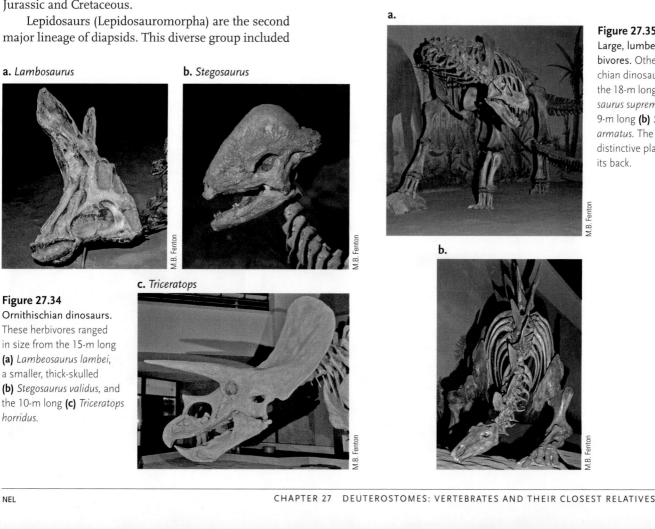

Figure 27.35

Large, lumbering herbivores. Other ornithischian dinosaurs included the 18-m long **(a)** *Camarasaurus supremus* and the 9-m long **(b)** *Stegosaurus armatus*. The latter had distinctive plates along its back.

b.

c. *Triceratops*

Figure 27.34

Ornithischian dinosaurs. These herbivores ranged in size from the 15-m long **(a)** *Lambeosaurus lambei*, a smaller, thick-skulled **(b)** *Stegosaurus validus*, and the 10-m long **(c)** *Triceratops horridus*.

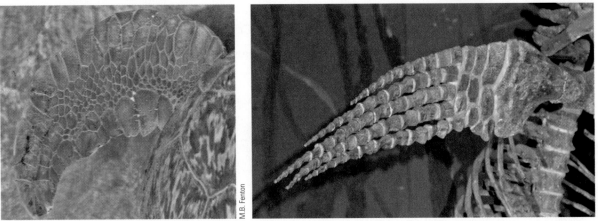

Figure 27.36

Paddles. Paddlelike forelimbs developed in sea turtles (left) and pleisiosaurs (right, *Trinacromerum bonneri*).

The teeth of reptiles provide important clues about their diets **(Figure 27.37)** and show interesting parallels with the teeth of other vertebrates.

27.10 Subclass Testudinata: Turtles and Tortoises

The turtle body plan, largely defined by a bony, boxlike shell, has changed little since the group first appeared during the Triassic **(Figure 27.38).** A turtle's ribs are fused to the inside of the shell, and in contrast to other tetrapods, the pectoral and pelvic girdles lie within the rib cage. The shell is formed from large keratinized scales covering the bony plates.

The 250 living species occupy terrestrial, freshwater, and marine habitats. They range from 8 cm to

Figure 27.37

Reptile teeth. As usual, teeth reflect the dietary habits of vertebrates. Herbivorous dinosaurs (**a**, *Diplodocus longus*, and **b**, hadrasaur) had teeth adapted for gathering plant material (**a**) and grinding it (**b**). They differ from those of a carnivorous dinosaur (**c**, *Daspletosaurus*) or a fish-eating reptile such as a camphosaur (**d**). A tooth of a *Tyrannosaurus rex* changed distinctly over its length. The biting part of the tooth (**e**) had enamel and serrated edges. There was no enamel on the part of the tooth located within the socket of the skull (**e, f**).

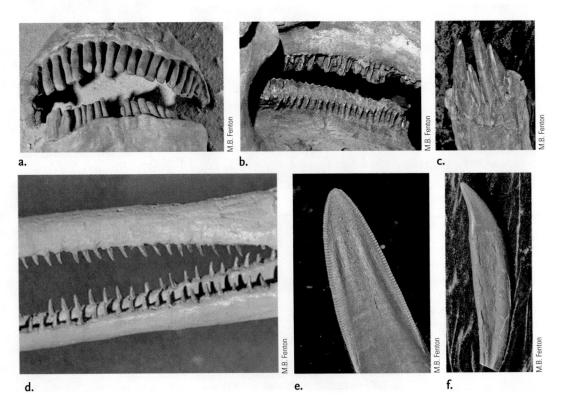

a. The turtle skeleton

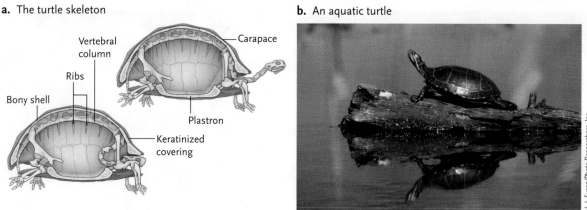

b. An aquatic turtle

Paul J. Fusco/Photo Researchers, Inc.

Figure 27.38

Testudines. Most turtles **(a)** can withdraw their heads and legs into a bony shell. Aquatic turtles **(b)**, such as the eastern painted turtle (*Chrysmys picta*), often bask in the sun to warm up. The sunlight may help eliminate parasites that cling to the turtle's skin.

2 m in length. Turtles use a keratinized beak in feeding, whether they eat animal or plant material. When threatened, most species retract into their shells. Many species are now endangered because adults are hunted for meat and their eggs are eaten by humans and other predators. Young are often collected for the pet trade, and the beaches favoured as nesting sites by marine species are too often used as tourist attractions (see Chapter 48).

STUDY BREAK

Describe the body plan of a turtle.

27.11 Living Diapsids: Sphenodontids, Squamates, and Crocodilians

27.11a Infraclass Lepidosaura, Order Rhynchocephalia: The Tuatara

Sphenodon punctatus is one of two living species of sphenodontids (*sphen* = wedge; *dont* = tooth) or tuataras, a lineage that was diverse in the Mesozoic **(Figure 27.39a, p. 644).** These lizardlike animals are best known for having a "third" or pineal eye. They survive on a few islands off the coast of New Zealand. Adults are about 60 cm long. They live in dense colonies, where males and females defend small territories. They often share underground burrows with seabirds and eat invertebrates and small vertebrates. They are primarily nocturnal and maintain low body temperatures during periods of activity. Their survival is threatened by two introduced predators, cats and rats.

27.11b Infraclass Lepidosaura, Order Squamata: Lizards and Snakes

Lizards and snakes are covered by overlapping, keratinized scales (*squam* = scale) that protect against dehydration. Squamates periodically shed their skin

while growing, much the way arthropods shed their exoskeletons (see Chapter 26). Most squamates regulate their body temperature behaviourally (see Chapter 43), so they are active only when weather conditions are favourable. They shuttle between sunny and shady places to warm up or cool down as needed.

Most of the 3700 lizard species are less than 15 cm long, but Komodo dragons (*Varanus komodoensis*) grow to nearly 3 m in length (see Figure 34.16c). Lizards occupy a wide range of habitats and are especially common in deserts and the tropics. One species (*Lacerta vivipara*) occurs within the Arctic Circle. Most lizards eat insects, although some consume leaves or meat.

The 2300 species of snakes evolved from a lineage of lizards that lost their legs over evolutionary time. Streamlined bodies make snakes efficient burrowers or climbers **(Figure 27.39c)**. Many subterranean species are 10 or 15 cm long, whereas the giant constrictors may grow to 10 m. Unlike lizards, all snakes are predators that swallow prey whole. Compared with their lizard ancestors, snake skull bones are reduced in size and connected to each other by elastic ligaments. This gives snakes remarkable capacity to stretch their mouths. Some snakes can swallow food items that are larger than their heads (see Chapter 41). Snakes also have well-developed sensory systems for detecting prey. The flicking tongue carries airborne molecules to sensory receptors in the roof of the mouth (see Box 34.4). Most snakes can detect vibrations on the ground, and some, like rattlesnakes, have heat-sensing organs (see Figure 34.32). Many snakes kill by constriction, which suffocates prey, whereas several species produce venoms, toxins that immobilize, kill, and partially digest prey (see Box 46.1).

27.11c Infraclass Archosauria, Order Crocodylia: Crocodiles, Alligators, and Gavials

The 21 species of alligators and crocodiles (*crocodil* = crocodile), along with the birds, are the living remnants of the archosaurs **(Figure 27.39d)**. Australian saltwater

CHAPTER 27 DEUTEROSTOMES: VERTEBRATES AND THEIR CLOSEST RELATIVES

a. Sphenodontia includes the tuatara (*Sphenodon punctatus*) and one other species.

b. Basilisk lizards (*Basiliscus basiliscus*) escape from predators by running across the surface of streams.

c. A western diamondback rattlesnake (*Crotalus atrox*) of the American southwest bares its fangs with which it injects a powerful toxin into prey.

d. Crocodilia includes semiaquatic predators, like this resting African Nile crocodile (*Crocodylus niloticus*), that frequently bask in the sun.

Figure 27.39
Living nonfeathered diapsids.

crocodiles (*Crocodylus porosus*) are the largest, growing to 7 m in length. Crocodilians are aquatic predators that eat other vertebrates. Striking anatomical adaptations distinguish them from living lepidosaurs, including a four-chambered heart that is homologous to the heart in birds. In some crocodilians, muscles that originate on the pubis insert on the liver. When these muscles contract, the liver moves toward the tail, creating negative pressure in the chest cavity, a situation analogous to the role of the diaphragm in mammals.

American alligators (*Alligator mississippiensis*) exhibit strong maternal behaviour, perhaps reflecting their relationship to birds. Females guard their nests ferociously and, after the young hatch, free their offspring from the nest. The young stay close to the mother for about a year, feeding on scraps that fall from her mouth and living under her watchful protection.

Many species of alligators and crocodiles are endangered because their habitats have been dis-

rupted by human activities. They have been hunted for meat and leather and because larger individuals are predators of humans. There is hope, however, as some populations of *A. mississippiensis* have recovered in the wake of efforts to protect them. In Africa and Australia, crocodiles are farmed for their meat and skin.

In the past, crocodilians were more diverse in body form than they are today. *Dakosaurus andiniensis*, a Jurassic–Cretaceous marine crocodilian from western South America, differed dramatically from "typical" crocodilians **(Figure 27.40)**.

STUDY BREAK

1. How do snakes kill their prey?
2. What features of crocodilians are homologous to those of birds? Which ones are analogous to those of mammals?

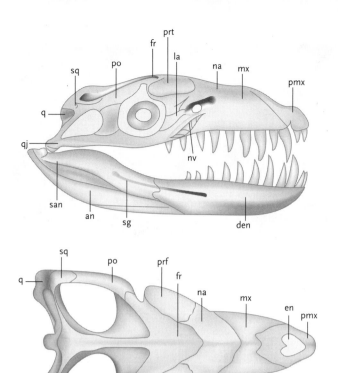

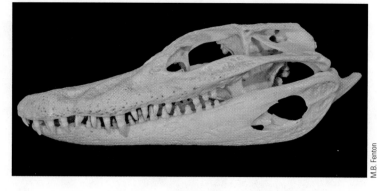

Figure 27.40

Crocodilians. *Dakosaurus andinensis*, a crocodile from the Jurassic–Cretaceous boundary in Patagonia (left), has a more robust skull and jaw than a more typical member of the group (above, *Alligator mississipiensis*). The skull of *Dakosaurus* is more rounded than the wedge-shaped skull of *Alligator*. Bones are abbreviated: an – angular; den – dentary; en – external nares; eoc – exoccipital; fr – frontal; ic – internal carotid formane; la – lacrimal; na – nasal; nv – neurovascular formina; pmx – premaxilla; po – postorbital; prf – prefrontal; pt – pterygoid; q – quadrate; qj – quadratojugal; san – surangular; sg – surangular groove; soc – supraoccipital; sq – squamosal.

27.12 Aves: Birds

Birds (Aves; *avis* = bird) appeared in the Jurassic as descendants of carnivorous, bipedal dinosaurs (see Figure 19.14). Birds belong to the archosaur lineage, and their evolutionary relationship to dinosaurs is evident in their skeletal anatomy and in the scales on their legs and feet. Powered flight gave birds access to new adaptive zones, likely contributing to their astounding evolutionary success **(Figure 27.41, p. 646)**. Some species of birds are flightless, and some of these are bipedal runners. Other birds are weak fliers.

Three skeletal features associated with flight in birds are the **keeled sternum** (breastbone), the furculum (wishbone), and the uncinate processes on the ribs **(Figure 27.42, p. 647)**. The keel on the sternum anchors the flight muscles (see Figure 27.41c), the furculum acts like a spring, and the uncinate processes, which effect overlap of adjoining ribs, give the rib cage strength. In flightless species, the sternum often lacks a keel (see Figure 27.42), an exception being penguins that "fly" through the water. However, flightless species often have uncinate processes.

Birds' skeletons are light and strong (see Figure 27.41b). The skeleton of a 1.5-kg frigate bird (*Fregata magnificens*) weighs just 100 g, far less than the weight of its feathers. Although the skeleton of a 20-g mammal weighs the same as that of a 20-g bird, the bird's bones are larger and lighter. Most birds have hollow limb bones with small supporting struts that criss-cross the internal cavities. Birds have reduced numbers of separate bony elements in the wings, skull, and vertebral column (especially the tail), so the skeleton is rigid. The bones associated with flight are generally large, and the wingbones are long (see Figure 27.41).

All extant birds **(Figure 27.43, p. 647)** use a keratinized bill for feeding rather than teeth, which are dense and heavy. Many species have a long, flexible neck that allows them to use their bills for feeding, grooming, nest building, and social interactions. Birds' soft internal organs are modified to reduce mass. Most birds lack a urinary bladder, so uric acid paste is eliminated with digestive wastes. Females have only one ovary and never carry more than one mature egg at a time. Eggs are laid as soon as they are shelled. Egg sizes give an indication of the range of size in birds **(Figure 27.44, p. 648)**. Birds range in size from a bee hummingbird (*Mellisuga helenae*) at 2 g to ostriches (*Struthio camelus*) at about 150 kg. The size spectrum is illustrated by a comparison of breast bones **(Figure 27.45, p. 648)**.

All birds have feathers (see Figure 27.42d), sturdy, lightweight structures derived from scales in the skin of their reptilian ancestors. Each feather has numerous barbs and barbules with tiny hooks and grooves that maintain the feathers' structures, even during vigorous activity. Flight feathers on the wings provide lift, whereas contour feathers streamline the surface of the body. Down feathers form an insulating cover close to the skin. Moulting replaces feathers once or twice each year. But not all animals with feathers are birds. Several extinct archosaurs had

a. Wing movements of an owl during flight

Gerard Lacz/ANT Photolibrary

b. Skeletal system of birds

Skull
Radius
Ulna
Pectoral girdle
Humerus
Scapula
Furculum (wishbone)
Pelvic girdle
Coracoid
Keeled sternum

c. Pectoral girdle and flight muscles of bird in frontal view

Humerus
Tendon
Humerus
Scapula
Furculum (wishbone)
Sternum
Pectoralis major (lowers wings)
Supracoracoideus (raises wings)
Keel of sternum

Internal structure of bird limb bones

d. Feather structure

Barbule
Barb
Shaft

Figure 27.41

Adaptations for flight in birds. The flapping movements **(a)** of a bird's wing provide thrust for forward momentum and lift to counteract gravity. The bird skeleton **(b)** includes a boxlike trunk, short tail, long neck, lightweight skull and beak, and well-developed limbs. In large birds, limb bones are hollow. Two sets of flight muscles **(c)** originate on the keeled sternum; one set raises the wings, whereas the other lowers them. Flexible feathers **(d)** form an airfoil on the wing surface.

feathers but these animals had none of the adaptations for flight.

Other adaptations for flight allow birds to harness the energy needed to power their flight muscles. Their metabolic rates are 8 to 10 times higher than those of comparably sized reptiles, allowing them to process energy-rich food rapidly. A complex and efficient respiratory system (see Chapter 42) and a four-chambered heart (see Chapter 37) enable them to consume and distribute oxygen efficiently. As a consequence of high rates of metabolic heat production, most birds maintain a high and constant body temperature (see Chapter 43).

Flying birds were abundant by the Cretaceous. Even in the Jurassic, *Archaeopteryx* had a furculum and was capable of at least limited flight. Until 2008, two main theories purported to explain the evolution of flight in birds. Proponents of the "top-down" theory argued that ancestral birds lived in trees and glided down from them in pursuit of insect prey. Gliding and access to prey are key elements of this theory. Proponents of the "bottom-up" theory proposed that a protobird was a runner (cursorial) and ran in pursuit of prey and jumped up to catch it.

In 2008, Kenneth P. Dial and two colleagues proposed the "ontogenic–transitional wing" (OTW)

Figure 27.42

Bird skeletons and flight. Compared are the thoracic skeletons of Hudsonian curlew (**a**, *Numenius phaeopus*), kiwi (**b** and **d**, *Apteryx australis*), and a penguin (**c**). Note keels on the sterna of the curlew and the penguin but not on the kiwi. Neither the penguin nor the kiwi can fly, but the penguin "flies" in water. The wings of the kiwi are drastically reduced (**d**), and there is no furculum (wishbone), which is obvious in the penguin and the curlew. All three species have distinct uncinate processes on the ribs (**a, c, d**).

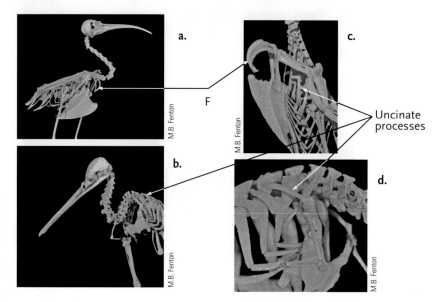

hypothesis to explain the evolution of flight in birds. They asserted that the transitional stages leading to the development of flight in modern birds corresponded to its evolutionary development. Key to the OTW theory is the observation that in developing from flightless hatchlings to flight-capable juveniles, individual birds move their protowings in the same ways as adults move fully developed wings. Dial and his colleagues noted that flap-running allows as yet flightless birds to move over obstacles. The OTW theory provides another look at the evolution of flight, and its predictions can be tested with fledglings of extant species. The combination of wings and **bipedalism** is central to the OTW hypothesis. Birds are bipedal, and pterosaurs may have been. Bats, however, are not bipedal, so the OTW hypothesis will not explain evolution of flight in that group.

The first known radiation of birds produced the enantiornithines ("opposite" birds), the dominant birds of the Jurassic and Cretaceous. Ornithurines

Figure 27.43
Bird diversity.

a. The Laysan albatross (Procellariiformes, *Phoebastria immutabilis*) has the long thin wings typical of birds that fly great distances.

b. The roseate spoonbill (Ciconiformes, *Ajaia ajaja*) uses its bill to strain food particles from water.

c. The bald eagle (Falconiformes, *Haliaeetus leucocephalus*) uses its sharp bill and talons to capture and tear apart prey.

d. A European nightjar (Caprimulgiformes, *Caprimulgus europaeus*) uses its wide mouth to capture flying insects.

e. A Bahama woodstar hummingbird (Apodiformes, *Calliphlox evelynae*) hovers before a hibiscus blossom to drink nectar from the base of the flower.

f. The chestnut-backed chickadee (Passeriformes, *Parus rufescens*) uses its thin bill to probe for insects in dense vegetation.

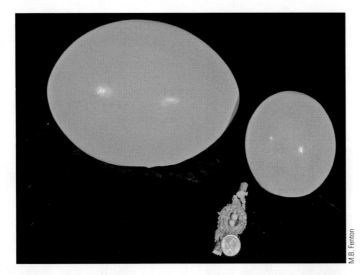

Figure 27.44

Bird eggs. Bird eggs range in size from those of elephant birds (left, *Aepyornis* of Madagascar) to ostriches (*Struthio camelus*, right) and a hummingbird (bottom). The scale, a Canadian $2 coin, is 2.8 cm in diameter.

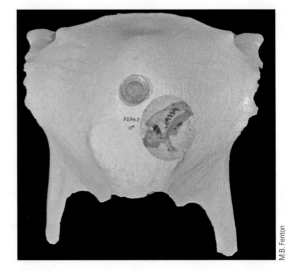

Figure 27.45

Breast bones of birds. Compared are the unkeeled breastbone of an ostrich (*Struthio camelus*) and a keeled breastbone of a hummingbird (*Trochilus polytmus*). A Canadian $2 coin (2.8 cm in diameter) is shown for scale.

are modern birds **(Figure 27.46)**. Like dinosaurs, many mammals, and other organisms, the enantiornithines did not survive the extinctions that marked the end of the Cretaceous (see Chapter 48). Many enantiornithines flew, reflected by keeled sterna, furcula, and other "modern" skeletal features. Others, such as Hesperornis, were swimmers that used their feet for propulsion and, unlike penguins, had keel-less sterna **(Figure 27.47)**. Ornithurines include modern groups of wading birds and seabirds, first known from late Cretaceous rocks. Woodpeckers, perching birds, birds of prey, pigeons, swifts, the flightless ratites, penguins,

Figure 27.46

Evolution of birds. Enantiornithines, or opposite birds, were dominant in the Mesozoic but coexisted with ornithurine (more modern) birds in the early Cretaceous. The enantiornithines did not survive the extinctions at the end of the Cretaceoous. By the Miocene, passerine birds became the dominant landbirds.

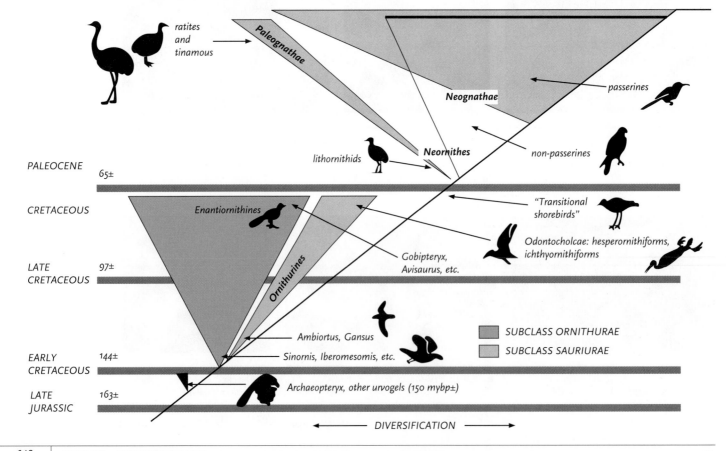

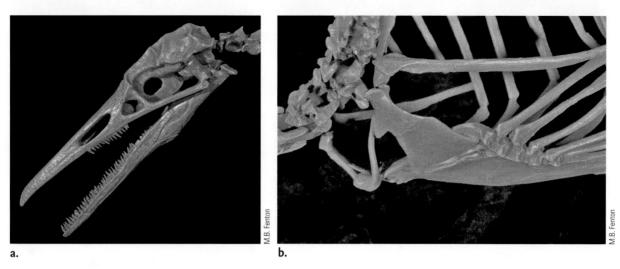

Figure 27.47

Skull **(a)** and sternum **(b)** of *Hesperornis*, a Cretaceous enantiornithine bird. Note the teeth, along with an unkeeled sternum and a furculum. This diving bird swam with its feet rather than its wings. The skull is 25 cm long.

and some other groups were all present by the end of the Oligocene. Birds continued to diversify through the Miocene.

The ~9000 living bird species show extraordinary ecological specializations built on the same body plan. Living birds are traditionally classified into nearly 30 orders. A bird's bill usually reflects its diet. Seed and nut eaters, such as finches and parrots, have deep, stout bills that crack hard shells. Carnivorous hawks and carrion-eating vultures have sharp beaks to rip flesh. Nectar-feeding hummingbirds and sunbirds have long slender bills to reach into flowers, although many perching birds also have slender bills to feed on insects. The bills of ducks are modified to extract particulate matter from water.

Birds also differ in the structure of their feet and wings. Predators have large, strong talons (claws), whereas ducks and other swimming birds have webbed feet that serve as paddles. Long-distance fliers such as albatrosses have narrow wings, whereas species that hover at flowers have short, broad wings. The wings of penguins and similar species are so specialized for swimming that they are incapable of aerial flight.

All birds have well-developed sensory and nervous systems, and their brains are proportionately larger than those of comparably sized diapsids. Large eyes provide sharp vision, and most species also have good hearing, which nocturnal hunters such as owls use to locate prey. Vultures and some other species have a good sense of smell, which they use to find food. Migrating birds use polarized light, changes in air pressure, and Earth's magnetic field for orientation (see Chapter 34).

Many birds exhibit complex social behaviour, including courtship, territoriality, and parental care. Many species use vocalizations and visual displays to challenge other individuals or attract mates. Most raise their young in nests, using body heat to incubate eggs. The nest may be a simple depression on a gravel beach, a cup woven from twigs and grasses, or a feather-lined hole in a tree.

Many bird species make semiannual long-distance migrations (see Chapters 3 and 40). Golden plovers (*Pluvialis dominica*) and the godwit (see *The Chemical and Physical Foundations of Biology* pages) migrate 20 000 km twice each year. Migrations are a response to seasonal changes in climate. Birds travel toward the tropics as winter approaches. In spring, they return to high latitudes to breed and to use seasonally abundant food sources.

STUDY BREAK

1. What three skeletal features are associated with bird flight? Which ones are missing in flightless birds?
2. What adaptations make flight possible in birds and pterosaurs?
3. What characteristics maintain the structure of feathers and make them important to flight in birds?

27.13 Mammalia: Monotremes, Marsupials, and Placentals

Mammals are part of the synapsid lineage, the first of the aminiotes to diversify. During the late Paleozoic, medium- to large-sized synapsids were the most abundant veretebrate predators in terrestrial habitats. Therapsids were one successful and persistent branch of synapids, and they were relatively

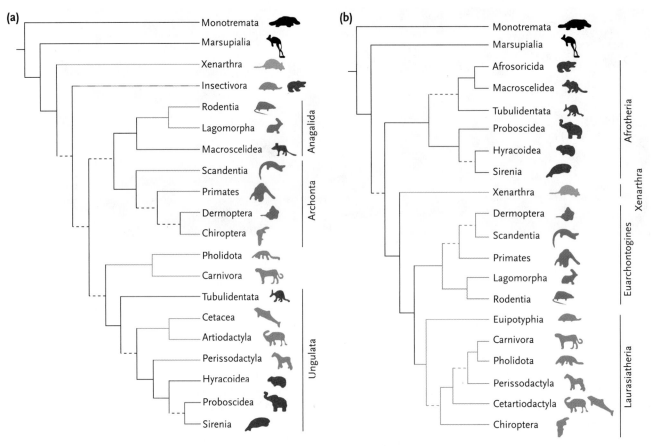

Figure 27.48

Modern mammals. In 2004, the prevailing phylogenies of mammals derived from **(a)** morphological and **(b)** molecular data.

mammal-like in their legs, skulls, jaws, and teeth. By the end of the Triassic, the earliest mammals (most of them no bigger than a rat) had appeared. Several lineages of early mammals, such as multituberculates (see Chapter 48) and the lineage that includes the Mesozoic beaver (see Figures 19.7 and 19.8), persisted and even flourished through much of the Mesozoic. These mammals coexisted with dinosaurs and other diapsids, as well as with the enantiornithine birds.

Paleontologists hypothesize that most Mesozoic mammals were nocturnal, perhaps to avoid diurnal predators and/or overheating. There are two living mammalian lineages **(Figure 27.48)**, the egg-laying Prototheria (or Monotremata) and the live-bearing Theria (marsupials and placentals).

Several features distinguish mammals from other vertebrates, but mammalian diversity makes it difficult to generalize absolutely about definitive characteristics. Living mammals are relatively easy to recognize. They are usually furry and have a diaphragm (a sheet of muscle separating the chest cavity from the viscera); most are **homeothermic** (warm-blooded) and bear live young. In mammals, most blood leaves the heart through the left aortic arch (the main blood vessel leaving the heart). Mammals have two occipital condyles where the skull attaches to the neck, as well

as a secondary palate (the plate of bones forming the roof of the mouth). They are *heterodont* and *diphyodont* **(Figure 27.49).** Heterodont means that different teeth are specialized for different jobs; diphyodont means that there are two generations of teeth (milk or deciduous teeth and adult teeth). But some mammals have no teeth, and others lay eggs. The secondary palate allows mammals to breathe while sucking, without releasing hold on the nipple—an essential part of nursing.

Homeothermy means that mammals typically maintain an elevated and stable body temperature so that they can be active under different environmental conditions. They can do this because of their metabolic rates and insulation. Heterodont teeth make mammals more efficient at mechanically dealing with their food (chewing), reducing the lag between the time food is consumed and when the energy in it is available to the consumer. Heterodont teeth are correlated with improved jaw articulation, in mammals between the dentary (lower jaw) and squamosal (bone on the skull). The diaphragm means that mammals are reasonably efficient at breathing, and the circulatory system with a four-chambered heart makes them efficient at internal circulation of resources or collection of wastes. Milk is a rich food source, and by feeding it to their young, female mammals

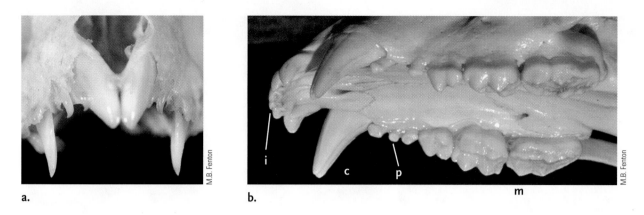

Figure 27.49

Mammal teeth. In most mammals, the teeth are diphyodont, meaning that milk (decidious) teeth are replaced by permanent teeth. The skull of a vampire bat (*Desmodus rotundus*) clearly shows four deciduous teeth, as well as permanent teeth **(a)**. The teeth of mammals are also heterodont **(b)**, meaning that different teeth are specialized to do different jobs. In this bear (*Ursus americana*), incisors (i), a canine (c), premolars (p), and molars (m) are obvious.

provide the best opportunity for growth and development. The **cortex** of the brain is central to information processing and learning. Mammals' brains are another key to their evolutionary success.

27.13a The Mammalian Radiation: Variation on Mammals

The egg-laying Prototheria (*proto* = first; *theri* = wild beast), also called Monotremata, and the live-bearing Theria are the two groups of living mammals. Among the Theria, the Metatheria (*meta* = between), also called marsupials, and the Eutheria (*eu* = good), or placentals, differ in their reproductive adaptations.

Monotremata. The monotremes (*mono* = one; *trema* = perforation) are represented by three living species that occur only in the Australian region. Females lay leathery-shelled eggs **(Figure 27.50)**, and newly hatched young lap up milk secreted by modified sweat glands (mammary glands) on the mother's belly. The duck-billed platypus (*Ornithorhynchus anatinus*) lives in burrows along riverbanks and feeds on aquatic invertebrates. The two species of echidnas or spiny anteaters (*Tachyglossus aculeatus* and *Zaglossus bruijnii*) feed on ants or termites.

Marsupialia. Represented by 240 species, marsupials (*marsupion* = purse) (Metatheria) are characterized by short gestation periods. The young are briefly (as few as 8 to 10 days in some species and up to 30 days in others) nourished in the uterus via a placenta and are then born at an early stage of development. Newborns use their forelimbs to drag themselves from the vagina and across the mother's belly fur to her abdominal pouch, the marsupium, where they complete their development attached to a teat. Marsupials are prevalent among the native mammals of Australia and also

a. Short-nosed echidna

b. Duck-billed platypus

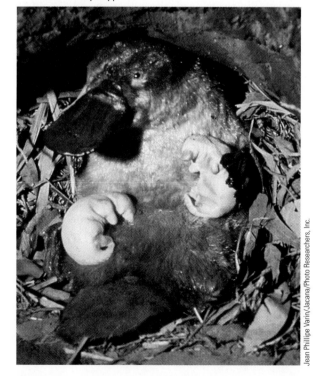

Figure 27.50

Monotremes. The short-nosed echidna (**a**, *Tachyglossus aculeatus*) is terrestrial. The duck-billed platypus (**b**, *Ornithorhynchus anatinus*) raises its young in a streamside burrow.

Figure 27.51

Marsupials. A kangaroo (*Macropus giganteus*) carries her "joey" in her pouch; a male koala (*Phascolarctos cinereus*) naps; and an opossum from Guyana (*Didelphis* species) emerges from its den after dark to feed.

are diverse in South America **(Figure 27.51)**. One species, the opossum (*Didelphis virginiana*), occurs as far north as Canada. South America once had a diverse marsupial fauna, which declined after the Isthmus of Panama bridged the seaway between North and South America (see Chapter 18), allowing placental mammals to move southward.

Placental mammals (Eutheria) are represented by 4000 living species. They complete embryonic development in the mother's uterus, nourished through a **placenta** until they reach an advanced stage of development (**viviparous**). Some species, such as humans, are helpless at birth (**altricial**), but others, such as horses, are born with fur and are quickly mobile (**precocial**). Biologists divide the eutherians into about 18 orders, of which only 8 have more than 50 living species **(Figure 27.52)**. Rodents (Rodentia) make up about 45% of eutherian species, and bats (Chiroptera) comprise another 22%. We belong to the primates, along with 169 other species, representing about 5% of the current mammalian diversity.

Some eutherians are obviously specialized for locomotion. Although whales and dolphins (order Cetacea) and manatees and dugongs (order Sirenia) are descended from terrestrial ancestors, they are aquatic (mainly marine) and can no longer function on land. By contrast, seals and walruses (order Carnivora) feed under water but rest and breed on land. Bats (order Chiroptera) use wings for powered flight.

Although early mammals appear to have been insectivorous, the diets of modern eutherians are diverse. Odd-toed ungulates (*ungula* = hoof) such as horses and rhinoceroses (order Perissodactyla), even-toed ungulates such as cows and camels (order Artiodactyla), and rabbits and hares (order Lago-

morpha) all eat vegetation. Some of the vegetarians use fermentation to digest cellulose (see Chapter 41). Carnivores (order Carnivora) usually consume other animals, but some, such as the giant panda (*Ailuropoda melanoluca*), are vegetarians. Most bats eat insects, but some feed on flowers, fruit, or nectar, and some, the vampires, consume blood. Many whales and dolphins prey on fishes and other animals, but some eat plankton. Some groups, including rodents and primates, feed opportunistically on both plant and animal matter. Ants and termites are the preferred food of a variety of mammals, both prototherian and therian.

STUDY BREAK

1. How do monotremes differ from marsupials and placentals?
2. How do marsupials and placentals differ?
3. Are all mammals viviparous?

27.14 Evolutionary Convergence and Mammalian Diversity: Tails to Teeth

In the discussion on the Mesozoic beaver (see Figures 19.6 and 19.7), we learned that a dorsoventrally flattened tail occurred in a Mesozoic mammal and today occurs in a monotreme (duck-billed platypus) and in beavers (*Castor* species). Evolutionary convergences in design features such as these are common in mammals. Other good examples are the development of protective spines (quills) from hairs. These occur in spiny anteaters (monotremes), porcupines (rodents), and hedgehogs and tenrecs (insectivores).

a. The capybara (Rodentia, *Hydrochoerus hydrochaeris*), the largest rodent, feeds on vegetation in South American wetlands.

b. Most bats, like the Yuma Myotis (Chiroptera, *Myotis yumanensis*), are nocturnal predators on insects.

c. Walruses (Carnivora, *Obodenus rosmarus*) feed primarily on marine invertebrates in frigid arctic waters.

d. The black rhinoceros (Perissodactyla, *Diceros bicornis*) feeds on grass in sub-Saharan Africa.

e. Arabian camels (Artiodactyla, *Camelus dromedarius*) use enlarged foot pads to cross hot desert sands.

Figure 27.52
Eutherian diversity.

Another striking example of convergence among mammals is provided by the teeth and lumbar vertebrae of the Mesozoic *Fruitafossor windscheffeli* **(Figure 27.53)** and some living edentates (armadillos and sloths). Like sloths and armadillos, *Fruitafossor* had round **molars** with open roots **(Figure 27.54, p. 654).** Also like sloths and armadillos, *Fruitafossor* had processes in its lumbar vertebrae known only from living edentates. An analysis of the morphological features of *Fruitafossor* was used with other data to establish its phylogenetic relationships with other mammals **(Figure 27.55, p. 654).** Although the teeth and vertebral structures converge between *Fruitafossor* and the edentates, *Fruitafossor* is not closely related to any living mammals. We do not even know if *Fruitafossor* had other features of mammals such as mammary glands, a diaphragm, and vivipary. But *Fruitafossor*'s bones, particularly its jaw joints and occipital condyles, make it a mammal.

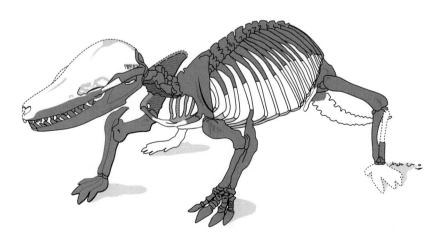

Figure 27.53
Fruitafossor, a mammal of the mid-Jurassic. Stippled bones are known as fossils, other bones presumed.

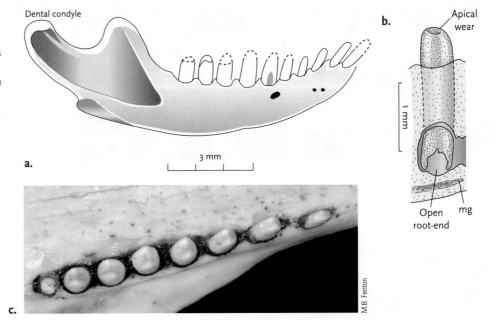

Figure 27.54

Convergences in Mammals. Round teeth with open roots are well known from edentate mammals like armadillos **(c)**, and tubulidentates, the aardvark (see Figure 27.59a). They also appear in *Fruitafossor* **(a, b)**.

Dental condyle

3 mm

a.

b.

Apical wear

1 mm

Open root-end

mg

M.B. Fenton

c.

27.14a Mammalian Teeth: Diversity of Form and Function

As in other vertebrates, mammals' teeth provide a good indication of diet. Some molars (cheek teeth) with "W"-shaped cusps cut and crush food **(Figure 27.56a, b, c)**, whereas others mainly crush **(Figure 27.56d, e)**. Grinding teeth have appeared in a wide range of forms in mammals **(Figure 27.57)** and show considerable variation in the details of their design.

Animals such as the walrus **(Figure 27.58a)** have tusks for digging and small flat molars for crushing the shells of bivalves (compare with Figures 27.19a and 27.21b). The molars of *Desmostylus* have an artistic circular pattern (see Figure 3.22c). These Miocene mammals were thought to have resembled Sirenia, the dugongs and manatees. Later discoveries

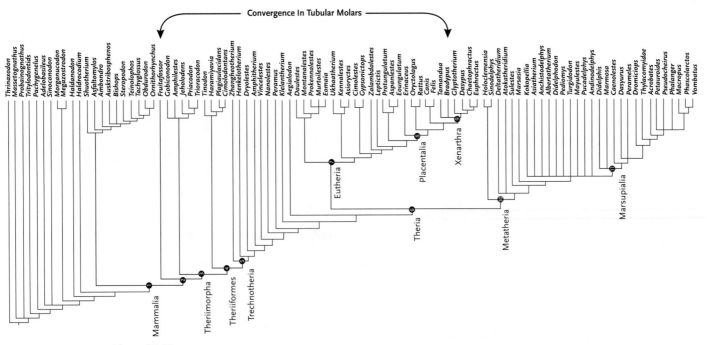

Figure 27.55

Fruitafossor as a mammal. In a phylogeny of mammals based on morphological characters, this species is not a monotreme and does not appear to be closely related to any living mammals.

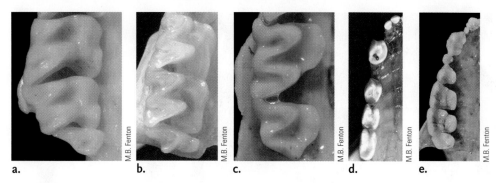

Figure 27.56

Teeth for cutting and crushing. The molar teeth of insectivores (shrews, moles, many bats) are "W" shaped, so they cut and crush at the same time. Bats that eat fruit have molars more specialized for crushing. Here *Suncus* **(a)** is a shrew, *Condylura* **(b)** a mole, and *Taphozous* **(c)** an insectivorous bat. *Pteropus* **(d)** and *Brachyphylla* **(e)** are fruit-eating bats.

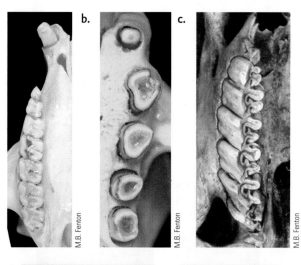

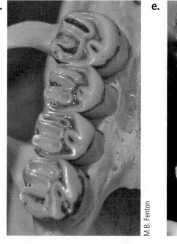

Figure 27.57

Molar teeth for crushing plant material. This selection of herbivores includes a hyrax (**a**, *Heterohyrax brucei* from Africa), a three-toed sloth (**b**, *Bradypus tridactylus* from South America), a black rhino (**c**, *Diceros bicornis* from Africa), a porcupine (**d**, *Erethizon dorsatum* from North America), and a paca (**e**, *Cuniculus paca* from South America). The hyrax belongs to the order Hyracoidea, the sloth to the order Edentata, the rhino to the order Persissodactyla, and the porcupine and the paca tothe order Rodentia.

revealed that they had massive limbs and, in body form, looked more like modern hippos. They presumably used their teeth for crushing aquatic vegetation.

Mammals that eat mainly ants and termites (see **Figure 27.59, p. 656**) often lack teeth entirely. This adaptive zone has been exploited by mammals across the tropics. The South American examples (*Dasypus* and *Myrmecophaga*, order Edentata) are different evolutionary lines (see Figure 27.48) from the African ones (*Orycteropus*, order Tubulidantata, and *Manis*, order Pholidota). Australia has both monotreme and marsupial anteaters. The most astonishing anteater is the aardwolf, a variation on a hyena **(Figure 27.60, p. 656)**; both of these species belong to the order Carnivora.

Whereas reptiles, amphibians, fish, and sharks can replace teeth many times (e.g., Figure 27.19), mammals replace them only once. Teeth wear with age **(Figure 27.61a** and **b, p. 656)**. When the teeth are worn out, the animal can no longer feed

Figure 27.58

Teeth for different jobs. Whereas walrus (**a**, *Odobenus rosmarus*) use tusks for digging clams, which they crush with their molars, flying lemurs (**b**, *Cynocephalus*) use comblike lower incisor teeth to comb their fur, and dolphins (**c**, *Tursiops*) have rows of similar teeth (homodont) for grasping fish.

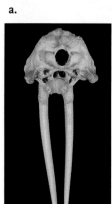

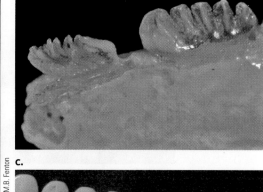

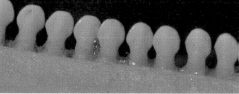

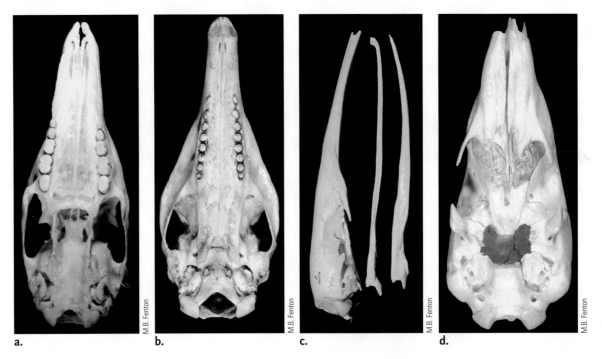

Figure 27.59

Ant- and termite-eating mammals, some with and some without teeth. The aardvark (**a**, *Orycteropus afer*) is from Africa and the armadillo (**b**, *Dasypus*) and giant anteater (**c**, *Myrmecophaga*) are from South America. Scaly anteaters (*Manis* species) occur from Africa to southeast Asia. The aardvark belongs to the order Tubulidentata, the armadillo and the giant anteater to the order Edentata, and the scaly anteater to the order Pholidota.

itself properly and dies. Elephants deal with this problem by having only four active molars in the jaw at any one time. The new molar grows in from the back **(Figure 27.61c)**, replacing the worn one. In rodents and some other mammals (and also in hydrasaur dinosaurs), molar (and for rodents and lagomorphs incisor) teeth grow continuously. Here the teeth are curved so that pressure during biting

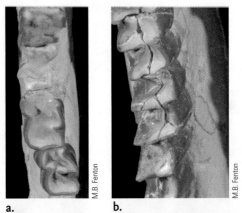

a.   **b.**

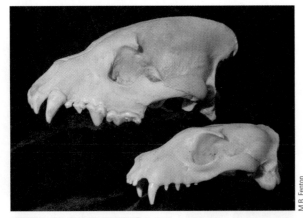

Figure 27.60

Divergence! Spotted hyena (top, *Crocuta crocuta*) and aardwolf (bottom, *Proteles capensis*) are in the same family (Hyaenidae). The spotted hyena is a carnivorous scavenger with massive teeth. The aardwolf eats mainly ants and termites and has reduced teeth (and a differently shaped skull). The *Crocuta* skull is about 30 cm long. Both belong to the order Carnivora.

c.

Figure 27.61

Tooth wear. The teeth of a fossil rhino. First, the worn teeth of an old *Hyracodon nebraskensis* are compared with those of a young one (**a** and **b**, respectively). Elephants (**c**, *Loxodonta africana*) have four functional molars in the mouth at any one time (one in each jaw quadrant). New molars push into the tooth row from the back.

Geckel®

Geckos **(Figure 1)** can cling to vertical and even inverted smooth surfaces such as window glass. They do this using specialized keratinous setae (fine hairs) on their feet. There are spatulate extensions at the end of each seta. The other element in the adhesive ability of geckos is an adhesive.

Figure 1
Geckos, such as this one, can walk on (stick to) glass.

But the remarkable feature of geckos is that the system allows rapid detachment of the foot. As many people have learned using Crazy Glue® and its equivalents, getting stuck to something is easy; getting unstuck is a different story.

As remarkable as geckos, some mussels (see Chapter 26) secrete a specialized adhesive with a high concentraton of catecholic amino acid 3,4-dihydroxy-l-phenlalanine (DOPA). DOPA allows the mussels to cling firmly to wet surfaces. In contrast, the adhesive ability of geckos is diminished by full immersion in water.

Geckel® is a new hybrid adhesive **(Figure 2)** combining the adhesive features of those used by geckos and mussels. Geckel® is a thin layer of a synthetic polymer that retains its adhesive properties in dry and wet environments for more than 1000 contact cycles.

Work with geckos (probably *Rhoptropus biporosus*) from the Namib desert sheds light on the evolutionary background of their extraordinary clinging power. These small geckos weigh about 2 g and show great mobility on the variety of substrates they encounter— rough, undulant, and unpredictable, often providing few points of adhesion. The adhesive pads under the geckos' toes allow them to cling to the full spectrum of surfaces, and their ability to stick to glass is coincidental.

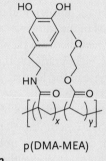

p(DMA-MEA)

Figure 2

Geckel®, a fabricated adhesive that mimics those produced and used by geckos and mussels.

---

is not directed at the points of growth (see Figures 19.8b and 48.4).

STUDY BREAK

1. What features are found in most mammals and distinguish them from other vertebrates?
2. How is heterodont different from diphyodont?
3. Distinguish among monotremes, marsupials, and placentals.

27.15 The Evolution of Humans

Genetic analyses of living hominoid species indicate that African hominoids diverged into several lineages between 10 and 5 million years ago. One lineage, the **hominids**, includes modern humans and our bipedal ancestors. Upright posture and bipedal locomotion are adaptations that distinguish hominids from apes. Bipedal locomotion largely freed the hands from locomotor functions, allowing them to become specialized for other activities, such as tool use. Evolutionary refinements in grasping ability

allow hominids to hold objects tightly with a *power grip* or manipulate them precisely with a *precision grip* **(Figure 27.62)**.

Female hominids suffer at least one consequence of being bipedal, namely the shift in the body's centre of mass during pregnancy. In humans, specialized adaptations of the axial skeleton include an increase in the number of lumbar vertebrae and the lengths of individual vertebra. There also is a marked posterior concavity of individual lumbar vertebrae (lordosis), which stabilizes the centre of mass of the upper body over the hips. Females have a derived curvature of the

a. Power grip   **b.** Precision grip

Figure 27.62
Power grip versus precision grip. Hominids grasp objects in two distinct ways. The power grip **(a)** allows us to grasp an object firmly, whereas the precision grip **(b)** allows us to manipulate objects by fine movements.

lumbar area and reinforcement of those vertebrae to compensate for the additional load associated with pregnancy. Evidence from *Australopithecus* fossils suggests that these adaptations to bipedalism preceded the evolution of species in the genus *Homo*.

In 2007, S.K.S. Thorpe, R.L. Holder, and R.H. Crompton proposed that bipedalism arose in an arboreal setting. Specifically, they asserted that hand-assisted bipedalism allowed the ancestors of humans and great apes to move on flexible supports (branches) that otherwise would be too small. Thorpe et al. compared human and orangutan (*Pongo abelii*) locomotion and found that organutans walking on flexible branches increase knee and hip extension, just like humans do when running on a springy track. In a bipedal gait, humans and orangutans do not flex the hind limbs in the same way as gorillas and chimps do.

This new theory explains the morphological adaptations to orthogrady (upright posture), such as lateral stiffness of the lumbar spine; both occur in more advanced hominids. In six-million-year-old fossils of *Orrorin tugensis*, the head of the femur suggests that this species resembles *Homo* and *Australopithecus*. Although *O. tugensis* is not more closely related to *Homo* than to *Australopithecus* **(Figure 27.63)**, its gait would have been more like that of *Australopithecus*.

Paleontologists have uncovered fossil remains of numerous hominids that lived in East Africa and South Africa from roughly 6 million to 1 million years ago (see Figure 27.63). In 2000, researchers found 13 fossils of *O. tugenensis* ("first man" in a local African language), a species that lived about 6 million years ago in East African forests. The best-studied early hominid fossils, the remains of 50 individuals discovered in the East African Rift Valley, date from about 5 million years ago. Named *Ardipithecus ramidus*, these hominids stood 120 cm tall and had apelike teeth. Other *Ardipithecus* fossils, recently discovered at a different site, appear to be much older (5.8 million years) and show evidence of bipedal locomotion.

Hominid fossils from 4.2 to 1.2 million years ago are known from many sites in East, Central, and South Africa. They are currently assigned to the genera *Australopithecus* (*australo* = southern; *pithecus* = ape) and *Paranthropus* (*para* = beside; *anthropus* = man). With their large faces, protruding jaws, and small skulls and brains, most of these hominids had an apelike appearance. *Australopithecus anamensis*, which lived in East Africa around 4 million years ago, is the oldest known species. It had thick enamel on its teeth, a derived hominid characteristic. A fossilized leg bone suggests that it was bipedal.

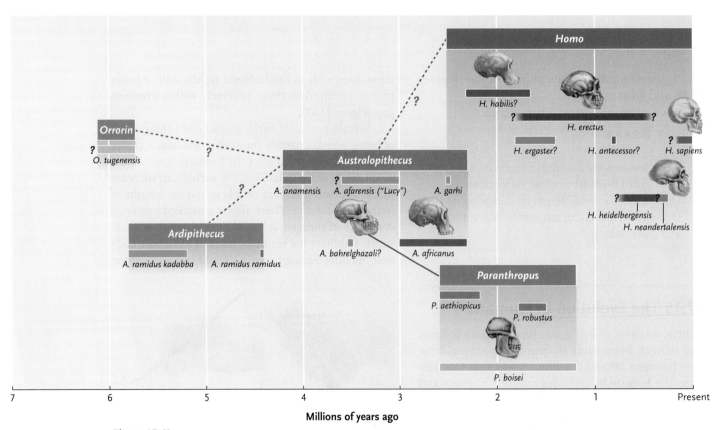

Figure 27.63

Hominid time line. Several species of hominids lived simultaneously at sites in eastern and southern Africa. The time line for each species reflects the ages of known fossils. Numerous question marks indicate uncertainty about classification and/or ages of fossils. Some skulls shown here are reconstructions from fragments.

Specimens of more than 60 individual *Australopithecus afarensis* have been found in northern Ethiopia, including about 40% of a female's skeleton, named "Lucy" by its discoverers (after the Beatles' song "Lucy in the Sky with Diamonds"; **Figure 27.64**). *A. afarensis* lived 3.5 to 3 million years ago, but it retained several ancestral characteristics. It had moderately large and pointed canine teeth and a relatively small brain. Males and females were 150 cm and 120 cm tall, respectively. Skeletal analyses suggest that Lucy was fully bipedal, a conclusion supported by fossilized footprints preserved in a layer of volcanic ash.

Other species of *Australopithecus* and *Paranthropus* lived in East Africa or South Africa between 3.7 and 1 million years ago. Adult males ranged from 40 to 50 kg in mass and from 130 to 150 cm in height; females were smaller. Most of these species had deep jaws and large molars. Several of them had a crest of bone along the midline of the skull, providing a large surface for the attachment of jaw muscles. These anatomical features suggest that they ate hard food, such as nuts, seeds, and other vegetable products. *Australopithecus africanus*, known only from South Africa, had small jaws and teeth, indicating that it probably had a softer diet. The phylogenetic relationships of the species classified as *Australopithecus* and *Paranthropus*, and their exact relationships to later hominids, are not yet fully understood.

Australopithecus was likely ancestral to humans, which are classified in the genus *Homo*.

Pliocene fossils of the earliest ancestors of humans are fragmentary and widely distributed in space and time. We can describe them as belonging to *Homo habilis* (meaning "handy man"). From 2.3 to 1.7 million years ago, *H. habilis* occupied the woodlands and **savannas** of eastern and southern Africa, sharing these habitats with various species of *Paranthropus*. The two genera are easy to distinguish because the brains of *H. habilis* were at least 20% larger, and they had larger **incisors** and smaller molars than their hominid cousins. They ate hard-shelled nuts and seeds, as well as soft fruits, tubers, leaves, and insects. They may also have hunted small prey or scavenged carcasses left by larger predators.

Researchers have found numerous tools dating to the time of *H. habilis* but are not sure which species made them. Many of the hominid species of that time probably cracked marrowbones with rocks or scraped flesh from bones with sharp stones. Paleoanthropologist Louis Leakey was the first to discover evidence of tool *making* at East Africa's Olduvai Gorge, which cuts through a great sequence of sedimentary rock layers. The oldest tools at this site are crudely chipped pebbles probably manufactured by *H. habilis*. However, humans are not the only animals to use tools (see Chapter 40).

Early in the Pleistocene, about 1.8 million years ago, a new species of humans, *Homo erectus* ("upright man"), appeared in East Africa, although several species may be involved. One nearly complete skeleton suggests that *H. erectus* was taller than its ancestors and had a much larger brain, a thicker skull, and protruding brow ridges.

H. erectus made fairly sophisticated tools, including the hand axe **(Figure 27.65b)** used to cut food

a. "Lucy"

b. Australopithecine footprints

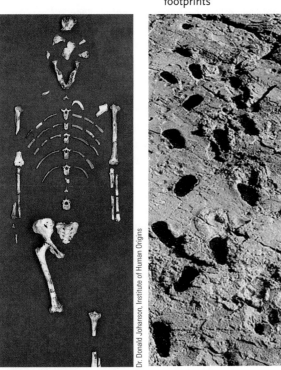

Dr. Donald Johanson, Institute of Human Origins

Louise M. Robbins

Figure 27.64

Australopithecines. "Lucy" is the most complete fossil of *Australopithecus afarensis* **(a).** Mary Leakey discovered footprints of australopithecines made in soft damp volcanic ash dating to about 3.7 million years ago. The **(b)** footprints indicate that these animals were fully bipedal.

a. *Homo erectus*

b. Hand axe

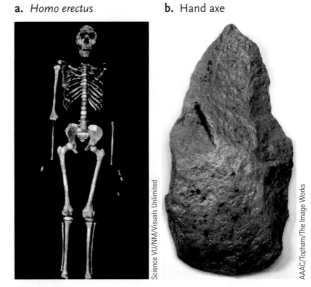

Science VU/NM/Visuals Unlimited

AAAC/Topham/The Image Works

Figure 27.65

Homo erectus. A nearly complete skeleton from Kenya **(a).** Hand tools **(b)** are often found at sites used by *H. erectus*.

Norman John (Jack) Berrill, McGill University

Growing up on the edge of a city gave Jack Berrill ready access to the fauna and flora of the surrounding countryside, the woods, the streams, the ponds. As a first year premedical student at the University of Bristol, he was offered the chance to join a zoological expedition to the Indian Ocean, a life-changing experience that drew him into zoology. In 1929, he completed his Ph.D. (University College, London, England) and became an assistant professor of zoology at McGill University in Montreal, Quebec, where he remained until his retirement.

Jack Berrill is distinguished for his research on development, **morphogenesis**, and regeneration in the Tunicata (phylum Urochordata). He chose these animals for study because they were transparent, allowing him to see what was going on inside them with minimum disturbance. His contribution to our knowledge of tunicates was profound and continues to strongly influence the field.

In addition to his research, Jack was also an innovative teacher. He used 16-mm film (silent and in black and white) to illustrate some of his lectures. He provided commentary as he showed the film, stopping here and there, backing up, and then continuing. One can only imagine what he could have done with videos and PowerPoint.

But Jack's contributions did not stop there. He also wrote 10 books that popularized zoology, such as *The Living Tide* (1951), *Inherit the Earth* (1966), and *Animals in Action* (1972).

Jack Berrill influenced the lives of others through his research. His published findings opened new avenues of thought. He also influenced people through his teaching and nontechnical publications.

---

and other materials, to scrape meat from bones, and to dig for roots. *H. erectus* probably ate both plants and animals and may have hunted and scavenged animal prey. Archaeological data point to their use of fire to process food and to keep warm. Near Lake Turkana in Kenya, fossils identified as *Homo* and dating from 1.45 to 1.55 million years ago were described in 2007. These data suggest that *H. erectus* and *H. habilis* lived together in the same habitats for a considerable time, much as chimps and gorillas do today. Adult male *H. erectus* were much larger than adult females, suggesting a polygynous lifestyle, one male with several females (see Chapter 40).

About 1.5 million years ago, the pressure of growing populations apparently forced groups of *H. erectus* out of Africa. They dispersed northward from East Africa into both northwestern Africa and Eurasia. Some moved eastward through Asia as far as the island of Java. Recent discoveries in Spain indicate that *H. erectus* also occupied parts of Western Europe.

Judging from its geographic distribution, *H. erectus* was successful in many environments. It produced several descendant species, of which modern humans (*H. sapiens*, meaning "wise man") are the only survivors. Extinct descendants of *H. erectus*, archaic humans, first appeared at least 400 000 years ago. They generally had larger brains, rounder skulls, and smaller molars than *H. erectus*.

Neanderthals (*Homo neanderthalensis*), which lived in Europe and western Asia from 150 000 to 28 000 years ago, are the best-known archaic humans. Compared with modern humans, they had a heavier build, pronounced brow ridges, and slightly larger brains. Neanderthals were culturally and technologically sophis-

ticated. They made complex tools, including wooden spears, stone axes, and flint scrapers and knives. At some sites, they built shelters of stones, branches, and animal hides, and they routinely used fire. They were successful hunters and probably ate nuts, berries, fishes, and bird eggs. Some groups buried their dead, and they may have had rudimentary speech.

Researchers once classified Neanderthals as a subspecies of *H. sapiens*, but most now believe that they were a separate species. In 1997, two teams of researchers independently analyzed short segments of mitochondrial DNA (mtDNA) extracted from the fossilized arm bone of a Neanderthal. Unlike nuclear DNA, which individuals inherit from both parents, only mothers pass mtDNA to offspring. It does not undergo genetic recombination (see Chapter 10), and it has a high mutation rate, making it useful for phylogenetic analyses. If mutation rates in mtDNA are fairly constant, this molecule can serve as a molecular clock (see Chapter 19). Comparing the Neanderthal sequence with mtDNA from 986 living humans revealed three times more differences between the Neanderthals and modern humans than between pairs of modern humans in their sample. These results suggest that Neanderthals and modern humans are different species that diverged from a common ancestor 690 000 to 550 000 years ago, well before modern humans appeared.

Modern humans (*H. sapiens*) differ from Neanderthals and other archaic humans in having a slighter build, less protruding brow ridges, and a more prominent chin. The earliest fossils of modern humans found in Africa and Asia are 150 000 years old; those from the Middle East are 100 000 years old. Fossils from about 20 000 years ago are known from

Western Europe, the most famous being those of the Cro-Magnon deposits in southern France. The widespread appearance of modern humans roughly coincided with the demise of Neanderthals in Western Europe and the Middle East 40 000 to 28 000 years ago. Although the two species apparently coexisted in some regions for thousands of years, we have little concrete evidence that they interacted, let alone interbred.

But when and where did modern humans first arise? Researchers use fossils and genetic data from contemporary human populations to address two competing hypotheses about this question.

The early descendants, archaic humans, left Africa and established populations in the Middle East, Asia, and Europe. Some time later, 200 000 to 100 000 years ago, *H. sapiens* arose in Africa. These modern humans also migrated into Europe and Asia and, through competition, eventually drove archaic humans to extinction. Thus, the **African Emergence Hypothesis** suggests that all modern humans are descended from a fairly recent African ancestor.

According to the Multiregional Hypothesis, populations of *H. erectus* and archaic humans had spread through much of Europe and Asia by 0.5 million years ago. Modern humans then evolved from archaic humans in many regions simultaneously. Although these geographically separated populations may have experienced some evolutionary differentiation (see Chapter 19), gene flow between them prevented reproductive isolation and maintained them as a single but variable species, *H. sapiens*.

Paleontological data do not clearly support either hypothesis, but in 2008, genetic data **(Figure 27.66)** generally support the African Emergence Hypothesis. Some scientists argue that human remains with a mixture of archaic and modern characteristics confirm the **Multiregional Hypothesis**. In late 1998, researchers in Portugal discovered a fossilized child that had been

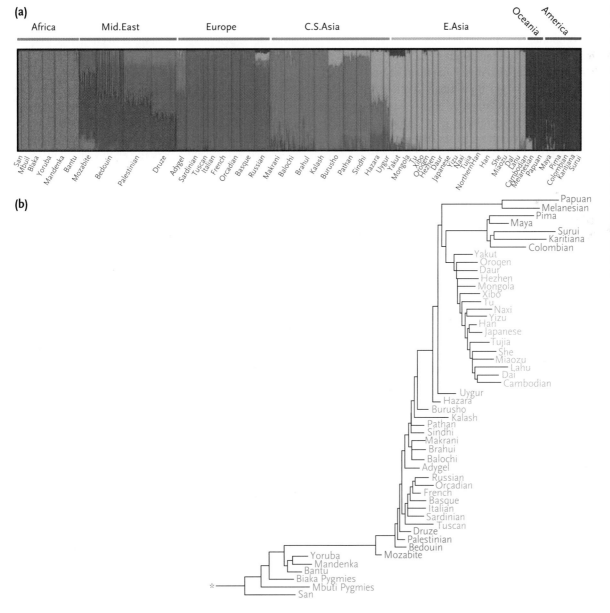

Figure 27.66

Out of Africa. Genetic data from 650 000 common single-nucleotide polymorphism loci from 928 humans were used to construct an individual ancestry and population dendogram. This maximum likelihood tree of 51 populations shows a single origin in sub-Saharan Africa and a subsequent radiation across Asia to the New World and Polynesia.

buried 24 000 years ago, when only modern humans were thought to have occupied Europe. This fossil shows a surprising mix of Neanderthal and modern human traits, possibly indicating that the two groups interbred. On the other hand, recent finds in the Middle East indicate that Neanderthals and modern humans coexisted without interbreeding for 50 000 years.

Scientists use DNA sequences from modern humans to evaluate the two hypotheses. In 1987, Rebecca Cann and colleagues published an analysis of mtDNA sequences from more than 100 ethnically diverse humans on four continents. They found that contemporary African populations contain the greatest variation in mtDNA. One explanation for this observation is that neutral mutations have been accumulating in African populations longer than in others, marking the African populations as the oldest on Earth. They also found that all human populations contain at least one mtDNA sequence of African origin, suggesting an African ancestry for all modern humans. Cann and her colleagues named the ancestral population, which lived approximately 200 000 years ago, the "mitochondrial Eve."

Proponents of the Multiregional Hypothesis criticized the statistical techniques used by Cann and her colleagues. Some also noted that if ancient populations in Africa were larger than those in other parts of the world, population size, rather than age, could account for high genetic variability (see Chapter 17). Moreover, recent research suggests that mutation rates in mtDNA might not be constant and that natural selection can influence mtDNA sequences, calling into question mtDNA's usefulness as a molecular clock.

Other researchers have examined genetic material that males inherit from their fathers. In 1995, L. Simon Whitfield and colleagues published a study of an 18 000 base-pair sequence from the Y chromosome, which does not undergo recombination with the X chromosome. Because the sequence contains no genes, it should not be subject to natural selection. Thus, sequence variations should result only from random mutations, which can serve as a molecular

clock. The researchers discovered only three sequence mutations among the five subjects they examined. This was surprising because their sample included a European, a Melanesian, a native South American, and two Africans. By contrast, a chimpanzee exhibited 207 differences from the human version of the sequence. Using a sophisticated statistical analysis, the Whitfield team calculated that the common ancestor of these diverse humans, dubbed the "African Adam," lived between 37 000 and 49 000 years ago. The limited genetic diversity and relatively recent origin of a common ancestor clearly support the African Emergence Hypothesis. Follow-up studies on the Y chromosomes of thousands of men from Africa, Europe, Asia, Australia, and the Americas have confirmed that all modern humans are the descendants of a single migration out of Africa.

Some controversies about human evolution arise because researchers who use genetic data must make assumptions about the sizes and geographic ranges of ancient populations. They also must make assumptions about the amount of gene flow that was involved and how natural selection may have affected our ancestors. Scientists are obliged to challenge assumptions and conclusions arising from statistical analyses. Intellectual disputes are routine in science, and they challenge researchers to refine their hypotheses and to test them in new ways. Questions about the details of human origins are at the centre of one of the liveliest debates in evolutionary biology today; additional research will surely clarify the evolutionary history of our species.

STUDY BREAK

1. What key adaptations distinguish humans from apes? How did they arise?
2. What features distinguish *H. erectus* from its ancestors?
3. Describe Neanderthals and compare them with modern humans.

UNANSWERED QUESTIONS

Should birds be considered reptiles, or do they merit separation into a distinct class? (See also Chapter 19.)

How long ago did humans first arrive in the New World (North America, South America, Central America)? How do we know? Before

1000 A.D., was there one or were there several waves of human immigration into the New World?

Review

27.2 Phylum Echinodermata

- Echinodermata are slow-moving or sessile, bottom-dwelling animals. They are important herbivores and predators that occur from shallow coastal waters to the oceans' depths. Adult echinoderms develop from bilaterally symmetrical, free-swimming larvae. Developing larvae assume a secondary radial symmetry, often organized around five rays or "arms." The table below provides a comparison of echinoderms and humans:

System	Echinoderms	Humans
digestive	complete system	complete system
excretory	not present	complete system
respiratory	not present	complete system
circulatory	minimal system	closed, complete system
nervous system	no head or central	cephalized system

- Water enters the fluid-filled canals of the water vascular system through the madreporite (a sievelike plate) on the aboral surface. A tube connects the madreporite to the ring canal, which surrounds the esophagus. The ring canal branches into radial canals that extend into each arm and is connected to numerous mucus-covered tube feet. When ampullae, small muscular bulbs in each tube foot, contract, they force water into the tube foot, causing it to lengthen and attach to a substrate. The tube foot contracts, pulling the animal along and pushing water back into the ampulla; this causes the tube foot to release the substrate. Echinoderms reproduce either sexually or asexually. Sexual reproduction is usually achieved by releasing gametes into the water. Asexual reproduction involves clonal budding and may be stimulated by the odour of a predator.
- Asteroidea (sea stars) consist of a central disk surrounded by 5 to 20 radiating "arms." Small pincers at the base of pedicellariae (short spines) are used to remove debris that falls onto the animal's surface. The ossicles of their endoskeleton are not fused, permitting flexibility of the arms and disk. Most sea stars eat invertebrates and small fish.
- Ophiuroidea (brittle stars and basket stars) have a well-defined central disk and slender, elongated arms that are sometimes branched. They crawl swiftly across substrates by moving their arms in a coordinated fashion. They feed on small prey, suspended plankton, or detritus extracted from muddy deposits.
- Echinoidea (sea urchins and sand dollars) lack arms. Their ossicles are fused into tests that provide excellent protection but restrict flexibility. Echinoids use tube feet in locomotion. They graze on algae and other organisms that cling to marine surfaces.
- Holothuroidea (sea cucumbers) have a reduced endoskeleton consisting of widely separated microscopic plates. They have five rows of tube feet and a soft body elongated along the oral–aboral axis. Modified tube feet form a ring of tentacles around the mouth. Some species secrete a mucus net that traps plankton or other food particles. The net and tentacles are inserted into the mouth, where the food is ingested. Other species extract food from bottom sediments.
- Crinoidea (sea lilies and feather stars) have five to several hundred branched arms surrounding the disk containing the mouth. Branches of the arms are covered with mucus-coated tube feet that trap suspended microscopic organisms. Sessile sea lilies have a central disk attached to a flexible stalk that can reach a metre in length, whereas adult feather stars swim or crawl weakly.

27.3 Phylum Hemichordata

- Hemichordates (acorn worms) use a muscular, mucus-coated proboscis to construct burrows and trap food particles. Drawn in by beating cilia, water enters the pharynx and exits through the pharyngeal gill slits. As the water passes, suspended food is trapped and directed to the digestive system, while gases are exchanged across the partitions between gill slits.

27.4 Phylum Chordata

- A notochord, a dorsal hollow nerve cord, and gill slits distinguish chordates from all other deuterosomes. Gill slits are sets of paired openings in the pharynx. Water is drawn into the mouth, food is filtered out, and the water passes through the pharynx, where gas exchange takes place, and then out through the gill slits.
- Tunicates (sea squirts) belong to the subphylum Urochordata. They float in surface waters or attach to substrates in shallow waters. Many are sessile as adults and secrete a gelatinous or leathery "tunic" around their bodies. They squirt water through a siphon when disturbed. Some urochordates have larvae that resemble cephalochordates (or lancelets), and in a few species, these larvae are neotenous. Adult lancelets are mainly sedentary, lying partly buried in sand of shallow marine waters. They have well-developed body wall muscles and a prominent notochord. Adults have light receptors on the head and chemical sense organs on tentacles.

27.5 The Origin and Diversification of Vertebrates

- The internal skeleton of vertebrates provides structural support for muscles and protects the nervous system and other internal organs. The backbone surrounds and protects the dorsal nerve cord, and a bony cranium provides protection for the brain. The backbone acts as a place for muscle attachments, which allows quick movement.
- Homeotic (*Hox*) genes influence the three-dimensional shape of an animal and the locations of structures such as eyes, wings, and legs. *Hox* genes are arranged on chromosomes in a specific order to form the *Hox* gene complex. Each gene in the complex governs the development of particular structures. Species with simple anatomy have fewer *Hox* genes than more complex species, which have duplicated copies. These duplicate copies assumed new functions, directing the development of novel structures, such as the vertebral column and jaws.
- Vertebrates have four characteristic morphological innovations: cranium, vertebrae, bone, and neural crest cells.

27.6 Agnathans: Hagfishes and Lampreys, Conodonts, and Ostracoderms

- Agnatha are primitive vertebrates that use a muscular pharynx to suck water containing food particles into their mouths and gills to filter the food and perform gas exchange. Hagfishes and lampreys have a well-developed notochord but lack true vertebrae and paired fins. The hagfish skeleton is a cranium and a notochord. These marine scavengers feed on invertebrate prey and dead fish. They lack a larval stage. Lampreys have a more derived axial skeleton than hagfishes. Their notochord is surrounded by cartilage that partially covers the nerve cord, whereas hagfish have no specialized structures surrounding the nerve cord. Some species of lampreys are parasitic as adults, attaching to a host. Ammocoetes, the larval stage of lampreys, resemble cephalochordates and may develop for up to seven years before metamorphosing into adults.

27.7 Jawed Fishes: Jaws Expanded the Feeding Opportunities for Vertebrates

- Jaws meant that fishes could feed on larger items of food with higher energy content. Jaws also function to defend against predators, groom, transport young, and grasp, kill, and shred food items.

- Flexible fins, lightweight skeletons, streamlined bodies, and an absence of heavy body armour allow sharks to pursue prey rapidly. Sharks and their relatives have squalene, an oily substance contained within the liver. Squalene is lighter than water and increases the animals' buoyancy.

- The lateral line system of elasmobranchs and other fishes consists of a row of tiny sensors in canals along both sides of the body. This system allows detection of vibrations in water, which can be used when hunting.

- In many bony fishes, a gas-filled swim bladder serves as a hydrostatic organ to increase buoyancy. Bony fish also have small, smooth, lightweight scales and bodies that are covered with a protective coat of mucus that retards bacterial growth and smooths the flow of water past the body.

27.8 Early Tetrapods and Modern Amphibians

- Osteolepiforms (fleshy-finned fishes) and tetrapods had infoldings of their tooth surfaces. The shapes and positions of bones on the dorsum and side of their crania and in their appendages were similar. Osteolepiformes had strong fins enabling them to crawl on mud (making their move onto land) and possessed vertebral columns with crescent-shaped bones for support. Osteolepiformes had lungs allowing them to breathe atmospheric oxygen. They could excrete urea or uric acid rather than ammonium.

- The body wall of fish picks up sound vibrations and directly transfers them to sensory receptors. Sound waves are harder to detect in air. The development of a tympanum, or eardrum, allowed tetrapods to detect airborne vibrations and transfer them to the sensory cells of their inner ear.

- Amphibians have thin, scaleless skin, well supplied with blood vessels. Since some oxygen and carbon dioxide enter the body across a thin layer of water, most amphibians need moist skin, restricting them to aquatic or wet terrestrial habitats. Many amphibians need access to free-standing water to reproduce.

27.9 The Origin and Mesozoic Radiations of Amniotes

- Amniotes get their name from the amnion, a fluid-filled sac surrounding the embryo during development. Amniote eggs are resistant to desiccation because the developing embryos excrete uric acid that is stored in the allantois.

- Amniote eggs have four specialized membranes that protect the embryo and facilitate gas exchange and excretion. They also have a hard or leathery shell perforated by microscopic pores that mediates the exchange of air and water between the egg and its environment. Keratin and lipids are partly responsible for making the skin waterproof.

27.10 Sublcass Testudinata: Turtles and Tortoises

- There have been three major radiations of amniotes: anapsids, synapsids, and diapsids, distinguishable by the numbers of bony arches in the temporal region of the skull. The bony arches

allow space for contraction (and expansion) of large and powerful jaw muscles. Anapsids lacked temporal arches, synapsids have one pair of temporal arches, and diapsids have two pairs of arches.

- Surviving anapsids are turtles and tortoises. A turtle's body is defined by a bony, boxlike shell, which includes a dorsal carapace and a ventral plastron. Its ribs are fused to the inside of the carapace, and the pectoral and pelvic girdles lie within the rib cage. Large keratinized scales cover the bony plates that form the shell.

27.11 Living Diapsids: Spenodontids, Squamates, and Crocodilians

- Diapsids evolved in two lines, lepidosaurs and archosaurs. Lepidosaurs include snakes and lizards and many extinct forms. Snakes and lizards use olfactory and vibrational cues to detect prey. Some even have thermal perception.

- Living archosaurs include crocodilians, animals with a four-chambered heart that is homologous to the heart in birds. Some crocodilians have muscles that originate on the pubis insert on the liver. When these muscles contract, the liver moves toward the tail, creating negative pressure in the chest cavity. This situation is analogous to the role of the diaphragm in mammals.

27.12 Aves: Birds

- Birds' ability to fly reflects a keeled sternum (breastbone), a furculum (wishbone), and uncinate processes on the ribs. These main adaptations, coupled with lightweight, strong bones and feathers, contributed to the success of birds. Flightless birds often lack a keeled sternum. Most birds have hollow limb bones with small supporting struts that criss-cross the internal cavities. Birds have fewer separate bony elements in the wings, skull, and vertebral column, so the skeleton is light and rigid. All modern birds have replaced dense and heavy teeth with a lightweight keratinized bill. Birds have much higher metabolic rates than comparably sized reptiles do, and they depend on energy-rich food. A complex and efficient respiratory system and a four-chambered heart enable them to consume and distribute oxygen efficiently. Other adaptations include modification of internal organs to reduce weight, elimination of a urinary bladder so that uric paste is eliminated with digestive wastes, and laying eggs as soon as they are shelled.

- Each feather has numerous barbs and barbules with tiny hooks and grooves that maintain the feathers' structure, even during vigorous activity. Flight feathers on the wings provide lift, whereas contour feathers streamline the surface of the body. Down feathers form an insulating cover close to the skin.

- The "top-down" theory suggests that ancestral birds lived in trees and glided down from those trees in pursuit of insect prey. The "bottom-up" theory proposes a cursorial ancestor that ran along in pursuit of prey and jumped up to catch it. The "ontogenic–transitional wing" (OTW) hypothesis is a third effort to explain the evolution of flight in birds. Its proponents suggest that flapping protowings gave the ancestors of birds greater mobility.

27.13 Mammalia: Monotremes, Marsupials, and Placentals

- Most living mammals are furry and endothermic (warm-blooded). Mammals usually bear live young and have a diaphragm, a left aortic arch leaving the heart, and two occipital condyles. Mammals also have a secondary palate and are heterodont (teeth specialized for different jobs) and diphyodont (two generations of teeth, milk or deciduous teeth and adult teeth). Heterodont teeth make mammals more efficient at mechanically dealing with their food (chewing), reducing the lagtime between consumption of food and availability of the food's energy.

- Monotremes lay leathery-shelled eggs. When newborns hatch, they lap up milk secreted by the mammary glands located on the mother's belly. Marsupials have short gestation periods of as few as 8 to 10 days. Young are born at an early stage of development and complete their development attached to a teat in the abdominal pouch (the marsupium) of their mother. Placental mammals complete embryonic development in the mother's uterus, nourished through a placenta until they reach a fairly advanced stage of development.

27.15 The Evolution of Humans

- Upright posture and bipedal locomotion are key adaptations distinguishing hominids from apes. Bipedalism may have arisen in an arboreal setting that allowed the ancestors of humans to move on flexible supports (branches). Bipedal locomotion freed the hands from locomotor functions, allowing them to become adapted for other activities, such as tool use.

- *Homo erectus* ("upright man") was taller than its ancestors and had a much larger brain, a thicker skull, and protruding brow ridges. *H. erectus* was able to make tools to cut food and other materials, to scrape meat from bones, and to dig for roots. They had a more complex diet, probably eating both plants and animals, and may have hunted and scavenged animal prey. They used fire to process food and keep themselves warm.

- Neanderthals had a heavier build, pronounced brow ridges, and slightly larger brains compared with modern humans. They were technologically sophisticated, making wooden spears, stone axes, and flint scrapers and knives. They built shelters and routinely used fire. They were successful hunters and used rudimentary speech. Modern humans differ from Neanderthals in having a slighter build, less protruding brow ridges, and a more prominent chin.

- The African Emergence Hypothesis states that between 1.5 and 0.5 million years ago, a population of *H. erectus* gave rise to several descendant species. These archaic humans left Africa and established populations in the Middle East, Asia, and Europe. Some time later, *H. sapiens* arose in Africa. These modern humans also migrated into Europe and Asia and eventually drove archaic humans to extinction. This hypothesis suggests that all modern humans are descended from a fairly recent African ancestor.

- The Multiregional Hypothesis proposes that populations of *H. erectus* and archaic humans had spread through much of Europe and Asia by 0.5 million years ago. Modern humans (*H. sapiens*) then evolved from archaic humans in many regions simultaneously. Although they were geographically separated, these populations may have experienced some evolutionary differentiation; gene flow between them prevented reproductive isolation and maintained them as a single species, *H. sapiens*.

Questions

Self-Test Questions

1. Which phylum includes animals with a water vascular system?
   a. Echinodermata
   b. Hemichordata
   c. Chordata
   d. Arthropoda
   e. Annelida

2. Which of the following is *not* a characteristic of all chordates?
   a. notochord
   b. segmental body wall and tail muscles
   c. segmented nervous system
   d. dorsal hollow nerve cord
   e. perforated pharynx

3. Which group of vertebrates has adaptations allowing reproduction on land?
   a. agnathans
   b. tetrapods
   c. gnathostomes
   d. amniotes
   e. ichthyosaurs

4. Which group of fishes has the most living species today?
   a. sarcopterygians
   b. actinopterygians
   c. chondrichthyans
   d. acanthodians
   e. ostracoderms

5. Modern amphibians
   a. closely resemble their Paleozoic ancestors.
   b. always occupy terrestrial habitats as adults.
   c. never occupy terrestrial habitats as adults.
   d. are generally larger than their Paleozoic ancestors.
   e. are generally smaller than their Paleozoic ancestors.

6. Which one of the following key adaptations allows amniotes to occupy terrestrial habitats?
   a. production of carbon dioxide as a metabolic waste product
   b. an unshelled egg protected by jellylike material
   c. a dry skin largely impermeable to water
   d. a lightweight skeleton with hollow bones
   e. feathers or fur providing insulation against cold weather

7. Which of the following characteristics are central to powered flight in birds?
   a. webbed feet, long legs, feathers
   b. efficient respiratiory and excretory systems, flight muscles
   c. elongated forelimbs, keeled breast bone, flight muscles
   d. feathers, furculum, eyes
   e. short tail vertebrae, large nostrils, feathers.

8. Which of the following characteristics did *not* contribute to the evolutionary success of mammals?
   a. extended parental care of young
   b. an erect posture and flexible hip and shoulder joints
   c. specializations of the teeth and jaws
   d. enlarged brain
   e. high metabolic rate and homeothermy

9. The Hominoidea (hominids) is a monophyletic group that includes
   a. apes and monkeys.
   b. apes only.
   c. humans and human ancestors.
   d. apes and humans.
   e. monkeys, apes, and humans.

10. Which of the following hominids was the earliest?
   a. *Ardipithecus ramidus*
   b. *Australopithecus afarensis*
   c. *Homo habilis*
   d. *Homo erectus*
   e. *Homo neanderthalensis*

Questions for Discussion

1. Most sharks and rays are predatory, but the largest species feed on plankton. Construct a hypothesis to explain this observation. How would you test your hypothesis?

2. What selection pressures did tetrapods face when they first ventured onto land? What characteristics allowed them to meet these pressures?

3. Use binoculars to observe several species of birds in different environments, such as lakes and forests. How are their beaks and feet adapted to their habitats and food habits?

4. Imagine that you unearthed the complete fossilized remains of a mammal. How would you determine its diet?

5. Many myths about human evolution are embraced by popular culture. Using the information you have learned about human evolution, argue against each of the following myths:
   a. Humans evolved from chimpanzees.
   b. Evolution occurred in a steady linear progression from primitive primate to anatomically modern humans.
   c. All human characteristics, such as bipedal locomotion and an enlarged brain, evolved simultaneously and at the same rate.

(a) Banyan tree (*Ficus* sp.), one type of "strangler fig."
(b) Close-up view of strangler fig roots on the trunk of a host plant.

Isabella M. Gioia

Adrian Jones, IAN Image Library
(www.ian.umces.edu/imagelibrary/)

28 The Plant Body

WHY IT MATTERS

What is the largest plant in the world? The answer depends on how we define largest—is it the tallest? The one with the greatest mass? If we define largest as the plant with the biggest canopy (stem and branches), then the winner of the contest would be the banyan tree (see opening photograph). The banyan is one of several kinds of figs (*Ficus* species) that are known as strangler figs due to their aggressive growth habit. The seeds of strangler figs, dispersed by birds, are often deposited high up on the branches of other tree species in tropical rain forests. The seeds germinate in the bark of their host tree and send thin roots down the trunk of the host plant to the ground. Once the roots enter the ground, they grow and thicken quickly. Roots that cross over each other fuse together, trapping the host plant's trunk in a cage of roots that eventually fuse into a more or less solid mass. Meanwhile, the stem of the fig climbs upward, twining itself around the host's stem, and soon overtops the host, putting out many thick leaves that shade the host plant's leaves. The strangler fig can now outcompete the host plant for sunlight and for water and nutrients from the soil. The network of roots that surround the host's trunk prevent further lateral growth of the host, which eventually starves to death. The host trunk rts away, leaving a hollow cylinder of roots that form the main trunk of the fig tree. Some of these fig species continue to send down roots from their branches. When these aerial roots reach the ground, they become additional trunks to help support the canopy, which can become massive. In this way, a single fig tree and its numerous, interconnected trunks can spread out over a very large area. The largest banyan tree in the world has a canopy that is 420 m in diameter! This aggressive growth strategy is a definite advantage in rainforests, where competition for light is fierce as very little light penetrates beyond the upper canopy.

Even though strangler figs are unusual in that their seeds germinate in the bark of another plant rather than in the soil, fig seedlings develop into mature plants via the same processes as other plants. As you saw in Chapter 25, plants were able to successfully colonize diverse land habitats only as adaptations in form and function helped them solve problems posed by the terrestrial environment. These evolutionary adaptations included

- a *shoot system* that helps support leaves and other body parts in air,
- a *root system* that anchors the plant in soil and provides access to soil nutrients and water,
- tissues for internal transport of water and nutrients, and
- specializations for preventing water loss.

What structures make up the root and shoot systems of a plant? How do the different parts of a plant develop? How do some plants, such as these strangler figs, become woody? Starting in this chapter and continuing through the next three chapters, we investigate these questions and explore the structure and functioning of plants—their morphology, anatomy, and physiology.

A plant's *morphology* is its external form, such as the shape of its leaves, and its *anatomy* is the structure and arrangement of its internal parts. Plant *physiology* refers to the mechanisms by which the plant's body functions in its environment. Our focus in this chapter is the plant division called angiosperms, or flowering plants, which are the most successful plants on Earth in terms of distribution and sheer numbers of species.

28.1 Plant Structure and Growth: An Overview

In this chapter, we focus on the key characteristics of plant structure and growth and make several comparisons between land plants and terrestrial animals. We could compare plants with many other organisms since plants and animals are just two of the many kingdoms of life, but we tend to be most familiar with animals. It is obvious that plants are very different from animals, but why are they so different? We can think of plants and animals as representatives of two very

different solutions to the challenges of life on land. If we generalize about "typical" plants and "typical" animals, we can get a clearer picture of these two different strategies. Animals are chemoheterotrophs: they obtain both energy and carbon from the food they eat. Their food sources tend to be fairly concentrated sources of nutrients. All terrestrial animals are motile (some aquatic animals are stationary) and can move from one place to another in search of food, water, or a mate. They can also flee from predators or move away from unfavourable conditions. Animal bodies, then, need to be fairly compact to facilitate moving around.

In contrast, plants are photosynthetic autotrophs—"self-feeders"—that need sunlight, carbon dioxide (available in air), and water (available in soil). In addition, plants require other nutrients that are usually available only in soil; these nutrients are usually patchily distributed in the soil and often available only at low concentrations. Thus, unlike animals, plants have to gather diffuse nutrients from both air and soil. How best to capture these diffuse nutrients? A large surface area is important, both above ground and below ground, so plant bodies are not compact but spreading and branched in form (the term for this form is *dendritic*, which literally means "treelike"). To visualize this dendritic growth, think about how the branches of an aspen or another poplar tree look in the spring before they have leafed out **(Figure 28.1)**. The root system of the tree is also dendritic, branching and spreading below ground. Thus, the evolutionary response to the challenges posed by life on land has resulted in a plant body consisting of two closely linked but quite different components—a photosynthetic *shoot system* extending upward into the air and a nonphotosynthetic *root system* extending downward into the soil **(Figure 28.2)**.

Figure 28.1
Dendritic growth shown by the above-ground portion of a tree.

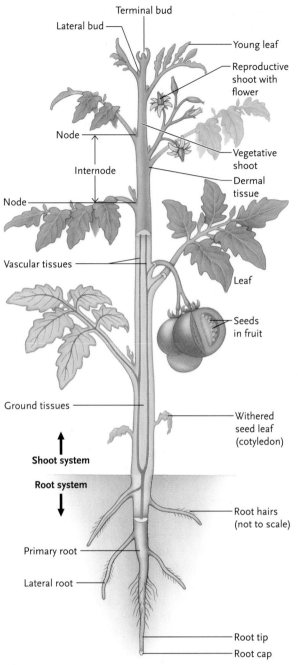

Figure 28.2

Body plan for the commercially grown tomato plant *Solanum lycopersicum*, a typical angiosperm. Vascular tissues (purple) conduct water, dissolved minerals, and organic substances. They thread through ground tissues, which make up most of the plant body. Dermal tissues (epidermis, in this case) cover the surfaces of the root and shoot systems.

Obviously, a plant cannot just pick up this extensive root system and move around in search of better conditions. Instead, plants are fixed in place (sessile), and they must therefore search for nutrients and water, find mates, and defend themselves from predators—everything that animals have to do—but while being fixed in place. As you read through this chapter, think about how plant morphology and growth relate to being sessile photoautotrophs.

28.1a Cells of All Plant Tissues Share Some General Features

Both root and shoot systems consist of various **organs**—body structures that contain two or more types of tissues and have a definite form and function. Plant organs include leaves, stems, and roots. A **tissue** is a group of cells and intercellular substances that function together in one or more specialized tasks.

Plant cells share some features with animal cells but differ in that they typically have a cell wall, a large vacuole, and, in many cells, chloroplasts. Chloroplasts function in photosynthesis and are discussed in more detail in Chapter 7. The vacuole may occupy most of the volume in a mature plant cell and plays an important role in cell elongation and maintenance of rigid tissues. Vacuoles may also act as storage compartments. In all plant tissues, the cells have a **primary cell wall** surrounding the plasma membrane and cell contents (cytoplasm and organelles) **(Figure 28.3a, p. 670)**. These cell walls are the "skeleton" of a plant, serving as support, just as the skeleton for an animal does. A primary cell wall is made largely of microfibrils of **cellulose**, a polymer of glucose, embedded in a matrix of other polysaccharides. Cellulose is the most abundant polysaccharide on earth and is currently being investigated as a source of biofuel (see *Molecule Behind Biology*). The combination of cellulose fibrils and other polysaccharides gives the cell wall strength and flexibility. Primary cell walls also contain various proteins. Some of these are structural proteins that contribute to the wall's strength, whereas others are enzymes that catalyze the formation and modification of the cell wall. Don't think of the cell wall as a solid barrier, like a cement wall, but rather as a semipermeable "mesh" or filter, which allows some molecules (e.g., water) to pass through into the cell. As well, cytoplasmic connections between adjacent cells, called **plasmodesmata** (singular, plasmodesma), allow solutes such as amino acids and sugars to move from one cell to the next. The space between the primary cell walls of adjacent cells is filled with a polysaccharide layer called the **middle lamella**.

As a young plant grows, different types of cells deposit additional cellulose and other materials inside the primary wall, forming a strong **secondary cell wall (Figure 28.3b, p. 670)**. Secondary walls often contain **lignin**, a complex water-insoluble polymer (see Chapter 24), which makes cell walls very strong, rigid, and impermeable to water. As we learned in Chapter 25, the evolution of large vascular plants became possible only after biochemical pathways producing lignin evolved, through modification of existing pathways, allowing a plant to produce lignified cells that both provided support and conducted water through the plant body. Lignin is also very resistant to decomposition, so its presence in cell walls makes the cell more resistant to attack by microbes (see Chapter 24). As you can see

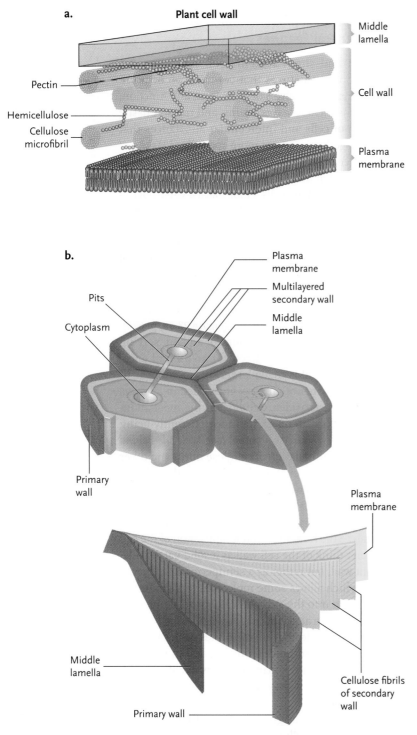

a.

Plant cell wall

Middle lamella

Pectin

Hemicellulose

Cellulose microfibril

Cell wall

Plasma membrane

b.

Plasma membrane

Multilayered secondary wall

Middle lamella

Pits

Cytoplasm

Primary wall

Plasma membrane

Middle lamella

Cellulose fibrils of secondary wall

Primary wall

Figure 28.3

(a) Structure of a plant primary cell wall. **(b)** Structure of a plant cell wall. Upper figure shows cross-section of plant cells in which secondary wall layers have been deposited inside the primary wall. The lower figure is a close-up of the arrangement of primary and secondary layers.

Most plant cells have a much more flexible differentiation than do animal cells. In general, once an animal cell has differentiated, it cannot dedifferentiate or "turn back" into an unspecialized cell (this is why it has proved so difficult to clone animals). Almost any plant cell, even one that has become specialized, can dedifferentiate and divide to produce an entire plant (obviously, cells in which the cytoplasm has been lost, such as xylem cells, are not able to dedifferentiate). This ability of almost any cell to give rise to all other parts of a plant is known as **totipotency.** You can see totipotency in action if you take a cutting of a shoot and place it in water: in a few days, roots will form on the bottom of the stem. Cloning of plants is very easy, something that many plants do all the time as a means of reproduction and many gardeners use as a means of propagation. What are the advantages of totipotency? It allows plants to heal wounds and, as mentioned above, is also one means of asexual reproduction; for example, in many plants (such as raspberries), if a branch or stem comes into contact with the soil for long enough, roots will develop at the point where the stem touches the ground, forming a new plant.

28.1b Shoot and Root Systems Perform Different but Integrated Functions

A flowering plant's **shoot system** typically consists of stems, leaves, buds, and—during part of the plant's life cycle—reproductive organs known as flowers (see Figure 28.2). A stem with its attached leaves and buds is a *vegetative* (nonreproductive) shoot; a bud eventually gives rise to an extension of the shoot or to a new, branching shoot. A *reproductive* shoot produces flowers, which later develop fruits containing seeds.

The shoot system is highly adapted for photosynthesis. Leaves greatly increase a plant's surface area and thus its exposure to light. Stems are frameworks for upright growth, which favourably positions leaves for light exposure and flowers for pollination. Some parts of the shoot system also store carbohydrates manufactured during photosynthesis. Many plants can change the orientation of their leaves to maximize light absorption or, in arid habitats, to prevent overheating.

The **root system** usually grows below ground. It anchors the plant and supports its upright parts. It also absorbs water and dissolved minerals from soil and stores carbohydrates. Adaptations in the structure and function of plant cells and tissues were an integral part of the evolution of shoots and roots, for example, the development of vascular tissues specialized to serve as internal pipelines that conduct water, minerals, and organic substances throughout the plant. The root hairs sketched in Figure 28.2 are surface cells specialized for absorbing water and nutrients from soil.

from Figure 28.3b, some cells are very small relative to the amount of wall material that surrounds them.

As in animals, all of a plant's cells have the same genes in their nuclei. So how do specialized cells such as xylem arise in plants? As each cell matures and *differentiates* (becomes specialized for a particular function), specific genes are activated. For the most part, fully differentiated animal cells perform their functions while alive, but some types of plant cells die after differentiating, and their cytoplasm disappears. The walls that remain, however, serve key functions, particularly in xylem.

MOLECULE BEHIND BIOLOGY

Cellulose

Cellulose (**Figure 1**) is the most abundant organic compound on Earth, thanks to its presence in every cell wall of every plant. We have many uses for cellulose already: in paper, clothing, insulation, and a variety of industrial uses. But could we also use this abundant substance as a source of fuel? Driven by a desire for more "green" sources of energy and the high price of oil, people have been looking at various sources of biofuel—fuel from plants.

One such biofuel, ethanol, is currently produced primarily from corn. Corn kernels are mostly starch (and water), which is easily broken down into sugars that are then fermented to produce ethanol. Like starch, cellulose is also a polymer of glucose, so it, too, can be broken down to sugars that can be fermented. However, it is much more difficult to do this with cellulose. Why? The linkages between glucose monomers in cellulose are different from those in starch (see *The Chemical and Physical Foundations of Biology* pages). This seemingly minor difference makes a very big difference

in not only the characteristics of the resulting polymers—cellulose is linear, whereas starch is coiled—but also in how difficult it is for decomposers to break the bonds between the monomers. Starch is readily decomposed by many organisms, including humans, but cellulose can be broken down only by a few organisms, mostly fungi and prokaryotes. Moreover, cellulose may be protected by lignin in some plant tissues, making the cellulose even harder to break down. Consequently, converting cellulose into liquid fuel is currently a very complex, difficult, and energy-consuming process.

But there are issues related to the use of corn for ethanol. World food prices rose 10% in 2006 partly because of rising biofuel demand; diverting corn from food to fuel use may be contributing to food shortages in some countries. There is also concern about the long-term effects on soil fertility of cultivating corn.

An advantage of converting cellulose to fuel is that all parts of the plants, not just the starch- and sugar-rich parts, could be converted to fuel.

In Canada and the United States, a very promising source of cellulose for biofuel is switchgrass (*Panicum virgatum*), a native grass of the tall-grass prairies. It grows very quickly, is able to grow on marginal land that is unsuitable for crop production, and can withstand both drought and flooding. Switchgrass is perennial, so it would not need to be replanted every year. Although the problems related to converting cellulose from switchgrass to liquid fuel (ethanol) remain, we could avoid those problems if we focused on other forms of fuel. For example, in Canada, the biggest contributor to greenhouse gases is heating, not transportation. Researchers have found that switchgrass stems can be dried and compressed into fuel pellets that can be burned. Used in this way, switchgrass produced a whopping 540 times the amount of energy than was needed to grow, harvest, and process it. This yield is seven times more energy per hectare than corn yields. Switchgrass pellets could also be used to generate electricity.

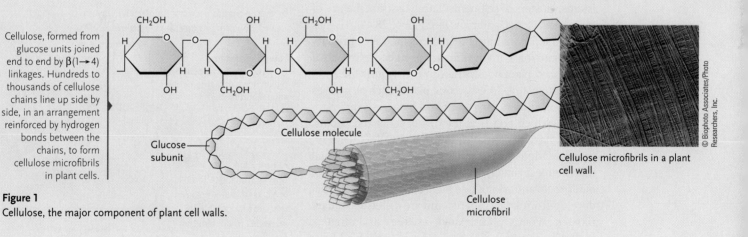

Cellulose, formed from glucose units joined end to end by β(1→4) linkages. Hundreds to thousands of cellulose chains line up side by side, in an arrangement reinforced by hydrogen bonds between the chains, to form cellulose microfibrils in plant cells.

Glucose subunit

Cellulose molecule

Cellulose microfibril

Cellulose microfibrils in a plant cell wall.

© Biophoto Associates/Photo Researchers, Inc.

Figure 1
Cellulose, the major component of plant cell walls.

28.1c Meristems Produce New Tissues Throughout a Plant's Life

Most animals grow to a certain size, and then their growth slows dramatically or stops. This pattern is called **determinate growth.** In contrast, plants can grow throughout their lives, a pattern called **indeterminate growth.** Individual plant parts exhibit determinate growth, such as leaves, flowers, and fruits,

but every plant also has self-perpetuating embryonic tissue, called meristem (*merizein* = to divide), at the tips of shoots and roots. Under the influence of plant hormones, these **meristems** produce new tissues more or less continuously while the plant is alive.

Why do plants have indeterminate growth? A capacity for indeterminate growth gives plants a great deal of flexibility—or what biologists often call *plasticity*—in their possible responses to changes in environmental factors such as light, temperature, water, and nutrients. This plasticity has major adaptive benefits for an organism that cannot move about, as most animals can. For example, if external factors (such as a houseplant's owner) change the direction of incoming light for photosynthesis, stems can "shift gears" and grow in that direction. These and other plant movements, called **tropisms**, are a major topic of Chapter 31.

Remember, too, that nutrients are patchily distributed and diffuse in soil. Indeterminate growth allows a root system to extend and grow out of regions in which nutrients have been depleted and forage for patches with more nutrients; if plant root systems were determinate, plants would soon exhaust local nutrient supplies and be unable to forage for more.

As you know, animals grow mainly by mitosis, which increases the number of body cells. Plants, however, grow by two mechanisms—an increase in the number of cells by mitotic cell division in the meristems *and* an increase in the size of individual cells. In regions adjacent to the meristems in the tips of shoots and roots, the daughter cells rapidly increase in size—especially in length—for some time after they are produced. In contrast, when animal cells divide mitotically, the daughter cells are usually roughly the same size as the parent cell.

28.1d Meristems Are Responsible for Growth in Both Height and Girth

Some plants have only one kind of meristem, whereas others have two **(Figure 28.4)**. All plants have **apical meristems**, clusters of self-perpetuating tissue at the tips of their buds, stems, and roots (see Figure 28.4a). Tissues that develop from apical meristems are called **primary tissues** and make up the **primary plant body**. Growth of the primary plant body is called **primary growth.**

Some plants—herbaceous plants such as grasses and dandelions, for example—have only primary growth, which occurs at the tips of roots and shoots. Others have **secondary growth**, as well as primary growth. Originating at cylinders of tissue called **lateral meristems**, secondary growth increases the diameter of older roots and stems (see Figure 28.4b). Tissues that develop from lateral meristems are called **secondary tissues**. Woody plants, such as trees and shrubs, including the strangler fig discussed earlier, all have secondary tissues.

Primary and secondary growth can go on simultaneously in a single plant, with primary growth increasing the length of shoots and roots, whereas secondary growth adds girth to these organs. Each spring, for example, a poplar tree undergoes primary growth at each of its root and shoot tips, whereas secondary growth increases the diameter of its older, woody parts. Plant hormones govern these growth processes and other key events described in Chapter 31.

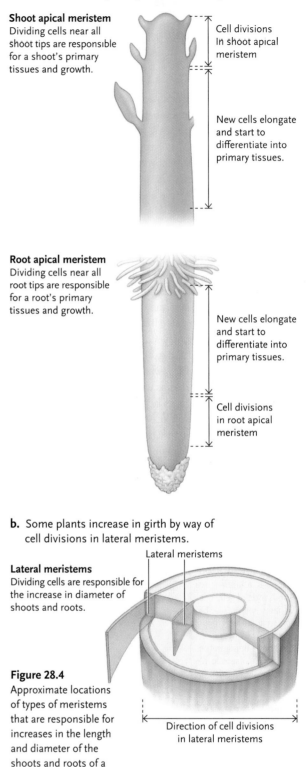

a. Plants increase in length by cell divisions in apical meristems and by elongation of the daughter cells.

Shoot apical meristem
Dividing cells near all shoot tips are responsible for a shoot's primary tissues and growth.

Cell divisions in shoot apical meristem

New cells elongate and start to differentiate into primary tissues.

Root apical meristem
Dividing cells near all root tips are responsible for a root's primary tissues and growth.

New cells elongate and start to differentiate into primary tissues.

Cell divisions in root apical meristem

b. Some plants increase in girth by way of cell divisions in lateral meristems.

Lateral meristems

Lateral meristems
Dividing cells are responsible for the increase in diameter of shoots and roots.

Figure 28.4
Approximate locations of types of meristems that are responsible for increases in the length and diameter of the shoots and roots of a vascular plant.

Direction of cell divisions in lateral meristems

28.1e Monocots and Eudicots Are the Two General Structural Forms of Flowering Plants

Several broad categories of body architecture arose as flowering plants evolved, with the two major categories being the **monocot** and **eudicot** lineages. Grasses, lilies, cattails, corn, and rice are examples of monocots. Eudicots include nearly all familiar angiosperm trees and shrubs, as well as many nonwoody (herbaceous) plants. Examples are poplars, willows, oaks, cacti, roses, poppies, sunflowers, and garden beans and peas.

Monocots and eudicots get their names from the number of *cotyledons*—the seed leaves associated with plant embryos (see Chapter 25). Monocot seeds have one cotyledon and eudicot seeds have two. Although monocots and eudicots have similar types of tissues, their body structures differ in distinctive ways **(Table 28.1)**. As we discuss the morphology of flowering plants, we refer frequently to these structural differences.

28.1f Flowering Plants Can Be Grouped According to Type of Growth and Life Span

As you learned above, we can distinguish between flowering plants depending on whether they are herbaceous or woody plants and whether they are monocots or eudicots. We can also distinguish plants by life span. **Annuals** are herbaceous plants in which the life cycle is completed in one growing season. With minimal or no secondary growth, annuals typically have only apical meristems. Examples are tomatoes (a eudicot) and corn (a monocot). **Biennials** such as carrots complete their life cycle in two growing seasons, and limited secondary growth occurs in some species. In the first season, roots, stems, and leaves form; in its second year of growth, the plant flowers, forms seeds, and dies. In **perennials**, vegetative growth and reproduction continue year after year. Many perennials, such as trees, shrubs, and some vines, have secondary tissues, although others, such as irises and daffodils, do not.

STUDY BREAK

1. Compare the components and functions of a land plant's shoot and root systems.
2. Explain what meristem tissue is and name and describe the functions of the basic types of meristems.

28.2 The Three Plant Tissue Systems

As in animals, plant organs are composed of tissue systems. Each tissue system includes several types of tissue, and each tissue is made up of cells with specializations for different functions **(Table 28.2, p. 674).** *Simple* tissues have only one type of cell. Other tissues are *complex,* with organized arrays of two or

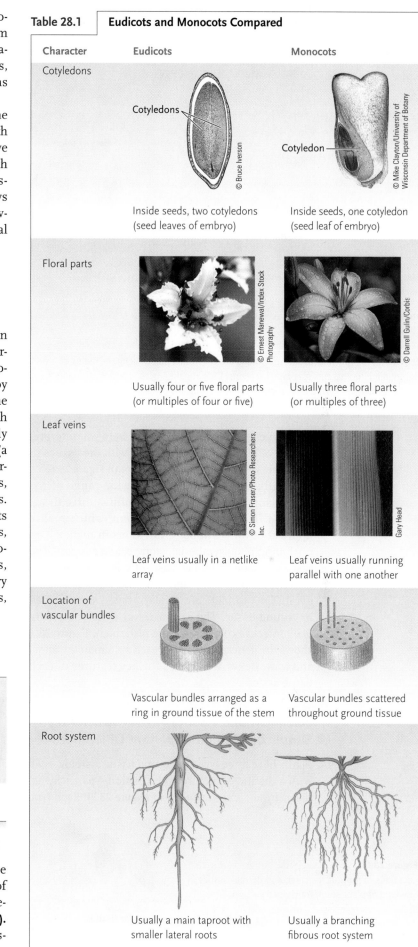

Table 28.1 **Eudicots and Monocots Compared**

Character	Eudicots	Monocots
Cotyledons	Inside seeds, two cotyledons (seed leaves of embryo)	Inside seeds, one cotyledon (seed leaf of embryo)
Floral parts	Usually four or five floral parts (or multiples of four or five)	Usually three floral parts (or multiples of three)
Leaf veins	Leaf veins usually in a netlike array	Leaf veins usually running parallel with one another
Location of vascular bundles	Vascular bundles arranged as a ring in ground tissue of the stem	Vascular bundles scattered throughout ground tissue
Root system	Usually a main taproot with smaller lateral roots	Usually a branching fibrous root system

Table 28.2

Table 28.2	Summary of Flowering Plant Tissues and Their Components		
Tissue System	Name of Tissue	Cell Types in Tissue	Tissue Function
Ground tissue	Parenchyma	Parenchyma cells	Photosynthesis, respiration, storage, secretion
	Collenchyma	Collenchyma cells	Flexible strength for growing plant parts
	Sclerenchyma	Fibres or sclereids	Rigid support, deterring herbivores
Vascular tissue	Xylem	Conducting cells (tracheids, vessel members), parenchyma cells, sclerenchyma cells	Transport of water and dissolved minerals
	Phloem	Conducting cells (sieve tube members), parenchyma cells, sclerenchyma cells	Sugar transport
Dermal tissue	Epidermis	Undifferentiated cells, guard cells, other specialized cells	Control of gas exchange, water loss, protection
	Periderm	Cork, cork cambium, secondary cortex	Protection

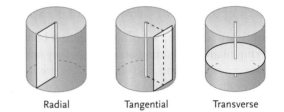

Figure 28.5

Terms that identify how tissue specimens are cut from a plant. Along the radius of a stem or root, longitudinal cuts give radial sections. Cuts at right angles to a root or stem radius give tangential sections. Cuts perpendicular to the long axis of a stem or root give transverse sections (cross sections).

Radial   Tangential   Transverse

more types of cells. **Figure 28.5** will help you interpret images of plant tissues, beginning with the tissues in a transverse section of a stem shown in **Figure 28.6.**

Unlike animals that have a wide range of tissues, plant organs are composed of just three tissue systems. The **ground tissue system**, which makes up most of the plant body, functions in metabolism (including photosynthesis), storage, and support. The **vascular tissue system** consists of xylem and phloem, which transport water and nutrients throughout the plant. The cylinders of vascular tissue are embedded in ground tissue. The **dermal tissue system** is a skin-like protective covering for the plant body. Figure 28.2 shows the general location of each system in the shoot and root. Below we discuss the key features of each tissue system.

28.2a Ground Tissues Are All Structurally Simple but Exhibit Important Differences

Plants have three types of ground tissue systems, each with a distinct structure and function—*parenchyma, collenchyma,* and *sclerenchyma* (**Figure 28.7**). Each type

is structurally simple, being composed mainly of one kind of cell. In a very real sense, the cells in ground tissues are the "worker bees" of plants, carrying out photosynthesis, storing carbohydrates, providing mechanical support for the plant body, and performing other basic functions. Each kind of cell has a distinctive wall structure, and some have variations in the cytoplasmic contents as well.

Parenchyma: Soft Primary Tissues. Parenchyma (*para* = around; *chein* = fill in or pour) makes up the bulk of the primary growth of roots, stems, leaves, flowers, and fruits. Most parenchyma cells have only a thin primary wall and so are pliable and permeable to water. Often the cells are spherical or many-sided, although they also can be elongated like a sausage, as in Figure 28.7a. Parenchyma cells typically have air spaces between them, especially in leaves (see Section 28.3). Stems and leaves in aquatic plants often have very large air spaces between parenchyma cells, which facilitate the movement of oxygen to submerged parts of the plant and help the leaves float upward toward the light.

Figure 28.6

Locations of ground, vascular, and dermal tissues in one kind of plant stem, transverse section. Ground tissues are simple tissues, whereas vascular and dermal tissues are complex, containing various types of specialized cells (Micrograph:, Ed Reschke / Peter Arnold Inc.).

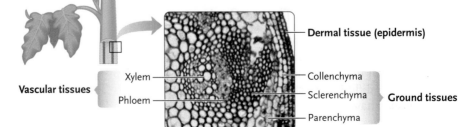

Vascular tissues

Xylem
Phloem

Dermal tissue (epidermis)
Collenchyma
Sclerenchyma — **Ground tissues**
Parenchyma

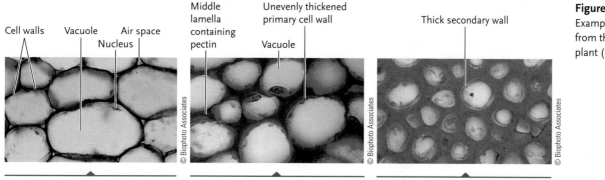

Cell walls   Vacuole   Air space
         Nucleus

Middle lamella containing pectin   Unevenly thickened primary cell wall
         Vacuole

Thick secondary wall

© Biophoto Associates

Figure 28.7
Examples of ground tissues from the stem of a sunflower plant (*Helianthus annuus*).

a. Parenchyma tissues consist of soft, living cells specialized for storage, other functions.

b. Collenchyma tissues provide flexible support.

c. Sclerenchyma tissues provide rigid support and protection.

Parenchyma cells may be specialized for tasks as varied as storage, secretion, and photosynthesis. For example, the photosynthetic cells of leaves are parenchyma cells. In many plant species, modified parenchyma cells are specialized for short-distance transport of solutes. Such cells are common in tissues in which water and solutes must be rapidly moved from cell to cell. Parenchyma cells usually remain alive and metabolically active when mature.

Collenchyma: Flexible Support. The "strings" in celery are examples of the flexible ground tissue called **collenchyma** (*kolla* = glue; see Figure 28.7b), which helps strengthen plant parts that are still elongating. Collenchyma cells are typically elongated, and collectively, they often form strands under the dermal tissue of growing shoot regions and leaf stalks.

The primary walls of collenchyma cells are built of alternating layers of cellulose and pectin and are unevenly thickened. These walls can stretch as the cell enlarges, making them very suitable for support of young, growing organs. Mature collenchyma cells are alive and metabolically active, and they continue to synthesize primary wall layers as the plant grows.

Sclerenchyma: Rigid Support and Protection. Mature plant parts gain additional mechanical support and protection from **sclerenchyma** (*skleros* = hard), cells with thick, lignified secondary walls (see Figure 28.7c). Some regions of the cell wall lack secondary wall material, forming a *pit* where the cell wall is more porous than elsewhere. Water can flow from one sclerenchyma cell to another through these pits. After **lignification** occurs, sclerenchyma cells die because their cytoplasm can no longer exchange gases, nutrients, and other materials with the environment. The walls, however, continue to provide protection and support.

The two types of sclerenchyma cells—*sclereids* and *fibres*—differ in their shape and arrangement. **Sclereids** tend to be short and are often branched; they sometimes aggregate into protective sheets, forming the hard casings of a coconut shell or a peach pit, for example. Sclereids can also be scattered in tissue—cube-shaped sclereids dispersed in the flesh of a pear give it its gritty texture **(Figure 28.8a)**. **Fibres** are long, tapered cells **(Figure 28.8b)** that resist stretching but are more pliable than sclereids. Fibres often occur in bundles in stems and leaves, strengthening and supporting these tissues. We use plant fibres to manufacture rope, paper, and cloth. Linen, for example, is made of fibres extracted from the stems of flax plants (*Linum usitatissimum*).

28.2b Vascular Tissues Are Specialized for Conducting Fluids

Vascular tissue systems consist of complex tissues composed of specialized conducting cells, parenchyma cells, and fibres. *Xylem* and *phloem,* the two kinds of vascular tissues in flowering plants, are organized into cylinders of interconnected cells that extend throughout the plant.

Xylem: Transporting Water and Minerals. **Xylem** (*xylon* = wood) conducts water and dissolved minerals absorbed from the soil upward from a plant's roots to

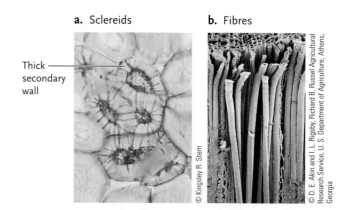

a. Sclereids   **b.** Fibres

Thick secondary wall

© Kingsley R. Stern

© D. E. Akin and I. L. Rigsby, Richard B. Russel Agricultural Research Service, U. S. Department of Agriculture, Athens, Georgia

Figure 28.8
Examples of sclerenchyma cells. **(a)** From the flesh of a pear (*Pyrus*), one type of sclereid: stone cells, each with a thick, lignified wall. **(b)** Strong fibres from stems of a flax plant (*Linum*).

the shoot. It was a key adaptation allowing plants to make the transition to life on land (see Chapter 25). Xylem contains two types of conducting cells: *tracheids* and *vessel members*. Both develop thick, lignified secondary cell walls and die at maturity. The empty cell walls of abutting cells serve as pipelines for water and minerals.

Tracheids are elongated, with tapered, overlapping ends **(Figure 28.9a).** In plants adapted to drier soil conditions, they have strong secondary walls that keep them from collapsing when water becomes scarce. As in sclerenchyma, water can move from cell to cell through pits. Usually, a pit in one cell is opposite a pit of an adjacent cell, so water seeps laterally from tracheid to tracheid.

Vessel members (or vessel elements) are shorter cells joined end to end in tubelike columns called vessels **(Figure 28.9b). Vessels** are typically several centimetres long, and in some vines and trees, they may be many metres long. Like tracheids, vessel members have pits. However, they have another adaptation that greatly enhances water flow. As vessel members mature, enzymes break down portions of their end walls, producing perforations. Some vessel members have a single, large perforation, so that the end is completely open (see Figure 28.7b). Others have a cluster of small, round perforations, or ladderlike bars, extending across the open end. Water moves more efficiently through vessels than tracheids due to their greater diameter and perforated ends.

Fossil evidence shows that the forerunners of modern plant species relied solely on tracheids for water transport, and today ferns and most gymnosperms still have only tracheids. Nearly all angiosperms and a few gymnosperms and seedless vascular plants have *both* tracheids and vessel members, however, which confers an adaptive advantage. Flowing water sometimes contains air bubbles, which are a potentially lethal threat to the plant. Water can flow rapidly through vessel members that are linked end to end, but the open channel cannot prevent air bubbles from forming and possibly blocking the flow through the whole vessel. By contrast, even though water moves more slowly in tracheids, the pits are impermeable to air bubbles, and a bubble that forms in one tracheid stays there; water continues to move between other tracheids.

At maturity, tracheids and vessel members die as genetic cues cause their **protoplasts** to degenerate and lignin to be deposited in the cell walls.

Phloem: Transporting Sugars and Other Solutes. The vascular tissue **phloem** (*phloios* = tree bark) transports solutes, notably the sugars made in photosynthesis, throughout the plant body. The main conducting cells of phloem are **sieve tube members (Figure 28.10),** which are connected end to end, forming a **sieve tube.** As the name implies, their end walls, called sieve plates, are studded with pores. In flowering plants, the phloem is strengthened by fibres and sclereids.

Immature sieve tube members contain the usual plant organelles. Over time, however, the cell nucleus and internal membranes in plastids break down, mitochondria shrink, and the cytoplasm is reduced to a thin layer lining the interior surface of the cell wall. Even without a nucleus, the cell lives up to several years in most plants and much longer in some trees.

In many flowering plants, specialized parenchyma cells known as **companion cells** are connected to mature sieve tube members by plasmodesmata.

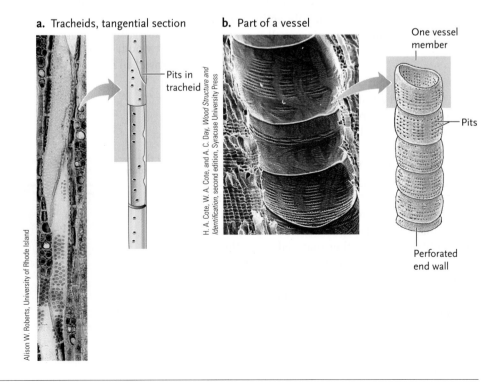

a. Tracheids, tangential section — Pits in tracheid

b. Part of a vessel — One vessel member — Pits — Perforated end wall

H. A. Cote, W. A. Cote, and A. C. Day, *Wood Structure and Identification*, second edition, Syracuse University Press

Alison W. Roberts, University of Rhode Island

Figure 28.9
Representative tracheids and vessel members from woody stems, elements in xylem that conduct water and dissolved mineral salts through the body of a vascular plant. The electron micrographs show **(a)** tracheids from a pine (*Pinus*) and **(b)** a vessel from a red oak (*Quercus rubra*).

a. Sieve-tube members

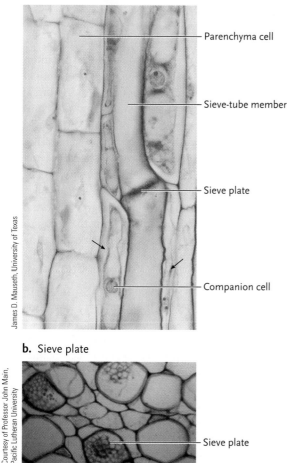

Parenchyma cell

Sieve-tube member

Sieve plate

Companion cell

James D. Mauseth, University of Texas

b. Sieve plate

Sieve plate

Courtesy of Professor John Main, Pacific Lutheran University

Figure 28.10

Structure of sieve tube members. **(a)** Micrograph showing sieve tube members in longitudinal section. The arrows point to companion cells. Long tubes of sieve tube members conduct sugars and other organic compounds. **(b)** Sieve plate in a cell in phloem, cross section.

Unlike sieve tube members, companion cells retain their nucleus when mature. They assist sieve tube members with both the uptake of sugars and the unloading of sugars in tissues engaged in food storage or growth. They may also help regulate the metabolism of mature sieve tube members. We

return to the functions of xylem and phloem cells in Chapter 29.

28.2c The Dermal Tissue System Protects Plant Surfaces

A complex tissue called **epidermis** covers the primary plant body in a single continuous layer **(Figure 28.11a)** or sometimes in multiple layers of tightly packed cells. The external surface of epidermal cell walls is coated with waxes that are embedded in cutin, a network of chemically linked fats. Epidermal cells secrete this coating, or **cuticle**, which resists water loss and helps protect against attacks by microbes. A cuticle coats all plant parts except the very tips of the shoot and the most absorptive parts of roots; other root regions have an extremely thin cuticle.

Most epidermal cells are relatively unspecialized, but some are modified in ways that represent important adaptations for plants. Young stems, leaves, flower parts, and even some roots have pairs of crescent-shaped **guard cells (Figure 28.11b)**. Unlike other cells of the epidermis, guard cells contain chloroplasts and so can carry out photosynthesis. The pore between a pair of guard cells is called a **stoma** (plural, stomata). Water vapour, carbon dioxide, and oxygen cross the epidermis through the stomata. Guard cells regulate opening and closing of stomata via mechanisms we consider in Chapter 29.

Other epidermal specializations are the single-celled or multicellular outgrowths collectively called **trichomes**, which give the stems or leaves of some plants a hairy appearance. Some trichomes exude sugars that attract insect pollinators. Leaf trichomes of *Urtica,* the stinging nettle, provide protection by injecting an irritating toxin into the skin of animals that brush against the plant or try to eat it. **Root hairs**, extensions of the outer wall of root epidermal cells **(Figure 28.11c)**, are also trichomes. Root hairs absorb much of a plant's water and minerals from the soil.

The epidermal cells of flower petals (which are modified leaves) synthesize pigments that are partly responsible for a blossom's colours.

a. Leaf epidermis

Cuticle   Epidermal cell

Parenchyma cell inside leaf

George S. Ellmore

b. Leaf surface

Cuticle-coated cell of lower epidermis   Guard cells

One stoma

© Dr. Jeremy Burgess/SPL/Photo Researchers, Inc.

c. Root hairs

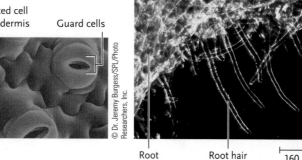

Root   Root hair   160 µm

Courtesy Mark Holland, Salisbury University

Figure 28.11

Structure and examples of epidermal tissue. **(a)** Cross section of leaf epidermis from a bush lily (*Clivia miniata*). **(b)** Scanning electron micrograph of a leaf surface, showing cuticle-covered epidermal cells and stomata. **(c)** Root hairs, an epidermal specialization.

28.3 Primary Shoot Systems

A young flowering plant's shoot system consists of the main stem, leaves, and buds, as well as flowers and fruits. Chapter 30 looks more closely at flowers and fruits; here we focus on the growth and organization of stems, buds, and leaves of the primary shoot system.

28.3a Stems Are Adapted to Provide Support, Routes for Vascular Tissues, Storage, and New Growth

Stems are structurally adapted for four main functions:

- Stems provide mechanical support, generally along a vertical (upright) axis, for body parts involved in growth, photosynthesis, and reproduction. These parts include meristematic tissues, leaves, and flowers.
- Stems house the vascular tissues (xylem and phloem), which transport products of photosynthesis, water and dissolved minerals, hormones, and other substances throughout the plant.
- Stems are often modified to store water and food.
- Buds and specific stem regions contain meristematic tissue that gives rise to new cells of the shoot.

The Modular Organization of a Stem. A plant stem develops in a pattern that divides the stem into modules, each consisting of a *node* and an *internode*. A **node** is a place on the stem where one or more leaves are attached; the area between two nodes is thus an **internode**. New primary growth occurs in buds—a **terminal bud** at the apex of the main shoot, and **lateral buds**, which produce branches (lateral shoots) at the point where leaves meet the stem. Meristematic tissue in buds gives rise to leaves, flowers, or both **(Figure 28.12)**.

In eudicots, most growth in a stem's length occurs directly below the apical meristem as internode cells divide and elongate. Internode cells nearest the apex are most active, so the most visible new growth occurs at the ends of stems. So why isn't the growth of grasses stopped when you mow your lawn or when cattle graze on them? In grasses and some other monocots, the upper cells of an internode stop dividing as the internode elongates, and cell divisions are limited to a meristematic region at the base of the internode. The stems of bamboo and other grasses elongate as the internodes are "pushed up" by the growth of such meristems. This adaptation allows grasses to grow back readily after grazing or mowing because the meristem is not removed.

Terminal buds release a hormone that inhibits the growth of nearby lateral buds, a phenomenon called **apical dominance**. Gardeners who want a bushier plant can stimulate lateral bud growth by periodically cutting off the terminal bud. The flow of hormone signals then dwindles to a level low enough that lateral buds begin to grow. In nature, apical dominance is an adaptation that directs the plant's resources into growing up toward the light.

Primary Growth and Structure of a Stem. Primary growth, the cell divisions and enlargement that produce the primary plant body, begins in the shoot and root apical meristems. The sequence of events is sim-

a. Location of nodes and buds

b. Leaves at a terminal bud

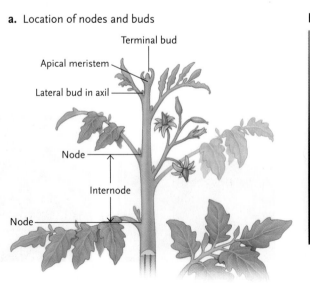

Figure 28.12

Modular structure of a stem. **(a)** The arrangement of nodes and buds on a plant stem. **(b)** Formation of leaves at a terminal bud of a dogwood (genus *Cornus*).

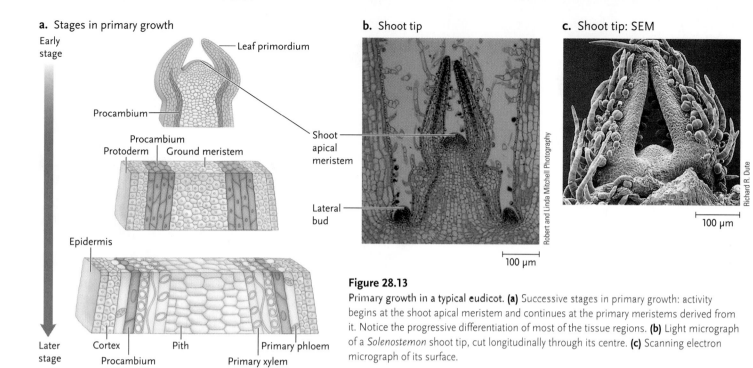

a. Stages in primary growth

Early stage

Leaf primordium

Procambium

Procambium
Protoderm
Ground meristem

Epidermis

Later stage
Cortex
Procambium
Pith
Primary xylem
Primary phloem

b. Shoot tip

Shoot apical meristem

Lateral bud

Robert and Linda Mitchell Photography

100 µm

c. Shoot tip: SEM

Richard R. Dute

100 µm

Figure 28.13

Primary growth in a typical eudicot. **(a)** Successive stages in primary growth: activity begins at the shoot apical meristem and continues at the primary meristems derived from it. Notice the progressive differentiation of most of the tissue regions. **(b)** Light micrograph of a *Solenostemon* shoot tip, cut longitudinally through its centre. **(c)** Scanning electron micrograph of its surface.

ilar in roots and shoots; it is shown for a eudicot shoot in **Figure 28.13.**

The shoot apical meristem is a dome-shaped mass of cells at the tip of shoots, surrounded by developing leaves. When a cell of this meristem divides, one of its daughter cells remains part of the meristem, whereas the other begins to differentiate to follow a particular developmental path.

The differentiating cells give rise to three **primary meristems:** *protoderm, procambium,* and *ground meristem* (see Figure 28.13a). These primary meristems are relatively unspecialized tissues with cells that differentiate, in turn, into specialized cells and tissues. In eudicots, the primary meristems are also responsible for elongation of the plant body.

Each primary meristem occupies a different position in the shoot tip, as shown in Figure 28.13a. Outermost is **protoderm,** a meristem that will produce the stem's epidermis. Inward from the protoderm is the **ground meristem,** which will give rise to ground tissue, most of it parenchyma. **Procambium,** which produces the primary vascular tissues, is sandwiched between ground meristem layers. Procambial cells are long and thin, and their spatial orientation foreshadows the future function of the tissues they produce. In most plants, inner procambial cells give rise to xylem and outer procambial cells to phloem. In plants with secondary growth, a thin region of procambium between the primary xylem and phloem remains undifferentiated. Later it will give rise to a lateral meristem.

The developing vascular tissues become organized into **vascular bundles,** cylinders of primary xylem and phloem that are wrapped in sclerenchyma. Eudicot stems have vascular bundles arranged in a circle that

separates the ground tissue in the centre of the stem (the pith) from the ground tissue under the epidermis (the cortex) **(Figure 28.14a, p. 680).** Both cortex and pith consist mainly of parenchyma; in some plant species, the pith parenchyma stores starch reserves. Monocot stems also have vascular bundles, but these are scattered throughout the ground tissue, so distinct pith and cortical regions do not form **(Figure 28.14b).** In some monocots, including bamboo, the pith breaks down, leaving the stem with a hollow core. The hollow stems of certain hard-walled bamboo species are used to make bamboo flutes.

As leaves and buds develop along a stem, some vascular bundles in the stem branch off into these tissues. The arrangement of vascular bundles in a plant ultimately depends on the number of branch points to leaves and buds and on the number and distribution of leaves.

Stem Modifications. Evolution has produced a range of stem specializations, including structures modified for reproduction, food storage, or both **(Figure 28.15, p. 681).** An onion or a garlic head is a *bulb,* a modified shoot that consists of a bud with fleshy leaves. *Tubers* are stem regions enlarged by the presence of starch-storing parenchyma cells; examples of plants that form tubers are the potato and the cassava (the source of tapioca). The "eyes" of a potato are buds at nodes of the modified stem. Many grasses, such as quackgrass (*Elymus repens*), and some weeds are difficult to eradicate because they have *rhizomes*—long underground stems that can extend as much as 50 cm deep into the soil and rapidly produce new shoots when existing ones are pulled out. The pungent, starchy "root" of

Figure 28.14
Organization of cells and tissues inside the stem of a eudicot and a monocot. **(a)** Part of a stem from alfalfa (*Medicago*), a eudicot. In many species of eudicots and conifers, the vascular bundles develop in a more or less ringlike array in the ground tissue system, as shown here. **(b)** Part of a stem from corn (*Zea mays*), a monocot. In most monocots and some herbaceous eudicots, vascular bundles are scattered through the ground tissue, as shown here.

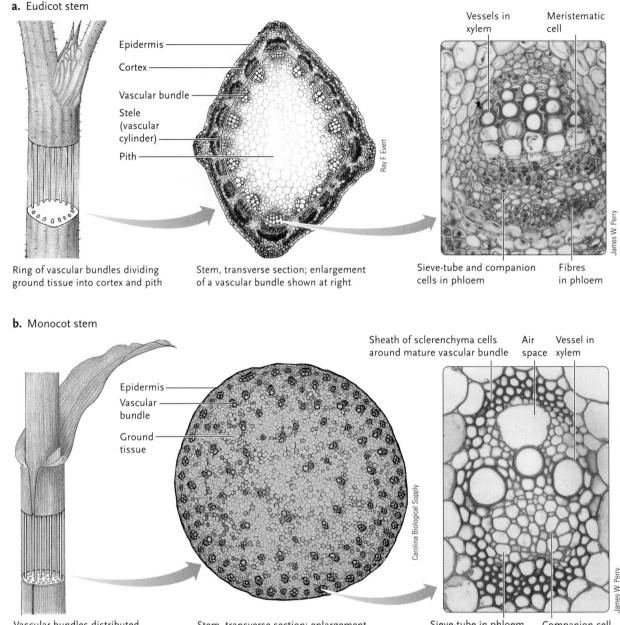

a. Eudicot stem

Epidermis
Cortex
Vascular bundle
Stele (vascular cylinder)
Pith

Ring of vascular bundles dividing ground tissue into cortex and pith

Stem, transverse section; enlargement of a vascular bundle shown at right

Vessels in xylem
Meristematic cell
Sieve-tube and companion cells in phloem
Fibres in phloem

Ray F. Evert

James W. Perry

b. Monocot stem

Epidermis
Vascular bundle
Ground tissue

Vascular bundles distributed throughout ground tissue

Stem, transverse section; enlargement of a vascular bundle shown at right

Sheath of sclerenchyma cells around mature vascular bundle
Air space
Vessel in xylem
Sieve-tube in phloem
Companion cell in phloem

Carolina Biological Supply

James W. Perry

ginger is also a rhizome. Crocuses and some other ornamental plants develop elongated, fleshy underground stems called *corms*, another starch-storage adaptation. Tubers, rhizomes, and corms all have meristematic tissue at nodes from which new plants can be propagated—a vegetative (asexual) reproductive mode. Other plants, including strawberries (*Fragaria* spp.), reproduce vegetatively via slender stems called *stolons*, which grow along the soil surface. New plants arise at nodes along the stolon.

28.3b Leaves Carry Out Photosynthesis and Gas Exchange

Each spring, a mature maple tree heralds the new season by unfurling roughly 100 000 leaves. Some other tree species produce leaves by the millions.

For these and most other plants, leaves are the main organs of photosynthesis and gas exchange (the movement of carbon dioxide and oxygen into and out of the leaf).

Leaf Morphology and Anatomy. In both eudicots and monocots, the leaf **blade** provides a large surface area for absorbing sunlight and carbon dioxide **(Figure 28.16)**. Leaves of flowering plants are generally oriented on the stem axis so that they can capture the maximum amount of sunlight; the stems and leaves of some plants change position to follow the sun's movement during the day (this phenomenon is described in Chapter 31).

Many eudicot leaves, such as those of maples, have a broad, flat blade attached to the stem by a stalklike **petiole** (see Figure 28.16a); the celery stalks that we eat

a. Onion bulb   **b.** Potato tuber   **c.** Ginger rhizome   **d.** Crocus corm   **e.** Strawberry stolons

Figure 28.15

A selection of modified stems. **(a)** The fleshy bulbs of onions (*Allium cepa*) are modified shoots in which the plant stores starch. **(b)** A potato (*Solanum tuberosum*), a tuber. **(c)** Ginger "root," the pungent, starchy rhizome of the ginger plant (*Zingiber officinale*). **(d)** Crocus plants (genus *Crocus*) typically grow from a corm. **(e)** A strawberry plant (*Fragaria ananassa*) and stolon.

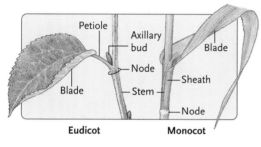

Figure 28.16

Leaf forms. Common forms of eudicot and monocot leaves.

Leaf Primary Growth and Internal Structure. As the shoot apical meristem divides, it produces a series of bumps on its sides, the **leaf primordia**, which give rise to leaves (see Figure 28.13a). As the plant grows and the internodes elongate, the leaves that form from leaf primordia become spaced at intervals along the length of the stem or its branches.

A leaf is typically composed of several layers **(Figure 28.18, p. 682)**. Uppermost is epidermis, with cuticle covering its outer surface. Just beneath the epidermis is **mesophyll** (*mesos* = middle; *phyllon* = leaf), ground tissue composed of loosely packed paren-

are petioles. Petioles hold leaves away from the stem and help prevent individual leaves from shading one another. In many plant species, petioles allow leaves to move in the breeze—think about trembling aspen (*Populus tremuloides*) leaves rustling in a breeze—enhancing air circulation around leaves, thus replenishing the supply of carbon dioxide for photosynthesis. In most monocot leaves, such as those of grass or corn, the blade is longer and narrower and its base simply forms a sheath around the stem (see Figure 28.16b).

In plants of arid habitats, leaves may be reduced to spines to reduce water loss by evaporation **(Figure 28.17a)**; the stem takes over the task of photosynthesis. Leaves or parts of leaves may be modified into tendrils, such as those of the sweet pea (*Lathyrus odoratus*) **(Figure 28.17b)**, or other structures. Epidermal cells on the leaves of the saltbush *Atriplex spongiosa* form balloonlike structures **(Figure 28.17c)** that contain concentrated Na$^+$ and Cl taken up from the salty soil. Eventually, the salt-filled epidermal cells burst or fall off the leaf, releasing the salt to the outside. This adaptation helps control the salt concentration in the plant's tissues—another example of the link between structure, function, and the environment in which a plant lives.

a. Cactus spines   **b.** Tendrils

c. Salt bladders, a form of trichome

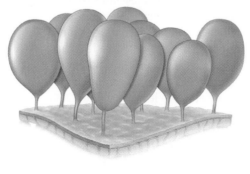

Figure 28.17

A few adaptations of leaves. **(a)** Spines on a barrel cactus (*Ferrocactus covillei*) thwart browsing herbivores and limit the surface area from which water is lost in the plant's arid environment. **(b)** The tendrils of a sweet pea (*Lathyrus odoratus*) help support the climbing plant's stem. **(c)** Salt bladders on the leaf of a saltbush plant (*Atriplex spongiosa*). The "bladders" are trichomes, specialized outgrowths of the leaf epidermis in which excess salt from the plant's tissue fluid accumulates. The salt-laden trichomes eventually burst or slough off.

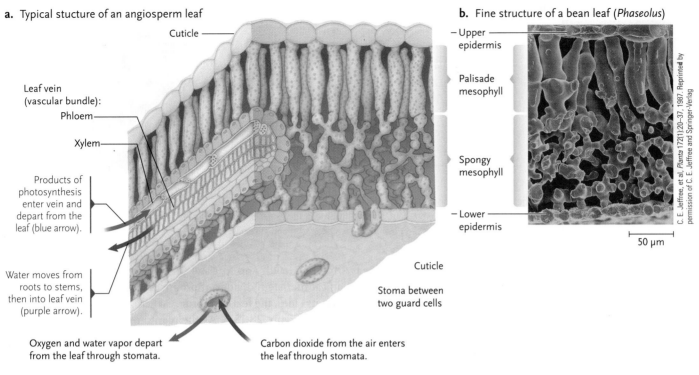

a. Typical stucture of an angiosperm leaf

Cuticle

Leaf vein
(vascular bundle):

Phloem

Xylem

Products of
photosynthesis
enter vein and
depart from the
leaf (blue arrow).

Water moves from
roots to stems,
then into leaf vein
(purple arrow).

Oxygen and water vapor depart
from the leaf through stomata.

Carbon dioxide from the air enters
the leaf through stomata.

b. Fine structure of a bean leaf (*Phaseolus*)

Upper
epidermis

Palisade
mesophyll

Spongy
mesophyll

Lower
epidermis

Cuticle

Stoma between
two guard cells

50 µm

C. E. Jeffree, et al, *Planta* 172(1):20–37, 1987. Reprinted by permission of C. E. Jeffree and Springer-Verlag

Figure 28.18

Internal structure of a leaf. (a) Diagram of a typical leaf structure for many kinds of flowering plants. **(b)** Scanning electron micrograph of tissue from the leaf of a kidney bean plant (*Phaseolus*), transverse section. Notice the compact organization of epidermal cells. See Figure 31.10 for a scanning electron micrograph of stomata.

chyma cells that contain chloroplasts. The leaves of many plants, especially eudicots, contain two layers of mesophyll. *Palisade mesophyll* cells contain more chloroplasts and are arranged in compact columns with smaller air spaces between them, typically toward the upper leaf surface. *Spongy mesophyll,* which tends to be located toward the underside of a leaf, consists of irregularly arranged cells with a conspicuous network of air spaces—between 15% and 50% of the leaf's volume—that give this layer a spongy appearance. What is the role of these air spaces? They enhance the uptake of carbon dioxide and release of oxygen during photosynthesis. Mesophyll also contains collenchyma and sclerenchyma cells, which support the photosynthetic cells.

Below the mesophyll is another cuticle-covered epidermal layer. Except in grasses and a few other plants, this layer contains most of the stomata through which water vapour exits the leaf and gas exchange occurs. For example, the upper surface of an apple leaf has no stomata, whereas a square centimeter of the lower surface has more than 20 000. A square centimeter of the upper epidermis of a tomato leaf has about 1200 stomata, whereas the same area of the lower epidermis has 13 000. Why are more stomata located on the underside of the leaf? This positioning protects stomata from direct exposure to sunlight, thus limiting water loss by evaporation through stomatal openings.

Vascular bundles form a lacy network of **veins** throughout the leaf. Eudicot leaves typically have a branching vein pattern; in monocot leaves, veins tend to run in parallel along the length of the leaf (see Table 28.1).

In temperate regions, most leaves are temporary structures. In deciduous species such as birches and maples, hormonal signals cause the leaves to drop from the stem as days shorten in autumn. Other temperate plants, such as most conifers, also drop their leaves (which are modified into needles in conifers), but they appear "evergreen" because the leaves may persist for several years and do not all drop at the same time.

STUDY BREAK

1. Describe the functions of stems and stem structures and list the basic steps in the primary growth of stems.
2. Explain the general function of leaves and how leaf anatomy supports this role in eudicots and monocots.
3. Describe the steps in the primary growth of a leaf and the structures that result from the process.

28.4 Root Systems

Plants cannot move around to find water and nutrients when they have depleted supplies in their immediate soil neighbourhood, so they must be able to forage for new supplies. Once found, the plant must absorb enough water and dissolved minerals to sustain growth and routine cellular maintenance. These tasks can require a tremendous root surface area, at least part of which is regularly replaced. In one study, rye plants (*Secale cereale*) that had been growing for only four months were measured. One plant's root system had a surface area of more than 700 m²— about 130 times greater than the surface area of its shoot system!

In addition to taking up water and nutrients, roots store nutrients produced by photosynthesis, some of which is used by root cells and some transported later to cells of the shoot. As the root system penetrates downward and spreads out, it also anchors the aboveground parts.

28.4a Taproot and Fibrous Root Systems Are Specialized for Particular Functions

Most eudicots have a **taproot system**—a single main root, or taproot, that is adapted for storage, plus smaller branching roots called **lateral roots (Figure 28.19a)**. As the main root grows downward, its diameter increases, and the lateral roots emerge along the length of its older, differentiated regions. The youngest lateral roots are near the root tip. Carrots and dandelions have a taproot system, as do pines and many other conifers. A pine's taproot system can penetrate 6 m or more into the soil.

Grasses and many other monocots develop a **fibrous root system** in which several main roots branch to form a dense mass of smaller roots **(Figure 28.19b)**. Fibrous root systems are adapted to absorb water and nutrients from the upper layers of soil and tend to spread out laterally from the base of the stem. Fibrous roots are important ecologically because dense root networks help hold topsoil in place and prevent erosion. During the 1930s, overgrazing by livestock and intensive farming in the prairie provinces of Canada and the US Midwest destroyed hundreds of thousands of acres of native prairie grasses, contributing to soil erosion on a massive scale. Swirling clouds of soil particles prompted journalists to name the area the Dust Bowl and gave this decade the name "the Dirty Thirties."

In some plants, **adventitious roots** arise from the stem of the young plant. "Adventitious" refers to any structure arising at an unusual location, such as roots that grow from stems or leaves. Adventitious roots of Virginia creeper (*Parthenociccus quinquefolia*) and some other climbing plants produce a gluelike substance that allows them to cling to vertical surfaces. The *prop roots* of a corn plant are adventitious roots that develop from the shoot node nearest the soil surface; they both support the plant and absorb water and nutrients. Mangroves and other trees that grow

a. Taproot system

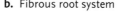

b. Fibrous root system

c. Adventitious roots

© Beth Davidow/Visuals Unlimited

Figure 28.19
Types of roots.
(a) Taproot system of a California poppy (*Eschscholzia californica*). **(b)** Fibrous root system of a grass plant. **(c)** Example of adventitious roots, the numerous prop roots of red mangrove trees (*Rhizophora*).

in marshy habitats often have huge prop roots, which develop from branches and from the main stem **(Figure 28.19c).**

28.4b Root Structure Is Specialized for Underground Growth

Like shoots, roots have distinct anatomical parts, each with a specific function. In most plants, primary growth of roots begins when an embryonic root emerges from a germinating seed and its apical meristem becomes active. **Figure 28.20** shows the structure of a root tip. Notice that the root apical meristem terminates in a dome-shaped cell mass, the **root cap.** The meristem produces the cap, which, in turn, surrounds and protects the meristem as the root elongates through the soil. Certain cells in the cap respond to gravity, guiding the root tip downward. Cap cells also secrete a polysaccharide-rich substance that lubricates the tip and eases the growing root's passage through the soil. Outer root cap cells are continually abraded off and replaced by new cells at the cap's base.

Zones of Primary Growth in Roots. Root primary growth takes place in successive stages, beginning at the root tip and progressing upward.

The root apical meristem and the actively dividing cells behind it form the **zone of cell division.** As in the stem, cells of the apical meristem divide to produce cells that remain as part of the meristem and other cells that differentiate into the three primary meristems. Cells in the centre of the root tip become the procambium, those just outside the procambium become ground meristem, and those on the periphery of the apical meristem become protoderm.

The zone of cell division merges into the **zone of elongation.** Most of the increase in a root's length comes from this region, where cells become longer as their vacuoles fill with water. This "hydraulic" elongation pushes the root cap and apical meristem through the soil by as much as several centimetres a day.

Above the zone of elongation, cells do not increase in length, but they may differentiate further and take on specialized roles in the **zone of maturation.** For example, epidermal cells in this zone give rise to root hairs, and the procambium, ground meristem, and protoderm complete their differentiation in this region.

Tissues of the Root System. Coupled with the primary growth of the shoot, primary root growth produces a unified system of vascular pipelines extending from root tip to shoot tip. The root procambium produces cells that mature into the root's xylem and phloem **(Figure 28.21).** Ground meristem gives rise to the root's cortex, its ground tissue of starch-storing parenchyma cells that surround the **stele.** In eudicots, the stele runs through the centre of the root (see **Figure 28.21a**). In corn and some other monocots, the stele forms a ring that divides the ground tissue into cortex and pith (see **Figure 28.21b**).

The root cortex often contains air spaces that allow oxygen to reach all of the living root cells. In many flowering plants, the outer root cortex cells give rise to an **exodermis,** a thin band of cells that, among other functions, may limit water losses from roots and help regulate the absorption of ions. The innermost layer of the root cortex is the **endodermis,** a thin, selectively permeable barrier that helps control the movement of water and dissolved minerals into the stele. We look in more detail at the roles of exodermis and endodermis in Chapter 29.

a.

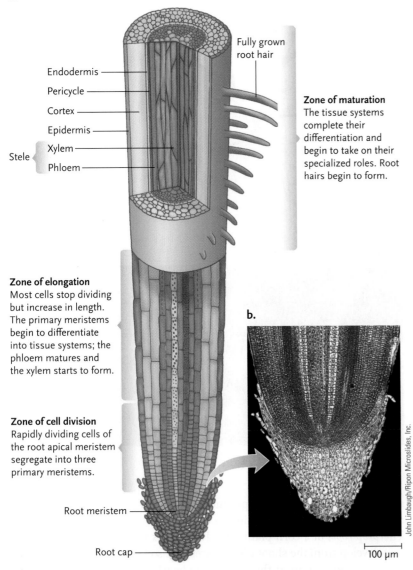

Endodermis
Pericycle
Cortex
Epidermis
Xylem
Phloem
Stele {

Fully grown root hair

Zone of maturation
The tissue systems complete their differentiation and begin to take on their specialized roles. Root hairs begin to form.

Zone of elongation
Most cells stop dividing but increase in length. The primary meristems begin to differentiate into tissue systems; the phloem matures and the xylem starts to form.

Zone of cell division
Rapidly dividing cells of the root apical meristem segregate into three primary meristems.

Root meristem

Root cap

b.

100 μm

John Limbaugh/Ripon Microslides, Inc.

Figure 28.20
Tissues and zones of primary growth in a root tip. **(a)** Generalized root tip, longitudinal section. **(b)** Micrograph of a corn root tip, longitudinal section.

a. Eudicot root

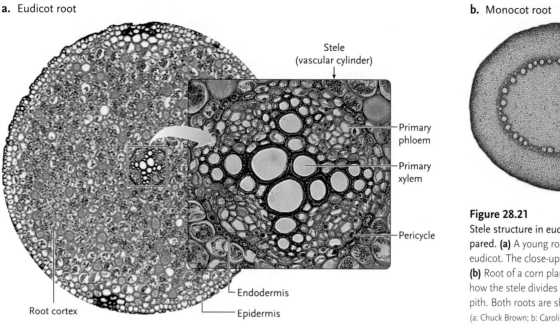

Stele (vascular cylinder)

Primary phloem

Primary xylem

Pericycle

Endodermis

Epidermis

Root cortex

b. Monocot root

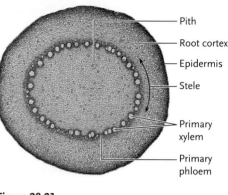

Pith

Root cortex

Epidermis

Stele

Primary xylem

Primary phloem

Figure 28.21

Stele structure in eudicot and monocot roots compared. **(a)** A young root of the buttercup *Ranunculus*, a eudicot. The close-up shows details of the stele. **(b)** Root of a corn plant (*Zea mays*), a monocot. Notice how the stele divides the ground tissue into cortex and pith. Both roots are shown in transverse section.

(a: Chuck Brown; b: Carolina Biological Supply.)

Between the stele and the endodermis is the **pericycle**, consisting of one or more layers of parenchyma cells that have retained the ability to function as meristem. The pericycle produces lateral roots **(Figure 28.22)** in response to chemical growth regulators. These lateral roots grow out through the cortex and epidermis, producing enzymes that help break down the intervening cells. The distribution and frequency of lateral root formation partly control the overall shape of the root system and the extent of the soil area it can penetrate.

The outer surface of some cells in the developing root epidermis become elongated into root hairs (see Figure 28.20). Root hairs can be more than a centimeter long and can form in less than a day. Collectively, the thousands or millions of them on a plant's roots greatly increase the plant's absorptive surface. But it is not just the increased surface area provided by root hairs that increases nutrient uptake: each hair is a slender tube with thin walls made sticky on their surface by a coating of pectin. Soil particles tend to adhere to the walls, providing an intimate association between the hair and the surrounding earth, thus facilitating the uptake of water molecules

and mineral ions from soil. When plants are transplanted, rough handling can tear off much of this fragile absorptive surface. Unable to take up enough water and minerals, the transplant may die before new root hairs can form.

STUDY BREAK

1. Compare the two general types of root systems.
2. Describe the zones of primary growth in roots.
3. Describe the various tissues that arise in a root system and their functions.

28.5 Secondary Growth

All plants undergo primary growth of the root and stem. In addition, some plants have secondary growth processes that add girth to roots and stems over two or

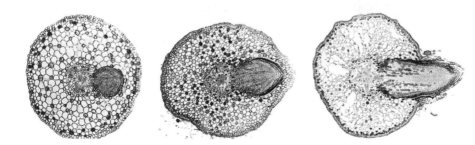

Figure 28.22

Micrographs showing the formation of a lateral root from the pericycle of a willow tree (*Salix*). These micrographs show transverse sections. (All images: © Omnikron/Photo Researches, Inc.)

more growing seasons. In plant species that have secondary growth, older stems and roots become more massive and woody through the activity of two types of lateral meristems called *cambia* (singular, cambium). One of these meristems, the **vascular cambium**, produces secondary xylem and phloem. The other, called the **cork cambium**, produces **cork**, a secondary tissue that replaces the original epidermis of the plant. In contrast to the cells of the apical meristerms, the cells of the lateral meristems divide perpendicular to the stem's longitudinal axis, so their descendants add girth to the stem instead of length.

28.5a Vascular Cambium Gives Rise to Secondary Growth in Stems

Recall that after the stem of a woody plant completes its primary growth, each vascular bundle contains a layer of undifferentiated cells between the primary xylem and the primary phloem. These cells, along with parenchyma cells between the bundles, eventually give rise to a continuous cylinder of vascular cambium that surrounds the xylem and pith of the stem **(Figure 28.23)**. Secondary growth takes place as the cells of the vascular cambium divide. Division of the vascular cambium produces secondary xylem to the inside of the cambium and secondary phloem to the outside of the cambium.

With time, the mass of secondary xylem inside the ring of vascular cambium increases, forming the hard tissue known as **wood**. Outside the vascular cambium, secondary phloem cells are also added each year **(Figure 28.24)**. (The primary phloem cells, which have thin walls, are destroyed as they are pushed outward by secondary growth.) As a stem increases in diameter, the growing mass of new tissue eventually causes the cortex, and the epidermis beyond it, to rupture. Such breaks in the outer protective "skin" of the plant are potentially harmful as they would allow easy entrance for pathogens. The cork cambium—produced early in the stem's secondary

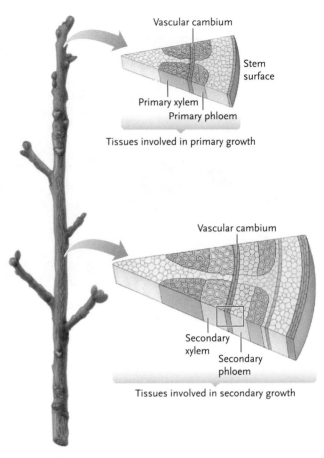

Figure 28.23
Secondary and primary growth compared. In a woody plant, primary growth resumes each spring at the terminal and lateral buds. Secondary growth resumes at the vascular cambium inside the stem.

development by meristem cells in the cortex or epidermis—replaces the lost epidermis with cork cells. The walls of cork cells contain lignin and thick layers of **suberin**, a waxy substance that is very impermeable to water and gases. Cork cells are dead at maturity.

Bark encompasses all the tissues outside the vascular cambium; it thus includes the secondary phloem,

Figure 28.24
Relationship between the vascular cambium and its derivative cells (secondary xylem and phloem). The drawing shows stem growth through successive seasons. Notice how the ongoing divisions displace the cambial cells, moving them steadily outward even as the core of xylem increases the stem or root thickness.

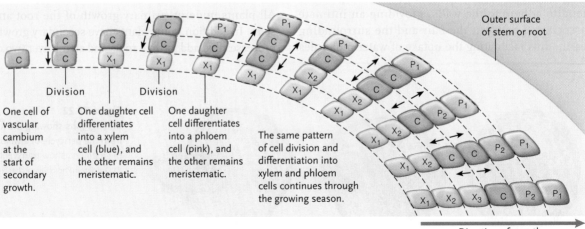

One cell of vascular cambium at the start of secondary growth.

One daughter cell differentiates into a xylem cell (blue), and the other remains meristematic.

One daughter cell differentiates into a phloem cell (pink), and the other remains meristematic.

The same pattern of cell division and differentiation into xylem and phloem cells continues through the growing season.

Outer surface of stem or root

Direction of growth

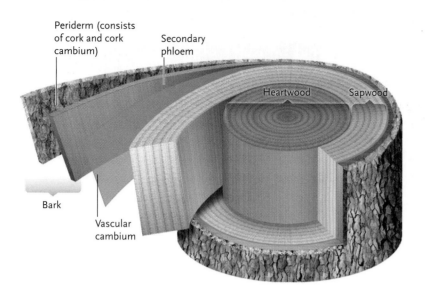

Periderm (consists of cork and cork cambium)

Secondary phloem

Heartwood

Sapwood

Bark

Vascular cambium

Figure 28.25
Structure of a woody stem showing extensive secondary growth. Heartwood, the mature tree's core, has no living cells. Sapwood, the cylindrical zone of xylem between the heartwood and vascular cambium, contains some living parenchyma cells among the nonliving vessels and tracheids. Everything outside the vascular cambium is bark. Everything inside it is wood.

the cork cambium, and the cork **(Figure 28.25)**. Girdling a tree by removing a strip of bark around the trunk is lethal because it destroys the secondary phloem layer, so nutrients from photosynthesis in leaves cannot reach the tree's roots. Cork for use in flooring and as bottle stoppers is harvested from the thick outer bark of the cork oak, *Quercus suber* **(Figure 28.26)**. Cork can be harvested from these trees once they are 25 years old and can be sustainably harvested every 9 to 12 years thereafter. Some trees can yield about 1 tonne of cork over the course of their lives!

How do the vascular cambium and other living tissues in a secondary stem obtain oxygen, given that the bark can be very thick on some trees? In some regions of the stem, the cork cambium divides very actively, forming spongy tissue with abundant air spaces (*lenticels*). Lenticels allow exchanges of oxygen and carbon dioxide between the living tissues and the outside air.

As a tree ages, changes also unfold in the appearance and function of the wood itself. In the centre of its older stems and roots is **heartwood**, dry tissue that no longer transports water and solutes and is a storage depot for some defensive compounds. In time, these substances—including resins, oils, gums, and tannins—clog and fill in the oldest xylem pipelines. Typically, they darken the heartwood, strengthen it, and make it more aromatic and resistant to decay. **Sapwood** is secondary growth located between heartwood and the vascular cambium. Compared with heartwood, it is wet and not as strong (see Figure 28.25).

In temperate climates, trees produce secondary xylem seasonally, with larger diameter cells produced in spring, when water is generally abundant, and smaller diameter cells in summer, when less water is available to be transported. The resulting "spring wood" and "summer wood" reflect light differently, and it is possible to identify them as alternating light and dark bands. The alternating bands represent annual growth layers known as "growth rings" **(Figure 28.27, p. 688)**. The age of a tree can be determined by counting the growth rings.

Growth rings also provide information on past climates: the wider spaced the rings, the more growth a tree was able to put on in one year, so the better the conditions (i.e., warmer and wetter). Dendroclimatologists use tree rings and other biological information to reconstruct past environments. This line of research is making significant contributions to our understanding of how the global climate has changed over time (see *People Behind Biology*).

Daniel Mosquin

Figure 28.26
Cork oak (*Quercus suber*) that has recently had part of its bark harvested.

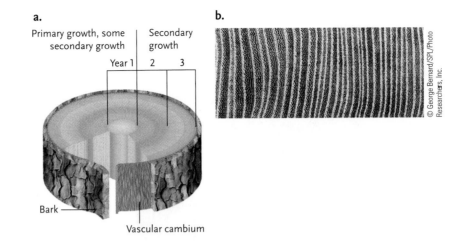

Figure 28.27

Secondary growth and tree ring formation. **(a)** Radial cut through a woody stem that has three annual rings, corresponding to secondary growth in years 2 through 4. **(b)** Tree rings in an elm (*Ulmas*). Each ring corresponds to one growing season. Differences in the widths of tree rings correspond to shifts in climate, including the availability of water.

28.5b Secondary Growth Can Also Occur in Roots

The roots of grasses, palms, and other monocots are almost always produced by primary growth alone, but in some plants, secondary growth also occurs in roots, although it is different from that in stems. In a root, the vascular cambium arises in part from a procambium layer between the xylem and phloem (**Figure 28.28**, step 1) and in part from the pericycle (step 2), eventually

Figure 28.28
Secondary growth in the root of one type of woody plant.

forming a complete cylinder (step 3). The vascular cambium functions in roots as it does in stems, producing secondary xylem to the inside and secondary phloem to the outside. As secondary xylem accumulates, older roots can become extremely thick and woody. Their ongoing secondary growth is powerful enough to break through concrete sidewalks and even dislodge the foundations of homes.

The pericycle also produces cork cambium in roots. In many woody eudicots and in all gym-

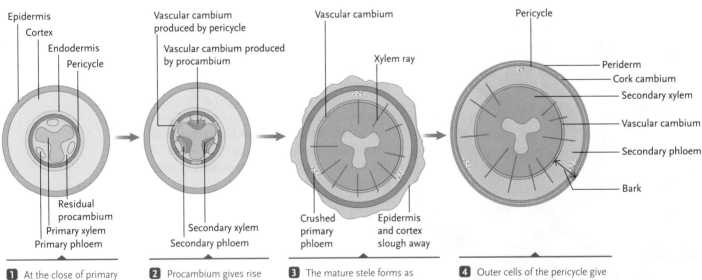

1 At the close of primary growth, the root's procambium has given rise to primary xylem and phloem. Thick root cortex surrounds thin layers of pericycle and endodermis. The epidermis is the outermost layer of the root.

2 Procambium gives rise to the pericycle and distinct regions of vascular cambium. One region gives rise to secondary xylem; the other gives rise to secondary phloem.

3 The mature stele forms as secondary xylem and phloem enlarge and vascular cambium becomes sandwiched between them. The pericycle forms the outer layer of the stele. Xylem rays develop, primary xylem is crushed by the expanding secondary phloem, and the epidermis and underlying root cortex begin to slough away.

4 Outer cells of the pericycle give rise to cork cambium, from which a layered periderm develops. Bark consists of all the tissues outside the vascular cambium, including secondary phloem.

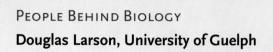

Douglas Larson, University of Guelph

You might think that the biggest trees would also be the oldest, but this isn't necessarily the case. Some big trees are very old—the giant sequoias of California for example—but sometimes the oldest trees are slow-growing survivors of marginal habitats. In Canada, the oldest trees east of the Rocky Mountains are white cedars (*Thuja occidentalis*) growing in "vertical forests" on the cliffs of the Niagara Escarpment **(Figure 1).** The escarpment runs through southwestern Ontario from near Niagara Falls north to the Bruce Peninsula that juts out into Lake Huron.

These ancient trees were discovered in the 1980s by Doug Larson, a biologist at the University of Guelph, Ontario, and his graduate students. Larson was interested in how environmental gradients influence a plant community and had decided that the cliffs of the Niagara Escarpment would be an interesting gradient to study. As part of describing the forest community on the cliffs, Larson and his students sampled the trees to determine their age. This step sounds simple, but because the trees grow on steep cliffs, sampling them meant dangling over the edge of a cliff in harness and helmet using rock climbing skills. The trees were stunted, twisted, and very small, ranging from a few centimetres to a

Figure 1
White cedar (*Thuja occidentalis*) growing on a cliff of the Niagara Escarpment, Ontario.

few metres in height and less than 25 cm in diameter. Thin cores were taken from living trees using a core borer. Rings are usually very obvious in both slices and cores (see Figure 28.27), but when Larson looked at the cores in the lab, he couldn't see any rings. Only after the cores were polished with sandpaper and checked under a microscope could the rings be counted. To the team's amazement, the tree was 350 years old! Larson did more extensive sampling of the cliff forests, in collaboration with Peter

Kelly, a dendrochronologist (a biologist who uses tree-ring data to date past events), and found that these trees were indeed ancient, with some living specimens that were more than 1300 years old (they germinated in about 690 C.E.). Larson had discovered an ancient forest that had survived for centuries in one of the most heavily populated parts of Canada. Other ancient cliff forests—which are, literally, life on the edge—have since been discovered elsewhere in the world.

nosperms, most of the root epidermis and cortex falls away, and the surface consists entirely of tissue produced by the cork cambium (see Figure 28.28, step 4).

28.5c Secondary Growth Is an Adaptive Response

Like all living organisms, plants compete for resources, and woody stems and roots confer some advantages. Plants with taller stems or wider canopies that defy the pull of gravity can intercept more of the light energy from the sun. With a greater energy supply for photosynthesis, they have the metabolic means to increase

their root and shoot systems and thus are better able to acquire resources—and ultimately to reproduce successfully.

In every stage of a plant's growth cycle, growth maintains a balance between the shoot system and the root system. Leaves and other photosynthetic parts of the shoot must supply root cells with enough sugars to support their metabolism, and roots must provide the shoot structures with water and minerals. As long as a plant is growing, this balance is maintained, even as the complexity of the root and shoot systems increases. This happens in all plants, whether they live only a few months or—like some bristlecone pines—for 6000 years.

Figure 1
Welwitschia mirabilis growing in the Namib desert of Africa.

In this chapter, we've established the basic anatomy and morphology of the plant body, with an emphasis on angiosperms. In Chapter 31, we look at how plants control the patterns of growth and development described in this chapter. First, however, we need to consider how water and nutrients are transported in the plant body (see Chapter 29) and how angiosperm seedlings are formed (see Chapter 30).

(see Chapter 29) and how angiosperm seedlings are formed (see Chapter 30).

STUDY BREAK

1. Explain the nature of secondary growth and where it typically occurs in plants.
2. Describe the components of vascular cambium and their roles in secondary growth in stems, including the development of tissues such as bark, cork, and wood.
3. Compare secondary growth in stems and in roots.

UNANSWERED QUESTIONS

Are plants developmental procrastinators?

It is well established that plants can survive physical insults and exposure to a wide range of environmental fluctuations. What biological resources of plants make them so resilient given their lifestyle constraints? What is the source of phenotypic plasticity that allows a plant's body form to change in response to changes in its habitats? Perhaps the answer lies in the ability of plants to put off making developmental decisions in response to environmental shifts.

Unlike most animal cells, plant cells are pluripotent, retaining their developmentally flexibility. Thus, they can behave as stem cells capable of proliferating and producing new structures and even new individuals. Furthermore, many types of plant cells will readily transdifferentiate and assume a new cellular identity even after reaching developmental maturity. In other words, few developmental decisions appear to be final, and many can be tailored to the environmental constraints imposed on the plant. Some plant species appear to have this flexibility even during more global developmental events, such as switching from vegetative growth to reproductive growth or flowering. Why is that the case? Recent findings suggest that by "leaving all options open," plants can quickly adapt to environmental changes and produce progeny, which is the ultimate biological goal for all living organisms.

Research has documented that shifts in environmental context activate genetic changes underlying plants' developmental and phenotypic plasticity. For example, at the whole-organism level, some plants, such as *Impatiens balsamina*, can switch between making leaves and making flowers if relative day length changes. In fact, these plants can make leaves that are partial flowers, or flowers that are partial leaves, if light conditions are alternated between short days and long days. Nicholas Battey at the University of Reading in England and his colleagues, who have investigated this phenomenon for many years, have demonstrated that a genetic basis exists for this ability to change body form in response to changing environmental cues. Furthermore, Battey's group suggests that among flowering plants, a genetic continuum exists from species that require constant reminders to initiate flowering to species that require only a single signal. For perennial plants such as trees, developmental reprogramming is essential because it allows them to orchestrate seasonally appropriate formation and growth of different organs from the same meristem. Currently, a major effort is under way to understand the genetic basis of developmental evolution, as well as how genetic variation may influence phenotypic plasticity. Since plasticity appears to be closely associated with environmental factors, one approach is to study the natural variants of a species from different geographic origins.

Plants respond to environmental variation both spatially and temporally. Perhaps a sort of biological global positioning system (GPS) exists that provides developmentally relevant information in time and space, which the plant translates into a variety of responses. In some species, the GPS may be on all the time, whereas in other species, it may operate only at certain times of the year, or it may function only once during the plant's lifetime. What might these genetic GPS devices be? How would we test this idea? Have candidate genes already been identified that might be components within the GPS? Is there a link between a plant's GPS and the genetic basis for its ability to procrastinate developmentally? In short, the answer to all of these questions appears to be "maybe," and in all likelihood, the full answer will be a complex one. Research conducted by Christopher Cullis at Case Western Reserve University shows that environmentally induced changes in the physical features of flax plants (*Linum usitatissimum*) are accompanied by changes in the entire genome of affected plants, and some of these genetic alterations are heritable. These findings are particularly striking because they demonstrate that in the short term, plants can respond to environmental fluctuations not only by altering their developmental output (body form and phenotype) but also by "reserving" their genomes. That the very blueprint of life, DNA, is also imbued with significant plasticity is particularly exciting and opens a new realm of inquiry into the mechanisms by which plants may respond to environmental challenges. In some biological contexts, being a procrastinator can be advantageous.

Marianne Hopkins is a postdoctoral fellow in the Biology Department at the University of Waterloo in Waterloo, Canada. Her expertise lies in plant genetics and plant molecular biology.

Susan Lolle is an associate professor of biology at the University of Waterloo in Waterloo, Canada. Her research interests include plant development, genetics, and genome biology. To learn more go to http://www.biology.uwaterloo.ca.

Review

Go to CENGAGENOW™ at http://hed.nelson.com/ to access quizzing, animations, exercises, articles, and personalized homework help.

28.1 Plant Structure and Growth: An Overview

- Differences between the structures and growth of plants and animals reflect their modes of nutrition.

- The plant body of an angiosperm consists of an above-ground shoot system with stems, leaves, and flowers and an underground root system.

- Meristems give rise to the plant body and are responsible for a plant's lifelong growth. Each meristem cell produces two daughter cells, one of which remains part of the meristem, whereas the other differentiates into a cell of one of the three primary tissues (protoderm, ground tissue, or procambium).

- Primary growth of roots and shoots originates at apical meristems at root and shoot tips. Some plants have lateral meristems that produce secondary growth and increase the diameter of stems and roots.

- The two major classes of flowering plants (angiosperms) are monocots and eudicots; angiosperms can also be differentiated based on pattern of growth (annuals versus perennials, woody versus herbaceous).

28.2 The Three Plant Tissue Systems

- All plant cells have primary cell walls composed primarily of cellulose. In some cells, secondary walls are laid down inside the primary walls. Maturing cells become specialized for specific functions, with some functions accomplished by the walls of dead cells.

- Plants have three tissue systems. Ground tissues make up most of the plant body, vascular tissues serve in transport, and dermal tissue forms a protective cover.

- Of the three types of ground tissues, parenchyma is active in photosynthesis, storage, and other tasks, whereas collenchyma and sclerenchyma provide mechanical support.

- Xylem and phloem are the plant vascular tissues. Xylem conducts water and dissolved minerals taken up from the soil and consists of conducting cells called tracheids and vessel members. Phloem, which conducts the products of photosynthesis from the leaves to the rest of the plant, contains living cells (sieve tube members) joined end-to-end in sieve tubes.

- The dermal tissue, epidermis, is coated with a waxy cuticle that restricts water loss. Water vapour and other gases enter and leave the plant through pores called stomata, which are flanked by specialized epidermal cells called guard cells. Epidermal specializations also include trichomes, such as root hairs.

28.3 Primary Shoot Systems

- The primary shoot system consists of the main stem, leaves, and buds, plus any attached flowers and fruits. Stems provide mechanical support, house vascular tissues, and may store food and fluid.

- Stems are organized into modular segments. Nodes are points where leaves and buds are attached, and internodes are the regions between nodes. The terminal bud at a shoot tip consists of shoot apical meristem. Lateral buds occur at intervals along the stem. Meristem tissue in buds gives rise to leaves, flowers, or both.

- Derivatives of the apical meristem produce three primary meristems: protoderm makes the stem's epidermis, procambium gives rise to primary xylem and phloem, and ground meristem gives rise to ground tissue.

- Vascular tissues are organized into vascular bundles, with phloem outside of the xylem in each bundle.

- Monocot and eudicot leaves have blades of different forms, all providing a large surface area for absorbing sunlight and carbon dioxide. Leaf modifications are adaptive responses to environmental selection pressures. Leaf characteristics such as shape or arrangement may change over the life cycle of a long-lived plant.

28.4 Root Systems

- Roots absorb water and dissolved minerals and conduct them to aerial plant parts; they anchor and sometimes support the plant and often store food. Root morphologies include taproot systems, fibrous root systems, and adventitious roots.

- During primary growth of a root, the primary meristem and actively dividing cells make up the zone of cell division, which merges into the zone of elongation. Past the zone of elongation, cells may differentiate and perform specialized roles in the zone of cell maturation.

- A root's vascular tissues (xylem and phloem) usually are arranged as a central stele. Parenchyma tissue around the stele forms the root cortex. The root endodermis also wraps around the stele. Inside it is the pericycle, containing parenchyma that can function as meristem. It gives rise to root primordia from which lateral roots emerge. Root hairs from the epidermis greatly increase the surface available for absorbing water and solutes.

28.5 Secondary Growth

- In plants with secondary growth, older stems and roots become more massive and woody via the activity of vascular cambium and cork cambium.

- Vascular cambium produces secondary phloem to the outside and secondary xylem to the inside of the stem.

- Cork cambium gives rise to cork, which replaces epidermis lost when stems increase in diameter.

- Bark consists of all tissues outside of the vascular cambium (secondary phloem, cork cambium, and cork).

- In root secondary growth, a thin layer of procambium cells between the xylem and phloem differentiates into vascular cambium. The pericycle produces root cork cambium.

Questions

Self-Test Questions

1. With respect to growth, plants differ from animals in that
   a. plant growth involves only an increase in the total number of the organism's cells.
   b. plant cells remain roughly the same size after cell division, whereas animal cells increase in size after they form.
   c. all plants form woody tissues during growth.
   d. plants have indeterminate growth; most animals have determinate growth.
   e. plants can grow only when young; animals grow for many years.

2. Identify the correct pairing of a plant tissue and its function.
   a. epidermis: rigid support
   b. xylem: sugar transport
   c. parenchyma: photosynthesis, respiration
   d. phloem: water and mineral transport
   e. periderm: control of gas exchange

3. Identify the correct pairing of a structure and its component(s).
   a. epidermis: companion cells
   b. phloem: sieve tube members
   c. sclerenchyma: lignin
   d. secondary cell wall: cuticle
   e. parenchyma: sclereids

4. Which of the following would be absent in a eudicot leaf?
   a. spongy mesophyll
   b. palisade mesophyll
   c. pericycle
   d. vascular bundles
   e. stoma

5. A student left a carrot in her refrigerator. Three weeks later, she noticed slender white fibres growing from its surface. They were not a fungus. Instead, they were
   a. lateral roots on a taproot.
   b. adventitious roots.
   c. root hairs on a fibrous root.
   d. root hairs on a lateral root.
   e. young prop roots.

6. Which of the following is *not* a structure that results from secondary plant growth?
   a. periderm
   b. a mature oak leaf
   c. cork
   d. pith
   e. heartwood

7. The greatest mitotic activity in a root takes place in the
   a. zone of maturation.
   b. zone of cell division.
   c. zone of elongation.
   d. root cap.
   e. endodermis.

Questions for Discussion

1. While camping in a national park, you notice a "Do Not Litter" sign nailed onto the trunk of a mature fir tree about 2 m off the ground. When you return five years later, will the sign be at the same height, or will the tree's growth have raised it higher? Explain your answer.

2. African violets and some other flowering plants are propagated commercially using leaf cuttings. A leaf detached from a parent plant is placed in a growth medium. In time, adventitious shoots and roots develop from the leaf blade, producing a new plant. Are all cells in the original leaf tissue equally likely to give rise to the new structures? If not, which one(s) are most likely to have done so? What property of the cells makes this propagation method possible?

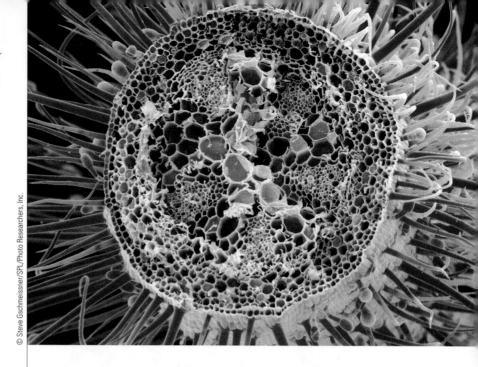

Cross section of the stem of a geranium (*Pelargonium*) showing parenchyma (pink) wrapping around vessels that transport water and nutrients in plants. In this false-colour SEM, large-diameter vessels (xylem) that carry water and minerals appear whitish and bundles of smaller vessels (phloem), which transport sugars, appear pale green.

© Steve Gschmeissner/SPL/Photo Researchers, Inc.

29 Transport in Plants

WHY IT MATTERS

The coast redwood, *Sequoia sempervirens* (**Figure 29.1, p. 696**), takes life to extremes. Redwood trees can live for more than 2000 years, and they can grow taller than any other organism on Earth. The tallest known specimen, located in Redwood National Park in California, soars 115.5 m from the dank forest floor. Botanists who have studied these giants estimate that such massive plants consume thousands of litres of water each day to survive. And that water—with its cargo of dissolved nutrients—must be transported the great distances between roots and leaves.

At first, movement of fluids and solutes 100 m or more from a mature redwood's roots to its leafy crown may seem to challenge the laws of physics. Raising water that high above ground in a pipe requires a powerful mechanical pump at the base and substantial energy to counteract the pull of gravity. You also require a pump—your heart—to move fluid over a vertical distance of less than 3 m. Yet a redwood tree has no pump. As you'll learn in this chapter, the evolutionary adaptations that move water and solutes throughout the plant body can move large volumes over great distances by harnessing the cumulative effects of seemingly weak interactions such as cohesion

Figure 29.1

Redwoods (*Sequoia sempervirens*), such as this tree growing in coastal California, have reached recorded heights of over 100 m during life spans of more than 2000 years.

Such extremely tall trees exemplify the ability of plants to move water and solutes from roots to shoots over amazingly long distances.

and evaporation. Overall, plant transport mechanisms solve a fundamental biological problem—the need to acquire materials from the environment and distribute them throughout the plant body.

Our discussion begins with a brief review of the principles of water and solute movement in plants, a topic introduced in Chapter 5. Then we examine how those principles apply to the movement of water and solutes into and through a plant's vascular pipelines.

29.1 Principles of Water and Solute Movement in Plants

In plants, as in all organisms, the movement of water and solutes begins at the level of individual cells and relies on mechanisms such as osmosis and the operation of transport proteins in the plasma membrane. Once water and nutrients enter a plant's specialized transport systems—the vascular tissues called xylem and phloem—other mechanisms carry them between various regions of the plant body in response to changing demands for those substances. Ultimately, these movements of materials result from the integrated activities of the individual cells, tissues, and organs of a single, smoothly functioning organism—the whole plant.

Plant transport mechanisms fall into two general categories—those for short-distance transport and those for long-distance transport. Short-distance transport mechanisms move substances into and between cells across membranes and to and from vascular tissues. For example, water, oxygen, and minerals enter roots by crossing the cell membranes of root hairs **(Figure 29.2a),** and nutrients such as carbohydrates from photosynthesis cross plasma membranes to nourish cells of the plant body. Similarly, water and other substances move short distances to and from a plant's xylem and phloem, which are arranged in vascular bundles **(Figure 29.2b).** Long-distance transport mechanisms move substances between roots and shoot parts **(Figure 29.2c).** Thus, water and dissolved minerals travel in the xylem from roots to other plant parts, and products of photosynthesis move in the phloem from the leaves and stems into roots and other structures. Carbon dioxide for photosynthesis enters photosynthetic tissues in the shoot.

We consider transport processes in the xylem and phloem later in this chapter. For the moment, our focus is on mechanisms that move water and solutes into and out of specific cells in roots, leaves, and stems. Keep in mind that the plant cell wall does not prevent solutes from moving into plant cells. Most solutes can cross the wall by way of the plasmodesmata that connect adjacent cells (see Chapter 28).

29.1a Both Passive and Active Mechanisms Move Substances into and out of Plant Cells

Recall from Chapter 5 that in all cells, there are two general mechanisms for transporting water and solutes across the plasma membrane into and between cells. In **passive transport,** substances move down a concentration gradient or, if the substance is an ion, down an electrochemical gradient. **Active transport** requires the cell to expend energy in moving substances *against* a gradient, usually by hydrolysis of ATP.

True to its name, simple diffusion is the simplest form of passive transport: oxygen, carbon dioxide, water, and some other small molecules can readily diffuse across cell plasma membranes, following a concentration gradient. By contrast, in all other types of membrane transport, ions and some larger molecules cross cell membranes assisted by carriers collectively called **transport proteins,** which are embedded in the membrane.

Passive transport of substances down an electrochemical gradient is called *facilitated diffusion* because the transport protein involved "facilitates" the process in some way. Transport proteins called *channel proteins* are configured to form a pore in the plasma membrane. Those called *carrier proteins* change shape in a way that releases the substance to the other side of the membrane.

In active transport, membrane transport proteins use energy to move substances against a concentration

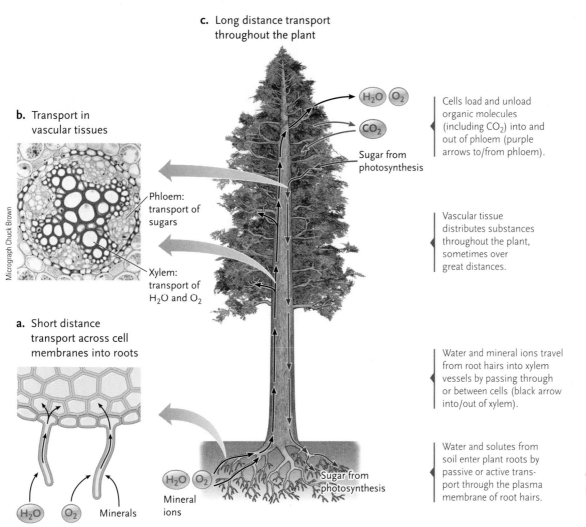

c. Long distance transport throughout the plant

b. Transport in vascular tissues

Micrograph Chuck Brown

Phloem: transport of sugars

Xylem: transport of H_2O and O_2

a. Short distance transport across cell membranes into roots

H_2O O_2 Minerals

H_2O O_2
Mineral ions

Sugar from photosynthesis

H_2O O_2

CO_2

Sugar from photosynthesis

Cells load and unload organic molecules (including CO_2) into and out of phloem (purple arrows to/from phloem).

Vascular tissue distributes substances throughout the plant, sometimes over great distances.

Water and mineral ions travel from root hairs into xylem vessels by passing through or between cells (black arrow into/out of xylem).

Water and solutes from soil enter plant roots by passive or active transport through the plasma membrane of root hairs.

Figure 29.2
Overview of transport routes in plants.

gradient or an electrochemical gradient. An electrochemical gradient exists across cell membranes when the concentrations of various ions differ between the inside and the outside of the cell. The differences in ion concentration result in a difference in electrical charge across the plasma membrane. In plant cells, the cytoplasm is slightly more negative than the fluid outside the cell. This charge difference is measured as an electrical voltage called the **membrane potential.** The word "potential" refers to the fact that the movement of ions across a membrane is a potential source of energy—that is, such ion movements can perform cellular work.

ATP provides the energy for active transport of substances into and out of plant cells. Hydrogen ions (protons), which tend to be more concentrated outside the cell than in the negatively charged cytoplasm, play a central role in the process. First, a proton pump pushes H^+ across the plasma membrane against its electrochemical gradient, from the inside to the outside of the cell **(Figure 29.3a, p. 698).** As protons accumulate outside the cell, the electrochemical gradient becomes steeper and significant potential energy is available. Crucial solutes such as cations (positively charged ions) often are more concentrated in the extracellular fluid. One result of the increased

charge difference created by proton pumping is that cations move into the cell through their membrane channels **(Figure 29.3b, p. 698).** These cations include mineral ions that have essential roles in plant cell metabolism.

The H^+ gradient also powers *secondary active transport,* a process in which a concentration gradient of an ion is used as the energy source for active transport of another substance. The two secondary mechanisms—*symport* and *antiport*—actively transport ions, sugars, and amino acids into and out of plant cells against their concentration gradient. In **symport,** the potential energy released as H^+ follows its gradient into the cell is coupled to the simultaneous uptake of another ion or molecule **(Figure 29.3c, p. 698).** In this way, plant cells can take up metabolically important ions such as nitrate (NO_3^-) and potassium (K^+). Nearly all organic substances that enter plant cells move in by symport as well.

In **antiport,** the energy released as H^+ diffuses into the cell powers the active transport of a second molecule, such as Ca^{2+}, in the opposite direction, *out of* the cell **(Figure 29.3d, p. 698).** One of antiport's key functions is to remove excess Na^+, which readily moves into plant cells by facilitated diffusion through channel proteins. If the Na^+ were not eliminated, it would quickly build up to toxic levels.

a. H⁺ pumped against its electrochemical gradient

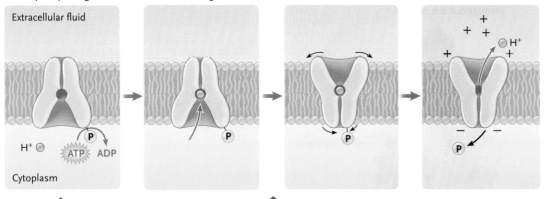

ATP energy pumps hydrogen ions (H⁺) out of the cytoplasm, creating an H⁺ gradient.

The concentration of H⁺ becomes higher outside the membrane than inside. Inward diffusion of H⁺ in response to the gradient becomes a source of energy for transporting other ions and neutral molecules such as sugar into the plant cell.

b. Uptake of cations

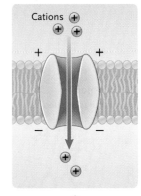

Some cations, such as NH₄⁺, enter the cell through selective channel proteins, following the electrochemical gradient created by H⁺ pumping.

c. Symport

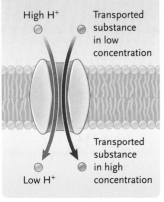

In symport, the inward diffusion of H⁺ is coupled with the simultaneous active transport of another substance into the cell.

d. Antiport

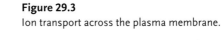

In antiport, H⁺ moving into the cell powers the movement of another solute in the opposite direction.

Figure 29.3
Ion transport across the plasma membrane.

Both passive and active transport are selective transport mechanisms that transport specific substances. Two factors govern this specificity. One is the size of the interior channel, which allows only molecules in a particular size range to pass through. The other factor is the distribution of charges along the inside of the channel. A channel that permits cations such as Na⁺ to pass through easily may completely bar anions, such as Cl⁻, and vice versa.

Relatively speaking, only small amounts of mineral ions and other solutes move into and out of plant cells. As we see next, H₂O is another matter. Throughout a plant's life, large volumes of water enter and exit its cells and tissues by way of osmosis.

29.1b Osmosis Governs Water Movement in Plants

One of the most important aspects of plant physiology is how water moves into and through plant cells and tissues. Inside a plant's tubelike vascular tissues, large amounts of water or any other fluid travel by **bulk flow**—the group movement of molecules in response to a difference in pressure between two locations, like water in a closed plumbing system gushing from an open faucet. For example, the dilute solution of water and ions that flows in the xylem, called **xylem sap**, moves by bulk flow from roots to shoot parts. The solution is pulled upward through the plant body in a process that relies on the cohesion of water molecules, which we consider more fully later in this chapter. Individual cells, however, gain and lose water by **osmosis**, the passive movement of water across a selectively permeable membrane in response to solute concentration gradients, a pressure gradient, or both (see Chapter 5). The driving force for osmosis is energy stored in the water itself. This potential energy, called **water potential**, is symbolized by the Greek letter psi (ψ). By convention, pure water has a ψ value of zero. Two factors that strongly influence this value in living plants are the presence of solutes and physical pressure.

The effect of dissolved solutes on water's tendency to move across a membrane is called *solute potential,* symbolized by ψ_S. In practical terms, water potential is higher where there are more water molecules in a solution relative to the number of solute molecules. Likewise, the water potential is *lower* in a solution with relatively more solutes. The relationship between water potential and solute potential is vital to understanding transport phenomena in plants because water tends to move by osmosis from regions where water potential is higher to regions where it is lower. Solutes are usually more concentrated inside plant cells than in the fluid surrounding them. This means that the water potential is higher outside plant cells than inside them, so water tends to enter the cells by osmosis. This, in fact, is the mechanism that draws soil water into a plant's roots.

Recall from Chapter 5 that an animal cell placed in a hypotonic solution may swell to the point of bursting. In plants, this is prevented by the cell wall, which exerts a pressure that counters the further inward movement of water. This pressure, called **turgor pressure**, rises until it is high enough to prevent more water from entering a cell by osmosis. In effect, when osmotic water movement stops,

turgor pressure has increased the water potential inside the cell until it equals the potential of the water outside the cell. The physical pressure required to halt osmotic water movement across a membrane is termed a solution's *pressure potential* and is symbolized as ψ_P.

By convention, plant physiologists measure water potential in units of pressure called **megapascals** (MPa). They use standard atmospheric pressure as a baseline, assigning it a value of zero. Accordingly, the water potential of pure water at standard atmospheric pressure is expressed as 0 MPa. This notation can be used to describe the changing effects under different conditions of solute potential and pressure potential **(Figure 29.4).** Adding pressure increases the water pressure, whereas adding solutes reduces it (because the relative concentration of water is lower), and water will flow from a solution of higher MPa to a solution of lower MPa. With these principles in mind, consider now how they operate in living plant cells.

A large **central vacuole** occupies most of the volume of a mature plant cell. The central vacuole, which is surrounded by a vacuolar membrane or **tonoplast**, contains a dilute solution of sugars, proteins,

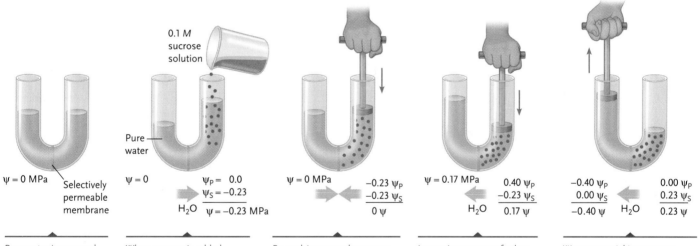

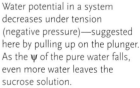

Pure water in a curved tube with compartments separated by a selectively permeable membrane

When sucrose is added to the water on one side to form a 0.1 *M* sucrose solution, the water potential on that side falls. Water moves into the solution by osmosis.

By applying enough pressure (ψ_P) to the solution to balance the osmotic pressure, water potential can be increased to zero, equaling that on the pure-water side of the membrane. Now there is no net movement of water across the membrane.

Increasing pressure further increases the water potential of the sucrose solution, so water moves back across the membrane into the compartment containing pure water.

Water potential in a system decreases under tension (negative pressure)—suggested here by pulling up on the plunger. As the ψ of the pure water falls, even more water leaves the sucrose solution.

> Plant physiologists assign a value of 0 MPa to the water potential (ψ) of pure water in an open container under normal atmospheric pressure and temperature.

Figure 29.4

The relationship between osmosis and water potential. If the water potential is higher on one side of a selectively permeable membrane, water will cross the membrane to the area of lower water potential. This diagram shows pure water on one side of a selectively permeable membrane and a simple sucrose solution on the other side. In an organism, however, the selectively permeable membranes of cells are rarely, if ever, in contact with pure water.

other organic molecules, and salts. The cell cytoplasm is confined to a thin layer between the tonoplast and the plasma membrane. A major role of the central vacuole is to maintain turgor pressure in the cell. Many solutes that enter a plant cell are actively transported from the cytoplasm into the central vacuole through channels in the tonoplast. As the solutes accumulate, water follows by osmosis.

The plant cell's relatively small amount of cytoplasm must compensate fairly quickly for water gains or losses caused by changes in osmotic flow. If the medium around a plant cell becomes hypertonic (has a high solute concentration), for example, water flows rapidly out of the cell. Water from the central vacuole replaces it, entering the cytoplasm through water-conducting channel proteins called **aquaporins.**

The water mechanics we have been discussing have major implications for land plants. For instance, the drooping of leaves and stems called **wilting** occurs when environmental conditions cause a plant to lose more water than it gains. Conditions that lead to wilting include dry soil, in which case, the water potential in the soil falls below that in the plant. Then the turgor pressure inside the cells falls, and the protoplast shrinks away from the cell wall **(Figure 29.5a).** By contrast, as long as the ψ of soil is higher than that in root epidermal cells, water will follow the ψ gradient and enter root cells, making them turgid, or firm **(Figure 29.5b).** As we see in the next section, water and solutes entering roots may move through the plant body by several routes.

STUDY BREAK

1. Explain the role(s) of a gradient of protons in moving substances across a plant cell's plasma membrane.
2. How do symport and antiport differ? Give examples of key substances each mechanism transports.
3. What is "water potential," and why is it important with respect to plant cells?

The experimenter begins with flaccid plant cells at atmospheric pressure and temperature. The cells contain enough water to prevent the plasma membrane from shrinking away from the cell wall, but lack turgor.

Flaccid cell

Plasma membrane   Tonoplast

a. A flaccid cell is placed in distilled water, which has a water potential of zero—much greater than the negative water potential inside the cell. The cell gains water by osmosis and swells until it is turgid. The cell wall prevents it from taking in more water and bursting.

Pure water

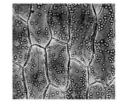

Turgid cells from an iris petal *(Iris)*

Distilled water

$\psi_P = 0$ MPa
$\psi_S = 0$ MPa

Turgid cell at equilibrium with its environment

$\psi_P = 0.7$ MPa
$\psi_S = -0.7$ MPa
$\psi = 0.0$ MPa

b. A flaccid cell is placed in a sucrose solution. The water potential inside the cell is much greater than that in the solute-rich solution, and the cell loses water until the vacuole shrinks and the protoplast shrinks away from the cell wall. This outcome of the experiment is called plasmolysis.

Sucrose solution

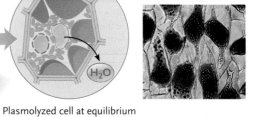

Plasmolyzed cells from a wilted iris petal

0.4 *M* sucrose

$\psi_P = 0.0$ MPa
$\psi_S = -0.9$ MPa
$\psi = -0.9$ MPa

Plasmolyzed cell at equilibrium with its environment

$\psi_P = 0.0$ MPa
$\psi_S = -0.9$ MPa
$\psi = -0.9$ MPa

Figure 29.5

An experiment to test the effects of different osmotic environments on plant cells. Notice that in both **(a)** and **(b)**, the final condition is the same: the water potential of the plant cell and its environment become equal. (Micrographs: © Claude Nuridsany and Marie Perennou/Science Photo Library/Photo Researchers, Inc.)

29.2 Transport in Roots

Soil around roots provides a plant's water and minerals, but roots don't simply "soak up" these essential substances. Instead, water and minerals that enter roots first travel laterally through the root cortex to the root xylem. Only then do they begin their journey upward to stems, leaves, and other tissues.

29.2a Water Travels to the Root Xylem by Three Pathways

Soil water always enters a root through the root epidermis. Once inside a root, however, water may take one of three routes into the root xylem, travelling either through living cells or in nonliving areas of the root **(Figure 29.6)**. Nonliving regions of a plant such as the continuous network of adjoining cell walls and air spaces in root tissue are called the *apoplast*. Thus, water follows an **apoplastic pathway** when it moves through the apoplast of roots, a route that does not cross cell membranes. Botanists refer to a plant's living parts as the *symplast*, and water moving through roots in the **symplastic pathway** moves from cell to cell through the open channels of plasmodesmata. Water also can enter root cells across the cell plasma membranes, a

transmembrane pathway. Water crosses the tonoplast of the central vacuole in this way as well.

When water enters a root, some diffuses into epidermal cells, entering the symplast. But a great deal of the water taken up by plant roots moves into the apoplast, moving along through cell walls and intercellular spaces. This apoplastic water (and any solutes dissolved in it) travels rapidly inward until it encounters the endodermis, the sheetlike single layer of cells that separates the root cortex from the stele. Cells in the root cortex generally have air spaces between them (which helps aerate the tissue), but endodermal cells are tightly packed **(Figure 29.7a , p. 702)**. Each one also has a beltlike **Casparian strip** in its radial and transverse walls, positioned somewhat like a ribbon of packing tape around a rectangular package **(Figure 29.7c and d, p. 702)**. The strip is impregnated with suberin, a waxy substance impermeable to water. Thus, the Casparian strip blocks the apoplastic pathway at the endodermis, preventing water and solutes in the apoplast from automatically passing on into the stele. Instead, if molecules are to move into the stele, they must detour across the plasma membranes of endodermal cells, entering the cells (and the symplast) where the wall is not blanketed by a Casparian strip (Figure 29.7d). From there, water and solutes can pass through plasmodesmata to cells in the outer layer of the stele (the pericycle) and then on into the xylem.

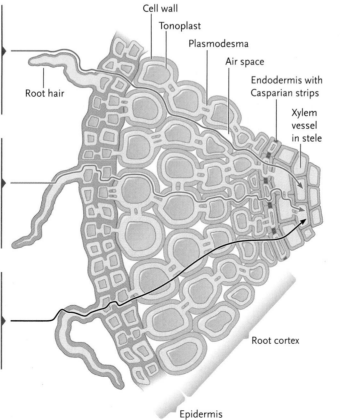

In the **apoplastic pathway** (red), water moves through nonliving regions—the continuous network of adjoining cell walls and tissue air spaces. However, when it reaches the endodermis, it passes through one layer of living cells.

In the **symplastic pathway** (green), water passes into and through living cells. After being taken up into root hairs water diffuses through the cytoplasm and passes from one living cell to the next through plasmodesmata.

In the **transmembrane pathway** (black), water that enters the cytoplasm moves between living cells by diffusing across cell membranes, including the plasma membrane and perhaps the tonoplast.

Cell wall
Tonoplast
Plasmodesma
Air space
Endodermis with Casparian strips
Xylem vessel in stele
Root hair
Root cortex
Epidermis

Figure 29.6
Pathways for the movement of water into roots.
Ions also enter roots via these three pathways but must be actively transported into cells when they reach the Casparian strips of the endodermis. In this way, only certain solutes in soil water are allowed to enter the stele.

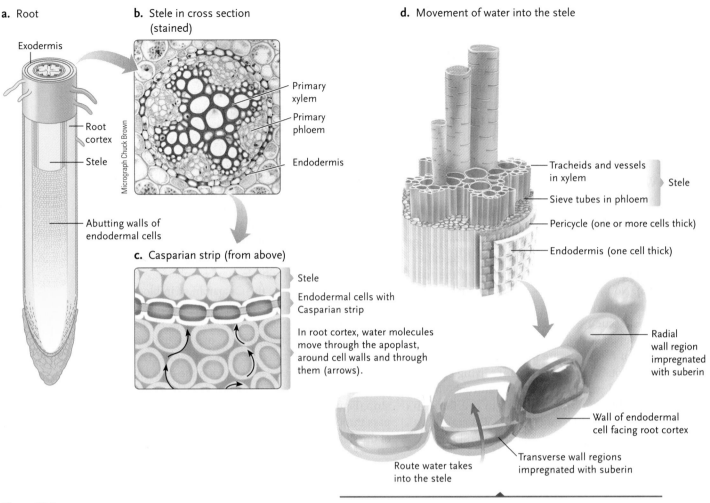

a. Root

Exodermis

Root cortex

Stele

Abutting walls of endodermal cells

b. Stele in cross section (stained)

Micrograph Chuck Brown

Primary xylem

Primary phloem

Endodermis

c. Casparian strip (from above)

Stele

Endodermal cells with Casparian strip

In root cortex, water molecules move through the apoplast, around cell walls and through them (arrows).

d. Movement of water into the stele

Tracheids and vessels in xylem

Stele

Sieve tubes in phloem

Pericycle (one or more cells thick)

Endodermis (one cell thick)

Radial wall region impregnated with suberin

Wall of endodermal cell facing root cortex

Transverse wall regions impregnated with suberin

Route water takes into the stele

Figure 29.7
Location and function of Casparian strips in roots.

Waxy, water-impervious Casparian strip (gold) in abutting walls of endodermal cells that control water and nutrient uptake

Although water molecules can easily cross an endodermal cell's plasma membrane, the semipermeable membrane allows only a subset of the solutes in soil water to cross. Undesirable solutes may be barred, whereas desirable ones may move into the cell by facilitated diffusion or active transport. Conversely, the endodermis prevents needed substances in the xylem from leaking out, back into the root cortex. In this way, the endodermis provides important control over which substances enter and leave a plant's vascular tissue. The roots of most flowering plants also have a second layer of cells with Casparian strips just inside the root epidermis. This layer, the exodermis (shown in Figure 29.7a), functions like the endodermis.

29.2b Roots Take Up Ions by Active Transport

Mineral ions in soil water also enter roots through the epidermis. Some enter the apoplast along with water, but most ions important for plant nutrition tend to be much more concentrated in roots than in the surrounding soil, so they cannot follow a concentration gradient into root epidermal cells. Instead, the epidermal cells actively transport ions inward—that is, ions enter the symplast immediately. They travel to the xylem via the symplastic or transmembrane pathways. Other ions can still move inward following the apoplastic pathway until they reach the Casparian strip of the endodermis. If they are to contribute to the plant's nutrition, however, they must be actively transported from the exodermis into cells of the root cortex and, as just described, from the endodermis into the stele. In short, mechanisms that control which solutes will be absorbed by root cells ultimately determine which solutes will be distributed through the plant.

Once an ion reaches the stele, it diffuses from cell to cell until it is "loaded" into the xylem. Experiments to determine whether the loading is passive (by diffusion) or active have been inconclusive, so the details of this final step are not entirely clear. Because the xylem's conducting elements are not living, water and ions in effect reenter the apoplastic pathway when they reach either tracheids or vessels. Once in the xylem, water can move laterally to and from tissues or travel upward in the conducting elements. Minerals are distributed to living cells and taken up by active transport. The following section examines how this "distribution of the wealth" takes place.

Suberin

Suberin is a complex cell wall polymer. It is found in specific cell types, including root epidermis, root endodermis (including Casparian bands), bundle sheath cells, and the periderm (bark) of woody species and underground organs (e.g., tubers). Suberin is a unique macromolecule that contains two distinct polymeric domains: poly(phenolic) and poly(aliphatic). Each domain has a unique chemical composition and contributes different properties to the walls in the specialized cells in which it is found. That is, the poly(phenolic) domain provides a structural barrier, whereas the poly(aliphatic) domain provides a nearly perfect water barrier, preventing water loss and regulating solute transport. Combined, these two domains provide protection against pathogens. Suberin is also a component of the wound-healing process in plants, serving to isolate damaged cells from undamaged ones beneath while closing off the exposed tissue from the external environment.

The chemical compositions of both suberin domains have been well characterized for a number of plant species, and recent attention has turned to the specifics of their biosynthesis within the context of suberization: that is, the process through which cells become suberized. Recent work carried out in the laboratory of Mark Bernards at the University of Western Ontario has focused on identifying key metabolic steps, cloning the genes encoding the enzymes responsible for these steps, and functionally characterizing them. Two model systems for studying suberin biosynthesis have emerged: wound-healing potato (*Solanum tuberosum*) tubers and *Arabidopsis* (*Arabidopsis thaliana*). Of these, the potato tuber system offers the advantage of generating a large amount of synchronously suberizing cells after a single wounding event derived by cutting the tuber under sterile conditions. The cut tissue rapidly heals, forming a suberized layer that closely resembles native potato periderm. In addition to delineating the biochemical pathways leading to the monomeric components of suberin, the induction of wound suberin in potatoes also allows the study of how two disparate metabolic pathways (fatty acid biosynthesis/modification and phenolic biosynthesis) are coordinately regulated and ultimately converge to generate a complex macromolecular structure.

STUDY BREAK

1. Explain two key differences in how the apoplastic and symplastic pathways route substances laterally in roots.
2. How does an ion enter a root hair and then move to the xylem?

29.3 Transport of Water and Minerals in the Xylem

We return now to the question that opened this chapter: How does the solution of water and minerals called xylem sap move—100 m or more in the tallest trees—from roots to stems and then into leaves? Xylem sap is mostly water, and we know that it moves upward by bulk flow through the tracheids and vessels in xylem. Yet because mature xylem cells are dead, they cannot expend energy to move water into and through the plant shoot. Instead, the driving force for the upward movement of xylem sap from root to shoot is sunlight, which causes water to evaporate from leaves and other aerial parts of land plants. Experiments show that only a small fraction of the water in xylem sap is used in a plant's growth and metabolism. The rest evaporates into the air in a phenomenon called **transpiration.** As described next, transpiration drives the ascent of sap.

29.3a The Mechanical Properties of Water Have Key Roles in Its Transport

The Chemical and Physical Foundations of Biology pages review several biologically important mechanical properties of water. Two of them interest us here. First, water molecules are strongly *cohesive:* they tend to form hydrogen bonds with one another. Second, water molecules are *adhesive:* they form hydrogen bonds with molecules of other substances, including the carbohydrates in plant cell walls. Water's cohesive and adhesive forces jointly pull water molecules into exceedingly small spaces, such as crevices in cell walls or narrow tubes such as xylem vessels in roots, stems, and leaves. In 1914, plant physiologist Henry Dixon explained the ascent of sap in terms of the relationship between transpiration and water's mechanical properties. His model of xylem transport is now called the **cohesion–tension mechanism of water transport (Figure 29.8, p. 704).**

According to the cohesion–tension model, water transport begins as water evaporates from the walls of mesophyll cells inside leaves and into the intercellular spaces. This water vapour escapes by transpiration through open stomata, the minute passageways in the leaf surface. As water molecules exit the leaf, they are replaced by others from the mesophyll cell cytoplasm. The water loss gradually reduces the water potential in a transpiring cell below the water potential in the leaf xylem. Now, water from the xylem in the leaf veins

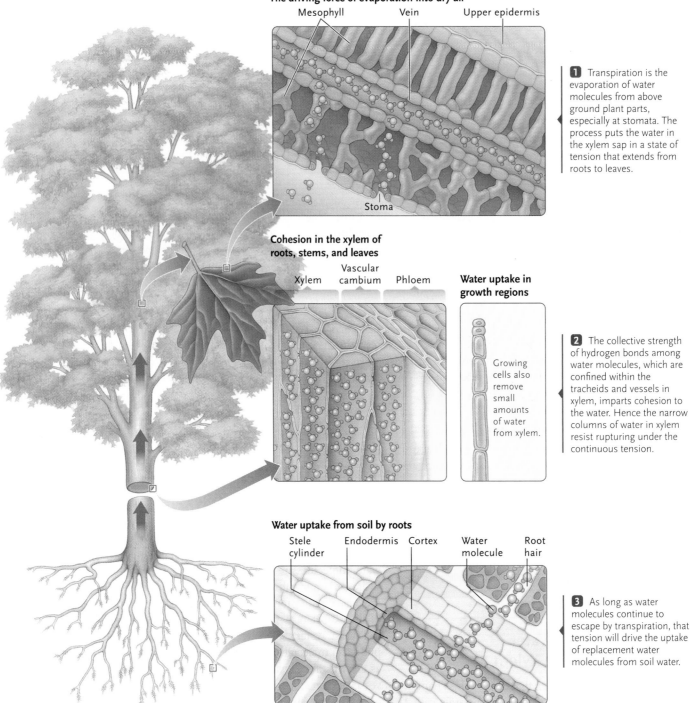

The driving force of evaporation into dry air

Mesophyll   Vein   Upper epidermis

Stoma

1 Transpiration is the evaporation of water molecules from above ground plant parts, especially at stomata. The process puts the water in the xylem sap in a state of tension that extends from roots to leaves.

Cohesion in the xylem of roots, stems, and leaves

Xylem   Vascular cambium   Phloem

Water uptake in growth regions

Growing cells also remove small amounts of water from xylem.

2 The collective strength of hydrogen bonds among water molecules, which are confined within the tracheids and vessels in xylem, imparts cohesion to the water. Hence the narrow columns of water in xylem resist rupturing under the continuous tension.

Water uptake from soil by roots

Stele cylinder   Endodermis   Cortex   Water molecule   Root hair

3 As long as water molecules continue to escape by transpiration, that tension will drive the uptake of replacement water molecules from soil water.

Figure 29.8

Cohesion–tension mechanism of water transport. Transpiration, the evaporation of water from shoot parts, creates tension on the water in xylem sap. This tension, which extends from root to leaf, pulls upward columns of water molecules that are hydrogen-bonded to one another.

follows the gradient into cells, replacing the water lost in transpiration.

In the xylem, water molecules are confined in narrow, tubular xylem cells. The water molecules form a long chain, like a string of weak magnets, held together by hydrogen bonds between individual molecules. When a water molecule moves out of a leaf vein into the mesophyll, its hydrogen bonds with the next molecule in line stretch but don't break. The stretching creates *tension*—a negative pressure gradient—in the column. **Adhesion** of the water column to xylem vessel walls adds to the tension. Under continuous tension from above, the entire column of water molecules in xylem is drawn upward, in a fashion somewhat analogous to the way water moves up through a drinking straw. Botanists refer to this root-to-shoot flow as the *transpiration stream*.

Transpiration continues regardless of whether evaporating water is replenished by water rapidly taken up from the soil. Wilting is visible evidence that the water-potential gradient between soil and a plant's shoot parts has shifted. Remember that as soil dries out, the remaining water molecules are held ever more tightly by the soil particles. In effect, the action of soil particles reduces the water potential in the soil surrounding plant roots, and as this happens, the roots take up water more slowly. However, because the water that evaporates from the plant's leaves is no longer being fully replaced, the leaves wilt as turgor pressure drops. Reducing the water potential in soil by adding solutes such as NaCl and other salts can have the same wilting effect. When the water potential in the soil finally equals that in leaf cells, a gradient no longer exists. Then movement of water from the soil into roots and up to the leaves comes to a halt.

29.3b Leaf Anatomy Contributes to Cohesion–Tension Forces

Leaf anatomy is key to the processes that move water upward in plants. To begin with, as much as two-thirds of a leaf's volume consists of air spaces—thus, there is a large internal surface area for evaporation. Leaves also may have thousands to millions of stomata, through which water vapour can escape. Both of these factors increase transpiration. Also, every square centimetre of a leaf contains thousands of tiny xylem veins, so most leaf cells lie within half a millimetre of a vein. This close proximity supplies water to cells and the spaces between them, from which the water can readily evaporate.

As water evaporates from a leaf, **surface tension** at the interface between the water film and the air in the leaf space translates into negative pressure that draws water from the leaf veins. This tension is multiplied many times over in all of the leaves and xylem veins of a plant. It increases further as the plant's metabolically active cells take up xylem sap.

29.3c In the Tallest Trees, the Cohesion– Tension Mechanism May Reach Its Physical Limit

A variety of experiments have tested the propositions of the cohesion–tension model, and thus far, the data strongly support it. For example, the model predicts that xylem sap will begin to move upward at the top of a tree early in the day when water begins to evaporate from leaves. Experiments with several different tree species have confirmed that this is the case. The experiments also showed that sap transport peaks at midday when evaporation is greatest and then tapers off in the evening as evaporative water loss slows.

Other experiments have probed the relationship between xylem transport and tree height. One team of researchers studied eight of the tallest living redwoods, including one that towers nearly 113 m above the forest floor. When the scientists measured the maximum tension exerted in the xylem sap in twigs at the tops of the trees, they discovered that it approached the known physical limit at which the bonds between water molecules in a column of water in a conifer's xylem will rupture. Based on this finding and other evidence, the team predicted that the maximum height for a healthy redwood tree is 122 to 130 m. Therefore, it is possible that the tallest redwoods alive today may grow taller still.

29.3d Root Pressure Contributes to Upward Water Movement in Some Plants

The cohesion–tension mechanism accounts for upward water movement in tall trees. In some nonwoody plant species, however—lawn grasses, for instance—a positive pressure can develop in roots and force xylem sap upward. This **root pressure** operates under conditions that reduce transpiration, such as high humidity or low light. In fact, the mechanism that produces root pressure often operates at night, when solar-powered transpiration slows or stops. Then active transport of ions into the stele sets up a water potential gradient across the endodermis. Because the Casparian strip of the endodermis tends to prevent ions from moving back into the root cortex, the water potential difference becomes quite large. It can move enough water and dissolved solutes into the xylem to produce a relatively high positive pressure. Although not sufficient to force water to the top of a very tall plant, in some smaller plant species, root pressure is strong enough to force water out of leaf openings, in a process called **guttation (Figure 29.9).** Pushed up and out of vein endings by root pressure, tiny droplets of water that look like dew in the early morning emerge from modified stomata at the margins of leaves.

Figure 29.9

Guttation, caused by root pressure. The drops of water appear at the endings of xylem veins along the leaf edges of a strawberry plant (*Fragaria*).

29.3e Stomata Regulate the Loss of Water by Transpiration

Three environmental conditions have major effects on the rate of transpiration: relative humidity, air temperature, and air movement. The most important is relative humidity, which is a measure of the amount of water vapour in air. The less water vapour in the air, the more evaporates from leaves (because the water potential is higher in the leaves than in the dry air). The air temperature at the leaf surface also speeds evaporation as it rises. Although evaporation does cool the leaf somewhat, the amount of water lost can double for each 10°C rise in air temperature. Air movement at the leaf surface carries water vapour away from the surface and so makes a steeper gradient. Together these factors explain why on extremely hot, dry, breezy days the leaves of certain plants must completely replace their water each hour.

Even when conditions are not so drastic, more than 90% of the water moving into a leaf can be lost through transpiration. Of the remaining water, about 2% is used in photosynthesis and other activities. These measurements emphasize the need for controls over transpiration for if water loss exceeds water uptake by roots, the resulting dehydration of plant tissues interferes with normal functioning, and the plant may wilt and die.

The cuticle-covered epidermis of leaves and stems reduces the rate of water loss from above-ground plant parts, but it also limits the rate at which CO_2 for photosynthesis can diffuse into the leaf. The functioning of stomata also affects a plant's water balance. When stomata are open, carbon dioxide can be absorbed, but unless the relative humidity of external air is 100%, water always moves out. However, plants have evolved adaptations that balance water loss with CO_2 uptake. This "transpiration–photosynthesis compromise" involves the regulation of transpiration and gas exchange by opening and closing stomata as environmental conditions change.

Opening and Closing of Stomata. Two guard cells flank each stomatal opening **(Figure 29.10)**. Their elastic walls are reinforced by cellulose microfibrils that wrap around the walls like a series of belts. The inward-facing walls are thicker and less elastic than the outer walls.

The opening and closing of stomata are good examples of a symport mechanism (see Figure 29.3c). Stomata open when potassium ions (K^+) flow into the guard cells through ion channels. As a first step, an active transport pump in the plasma membrane begins pumping H^+ ions out of the guard cells. The H^+ pumped out of the cell can then follow its concentration gradient back into the cell. This inward flow of H^+ powers the active transport of K^+ into the guard cell. As a result, the K^+ concentration in turgid guard cells may be four to eight times higher than that in flaccid (limp) guard cells **(Figure 29.11)**. Water follows inward by osmosis. As turgor pressure builds, the thick inner wall does not expand much, but the outer walls of each guard cell expand lengthwise, so the two cells bend away from each other and create a stoma ("mouth") between them. Stomata close when the H^+ active transport protein stops pumping. K^+ flows passively out of the guard cells, and water follows by osmosis. When the water content of the guard cells dwindles, turgor pressure drops. The guard cells collapse against each other, closing the stomata.

In most plants, stomata open at first light, stay open during daylight, and close at night. Experiments have shown that guard cells respond to a number of

a. Open stoma   **b.** Closed stoma

Guard cell   Guard cell

Chloroplast (guard cells are the only epidermal cells that have these organelles)

Stoma   20 μm

Figure 29.10
Guard cells and stomatal action. **(a)** An open stoma. Water entered collapsed guard cells, which swelled under turgor pressure and moved apart, thus forming the stoma in the needlelike leaf of the rock needlebush (*Hakea gibbosa*). **(b)** A closed stoma. Water exited the swollen guard cells, which collapsed against each other and closed the stoma.

a. Open stomata, with potassium mostly in guard cells

b. Closed stomata, with potassium mostly in epidermal cells

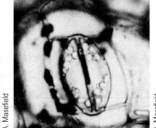

T. A. Masefield

Figure 29.11
Evidence for potassium accumulation in stomatal guard cells undergoing expansion. Strips from the leaf epidermis of a dayflower (*Commelina communis*) were immersed in a solution containing a stain that binds preferentially with potassium ions. **(a)** In leaf samples with open stomata, most of the potassium was concentrated in the guard cells. **(b)** In leaf samples with closed stomata, little potassium was in guard cells; most was present in adjacent epidermal cells.

environmental and chemical signals, any of which can induce the ion flows that open and close stomata. These signals include light, CO_2 concentration in the air spaces inside leaves, and the amount of water available to the plant.

Light and CO_2 Concentration. Light induces stomata to open through stimulation of blue-light receptors, probably located in the plasma membrane of guard cells. When stimulated, the receptors start the chain of events leading to stomatal opening by triggering activity of the H^+ pumps. Also, as photosynthesis begins in response to light, CO_2 concentration drops in the leaf air spaces as chloroplasts use the gas in carbohydrate production. In some way, this drop in CO_2 concentration sets off the series of events increasing the flow of K^+ into guard cells and furthers stomatal opening. The effects of reduced CO_2 concentration have been tested by placing plants in the dark in air containing no CO_2. Even in the absence of light, as the CO_2 concentration falls in leaves, guard cells swell and the stomata open.

Normally, when the sun goes down, a plant's demand for CO_2 drops as photosynthesis comes to a halt. Yet aerobic respiration continues to produce CO_2, which accumulates in leaves. As CO_2 concentration rises, and the blue-light wavelengths that activated the H^+ pumps wane, K^+ is lost from the guard cells and they collapse, closing the stomata. Thus, at night, transpiration is reduced and water is conserved.

Water Stress. As long as water is readily available to a plant's roots, the stomata remain open during daylight. However, if water loss stresses a plant, the stomata close or open only slightly, regardless of light intensity or CO_2 concentration. Some simple but elegant experiments have shown that the stress-related closing of stomata depends on a hormone, **abscisic acid (ABA)**, that is released by roots when water is unavailable. Test plants were suspended in containers so that only one-half of the root system received water. Even though the roots with access to water could absorb enough water to satisfy the needs of all the plants' leaves, the stomata still closed. Tissue analysis revealed that water-stressed roots rapidly synthesize ABA. Transported through the xylem, this hormone stimulates K^+ loss by guard cells, and water moves out of the cell by osmosis—so the stomata close **(Figure 29.12)**. Mesophyll cells also take up ABA from the xylem and release it, with the same effects on stomata, when their turgor pressure falls due to excessive water loss. ABA can also cause stomata to close when the hormone is added experimentally to leaves.

The Biological Clock. Besides responding to light, CO_2 concentration, and water stress, stomata apparently open and close on a regular daily schedule imposed by a biological clock. Even when plants are placed in

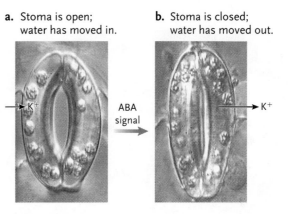

a. Stoma is open; water has moved in.　　**b.** Stoma is closed; water has moved out.

Figure 29.12

Hormonal control of stomatal closing. **(a)** When a stoma is open, high solute concentrations in the cytoplasm of both guard cells have raised the turgor pressure, keeping the cells swollen open. **(b)** In a water-stressed plant, the hormone abscisic acid (ABA) binds to receptors on the guard cell plasma membrane. Binding activates a signal transduction pathway that lowers solute concentrations inside the cells, which lowers the turgor pressure—so the stoma closes.

continuous darkness, their stomata open and close (for a time) in a cycle that roughly matches the day/night cycle of Earth. Such *circadian rhythms* (*circa* = around; *dies* = day) are also common in animals, and several, including wake/sleep cycles in mammals, are known to be controlled by hormones.

29.3f In Dry Climates, Plants Exhibit Various Adaptations for Conserving Water

Many plants have other evolutionary adaptations that conserve water, including modifications in structure or physiology **(Figure 29.13, p. 708)**. The stomata of oleanders, for example, lie at the bottom of pitlike invaginations that are lined by hairlike trichomes (see Figure 29.13b). Sunken stomata are less exposed to drying breezes, and trichomes help retain water vapour at the pore opening, so that water evaporates from the leaf much more slowly.

The leaves of *xerophytes*—plants adapted to hot, dry environments in which water stress can be severe—have a thickened cuticle that gives them a leathery feel and provides enhanced protection against evaporative water loss. An example is mesquite (*Prosopis*). In still other plants that inhabit arid landscapes, such as cacti, stems are thick, leaflike pads covered by sharp spines that actually are modified leaves (see Figure 29.13c). These structural alterations reduce the surface area for transpiration.

One intriguing variation on water-conservation mechanisms occurs in CAM plants, including cacti, orchids, and most succulents. As discussed in Chapter 7, **crassulacean acid metabolism** (CAM) is a biochemical variation of photosynthesis that was discovered in a member of the family Crassulaceae. CAM plants generally have fewer stomata than other types of plants, and their stomata follow a reversed

a. Oleanders

b. Oleander leaf

Cuticle

Multilayer epidermis

Recessed stoma

c. Spines (modified leaves) on a cactus stem

d. CAM plant

Figure 29.13

Some adaptations that enable plants to survive water stress. **(a)** Oleanders (*Nerium oleander*) are adapted to arid conditions. **(b)** As shown in the micrograph, oleander leaves have recessed stomata on their lower surface and a multilayer epidermis covered by a thick cuticle on the upper surface. **(c)** Like many other cacti, the leaves of the Graham dog cactus (*Opuntia grahamii*) are modified into spines that protrude from the underlying stem. Transpiration and photosynthesis occur in the green stems, such as the oval stem in this photograph. **(d)** *Sedum*, a CAM plant, in which the stomata open only at night.

schedule. They are closed during the day, when temperatures are higher and the relative humidity is lower, and open at night. At night, the plant temporarily fixes carbon dioxide by converting it to malate, an **organic acid**. In the daytime, the CO_2 is released from malate and diffuses into chloroplasts, so photosynthesis takes place even though a CAM plant's stomata are closed. This adaptation prevents heavy evaporative water losses during the heat of the day.

STUDY BREAK

1. Explain the key steps in the cohesion–tension mechanism of water transport in a plant.
2. How and when do stomata open and close? In what ways is their functioning important to a plant's ability to manage water loss?

29.4 Transport of Organic Substances in the Phloem

A plant's phloem is another major long-distance transport system, and a superhighway at that: it carries huge amounts of carbohydrates; lesser but vital amounts of amino acids, fatty acids, and other organic compounds; and still other essential substances, such as hormones. And unlike the xylem's unidirectional upward flow, the phloem transports substances throughout the plant to wherever they are used or stored. Organic compounds and water in the sieve tubes of phloem are under pressure and driven by concentration gradients.

29.4a Organic Compounds Are Stored and Transported in Different Forms

Plants synthesize various kinds of organic compounds, including large amounts of carbohydrates that are stored mainly as starch. Yet regardless of where in a plant a particular compound is destined to be used or stored, starch, protein, and fat molecules cannot leave the cells in which they are formed because all are too large to cross cell membranes. They also may be too insoluble in water to be transported to other regions of the plant body. Consequently, in leaves and other plant parts, specific reactions convert organic compounds to transportable forms. For example, hydrolysis of starch liberates glucose units, which combine with fructose to form sucrose—the main form in which sugars are transported through the phloem of most plants. Proteins are broken down into amino acids, and lipids are converted into fatty acids. These forms are also better able to cross cell membranes by passive or active mechanisms.

29.4b Organic Solutes Move by Translocation

In plants, the long-distance transport of substances is called **translocation**. Botanists most often use this term to refer to the distribution of sucrose and other organic compounds by phloem, and they understand the mechanism best in flowering plants. The phloem of flowering plants contains interconnecting sieve tubes formed by living sieve tube member cells (see Figure 28.10). Sieve tubes lie end to end within vascular bundles, and they extend through all parts of the plant. Water and organic compounds, collectively called **phloem sap**, flow rapidly through large pores on the sieve tubes' end walls—another example of a structural adaptation that suits a particular function.

29.4c Phloem Sap Moves from Source to Sink under Pressure

Over the decades, plant physiologists have proposed several mechanisms of translocation, but it was the tiny aphid, an insect that annoys gardeners, that helped demonstrate that organic compounds flow

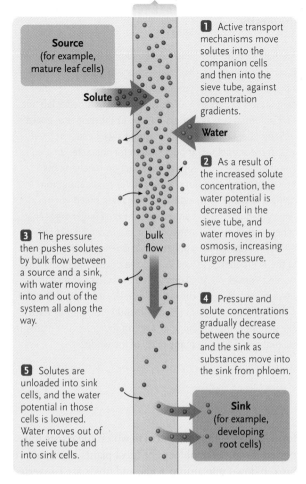

Sieve tube of the phloem

Source
(for example,
mature leaf cells)

Solute

Water

1 Active transport mechanisms move solutes into the companion cells and then into the sieve tube, against concentration gradients.

2 As a result of the increased solute concentration, the water potential is decreased in the sieve tube, and water moves in by osmosis, increasing turgor pressure.

3 The pressure then pushes solutes by bulk flow between a source and a sink, with water moving into and out of the system all along the way.

bulk flow

4 Pressure and solute concentrations gradually decrease between the source and the sink as substances move into the sink from phloem.

5 Solutes are unloaded into sink cells, and the water potential in those cells is lowered. Water moves out of the seive tube and into sink cells.

Sink
(for example,
developing
root cells)

Figure 29.14
Summary of the pressure flow mechanism in the phloem of flowering plants. Organic solutes are loaded into sieve tubes at a source, such as a leaf, and move by bulk flow toward a sink, such as roots or rapidly growing stem parts.

under pressure in the phloem. An aphid attacks plant leaves and stems, forcing its needlelike stylet (a mouthpart) into sieve tubes to obtain the dissolved sugars and other nutrients inside. Numerous experiments with aphids have shown that in most plant species, sucrose is the main carbohydrate being translocated through the phloem. Studies also verify that the contents of sieve tubes are under high pressure, often five times as much as that of an automobile tire. When a live aphid feeds on phloem sap, this pressure forces the fluid through the aphid's gut and (minus nutrients absorbed) out its anus as "honeydew." If you park your car under a tree being attacked by aphids, it might get spattered with sticky honeydew droplets, thanks to the high fluid pressure in the tree's phloem.

A great deal of what botanists know about the transport of phloem sap has come from studies of sucrose transport in flowering plants. A fundamental discovery is that in flowering plants, sucrose-laden phloem sap flows from a starting location, called the

source, to another site, called the *sink,* along gradients of decreasing solute concentration and pressure. A **source** is any region of the plant where organic substances are being loaded into the phloem's sieve tube system. A **sink** is any region where organic substances are being unloaded from the sieve tube system and used or stored. What causes sucrose and other solutes produced in leaf mesophyll to flow from a source to a sink? In flowering plants, the **pressure flow mechanism** builds up at the source end of a sieve tube system and pushes those solutes by bulk flow toward a sink, where they are removed. **Figure 29.14** summarizes this mechanism.

The site of photosynthesis in mature leaves is an example of a source. Another example is a tulip bulb. In spring, stored food is mobilized for transport upward to growing plant parts, but after the plants bloom, the bulb becomes a sink as sugars manufactured in the tulip plant's leaves are translocated into it for storage. Young leaves, roots, and developing fruits generally start out as sinks, only to become sources when the season changes or the plant enters a new developmental phase. In general, sinks receive organic compounds from sources closest to them. Hence, the lower leaves on a rose bush may supply sucrose to roots, whereas leaves farther up the shoot supply the shoot tip.

Most substances carried in phloem are loaded into sieve tube members by active transport **(Figure 29.15a)**. Sucrose is our example here. In leaves, sucrose formed inside mesophyll cells is exported and eventually reaches the apoplast (adjoining cell walls and air spaces) next to a small phloem vein. Here, it is actively pumped into companion cells by symport (see Figure 29.3), in which H^+ ions move into the cell through the same carrier that takes up the sugar molecules. From the companion cells, most sucrose crosses into the living sieve tube members through plasmodesmata. Some sucrose also is loaded into sieve tube members by symport.

In some plants, companion cells become modified into **transfer cells** that facilitate the short-distance transport of organic solutes from the apoplast into the symplast. Transfer cells generally form when large amounts of solutes must be loaded or unloaded into the phloem, and they shunt substances through plasmodesmata to sieve tube members. As a transfer cell is forming, parts of the cell wall grow inward like pleats. This structural feature increases the surface area across which solutes can be taken up. The underlying plasma membrane, packed with transport proteins, then expands to cover the ingrowths. Transfer cells also enhance solute transport between living cells in the xylem, and they occur in glandlike tissues that secrete nectar. Botanists have discovered transfer cells in species from every taxonomic group in the plant kingdom, as well as in fungi and algae. In part because they arise from differentiated cells (instead

a. Loading at a source

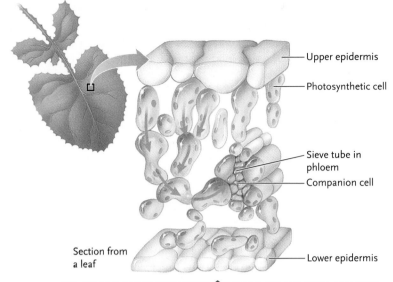

Upper epidermis

Photosynthetic cell

Sieve tube in phloem

Companion cell

Section from a leaf

Lower epidermis

Photosynthetic cells in leaves are a common source of carbohydrates that must be distributed throughout a plant. Small, soluble forms of these compounds move from the cells into phloem (in a leaf vein).

b. Translocation along a distribution path

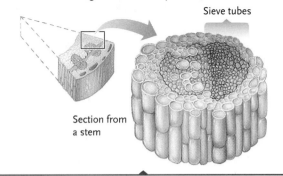

Sieve tubes

Section from a stem

Fluid pressure is greatest inside sieve tubes at the source. It pushes the solute-rich fluid to a sink, which is any region where cells are growing or storing food. There, the pressure is lower because cells are withdrawing solutes from the tubes and water follows the solutes.

c. Unloading at the sink

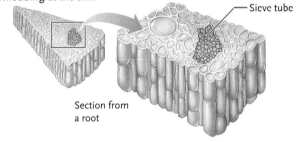

Sieve tube

Section from a root

Solutes are unloaded from sieve tubes into cells at the sink; water follows. Translocation continues as long as solute concentration gradients and a pressure gradient exist between the source and the sink.

Figure 29.15
Translocation in the tissues of *Sonchus*, commonly called sow thistle. Research on *Sonchus* provided experimental evidence for the pressure flow mechanism.

of from meristem cells like other plant types of plant cells), researchers are working to define the molecular mechanisms that trigger their development.

When sucrose is loaded into sieve tubes, its concentration rises inside the tubes. Thus, the water potential falls, and water flows into the sieve tubes by osmosis. In fact, the phloem typically carries a great deal of water. As water enters sieve tubes, turgor pressure in the tubes increases, and the sucrose-rich fluid moves by bulk flow into the increasingly larger sieve tubes of larger veins. Eventually, the fluid is pushed out of the leaf into the stem and toward a sink **(Figure 29.15b)**. When sucrose is unloaded at the sink, water in the tube "follows solutes," moving by osmosis into the surrounding cells **(Figure 29.15c)**.

Sieve tubes are mostly passive conduits for translocation. The system works because companion cells supply most of the energy that loads sucrose and other solutes at the source, and because solutes are removed at their sinks. As sucrose enters a sink, for example, its concentration in sieve tubes decreases, with a corresponding decrease in pressure. Thus, for sucrose and other solutes transported in the phloem, there is always

a gradient of concentration from source to sink—and a pressure gradient that keeps the solute moving along.

As noted previously, phloem sap moving through a plant carries a wide variety of substances, including hormones, amino acids, organic acids, and agricultural chemicals. The phloem also transports organic nitrogen compounds and mineral ions that are removed from dying leaves and stored for reuse in root tissue.

The transport functions of xylem and phloem are closely integrated with phenomena discussed later in this unit—reproduction and embryonic development and the hormone-based regulation of plant growth.

STUDY BREAK

1. Compare translocation and transpiration.
2. Using sucrose as your example, summarize how a substance moves from a source into sieve tubes and then is unloaded at a sink. What is this mechanism called, and why?

What are plasmodesmata made of, and exactly how do they function?

Plasmodesmata, the cytoplasmic channels through plant cell walls, connect plant cells to each other. Yet two fundamental questions about plasmodesmata remain unanswered: Exactly how do plasmodesmata function, and what are their structural components?

As described in this chapter, botanists have long assumed that nutrients, water, and small molecules that serve as growth regulators move through plasmodesmata, which form part of the symplastic pathway in plant tissues. Recent studies have demonstrated that larger molecules, including viruses and important proteins involved in plant growth and development, also move from cell to cell through plasmodesmata. For example, Patricia Zambryski and K.M. Crawford at the University of California at Berkeley reported that proteins, including transcription factors, travel via plasmodesmata from the cell that produces the proteins to adjacent cells where the factors promote or inhibit the expression of particular genes.

Although the normal functions of plasmodesmata in plant growth and development still are not well understood, ongoing research by Zambryski and other plant scientists has begun to shed light on the workings of these vital channels. For instance, a variety of studies of the processes by which viruses spread through plant tissues have revealed that plasmodesmata are not simply static, open channels. Instead, they are dynamic structures with the capacity to close, reopen, widen, and narrow. This capacity for structural change is not triggered by viral infection: rather, it seems that viruses simply take over the plant's natural mechanism for moving molecules from one cell to another.

Plasmodesmata were first observed using electron microscopy several decades ago, and they appear to be lined with proteins as well as membranes. Multiple biochemical approaches have failed to identify the proteins, probably because of the difficulty of purifying proteins that are associated with both a membrane and the cell wall. Genetic screens to identify plasmodesmata proteins, as well as the genes that regulate the functioning of plasmodesmata, are currently under way and may finally reveal details of plasmodesmata structure. As our understanding of the architecture of plasmodesmata and how they function grows, so will insights into the mechanisms of plant development, how plants interact with viral pathogens, and other questions as well.

Beverly McMillan

Review

Go to CENGAGENOW™ at http://hed.nelson.com/ to access quizzing, animations, exercises, articles, and personalized homework help.

29.1 Principles of Water and Solute Movement in Plants

- Plants have mechanisms for moving water and solutes (1) into and out of cells, (2) laterally from cell to cell, and (3) long distance from the root to shoot or vice versa.

- Both passive and active mechanisms move substances into and out of plant cells. Solutes generally are transported by carriers (facilitated diffusion), either passively down a concentration or electrochemical gradient (in the case of ions), or actively against a gradient, which requires cellular energy. An H^+ gradient creates the membrane potential that drives the cross-membrane transport of many ions or molecules.

- Most organic substances enter plant cells by symport, in which the energy of the H^+ gradient is coupled with uptake of a different solute. Some substances cross the plant cell membrane by antiport, in which energy of the H^+ gradient powers movement of a second solute out of cells.

- Water crosses plant cell membranes by osmosis, which is driven by water potential (ψ). Water tends to move osmotically from regions where water potential is higher to regions where it is lower.

- Water potential reflects a balance between turgor pressure and solute potential. Water potential is measured in megapascals (MPa).

- Water and solutes also move into and out of the cell's central vacuole, transported from the cytoplasm across the tonoplast. Aquaporins across the tonoplast enhance water movement. Water in the central vacuole is vital for maintaining turgor pressure inside a plant cell.

- Bulk flow of fluid occurs when pressure at one point in a system changes with respect to another point in the system.

29.2 Transport in Roots

- Water and mineral ions entering roots travel laterally through the root cortex to the root xylem, following one or more of three major routes: the apoplastic pathway, the symplastic pathway, and the transmembrane pathway.

- In the apoplastic pathway, water diffuses into roots between the walls of root epidermal cells. By contrast, water and solutes absorbed by roots can enter either the symplastic or transmembrane pathway, both of which pass through cells.

- Casparian strips form a barrier that forces water and solutes in the apoplastic pathway to pass through cells in order to enter the stele. When an ion reaches the stele, it diffuses from cell to cell to reach the xylem. The roots of many flowering plants have a second layer of cells with Casparian strips (exodermis) just inside the root epidermis.

29.3 Transport of Water and Minerals in the Xylem

- In the conducting cells of xylem, tension generated by transpiration extends down from leaves to roots. By the cohesion–tension mechanism of water transport, water molecules are pulled upward by tension created as water exits a plant's leaves.

- In tall trees, negative pressure generated in the shoot drives bulk flow of xylem sap. In some plants, notably herbaceous species, positive pressure sometimes develops in roots and can force xylem sap upward.

- Transpiration and carbon dioxide uptake occur mostly through stomata. Environmental factors such as relative humidity, air temperature, and air movement at the leaf surface affect the transpiration rate.

- Most plants lose water and take up carbon dioxide during the day, when stomata are open. At night, when stomata close, plants conserve water and the inward movement of carbon dioxide falls.

- Stomata open in response to falling levels of carbon dioxide in leaves and also to incoming light wavelengths that activate photoreceptors in guard cells.

- Activation of photoreceptors triggers active transport of K^+ into guard cells. Simultaneous entry of anions, such as Cl^-, and synthesis of negatively charged organic acids increase the solute concentration, lowering the water potential so that water enters by osmosis. As turgor pressure builds, guard cells swell and draw apart, producing the stomatal opening.

- Guard cells close when light wavelengths used for photosynthesis wane. The stomata of water-stressed plants close regardless of light or CO_2 needs, possibly under the influence of the plant hormone ABA. The leaves of species native to arid environments typically have adaptations (such as an especially thick cuticle) that enhance the plant's ability to conserve water.

29.4 Transport of Organic Substances in the Phloem

- In flowering plants, phloem sap is translocated in sieve tube members. Differences in pressure between source and sink regions drive the flow. Sources include mature leaves; sinks include growing tissues and storage regions (such as the tubers of a potato).

- In leaves, the sugar sucrose is actively transported into companion cells adjacent to sieve tube members and then loaded into the sieve tubes through plasmodesmata.

- In some plants, transfer cells take up materials and pass them to sieve tube members. Transfer cells in xylem enhance the transport of solutes between tissues.

- As the sucrose concentration increases in the sieve tubes, water potential decreases. The resulting influx of water causes pressure to build up inside the sieve tubes, so the sucrose-laden fluid flows in bulk toward the sink, where sucrose and water are unloaded and distributed among surrounding cells and tissues.

Questions

Self-Test Questions

1. Antiport transport mechanisms
   a. move dissolved materials by osmosis.
   b. transport molecules in the opposite direction of H^+ transported by proton pumps.
   c. transport molecules in the same direction as H^+ is pumped.
   d. are not affected by the size of molecules to be transported.
   e. are not affected by the charge of molecules to be transported.

2. All of the following have roles in transporting materials between plant cells except
   a. the stele.
   b. symport.
   c. the cell membrane.
   d. stomata.
   e. transport proteins.

3. Turgor pressure is best expressed as the
   a. movement of water into a cell by osmosis.
   b. driving force for osmotic movement of water (ψ).
   c. group movement of large numbers of molecules due to a difference in pressure between two locations.
   d. equivalent of water potential.
   e. pressure exerted by fluid inside a plant cell against the cell wall.

4. Water potential is
   a. the driving force for the osmotic movement of water into plant cells.
   b. higher in a solution that has more solute molecules relative to water molecules.
   c. a measure of the physical pressure required to halt osmotic water movement across a membrane.
   d. a measure of the combined effects of a solution's pressure potential and its solute potential.
   e. the functional equivalent of turgor pressure.

5. To regulate the flow of water and minerals in the root, the
   a. Casparian strip of endodermal cells blocks the apoplastic pathway, forcing water and solutes to cross cell plasma membranes in order to pass into the stele.
   b. apoplastic pathway is expanded, allowing a greater variety of substances to move into the stele.
   c. symplastic pathway is modified in ways that make plasma membranes of root cortex cells more permeable to water and solutes.
   d. symplastic pathway shuts down entirely so that substances can move only through the apoplast.
   e. transmembrane pathway augments transport via the apoplast, shunting substances around cells.

6. An indoor gardener leaving for vacation completely wraps a potted plant with clear plastic. Temperature and light are left at low intensities. The effect of this strategy is to
   a. halt photosynthesis.
   b. reduce transpiration.
   c. cause guard cells to shrink and stomata to open.
   d. destroy cohesion of water molecules in the xylem.
   e. increase evaporation from leaf mesophyll cells.

7. Stomata open when
   a. water has moved out of the leaf by osmosis.
   b. K^+ flows out of guard cells.
   c. turgor pressure in the guard cells lessens.
   d. the H^+ active transport protein stops pumping.
   e. outward flow of H^+ sets up a concentration gradient that moves K^+ in via symport.

8. A factor that contributes to the movement of water up a plant stem is
   a. active transport of water into the root hairs.
   b. an increase in the water potential in the leaf's mesophyll layer.
   c. cohesion of water molecules in the stem and leaf xylem.
   d. evaporation of water molecules from the walls of cells in the root epidermis and cortex and in the stele.
   e. absorption of raindrops on a leaf's epidermis.

9. In translocation of sucrose-rich phloem sap,
   a. the sap flows toward a source as pressure builds up at a sink.
   b. crassulacean acid metabolism reduces the rate of photosynthesis.
   c. companion cells use energy to load solutes at a source and the solutes then follow their concentration gradients to sinks.

d. sucrose diffuses into companion cells while H^+ simultaneously leaves the cells by a different route.

e. companion cells pump sucrose into sieve tube members.

10. In Eastern Canada in early spring, miles of leafless maple trees have buckets hanging from "spigots" tapped into them to capture the fluid raw material for making maple syrup. This fluid flows into the buckets because

a. the tap drains phloem sap stored in the heartwood.

b. phloem sap is moving from its source in maple tree roots to its sink in the developing leaf buds.

c. phloem sap is moving from where it was synthesized to the closest sink.

d. bulk flow results as phloem sap is actively transported from smaller to larger veins.

e. phloem sap is diverted into the tap from transfer cells.

Questions for Discussion

1. Many popular houseplants are native to tropical rain forests. Among other characteristics, many nonwoody species have extraordinarily broad-bladed leaves, some so large that indigenous people use them as umbrellas. What environmental conditions might make a broad leaf adaptive in tropical regions, and why?

2. Insects such as aphids that prey on plants by feeding on phloem sap generally attack only young shoot parts. Other than the relative ease of piercing less mature tissues, suggest a reason why it may be more adaptive for these animals to focus their feeding effort on younger leaves and stems.

3. So-called systemic insecticides often are mixed with water and applied to the soil in which a plant grows. The chemicals are effective against sucking insects no matter which plant tissue the insects attack, but often don't work as well against chewing insects. Propose a reason for this difference.

4. Concerns about global warming and the greenhouse effect centre on rising levels of greenhouse gases, including atmospheric carbon dioxide. Plants use CO_2 for photosynthesis, and laboratory studies suggest that increased CO_2 levels could cause a rise in photosynthetic activity. However, as one environmentalist noted, "What plants do in environmental chambers may not happen in nature, where there are many other interacting variables." Strictly from the standpoint of physiological effects, what are some possible ramifications of a rapid doubling of atmospheric CO_2 on plants in temperate environments? In arid environments?

The reproductive structures of an ornamental poppy (*Papaver rhoeas*). Male reproductive structures, which produce pollen, surround the female reproductive structure, which produces eggs and is the site of fertilization and seed development (photographer's close-up).

© Ted Kinsman/SPL/Photo Researchers, Inc.

30 Reproduction and Development in Flowering Plants

WHY IT MATTERS

What kinds of plants do we rely on most for our food? Think about the plants that you eat in a given day: most of what we eat comes from just one group of land plants, the angiosperms (flowering plants). Although we do eat the vegetative parts of these plants, we rely heavily on the seeds and fruits produced by these organisms. Worldwide, the top 10 crop plants are angiosperms; for example, consider the top three crop plants in the world: rice, maize, wheat **(Figure 30.1, p. 716)**. Millions of people rely on the seeds and/or fruit either directly or on products made from these parts (e.g., flour). As in other flowering plants, seeds of rice, wheat, and corn result from sexual reproduction. Angiosperms have elaborate reproductive systems—housed in flowers—that produce and protect gametes and developing embryos. The flowers of many species also serve as invitations to animal pollinators.

Is there a downside to our reliance on angiosperm seeds and fruit? Whereas some angiosperms (including the top three crop plants mentioned above) are wind-pollinated, many others rely on animals to carry pollen from one plant to another to complete sexual reproduction. When populations of these pollinators are threatened or decline, the plants' survival is also put at risk.

a.

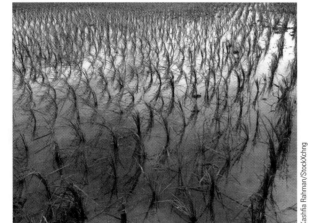

Kashfia Rahman/StockXchng

c.

Photographer: David/www.3d-images.ws

b.

Ian Britton/FreeFoto.com

Figure 30.1
The world's three most important crop plants (from a human perspective): **(a)** rice (*Oryza sativa*) plants in a rice paddy; **(b)** maize (*Zea mays*) plants; and **(c)** wheat (*Triticum aestivum*) plants.

Figure 30.2
Honeybee covered with pollen.

NASA Earth Observatory

This dire situation is now facing many angiosperms in North America that depend on honeybees for their pollination. About one-third of North American plants, including many important crop plants, rely on honeybees for pollination **(Figure 30.2)**. In North America, honeybees pollinate more than $16 billion dollars worth of almonds, cucumbers, berries, apples, and canola. These honeybees are not native to North America but were introduced (along with many crop plants that they pollinate) about 400 years ago from Europe. These introduced bees displaced most native honeybees by the 1920s, and we now depend on these honeybees to pollinate many crops. In 2004, some beekeepers started to report "disappearing colonies": hives that were virtually abandoned, containing only a few larvae, sometimes a queen, and a lot of honey—but no adults. By 2006, the scale of these disappearances was large enough that they hit the news and were termed "colony collapse disorder" (CCD).

The cause of CCD is still a mystery; explanations put forward include various pathogens and pests, the effects of genetically modified plants, drought, and even interference from cellular phone towers (this last hypothesis is not supported by any evidence). Perhaps several of these factors are acting together to create a "perfect storm" that results in the collapse of honeybee populations. If CCD spreads, populations of both cultivated and native angiosperms that rely on honeybees to complete their life cycles could be at risk.

In this chapter, we first investigate how sexual reproduction occurs in flowering plants. We then compare sexual reproduction with asexual reproduction, which occurs in many angiosperms under certain circumstances to produce clones that are genetically identical to their parents. Whether formed by sexual or asexual reproduction, once a new individual begins to grow, finely regulated gene interactions guide the development of flowers and other plant parts. Using methods of molecular biology and a variety of model organisms, plant biologists are beginning to understand some of the mechanisms by which these developmental pathways unfold; we conclude the chapter by looking at some of these mechanisms.

30.1 Overview of Flowering Plant Reproduction

In plants, as in animals, sexual reproduction occurs when male and female haploid gametes unite to create a diploid zygote, which then embarks on a developmental course of mitotic cell divisions, cell enlargement, and cell differentiation. In flowering plants, subsequent steps result in distinctive haploid and diploid forms of an individual.

30.1a Diploid and Haploid Generations Arise in the Angiosperm Life Cycle

An angiosperm zygote develops into an embryo enclosed within a seed. In a seed, early versions of the basic plant tissue systems are already in place, so the embryo technically is already a **sporophyte**—a term that refers to the diploid, spore-producing body of a plant (see Chapter 25). When most people look at a flowering plant, such as a wild rose (*Rosa acicularis*), what they think of as "the plant" is the sporophyte **(Figure 30.3).**

At some point during one or more seasons of an angiosperm sporophyte's growth and development, one or several of its vegetative shoots undergo changes in structure and function and become *floral shoots*—that is, reproductive shoots that will give rise to a flower or inflorescence (a group of flowers on the same floral shoot). Within the sexual organs of the flower, certain cells divide by meiosis. Unlike in animals, however, meiosis in plants does not yield gametes directly. Instead, meiosis gives rise to haploid **spores,** walled cells that develop by mitosis into multicellular haploid **gametophytes.** The gametophytes produce haploid gametes, again by mitosis. Male gametophytes produce sperm, and female gametophytes produce eggs. This division of a life cycle into a diploid, spore-producing generation and a haploid, gamete-producing one is called **alternation of generations** (a phenomenon described more fully in Chapter 25).

In virtually all plants, the gametophyte and the sporophyte are strikingly different from one another in both function and structure. As we learned in

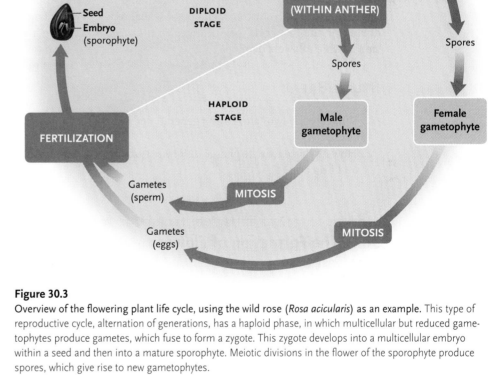

KEY
- Diploid
- Haploid

Figure 30.3

Overview of the flowering plant life cycle, using the wild rose (*Rosa acicularis*) as an example. This type of reproductive cycle, alternation of generations, has a haploid phase, in which multicellular but reduced gametophytes produce gametes, which fuse to form a zygote. This zygote develops into a multicellular embryo within a seed and then into a mature sporophyte. Meiotic divisions in the flower of the sporophyte produce spores, which give rise to new gametophytes.

Chapter 25, in mosses and other bryophytes, the gametophyte is usually larger than the sporophyte; the sporophyte grows out of the gametophyte and is nourished by it. In ferns, which are seedless vascular plants, the gametophyte is much smaller than the sporophyte and is free-living for much of its life span; in most fern species, the gametophyte nourishes itself by photosynthesis. In angiosperms and other seed plants, gametophytes are so reduced in size that they are retained *inside* the sporophyte for all or part of their lives. The female gametophyte of a flowering plant usually consists of only seven cells that are embedded in floral tissues, as you will read shortly. Male gametophytes are released into the environment as pollen grains that are so small that they are measured in micrometres. The pollen grain matures when it reaches floral tissue, producing a pollen tube that grows through floral tissue to the egg, carrying sperm with it. When the pollen tube reaches the egg, the sperm are released, resulting in fertilization and production of a new generation of seeds.

Sporophytes may also reproduce asexually. For instance, strawberry (*Fragaria* species) plants send out horizontal stolons, and new roots and shoots develop at each node along the stems. Short underground stems of onions and lilies put out buds that grow into new plants. In summer and fall, quackgrass (*Elymus repens*) produces new plants at nodes along its subterranean rhizomes. Asexual reproduction also can be induced artificially. Whole orchards of genetically identical fruit trees have been grown from the cuttings or buds of a single parent tree.

We turn now to our consideration of sexual reproduction in angiosperms, beginning with the crucial step in which flowers develop.

STUDY BREAK

1. What are the two "alternating generations" of plants?
2. How do these two life phases differ in structure and function?

30.2 The Formation of Flowers and Gametes

Flowering marks a developmental shift for an angiosperm. What triggers the formation of flowers? Biochemical signals—triggered in part by environmental cues such as day length and temperature—travel to the apical meristem of a shoot, as we will see in the next chapter, and set in motion changes in the activity of cells there. Instead of continuing vegetative growth, the shoot is modified into a floral shoot that will give rise to floral organs.

30.2a In Angiosperms, Flowers Contain the Organs for Sexual Reproduction

A flower develops from the end of the floral shoot, called the **receptacle.** Flowers consist of four concentric circles (*whorls*) of tissues, all of which are modified leaves; **Figure 30.4** shows a typical flower. The two outer whorls

consist of nonfertile, vegetative tissues. The outermost whorl (whorl 1) is made up of leaflike **sepals.** Sepals are usually green and, early in the flower's development, enclose all the other parts, as in an unopened rose bud. The next whorl is made up of **petals,** the "showy" parts of flowers. Petals have distinctive colours, patterning, and shapes, which play important roles in attracting bees and other animal pollinators. Glands that produce nectar, a sugary liquid that attracts animal pollinators, are often located at the base of petals.

A flower's two inner whorls comprise the sexual organs. Inside the petals are the **stamens** (whorl 3), in which male gametophytes form. In almost all living flowering plant species, a stamen consists of a slender **filament** (stalk) capped by a bilobed **anther.** Each anther contains four **pollen sacs,** in which pollen develops.

The innermost whorl (whorl 4) consists of one or more **carpels,** in which female gametophytes form. The lower part of a carpel is the **ovary.** Inside it is one or more **ovules,** in which an egg develops and fertilization takes place. A seed is a mature ovule. In many flowers that have more than one carpel, the carpels fuse into a single, common ovary containing multiple ovules. Typically, the carpel's slender **style** widens at its upper end, terminating in the **stigma,** which serves as a landing platform for pollen. Fused carpels may share a single stigma and style, or each may retain separate ones. The name angiosperm ("seed vessel") refers to the carpel.

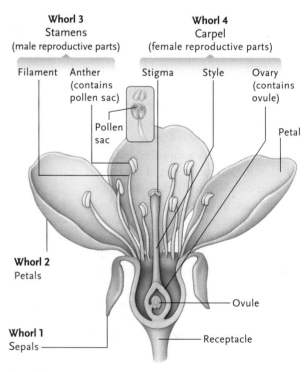

Figure 30.4

Structure of a wild rose (*Rosa acicularis*) flower, with the four whorls indicated. Like the flowers of many angiosperms, it has several stamens but also has numerous carpels. The anthers of the stamen produce haploid pollen. Stigmas of carpels receive pollen, and ovules inside the ovaries contain haploid eggs.

Not all plants have all four layers or whorls of tissue. Whereas many plants have flowers that have both male and female sexual organs, such as the flower shown in Figure 30.4, other plants' flowers have stamens or carpels, but not both. Some flowers lack the showy petals of the typical flower in Figure 30.4 or may have highly modified petals; these modifications often relate to attraction of specific pollinators (see *Molecule Behind Biology*). These **imperfect flowers** are further divided according to whether individual plants produce both sexual types of flowers or only one. In **monoecious** ("one house") species, such as corn (*Zea mays*), each plant has some "male" flowers with only stamens and some "female" flowers with only carpels. In **dioecious** ("two houses") species, such as willows (*Salix* species), a given plant produces flowers with only stamens or carpels **(Figure 30.5)**. With this basic angiosperm reproductive anatomy in mind, we now turn to the processes that produce male and female gametes.

30.2b Pollen Grains Arise from Microspores in Anthers

Most of a flowering plant's reproductive life cycle, from production of sperm and eggs to production of a mature seed, takes place within its flowers. **Figure 30.6, p. 720** shows this cycle as it unfolds in a flower with both stamens and carpels. The spores that give rise to male gametophytes are produced in anthers (see Figure 30.6, left). The pollen sacs inside each anther hold diploid microsporocytes (also called *microspore mother cells*); each microsporocyte produces four small haploid **microspores** by meiosis. Inside the spore wall, each microspore divides again, this time by mitosis. The result is an immature, haploid male gametophyte—a **pollen grain.**

This male gametophyte consists of three cells— two sperm cells plus a third cell that will form a **pollen tube.** When pollen lands on a stigma, this tube grows

a.

b.

Figure 30.5

Examples of monoecious and dioecious plants. **(a)** Corn (*Zea mays*) has separate male and female flowers on the same plant. **(b)** Willows (*Salix* species) have separate female (photo on the top) and male (photo on the bottom) plants.

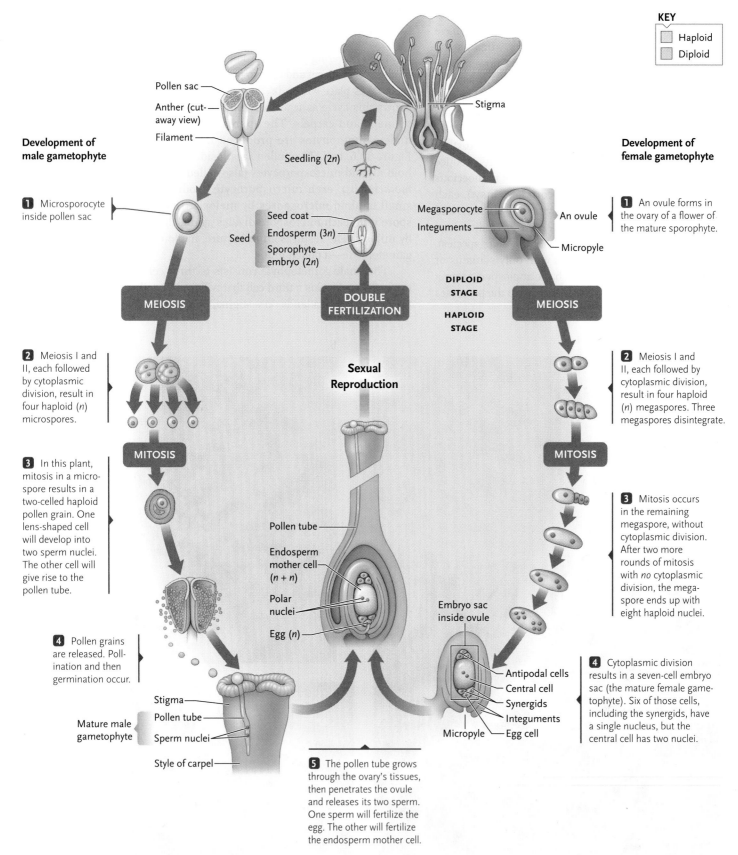

KEY

Haploid
Diploid

Development of male gametophyte

Pollen sac
Anther (cutaway view)
Filament

1 Microsporocyte inside pollen sac

2 Meiosis I and II, each followed by cytoplasmic division, result in four haploid (*n*) microspores.

3 In this plant, mitosis in a microspore results in a two-celled haploid pollen grain. One lens-shaped cell will develop into two sperm nuclei. The other cell will give rise to the pollen tube.

4 Pollen grains are released. Pollination and then germination occur.

Mature male gametophyte

Stigma
Pollen tube
Sperm nuclei
Style of carpel

Seedling (2*n*)

Seed coat
Endosperm (3*n*)
Seed
Sporophyte embryo (2*n*)

MEIOSIS

MITOSIS

DOUBLE FERTILIZATION

Sexual Reproduction

Pollen tube
Endosperm mother cell (*n* + *n*)
Polar nuclei
Egg (*n*)

5 The pollen tube grows through the ovary's tissues, then penetrates the ovule and releases its two sperm. One sperm will fertilize the egg. The other will fertilize the endosperm mother cell.

Stigma

DIPLOID STAGE

HAPLOID STAGE

Development of female gametophyte

Megasporocyte
Integuments
An ovule
Micropyle

1 An ovule forms in the ovary of a flower of the mature sporophyte.

MEIOSIS

2 Meiosis I and II, each followed by cytoplasmic division, result in four haploid (*n*) megaspores. Three megaspores disintegrate.

MITOSIS

3 Mitosis occurs in the remaining megaspore, without cytoplasmic division. After two more rounds of mitosis with *no* cytoplasmic division, the megaspore ends up with eight haploid nuclei.

Embryo sac inside ovule

Antipodal cells
Central cell
Synergids
Integuments
Micropyle
Egg cell

4 Cytoplasmic division results in a seven-cell embryo sac (the mature female gametophyte). Six of those cells, including the synergids, have a single nucleus, but the central cell has two nuclei.

Figure 30.6

Life cycle of the wild rose (*Rosa aciaularis*), a eudicot. Pollen grains develop in pollen sacs within the anthers. An embryo sac forms inside the ovules within an ovary, and an egg forms within the embryo sac. When the pollen grains are released and contact the stigma, double fertilization occurs. An embryo sporophyte and nutritive endosperm develop and become encased in a seed coat.

through the tissues of a carpel and carries the sperm cells to the ovary. A mature male gametophyte consists of the pollen tube and sperm cells—the male gametes.

The walls of pollen grains are tough enough to protect the male gametophyte during the somewhat precarious journey from anther to stigma. These walls are so distinctive that the family to which a plant belongs usually can be identified from pollen alone—based on the size and wall sculpturing of the grains, as well as the number of pores in the wall **(Figure 30.7)**. Because they withstand decay, pollen grains fossilize well and can provide revealing clues about the evolution of seed plants, as well as help biologists reconstruct ancient plant communities and determine how climates have changed over time.

30.2c Eggs and Other Cells of Female Gametophytes Arise from Megaspores in Ovaries

Meanwhile, in the ovary of a flower, one or more dome-shaped masses form on the inner wall. Each mass becomes an **ovule** (see Figure 30.6, right), which will develop into a seed after fertilization, if all goes well. Only one ovule forms in the carpel of some flowers, such as the cherry. Dozens, hundreds, or thousands may form in the carpels of other flowers, such as those of a bell pepper plant (*Capsicum annuum*). At one end, the ovule has a small opening, called the **micropyle**.

Inside the cell mass, a diploid megasporocyte (also called a *megaspore mother cell*) divides by meiosis, forming four haploid **megaspores.** In most plants, three of these megaspores disintegrate. The remaining megaspore enlarges and develops into the female gametophyte in a sequence of steps tracked in Figure 30.6.

First, three rounds of mitosis occur *without* cytoplasmic division; these divisions produce a single cell with eight nuclei arranged in two groups of four. Next, one nucleus in each group migrates to the centre of the cell; these two **polar nuclei** ("polar" because they migrate from opposite ends of the cell) may fuse or remain separate. The cytoplasm then divides, and a cell wall forms around the two polar nuclei, forming a single large *central cell.* A wall also forms around each of the other nuclei. Three of these walled nuclei

form a cluster near the micropyle; one of them is an **egg cell** that may eventually be fertilized. The other two, called *synergids,* will have a role in pollination. The eventual result of all of these events is an **embryo sac** containing seven cells and eight nuclei. This embryo sac is the female gametophyte.

As the male and female gametophytes complete their maturation, the stage is set for fertilization and the development of a new individual.

Study Break

1. What is the biological role of flowers, and what fundamental physiological change must occur before an angiosperm can produce a flower?
2. Explain the steps leading to the formation of a mature male gametophyte, beginning with microsporocytes in a flower's anthers. Which structures are diploid and which are haploid?
3. Trace the development of a female gametophyte, beginning with the megasporocyte in an ovule of a flower's ovary. Which structures are diploid and which are haploid?

30.3 Pollination, Fertilization, and Germination

The process by which plants produce seeds—which have the potential to give rise to new individuals—begins with *pollination,* when pollen grains make contact with the stigma of a flower. Air or water currents, birds, bats, insects, or other agents make the transfer. (Chapter 25 discusses the complex relationship between some flowering plants and their animal pollinators; also see *Molecule Behind Biology* box for more on how flowers attract pollinators.) Plants that produce pollen are no longer dependent on water for fertilization, but pollen may bring pathogens with it to the female reproductive tissues. How do plants protect themselves from these pathogens? See *People Behind Biology.*

Pollination is the first in a series of events leading to *fertilization,* the fusion of an egg and sperm inside

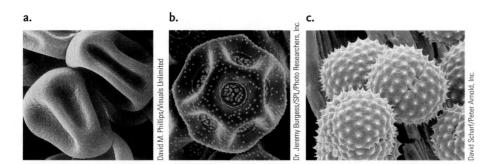

a. David M. Phillips/Visuals Unlimited

b. Dr. Jeremy Burgess/SPL/Photo Researchers, Inc.

c. David Scharf/Peter Arnold, Inc.

Figure 30.7

Examples of pollen grain diversity. Scanning electron micrographs of pollen grains from **(a)** a grass, **(b)** chickweed (*Stellaria*), and **(c)** ragweed (*Ambrosia*) plants.

the flower's ovary. The resulting embryo and its ovule mature into a seed housing a young sporophyte, and when the seed *germinates,* or sprouts, the sporophyte begins to grow.

30.3a Pollination Requires Compatible Pollen and Female Tissues

Even after pollen reaches a stigma, in most cases, pollination and fertilization can take place only if the pollen and stigma are compatible. For example, if pollen from one species lands on a stigma from another, chemical incompatibilities usually prevent pollen tubes from developing.

Even when the sperm-bearing pollen and a stigma are from the same species, pollination may not lead to fertilization unless the pollen and stigma belong to genetically distinct individuals. For instance, when pollen from a given plant lands on that plant's own stigma, a pollen tube may begin to develop but stop before reaching the embryo sac. How is self-pollination detected and blocked? **Self-incompatibility** is a biochemical recognition and rejection process that prevents self-fertilization, and it apparently results from interactions between proteins encoded by *S* (self) genes.

Research has shown that *S* genes usually have multiple alleles—in some species, there may be hundreds—and a common type of incompatibility occurs when pollen and stigma carry an identical *S* allele. The result is a biochemical signal that prevents proper formation of the pollen tube **(Figure 30.8).** For example, studies on plants of the mustard family (*Brassicaceae,* which includes canola) have revealed that pollen contacting an incompatible stigma produces a protein that prevents the stigma from hydrating the relatively dry pollen grain, an essential step if the pollen tube is to grow. A wide range of self-incompatibility responses have been discovered, however. In some plants, when incompatible pollen contacts a stigma, a pollen tube grows normally, but a hormonal response soon causes the flower to drop off the plant, preventing fertilization.

Why is it desirable for plants not to pollinate themselves? Self-incompatibility prevents inbreeding and promotes genetic variation, which is the raw material for natural selection and adaptation. Even so, many flowering plants do self-pollinate, either partly or exclusively, because that mode, too, has benefits in some circumstances. (Mendel's peas are a classic example.) For instance, "selfing" may help preserve adaptive traits in a population. It also reduces or

PEOPLE BEHIND BIOLOGY

Brett Poulis, University of Victoria

When pollen lands on the stigma of a flower (or on the female cone of a gymnosperm), it brings with it all sorts of unwelcome visitors: bacteria, viruses, and fungal spores are all present on the pollen. How can a plant allow pollen and pollen tubes to enter its tissue but still protect itself from these pathogens? Brett Poulis of the Centre for Forest Biology at the University of Victoria investigated this question in Douglas fir (*Pseudotsuga menziesii*), an important tree in Canada's forest industry, for his Ph.D. research. Conifers such as Douglas fir are all wind-pollinated; the contours of the female cones create air currents that draw the pollen toward the cones. Female cones also actively capture pollen by a variety of mechanisms, including sticky hairs and ovular secretions. These secretions, known as "pollination droplets," are released by

the ovule; once a droplet has trapped pollen, the droplet is retracted into the ovule, carrying pollen with it **(Figure 1** shows a pollen droplet produced by a different gymnosperm, not Douglas fir). The pollen will then germinate to produce a pollen tube that carries sperm to the egg. Earlier studies showed that pollen droplets consisted of sugars and other simple water-soluble compounds. Poulis and his advisor, Patrick von Aderkas, used new techniques to probe the protein composition of the droplets—the presence of proteins in the droplets indicates that these secretions play a more important role than just capturing pollen—and found that the droplets contain antimicrobial proteins. Not only does Poulis's research answer the important biological question of how these plants prevent pathogens from attacking the egg and developing

embryo, it may also have significant medical applications. The compounds identified in the secretions are effective against a wide range of pathogens, so perhaps they can be used as antibacterial and antifungal agents in humans. Since completing his Ph.D. research, Poulis, van Aderkas, and other colleagues have collaborated to start a biotechnology company that will develop medical products based on what they learned about conifer defence systems. For his work, Dr. Poulis was awarded a Networks of Centres of Excellence (NCE) Young Innovators Award in 2006.

(NCE are collaborations among universities, industry, not-for-profit organizations, and the federal government aimed at converting research findings into initiatives with economic and social benefits.).

Figure 1
Pollination droplet produced by an ovule of a gymnosperm.

William E. Friedman, University of Georgia

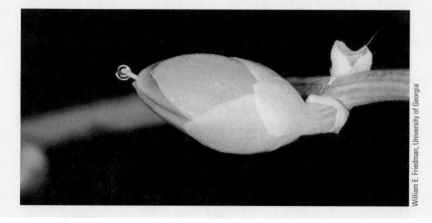

Figure 30.8

Self-incompatibility. When a pollen grain has an *S* allele that matches one in the stigma (which is diploid), the result is a biochemical response that prevents fertilization—in this illustration, by preventing the growth of a pollen tube.

CHAPTER 30 REPRODUCTION AND DEVELOPMENT IN FLOWERING PLANTS

eliminates a plant's reliance on wind, water, or animals for pollination and thus ensures that seeds will form when conditions for cross-pollination are unfavourable, as when pollinators or potential mates are scarce.

30.3b Double Fertilization Results in the Formation of Embryos and Endosperm

If a pollen grain lands on a compatible stigma, it absorbs moisture and germinates a pollen tube, which burrows through the stigma and style toward an ovule. We don't yet fully understand how the pollen tube finds an ovule, but it appears that chemical cues from the two synergid cells lying close to the egg cell help guide the pollen tube toward its destination (see *Unanswered Questions* at the end of this chapter). Before or during these events, the pollen grain's haploid sperm–producing cell divides by mitosis, forming two haploid sperm. When the pollen tube reaches the ovule, it enters through the micropyle, and an opening forms in its tip. By this time, one synergid has begun to die (an example of programmed cell death), and the two sperm are released into the disintegrating cell's cytoplasm. Experiments suggest that elements of the synergid's cytoskeleton guide the sperm onward, one to the egg cell and the other to the central cell.

Next a remarkable sequence of events occurs called **double fertilization**, which has been observed only in flowering plants and (in a somewhat different version) in the gnetophyte *Ephedra* (see Chapter 25). Typically, one sperm nucleus fuses with the egg to form a diploid (2*n*) zygote. The other sperm nucleus fuses with the central cell, forming a cell with a triploid (3*n*) nucleus. Tissues derived from that 3*n* cell are called **endosperm** ("inside the seed"). They nourish the embryo and, in monocots, the seedling, until its leaves form and photosynthesis has begun.

Embryo-nourishing endosperm forms only in flowering plants, and its evolution coincided with a reduction in the size of the female gametophyte. In other land plants, such as gymnosperms and ferns, the gametophyte itself contains enough stored food to nourish the embryonic sporophytes. Endosperm offers an advantage over female gametophyte tissue as a nutrient source for embryos because its development is tied to that of the embryo: if no embryo forms, the plant does not commit resources to endosperm. In gymnosperms, resources are committed to female gametophyte tissue even if no embryo forms. And if an angiosperm embryo is aborted, which can happen if environmental conditions become unfavourable for embryo development (e.g., in the case of drought), endosperm development also ceases, saving the plant energy and resources.

30.3c After Fertilization, Ovaries Develop into Fruits That Protect Seeds and Aid Seed Dispersal

Most angiosperm seeds are housed inside fruits, which provide protection and often aid seed dispersal. Contrary to popular assumption, the fruit does not provide any nutrients to the developing seeds. A **fruit** is a mature or ripened ovary. Usually, fruits begin to develop after ovules are fertilized. The fruit wall, called the **pericarp**, develops from the ovary wall and can have several layers. Hormones in pollen grains provide the initial stimulus that turns on the genetic machinery leading to fruit development; additional signals come from hormones produced by the developing seeds.

Fruits are extremely diverse, and biologists classify them into types based on combinations of structural features. A major defining feature is the nature of the pericarp, which may be fleshy (as in peaches) or dry (as in a hazelnut). A fruit also is classified according to the number of ovaries or flowers from which it develops. **Simple fruits**, such as peaches (*Prunus persica*) and tomatoes (*Solanum lycopersicum*), develop from a single ovary, and in many of them, at least one layer of the pericarp is fleshy and juicy **(Figure 30.9)**. Other simple fruits, including grains and nuts, have a thin, dry pericarp, which may be fused to the seed coat. The garden pea (*Pisum sativa*) is a simple fruit, the peas being the seeds and the surrounding pod the pericarp. **Aggregate fruits** are formed from several ovaries in a single flower. Examples are raspberries (*Rubus* species) and strawberries, which develop from clusters of ovaries. Strawberries also qualify as accessory fruits, in which floral parts in addition to the ovary become incorporated as the fruit develops. Anatomically, the fleshy part of a strawberry is an expanded receptacle (the end of the floral shoot) and the strawberry fruits are the tiny, dry nubbins (called *achenes*) you see embedded in the fleshy tissue of each berry. **Multiple fruits** develop from several ovaries in multiple flowers. For example, a pineapple (*Ananas* species) is a multiple fruit that develops from the enlarged ovaries of several flowers clustered together in an inflorescence. Figure 30.9 shows examples of some different types of fruits.

Fruits have two functions: they protect seeds, and they aid seed dispersal in specific environments. For example, the shell of a sunflower seed is a pericarp that protects the seeds within. A pea pod is a pericarp that in nature splits open to disperse the seeds (peas) inside. Maple fruits have winglike extensions for dispersal (see Figure 30.9e). When the fruit drops, the wings cause it to spin sideways and can carry it away on a breeze. This aerodynamic property propels maple seeds to new locations, where they will not have to

a. Peach (*Prunus*), a simple fruit **b.** Raspberry (*Rubus*), an aggregate fruit **c.** Strawberry (*Fragaria*), an accessory fruit

Fleshy pericarp

Fruit wall

d. Pineapple (*Ananus comosus*), a multiple fruit

e. Maple (*Acer*) fruit

One of many individual fruits

Wing
Seed (in carpel)

Figure 30.9

Fruits. **(a)** Peach (*Prunus persica*), a fleshy simple fruit. **(b)** Raspberry (*Rubus*), an aggregate fruit. **(c)** Strawberry (*Fragaria ananassa*), an accessory fruit that is also an aggregate fruit. **(d)** Pineapple (*Ananas comosus*), a multiple fruit. **(e)** Winged fruits of maple (*Acer*).

compete with the parent tree for water and minerals. Fruits also may have hooks, spines, hairs, or sticky surfaces, and they are ferried to new locations when they adhere to feathers, fur, or, sometimes, the socks of animals that brush against them. Fleshy fruits such as blueberries and cherries are nutritious food for many animals, and their seeds are adapted for surviving digestive enzymes in the animal gut. The seeds are distributed away from the parent plant in the animal's feces.

30.3d The Embryonic Sporophyte Develops Inside a Seed

When the zygote first forms, it starts to develop and elongate even before mitosis begins. Most of the organelles in the zygote, including the nucleus, become situated in the top half of the cell, whereas a vacuole takes up most of the lower half **(Figure 30.10, p. 726)**. The first round of mitosis divides the zygote into an upper *apical cell* and a lower *basal cell*. The apical cell then gives rise to the multicellular embryo, although most descendants of the basal cell form a simple row of cells, the **suspensor**, which transfers nutrients from the parent plant to the embryo (see Figure 30.10).

The first apical cell divisions produce a globe-shaped structure attached to the suspensor. As they continue to grow, eudicot embryos become heart-shaped (see Figure 30.10); each lobe of the "heart" is a developing **cotyledon** (seed leaf), which provides nutrients for growing tissues. By the time the ovule is mature—that is, a fully developed seed—it has become encased by a protective **seed coat**. Inside the seed, the sheltered embryo has a lengthwise axis with a root apical meristem at one end and a shoot apical meristem at the other.

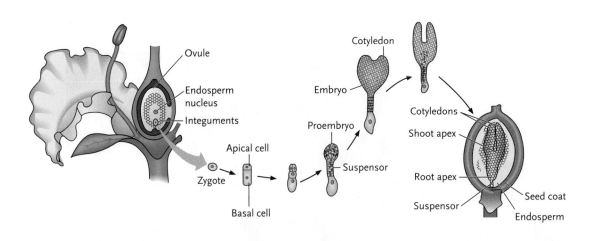

Figure 30.10
Stages in the development of a eudicot embryo. Structures of eudicot seeds.

In some eudicots, such as castor bean, endosperm is maintained as a tissue outside of the embryo. In the seeds of these eudicots, the cotyledons form an interface between the rest of the embryo and the endosperm; they produce enzymes that digest the endosperm and transfer the liberated nutrients to the seedling. In other eudicot seeds, the cotyledons absorb much of the nutrient-storing endosperm and become plump and fleshy. For instance, mature seeds of a sunflower (*Helianthus annuus*) have no endosperm at all. Monocots have one large cotyledon that acts like pea seed cotyledons; that is, they are an interface between the endosperm and the embryo, transferring nutrients to the embryo.

Figure 30.11a and **Figure 30.11b** illustrate the structure of the seeds of two eudicots, the kidney bean (*Phaseolus vulgaris*) and the castor bean (*Ricinus communis*). The kidney bean has broad, fleshy cotyledons, whereas the castor bean has much thinner ones, but in other ways, the embryos are quite similar. The **radicle**, or embryonic root, is located near the micropyle, where the pollen tube entered the ovule prior to fertilization. The radicle attaches to the cotyledon at a region of cells called the **hypocotyl** ("below the cotyledons"). Beyond the hypocotyl is the **epicotyl** ("above the cotyledons"), which has the shoot apical meristem at its tip and which often bears a cluster of tiny foliage leaves, the **plumule**. At germination, when the root and shoot first elongate and emerge from the seed, the cotyledons are positioned at the first stem node with the epicotyl above them and the hypocotyl below them.

The embryos of monocots such as corn differ structurally from those of eudicots in several ways **(Figure 30.11c)**. In addition to having only one very large cotyledon, they also have protective tissues shield the root and shoot apical meristems of monocots. The shoot apical meristem and first leaves are covered by a **coleoptile**, a sheath of cells that protects them during upward growth through the soil. A similar covering, the **coleorhiza**, sheathes the radicle

until it breaks out of the seed coat and enters the soil as the primary root. The actual embryo of a corn plant is buried deep within the corn "kernel," which technically is called a *grain*. Most of the moist interior of a fresh corn grain is endosperm; the single cotyledon forms a plump mass that absorbs nutrients from the endosperm.

30.3c Seed Germination Continues the Life Cycle

A mature seed is essentially dehydrated. Why is being dehydrated important? It allows the seed to stay in a state of "suspended animation." On average, only about 10% of a seed's weight is water—too little for **cell expansion** or metabolism. After a seed is dispersed and germinates, the embryo inside it becomes hydrated and resumes growth. Ideally, a seed germinates when external conditions favour the survival of the embryo and growth of the new sporophyte. This timing is important because once germination is under way, the embryo loses the protection of the seed coat and other structures that surround it. Overall, the amount of soil moisture and oxygen, the temperature, day length, and other environmental factors influence when germination takes place.

In some species, the life cycle may include a period of seed **dormancy** (*dormire* = to sleep), in which biological activity is suspended. Botanists have described a striking array of variations in the conditions required for dormant seeds to germinate. For instance, seeds may require minimum periods of daylight or darkness, repeated soaking, mechanical abrasion, or exposure to certain enzymes, the high heat of a fire, or a freeze–thaw cycle before they finally break dormancy. In some desert plants, hormones in the seed coat inhibit growth of a seedling until heavy rains flush the hormones away. This adaptation prevents seeds from germinating unless there is enough water in the soil to support

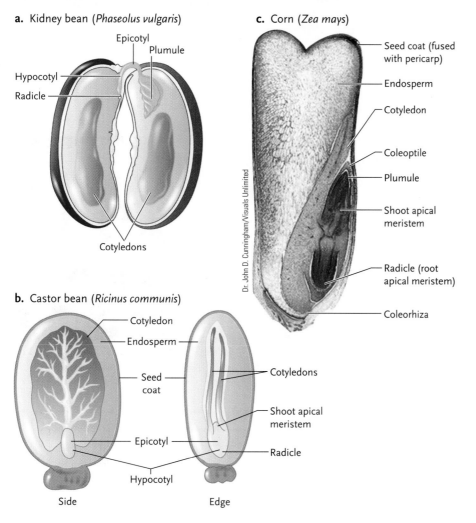

a. Kidney bean (*Phaseolus vulgaris*)

Epicotyl
Plumule
Hypocotyl
Radicle
Cotyledons

b. Castor bean (*Ricinus communis*)

Cotyledon
Endosperm
Seed coat
Epicotyl
Hypocotyl

Cotyledons
Shoot apical meristem
Radicle

Side   Edge

c. Corn (*Zea mays*)

Seed coat (fused with pericarp)
Endosperm
Cotyledon
Coleoptile
Plumule
Shoot apical meristem
Radicle (root apical meristem)
Coleorhiza

Dr. John D. Cunningham/Visuals Unlimited

Figure 30.11

The structure of eudicot and monocot seeds.
Eudicot seeds have two cotyledons, which store food absorbed from the endosperm, but the timing of this function varies in different species. **(a)** The cotyledons of a kidney bean (*Phaseolus vulgaris*) take up nutrients from endosperm while the seed develops, becoming plump and fleshy. **(b)** In the castor bean (*Ricinus communis*), the endosperm is thick and the cotyledons are thin until the seed germinates, when the cotyledons begin to take up endosperm nutrients. The drawing on the right gives a side view of the embryo. **(c)** A kernel of corn (*Zea mays*), a representative monocot seed, shown here in longitudinal section. Monocot seeds have a single cotyledon, which develops into a shield-shaped cotyledon that absorbs nutrients from endosperm.

the growth of the plant through the flowering and seed production stages before the soil dries once again. Many desert plants—and plants in harsh environments such as alpine tundra—cycle from germination to growth, flowering, and seed development in the space of a few weeks, and their offspring remain dormant as seeds until conditions once again favour germination and growth. Many seeds will not germinate until they have passed through the gut of an animal: their seed coats contain germination-inhibiting substances that are broken down by the acids and enzymes of an animal's digestive tract, allowing the seeds to germinate after they are deposited in the animal's feces.

The seeds of some species appear to remain viable for amazing lengths of time. Thousand-year-old lotus seeds (*Nelumbo lutea*) discovered in a dry lakebed have germinated trouble-free. The record for germination is held by a 2000-year-old date palm seed that germinated in 2005. To date, the seedling produced by this seed is thriving.

Germination begins with **imbibition**, in which water molecules move into the seed, attracted to hydro-

philic groups of stored proteins. As water enters, the seed swells, the coat ruptures, and the radicle begins its downward growth into the soil. Within this general framework, however, there are many variations among plants.

Once the seed coat splits, water and oxygen move more easily into the seed. Metabolism switches into high gear as cells divide and elongate to produce the seedling. Stable enzymes that were synthesized before dormancy become active; other enzymes are produced as the genes encoding them begin to be expressed. Among other roles, the increased gene activity and enzyme production mobilize the seed's food reserves in cotyledons or endosperm. Nutrients released by the enzymes sustain the rapidly developing seedling until its root and shoot systems are established.

The events of seed germination have been studied extensively in cereal grains, which are monocots. As a hydrating seed imbibes water, the embryo produces *gibberellin,* a hormone that stimulates the production of enzymes. Some of these enzymes digest components of endosperm cell

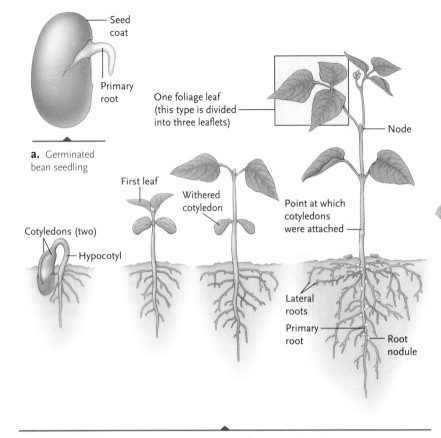

Seed coat

Primary root

a. Germinated bean seedling

One foliage leaf (this type is divided into three leaflets)

Node

Cotyledons (two)

Hypocotyl

First leaf

Withered cotyledon

Point at which cotyledons were attached

Lateral roots

Primary root

Root nodule

Herve Chaumeton/Agence Nature

c. Leaves breaking through the seed coat

b. Food-storing cotyledons are lifted above the soil surface when cells of the hypocotyl elongate. The hypocotyl becomes hook-shaped and forces a channel through the soil as it grows. At the soil surface, the hook straightens in response to light. For several days, cells of the cotyledons carry out photosynthesis; then the cotyledons wither and drop off. Photosynthesis is taken over by the first leaves that develop along the stem and later by foliage leaves.

Figure 30.12
Stages in the development of a representative eudicot, the kidney bean (*Phaseolus vulgaris*).

walls; others digest proteins, nucleic acids, and starch of the endosperm, releasing nutrient molecules for use by cells of the young root and shoot. Although it is clear that nutrient reserves are also mobilized by metabolic activity in eudicots and in gymnosperms, the details of the process are not well understood.

Inside a germinating seed, embryonic root cells are generally the first to divide and elongate, producing a radicle. When the radicle emerges from the seed coat as the primary root, germination is complete. **Figure 30.12** and **Figure 30.13** depict the stages of early development in a kidney bean, a eudicot, and in corn, a monocot. As the young plant grows, its development continues to be influenced by interactions of hormones and environmental factors, as you will read in the next chapter.

Many plants produce large numbers of seeds because, in nature, only a tiny fraction of seeds survive, germinate, and eventually grow into another mature plant. Also, flowers, seeds, and fruits represent major investments of plant resources. Asexual reproduction, discussed next, is a more "economical" means by which many plants can propagate themselves.

STUDY BREAK

1. Explain the sequence of events in a flowering plant that begins with formation of a pollen tube and culminates with the formation of a diploid zygote and the $3n$ cell that will give rise to endosperm in a seed.
2. Early angiosperm embryos undergo a series of general changes as a seed matures. Summarize this sequence and then describe the structural differences that develop in the seeds of monocots and eudicots.

30.4 Asexual Reproduction of Flowering Plants

As noted in Chapter 28, nodes in the stolons of strawberries and the rhizomes of quackgrass each can give rise to new individuals. So can "suckers" that sprout from the roots of raspberry bushes and "eyes" in the tubers of potatoes. All of these examples involve asexual or **vegetative reproduction** from a

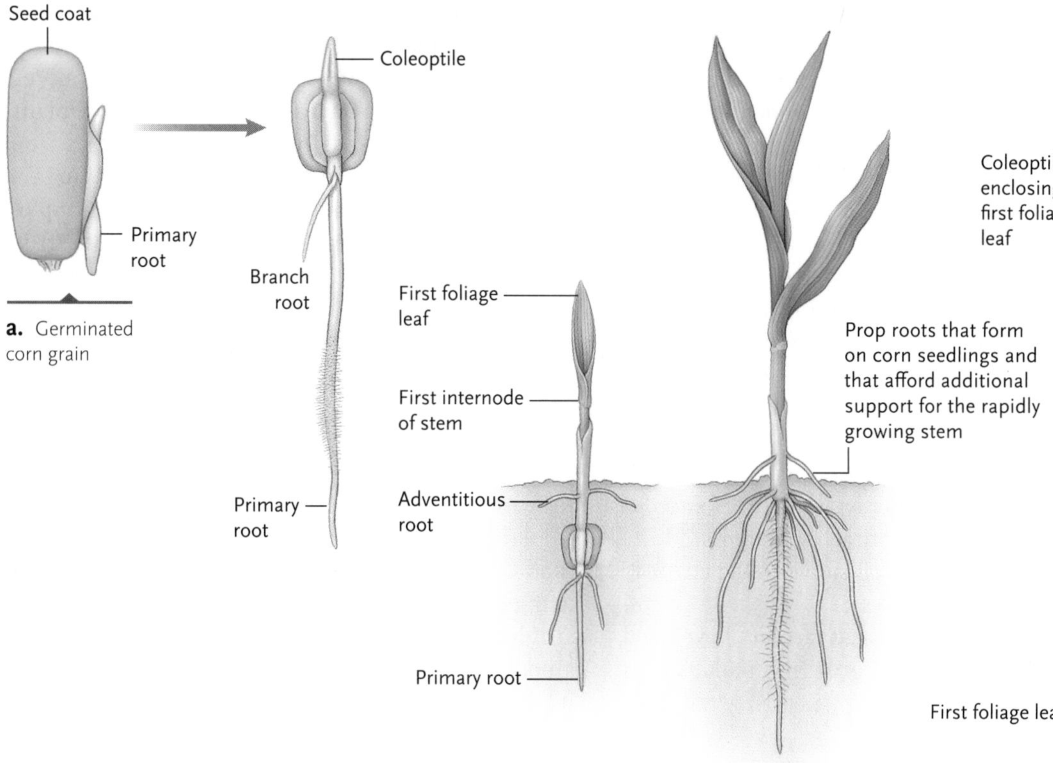

Seed coat

Primary root

a. Germinated corn grain

Coleoptile

Branch root

Primary root

First foliage leaf

First internode of stem

Adventitious root

Primary root

Prop roots that form on corn seedlings and that afford additional support for the rapidly growing stem

b. The young leaves are enclosed in a coleoptile, which protects them during upward growth through the soil. Adventitious roots develop from the first node at the base of the coleoptile. When a corn grain is planted deep, the first internode elongates, separating the primary and adventitious roots. When a grain is planted close to the soil surface, light inhibits elongation of the first internode and the primary and adventitious roots look as if they originate in the same region of the stem.

Figure 30.13
Stages in the development of a representative monocot, the corn plant (*Zea mays*).

Coleoptile enclosing first foliage leaf

Barry L. Runk/Grant Heilman, Inc.

c. Coleoptile and primary root

First foliage leaf

Coleoptile

James Mauseth

d. Coleoptile and first foliage leaf of two seedlings breaking through the soil surface

nonreproductive plant part, usually a bit of meristematic tissue in a bud on the root or stem. All of them produce offspring that are clones of the parent. Vegetative reproduction relies on an intriguing property of plants—namely, that many fully differentiated plant cells are **totipotent** ("all powerful"); that is, they have the genetic potential to develop into a whole, fully functional plant, as discussed in Chapter 28. Under appropriate conditions, a totipotent cell can *dedifferentiate*: it returns to an unspecialized embryonic state, and the genetic program that guides the development of a new individual is turned on.

Some animal stem cells are also totipotent (those in the first stage of embryo development); cells from later stages of animal development are *pluripotent* (cannot grow into a whole organism but can become many different kinds of cells) or *multipotent* (can only become some kinds of cells). In contrast, most plant cells are totipotent regardless of stage of development.

30.4a Vegetative Reproduction Is Common in Nature

Various plant species have developed different mechanisms for reproducing asexually. In the type of vegetative reproduction called **fragmentation**, cells in a piece of the

parent plant dedifferentiate and then regenerate missing plant parts. Many gardeners have discovered to their frustration that a chunk of dandelion root left in the soil can rapidly grow into a new dandelion plant in this way.

When a leaf falls or is torn away from a jade plant (*Crassula* species), a new plant can develop from meristematic tissue in the detached leaf adjacent to the wound surface. In the "mother of thousands" plant, *Kalanchoe daigremontiana*, meristematic tissue in notches along the leaf margin gives rise to tiny plantlets **(Figure 30.14)** that eventually fall to the ground, where they can sprout roots and grow to maturity.

Ed Reschke/Peter Arnold

Figure 30.14
Kalanchoe daigremontiana, the "mother of thousands" plant. Each tiny plant growing from the leaf margin can become a new, independent adult plant.

Some flowering plants, including Kentucky bluegrass (*Poa pratensis*), a common lawn grass in Canada, can reproduce asexually through a mechanism called **apomixis.** Typically, a diploid embryo develops from an unfertilized egg or from diploid cells in the ovule tissue around the embryo sac. The resulting seed is said to contain a **somatic embryo,** which is genetically identical to the parent.

In native plant species, most types of asexual reproduction result in offspring located near the parent. These clonal populations lack the variability provided by sexual reproduction, variation that enhances the odds for survival when environmental conditions change. Yet asexual reproduction offers an advantage in some situations. It usually requires less energy than producing complex reproductive structures such as seeds and showy flowers to attract pollinators. Moreover, clones are likely to be well suited to the environment in which the parent grows.

For centuries, gardeners and farmers have used asexual plant propagation to grow particular crops and trees and some ornamental plants. They routinely use *cuttings,* pieces of stems or leaves, to generate new plants; placed in water or moist soil, a cutting may sprout roots within days or a few weeks. Vegetative propagation can also be used to grow plants from single cells. Rose bushes and fruit trees from nurseries and commercially important fruits and vegetables such as Bartlett pears, McIntosh apples, Thompson seedless grapes, and asparagus come from plants produced vegetatively in tissue culture conditions that cause their cells to dedifferentiate to an embryonic stage.

30.4b Vegetative Propagation in Tissue Culture

Researchers have taken advantage of the totipotency of plant cells to develop plant tissue culture techniques, which allow them to produce clones of plants with desirable traits or to generate entire plants from single cells that have been genetically modified, among other goals. Plant tissue culture is simple in its general outlines **(Figure 30.15).** Bits of tissue are

1. Typically, bits of somatic tissue are excised, often from root and shoot tips or meristems, because these parts tend to be free of viruses. The excised tissue is cultured in a nutrient medium, under strictly controlled environmental conditions.

2. Within a few days, cells in the excised tissue dedifferentiate and form an unorganized tissue mass called a callus.

3. Individual callus cells can be separated out and cultured in a medium containing growth hormones.

4. Totipotent cells eventually give rise to plantlets with roots and shoots.

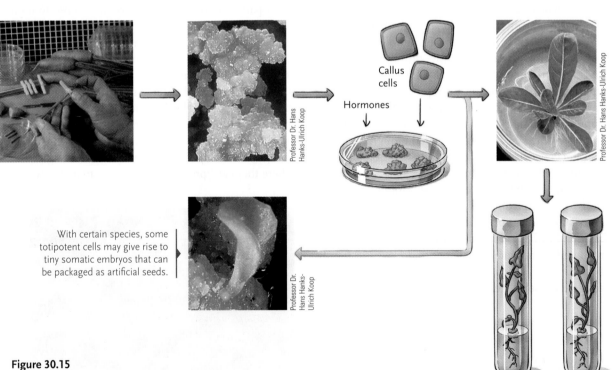

Callus cells

Hormones

With certain species, some totipotent cells may give rise to tiny somatic embryos that can be packaged as artificial seeds.

Figure 30.15
Plant tissue culture protocol.

excised from a plant and grown in a nutrient medium. The procedure disrupts normal interactions between cells in the tissue, and the cells dedifferentiate and form an unorganized cell mass called a **callus.** When cultured with nutrients and growth hormones, some cells of the callus regain totipotency and develop into plantlets with roots and shoots.

Plant tissue culture is the foundation for a new field of research dealing with *somatic embryogenesis* in plants. Single cells derived from a callus generated from shoot meristem are placed in a medium containing nutrients and hormones that promote cell differentiation. With some species, totipotent cells in the sample eventually give rise to diploid somatic embryos that can be packaged with nutrients and hormones in artificial "seeds." Endowed with the same traits as their parent, crop plants grown from somatic embryos are genetically uniform.

Regardless of how it comes into being, a young sporophyte changes significantly as it begins the developmental journey toward maturity, when it will be capable of reproducing. Next we explore what researchers are learning about these developmental changes.

STUDY BREAK

1. Describe three modes of asexual reproduction that occur in flowering plants.
2. What is totipotency, and how do methods of tissue culture exploit this property of plant cells?

30.5 Early Development of Plant Form and Function

As we learned in Chapter 28, one difference between plants and animals is that plant organs, such as leaves and flowers, may arise from meristems throughout an individual's life, sometimes over a period of thousands of years. Accordingly, in plants, the biological role of embryonic development is not to generate the tissues and organs of the adult but to establish a basic body plan—the root–shoot axis and the radial, "outside-to-inside" organization of epidermal, ground, and vascular tissues (see Chapter 28)—and the precursors of the primary meristems. Although they may sound simple, these fundamentals and the stages beyond them all require an intricately orchestrated sequence of molecular events that plant scientists are defining through sophisticated experimentation.

One of the most fruitful experimental approaches has been the study of plants with natural or induced gene mutations that block or otherwise affect steps in development and thus lend insight into the developmental roles of the normal, wild-type versions of those abnormal genes. Although researchers work with various species to probe the genetic underpinnings of early plant development, the thale cress (*Arabidopsis thaliana*) has become an important model organism for plant genetic research.

The entire *Arabidopsis* genome has been sequenced, providing a powerful molecular "database" for determining how various genes contribute to shaping the plant body. Experimenters' ability to trace the expression of specific genes has shed considerable light on how the root–shoot axis is set and how the three basic plant tissue systems arise.

30.5a Within Hours, an Early Plant Embryo's Basic Body Plan Is Established

What determines which part of the embryo will be the root and which part the shoot? Studies done with *Arabidopsis* have revealed that the first, asymmetrical division of the zygote, in which the apical cell receives the majority of the zygote's cytoplasm, whereas the basal cell receives the zygote's large vacuole and less cytoplasm, results in the two daughter cells receiving very different mixes of mRNAs. This means that the apical and basal cells will produce very different proteins; of particular interest are the different *transcription factors* (proteins that regulate transcription) that will be produced in the two daughter cells. With different transcription factors triggering the expression of different genes in the apical and basal cells, distinct biochemical pathways unfold in the two cells, which set in motion steps leading to the differentiation of root and shoot systems.

As development proceeds, cells at different sites become specialized in prescribed ways as a particular set of genes is expressed in each type of cell—a process known as *differentiation*. Differentiated cells, in turn, are the foundation of specialized tissues and organs. We are starting to unravel how plants regulate differentiation but much of this topic is beyond the scope of this chapter.

In nature, genes that govern plant development switch on or off in response to changing environmental conditions. Their signals determine the course of a plant's vegetative growth throughout its life. In many perennials, new leaves begin to develop inside buds in autumn and then become dormant until the following spring, when external conditions favour further growth. Environmental cues stimulate the gene-guided production of hormones that travel through the plant in xylem and phloem, triggering renewed leaf growth and expansion. Leaves and other shoot parts also age, wither, and fall away from the plant as hormonal signals change. The far-reaching effects of plant hormones on growth and development are the subject of Chapter 31.

What will happen to plant–pollinator relationships with climate change?

As you learned in this chapter and in Chapter 25, many plants and their pollinators have evolved together. This coevolution means that the life cycles of a plant must be in synchrony with that of its pollinator, so that both organisms will be at the right stage at the right time. For example, plants pollinated by honeybees need to have flowers producing pollen at the time that a honeybee colony has produced high numbers of mature workers. Lack of synchrony would mean either that there are no flowers ready for the bees and they would go hungry or that flowers do not get pollinated, potentially meaning that no seeds are produced. For many plant–pollinator partnerships, we don't yet know what the cues are or whether the two partners rely on the same cues. In many cases, the two likely use the same cue—such as air temperature—but in other cases, the two may use different cues. For example, the animal might use air temperature, whereas the plant would use snow melt, as the timing cue. So if climate change alters the timing for one partner, then synchrony might be lost. What will happen? Will the partnerships be disrupted? What effect will this have on the animal and plant populations? In the case of honeybees, there is evidence for such disruption: many of the plants they pollinate are flowering earlier, but the bees themselves are not developing earlier.

How does a pollen tube find the ovule?

This question has been investigated for over a century, and we still do not know exactly how a pollen tube is directed to an ovule—does the female gametophyte produce chemical signals that "lure" the pollen tube to an ovule? Or is there some mechanical guidance in the style; that is, do tissues of the style form "tracks" that direct the growth of the pollen tube? Evidence to support this latter hypothesis comes from research done with cut carpels that have had the ovary removed, leaving just the stigma and style. These studies reveal that pollen tubes will grow from the stigma down to the base of a style even if there is no female gametophyte. But biologists have investigated the other hypothesis: that the gametophyte produces directional signals that guide the pollen tube. Recent studies have indicated that the synergids (the cells on either side of the egg) appear to release an attractant, but it has not yet been identified. The two hypotheses aren't mutually exclusive; for example, chemical signals produced by the gametophyte might play a more important role later in pollen tube growth, once the tube gets closer to the ovule.

Review

Go to CENGAGENOW™ at http://hed.nelson.com/ to access quizzing, animations, exercises, articles, and personalized homework help.

30.1 Overview of Flowering Plant Reproduction

- In most flowering plant life cycles, a multicellular diploid stage, the sporophyte (spore-producing plant), alternates with a multicellular haploid stage, the gametophyte (gamete-producing plant). The sporophyte develops roots, stems, leaves, and, at some point, flowers. The separation of a life cycle into diploid and haploid stages is called alternation of generations.

30.2 The Formation of Flowers and Gametes

- A flower develops at the tip of a floral shoot. It can have up to four whorls supported by the receptacle. The outermost whorls consist of the sepals and petals, respectively. The third whorl consists of stamens, and carpels make up the innermost whorl.

- The anther of each stamen contains sacs where pollen grains develop. If compatible pollen lands on the stigma, the receptive surface of the carpel, it produces a pollen tube that grows down the style to the ovary, where ovules are formed. Eggs are produced by female gametophytes inside ovules.

- Flowers can contain both stamens and carpels, or they may contain only male or only female sex organs. Monoecious species have separate male and female flowers on the same plant; in dioecious species, the male and female flowers are on different plants.

- In pollen sacs, meiosis produces haploid microspores. Mitosis inside each microspore produces a pollen grain, an immature male gametophyte. One of its cells develops into two sperm cells, the male gametes of flowering plants. Another cell produces the pollen tube.

- In the ovule, four haploid megaspores form following meiosis. Usually all but one disintegrate. The remaining megaspore undergoes mitosis three times without cytokinesis, producing eight nuclei in a single large cell. Two of these, called polar nuclei, migrate to the centre of the cell. When cytokinesis occurs, cell walls form around the nuclei, with the two polar nuclei enclosed in a single wall. The result is the seven-celled embryo sac, one cell of which is the haploid egg. The cell with two polar nuclei will help give rise to endosperm.

30.3 Pollination, Fertilization, and Germination

- Upon pollination, the pollen grain resumes growth. A pollen tube develops from one cell, and mitosis of the male gametophyte's sperm-producing cell produces two sperm nuclei.

- In double fertilization, one sperm nucleus fuses with one egg nucleus to form a diploid ($2n$) zygote. The other sperm nucleus and the two polar nuclei of the remaining cell also fuse, forming a cell that will give rise to triploid ($3n$) endosperm in the seed.

- After the endosperm forms, the ovule expands, and the embryonic sporophyte develops. A mature ovule is a seed and is encased by a protective seed coat. Inside the seed, the embryo has a lengthwise axis with a root apical meristem at one end and a shoot apical meristem at the other.

- Eudicot embryos have two cotyledons. The embryonic shoot consists of an upper epicotyl and a lower hypocotyl; also present is an embryonic root, the radicle. The single cotyledon of a monocot absorbs nutrients from endosperm. The root and shoot apical meristems of a monocot embryo are protected by a coleoptile over the shoot tip and a coleorhiza over the radicle.

- A fruit is a matured or ripened ovary. Fruits protect seeds and disperse them by animals, wind, or water.

- Fruits are simple, aggregate, or multiple, depending on the number of flowers or ovaries from which they develop. Fruits also vary in the characteristics of their pericarp, which surrounds the seed.
- The seeds of most plants remain dormant until external conditions—moisture, oxygen, temperature, number of daylight hours, and other aspects—favour the survival of the embryo and the development of a new sporophyte.

30.4 Asexual Reproduction of Flowering Plants

- Many flowering plants also reproduce asexually, as when new plants arise by mitotic divisions at nodes or buds along modified

stems of the parent plant. New plants also may arise by vegetative propagation, either natural or induced.
- Tissue culture methods for developing new plants from a parent plant's somatic (nonreproductive) cells include somatic embryogenesis.

30.5 Early Development of Plant Form and Function

- In plants that reproduce sexually, development starts at fertilization. In a sequence of gene-guided processes, a new embryo acquires its root–shoot axis, and cells in different regions begin to differentiate, becoming specialized for particular functions.

Questions

Self-Test Questions

1. An angiosperm life cycle includes
   a. meiosis within the male gametophyte to produce sperm.
   b. meiosis within the female gametophyte to produce eggs.
   c. meiosis within the ovary to produce megaspores.
   d. fertilization to produce microspores.
   e. fertilization to produce megaspores.

2. In a flower,
   a. the ovary contains the ovule.
   b. the stamens support the petals.
   c. the anther contains the megaspores.
   d. the carpel includes the sepals.
   e. the corolla includes the receptacle.

3. Double fertilization in a flower means that
   a. six sperm fertilize two groups of three eggs each.
   b. one sperm fertilizes the egg, and a second sperm fertilizes the polar nuclei.
   c. one microspore becomes a pollen grain; the other microspore becomes a sperm-producing cell.
   d. one sperm fertilizes the egg, and a second sperm fertilizes a synergid, forming endosperm.
   e. one sperm can fertilize two endosperm mother cells.

4. A seed is best described as a (an)
   a. epicotyl.
   b. endosperm.
   c. mature ovary.
   d. mature spore.
   e. mature ovule.

5. The primary root develops from the embryonic
   a. epicotyl.
   b. hypocotyl.
   c. coleoptile.
   d. radicle.
   e. plumule.

Questions for Discussion

1. A plant physiologist has succeeded in cloning a gene for pest resistance into petunia cells. How can she use tissue culture to propagate a large number of petunia plants with the gene?

2. Grocery stores separate displays of fruits and vegetables according to typical uses for these plant foods. For instance, bell peppers, cucumbers, tomatoes, and eggplants are in the vegetable section, whereas apples, pears, and peaches are displayed with other fruits. How does this practice relate to the biological definition of a fruit?

3. Before cherries, blueberries, and many other fruits ripen and the seeds inside them mature, their flesh is bitter or sour. Only later does it become palatable to animals that assist in seed dispersal. Develop a hypothesis of how this sequence improves the odds for the plant's reproductive success and then propose an experiment (or series of experiments) for testing the hypothesis.

Sunflower plants (*Helianthus*) with flower heads oriented toward the Sun's rays—an example of a plant response to the environment.

© Garry Black/Masterfile

31 Control of Plant Growth and Development

WHY IT MATTERS

It's a warm, sunny day in the summer, and in a field of corn (*Zea mays*), a caterpillar (*Mythimna separata*) **(Figure 31.1a, p. 736)** is munching away at the leaves of a corn plant. Unlike an animal being attacked by a predator, the corn plant cannot run away, nor can it just flap its leaves to dislodge the caterpillar. But just because the plant doesn't move doesn't mean that it is not defending itself. Unbeknownst to the caterpillar, the plant is busily synthesizing chemical responses to the attack; some of these chemicals are transported to other cells within the plant, but others are volatile compounds that, when released to the air, send signals to animals that prey on this species of caterpillar. These animals are parasitic wasps (*Cotesia marginiventris*) **(Figure 31.1b)**, which soon descend on the unsuspecting caterpillar and lay eggs in its body, killing it **(Figure 31.1c)**. Neighbouring plants can also detect volatile signals and ramp up synthesis of defensive compounds in their leaves, making them less attractive targets to other caterpillars. Inside the plant that sent the signals, other chemical messengers have passed from the wounded leaf to undamaged tissues, increasing their

Figure 31.1

Some plants recruit animals to assist in their defence. **(a)** Common army-worm caterpillar (*Mythimna separata*, larval stage) feeding on corn (*Zea mays*). **(b)** Parasitic wasp (*Cotesia* species) that lays eggs in bodies of armyworm caterpillars. **(c)** Larvae of a parasitic wasp emerging from the body of an armyworm caterpillar.

a.

Christian Krupke, John Obermeyer, and Larry Bledsoe/Purdue University

b.

Dr. L. T. Kok, Professor of Entomology, Virginia Tech, Blacksburg, VA

|— 1 mm

c.

Marietta College

|—————| 10 mm

synthesis of defensive compounds. We don't yet understand all of the mechanisms by which these responses happen, but they are the subjects of intense research interest. Not only will studies of these responses help us understand how plants sense and respond to their environment, but we also might be able to use such a defence response to develop new pesticides that are toxic to the target pests but not to other organisms.

Defence responses such as those described above are one example of adaptations that promote the survival of plants as sessile organisms. These adaptations range from the triggers for seed germination to the development of a particular body form, the shift from a vegetative phase to a reproductive one, and the timed death of flowers, leaves, and other parts. Although many of the details remain elusive or disputed, ample evidence exists that an elaborate system of molecular signals regulates many of these phenomena. We know, for example, that plant hormones alter patterns of growth, cell metabolism, and morphogenesis in response to changing environmental rhythms, including seasonal changes in day length and temperature and the daily rhythms of light and dark. They also adjust those patterns in response to environmental conditions, such as the amount of sunlight or shade, moisture, soil nutrients, and other factors. Some hormones govern growth responses to directional stimuli, such as light, gravity, or the presence of nearby structures. Often hormonal effects involve changes in gene expression, although sometimes other mechanisms are at work.

We begin by surveying the different groups of plant hormones and other signalling molecules and then turn our attention to the remarkable diversity of responses to both internal and environmental signals.

31.1 Plant Hormones

The concept of hormones and their action was developed in the field of vertebrate animal physiology, but some aspects of animal hormones and how they work don't apply to plants. Animal hormones are chemicals that are produced by cells in one part of the body (often glands) and move via the circulatory systems to affect another part of the body. They are small molecules that are active at low concentrations to modify metabolism and development, and their various effects are integrated and coordinated by the central nervous system. There are a wide range of animal hormones (see Chapter 35). In contrast, plants lack a circulatory system comparable to the blood system of animals, so the long-distance action of hormones does not necessarily apply to plants; instead, plant hormones may have localized effects or effects on other parts of the plant (or both). Plant hormones can move via the vascular system, or just from cell to cell, or even via intercellular spaces. Plants also lack a central nervous system to integrate the action of various hormones. However, plants certainly do have molecules that regulate their growth and development and allow for communication between cells. There are fewer categories of plant hormones than animal hormones, and they do not all fit into the same classes as animal hormones; for example, ethylene, a plant hormone, is a gas.

In plants, a **hormone** (*horman* = to stimulate) is a signalling molecule that regulates or helps coordinate some aspect of the plant's growth, metabolism, or development. Plant hormones act in response to two general types of cues: (1) internal chemical conditions related to growth and development and (2) conditions in the external environment that affect plant growth, such as light or the availability of water. Some plant hormones are transported from the tissue that produces them to another plant part, whereas others exert their effects in the tissue where they are synthesized.

All plant hormones share certain characteristics. They are rather small organic molecules, and all are active in extremely low concentrations. Another shared feature is specificity: each one affects a given tissue in a particular way. Hormones that have effects outside the tissue where they are produced typically are transported to their target sites in vascular tissues, or they diffuse from one plant part to another. Within these general parameters, however, plant hormones vary greatly in their effects. Some stimulate one or more aspects of the plant's growth or development, whereas others have an inhibiting influence. Adding to the potential for confusion, a given hormone can have different effects in different tissues, and the effects also can differ depending on a target tissue's stage of development. And as researchers have increasingly discovered, many physiological responses result from the interaction of two or more hormones.

Biologists recognize at least seven major classes of plant hormones (Table 31.1): auxins, gibberellins, cytokinins, ethylene, brassinosteroids, abscisic acid (ABA), and jasmonates. Recent discoveries have added other substances to the list of hormonelike signalling agents in plants. We now consider each major class of plant hormones and discuss some of the newly discovered signalling molecules as well.

31.1a Auxins Promote Growth

Auxins are synthesized primarily in the shoot apical meristem and young stems and leaves. Their main effects are to stimulate plant growth by promoting cell elongation in stems and coleoptiles and by governing growth responses to light and gravity. Our focus here is indoleacetic acid (IAA), the most important natural auxin **(Figure 31.2)**. Botanists often use the general term "auxin" to refer to IAA, a practice we follow in the following discussion.

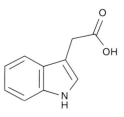

Figure 31.2
Structure of indoleacetic acid (IAA).

Experiments Leading to the Discovery of Auxins. Auxins were the first plant hormones identified. The path to their discovery began in the late nineteenth century in

Table 31.1	Major Plant Hormones and Signalling Chemicals		
Hormone/Signalling Compound	Where Synthesized	Tissues Affected	Effects
Auxins	Apical meristems, developing leaves and embryos	Growing tissues, buds, roots, leaves, fruits, vascular tissues	Promote growth and elongation of stems; promote formation of lateral roots and dormancy in lateral buds; promote fruit development; inhibit leaf abscission; orient plants with respect to light, gravity
Gibberellins	Root and shoot tips, young leaves, developing embryos	Stems, developing seeds	Promote cell divisions and growth and elongation of stems; promote seed germination
Cytokinins	Mainly in root tips	Shoot apical meristems, leaves, buds	Promote cell division; inhibit senescence of leaves; coordinate growth of roots and shoots (with auxin)
Ethylene	Shoot tips, roots, leaf nodes, flowers, fruits	Seeds, buds, seedlings, mature leaves, flowers, fruits	Regulates elongation and division of cells in seedling stems, roots; in mature plants, regulates senescence and abscission of leaves, flowers, and fruits
Brassinosteroids	Young seeds; shoots and leaves	Mainly shoot tips, developing embryos	Stimulate cell division and elongation, differentiation of vascular tissue
Abscisic acid	Leaves	Buds, seeds, stomata	Promotes responses to environmental stress, including inhibiting growth/promoting dormancy; stimulates stomata to close in water-stressed plants
Jasmonates	Roots, seeds, probably other tissues	Various tissues, including damaged ones	In defence responses, promote transcription of genes encoding protease inhibitors; possible role in plant responses to nutrient deficiencies
Oligosaccharins	Cell walls	Damaged tissues; possibly active in most plant cells	Promote synthesis of phytoalexins in injured plants; may also have a role in regulating growth
Systemin	Damaged tissues	Damaged tissues	To date, known only in tomato and closely related species; roles in defence, including triggering jasmonate-induced chemical defences
Salicylic acid	Damaged tissues	Many plant parts	Triggers synthesis of pathogenesis-related (PR) proteins, other general defences

Charles Darwin

When we think of Charles Darwin, we think of course of his theory of evolution by natural selection, which is the foundation of modern biology. But Darwin's contribution to biology is much more than just his work on evolution, key though it is: he was a very knowledgeable and creative naturalist, who carried out experiments on several other important biological questions. He published a detailed analysis of how earthworms improve the soil (The Formation of Vegetable Mould through the Action of Worms) and wrote books on several botanical topics, among them plants that eat animals (Insectivorous Plants), pollination and fertilization systems (Fertilisation in Orchids and The Effects of Self- and Cross-Fertilisation), and the tendency of plants to grow toward sunlight (The Power of Movement in Plants).

Experiments on this last topic, carried out with his son Francis, are still cited today for their role in helping us understand how plants respond to light.

Darwin's study. Darwin undertook most of his life's work in this room at Down House. He hesitated to discard old papers and specimens, believing that he would find a use for them as soon as they were carried away in the trash.

---

the library of Charles Darwin's home in the English countryside (see *People Behind Biology*).

Among his many interests, Darwin was fascinated by plant tropisms—movements such as the bending of a houseplant toward light. This growth response, triggered by exposure to a directional light source, is an example of a **phototropism**.

Working with his son Francis, Darwin explored phototropisms by germinating the seeds of two species of grasses, oat (*Avena sativa*) and canary grass (*Phalaris canariensis*), in pots on the sill of a sunny window. Recall from Chapter 30 that the shoot apical meristem and plumule of grass seedlings are sheathed by a protective coleoptile—a structure that is extremely sensitive to light. Darwin did not know this detail, but he observed that as the emerging shoots grew, within a few days, they bent toward the light. He hypothesized that the tip of the shoot somehow detected light and communicated that information to the coleoptile. Darwin tested this idea in several ways **(Figure 31.3)** and concluded that when seedlings are illuminated from the side, "some influence is transmitted from the upper to the lower part, causing them to bend."

The Darwins' observations spawned decades of studies—a body of work that illustrates how scientific understanding typically advances step by step, as one set of experimental findings stimulates new research. First, scientists in Denmark and Poland showed that the bending of a shoot toward a light source was caused by something that could move through agar (a jellylike culture material derived from certain red algae) but not through a sheet of the mineral mica. This finding prompted experiments establishing that, indeed, the stimulus was a chemical produced in the shoot tip. Soon afterward, in 1926, experiments by the Dutch plant physiologist Frits Went confirmed that the growth-promoting chemical diffuses downward from the shoot tip to the stem below **(Figure 31.4)**. Using oat seeds, Went first sliced the tips from young shoots that had been grown under normal light conditions. He then placed the tips on agar blocks and left them there long enough for diffusible substances to move into the agar. Meanwhile, the decapitated stems stopped growing, but growth quickly resumed in seedlings that Went "capped" with the agar blocks (see Figure 31.4a). Clearly, a growth-promoting substance in the excised shoot tips had diffused into the agar and from there into the seedling stems. Went also attached an agar block to one side of a decapitated shoot tip; when the shoot began growing again, it bent away from the agar (see Figure 31.4b). Importantly, Went performed his experiments in total darkness, to avoid any "contamination" of his results by the possible effects of light.

Went did not determine the mechanism—differential elongation of cells on the shaded side of a shoot—by which the growth promoter controlled phototropism.

QUESTION: Why does a plant stem bend toward the light?

EXPERIMENT 1: The Darwins observed that the first shoot of an emerging grass seedling, which is sheathed by a coleoptile, bends toward sunlight shining through a window. They removed the shoot tip from a seedling and illuminated one side of the seedling.

RESULT: The seedling neither grew nor bent.

EXPERIMENT 2: The Darwins divided seedlings into two groups. They covered the shoot tips of one group with an opaque cap and the shoot tips of the other group with a translucent cap. All the seedlings were illuminated from the same side.

Figure 31.3
The Darwins' experiments on phototropism.

Original observation

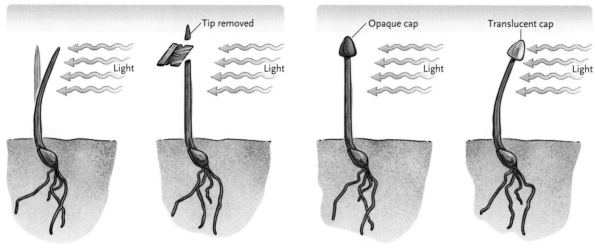

RESULT: The seedlings with opaque caps grew but did not bend. Those with translucent caps both grew and bent toward the light.

CONCLUSION: When seedlings are illuminated from one side, an unknown factor transmitted from a seedling's tip to the tissue below causes it to bend toward the light.

However, he did develop a test that correlated specific amounts of the substance, later named auxin (*auxein* = to increase), with particular growth effects.

This careful groundwork culminated several years later when other researchers identified auxin as IAA.

a. The procedure showing that IAA promotes elongation of cells below the shoot tip

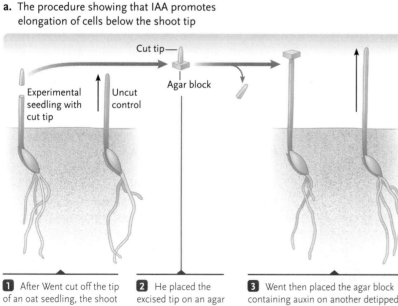

1 After Went cut off the tip of an oat seedling, the shoot stopped elongating, whereas a control seedling with an intact tip continued to grow.

2 He placed the excised tip on an agar block for 1–4 hours. During that time, IAA diffused into the agar block from the cut tip.

3 Went then placed the agar block containing auxin on another detipped oat shoot, and the shoot resumed elongation, growing about as rapidly as that of a control seedling with an intact shoot tip.

b. The procedure showing that cells in contact with IAA grow faster than those farther away

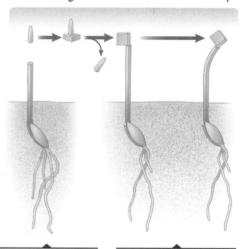

1 Went removed the tip of a seedling and placed it on an agar block.

2 He placed the agar block containing auxin on one side of the shoot tip. Auxin moved into the shoot tip on that side, causing it to bend away from the hormone.

Figure 31.4
Two experiments by Frits Went demonstrating the effect of IAA on an oat coleoptile. Went carried out the experiments in darkness to prevent the effects of light from skewing the results.

Effects of Auxins. As already noted, auxin stimulates aspects of plant growth and development. In fact, recent studies of plant development have revealed that auxin is one of the first chemical signals to help shape the plant body. When the zygote first divides, forming an embryo that consists of a basal cell and an apical cell, auxin exported by the basal cell to the apical cell helps guide the development of the various features of the embryonic shoot. As the embryo develops further, IAA is produced mainly by the leaf primordium of the young shoot (see Figure 28.14). While the developing shoot is underground, IAA is actively transported downward, stimulating the primary growth of the stem and root **(Figure 31.5)**. Once an elongating shoot breaks through the soil surface, its tip is exposed to sunlight, and the first leaves unfurl and begin photosynthesis. Shortly thereafter, the leaf tip stops producing IAA, and that task is assumed first by cells at the leaf edges and then by cells at the base of the young leaf. Even so, as Section 31.3 discusses more fully, IAA continues to influence a plant's responses to light and plays a role in plant growth responses to gravity as well. IAA also stimulates cell division in the vascular cambium and promotes the formation of secondary xylem, as well as the formation of new root apical meristems, including lateral meristems. Not all of auxin's effects promote growth, however. IAA also maintains apical dominance, which inhibits growth of lateral meristems on shoots and restricts the formation of branches (see Section 31.3). Hence, auxin is a signal that the shoot apical meristem is present and active.

Commercial orchardists spray synthetic IAA on fruit trees because it promotes uniform flowering and helps set the fruit; it also helps prevent premature fruit drop. These effects mean that all the fruit may be picked at the same time, with considerable savings in labour costs.

Some synthetic auxins are used as herbicides, essentially stimulating a target plant to "grow itself to death." A **herbicide** is any compound that, at proper concentration, kills plants. Some herbicides are selective, killing one class of plants and not others. The most widely used herbicide in the world is the synthetic auxin 2,4-D (2,4-dichlorophenoxyacetic acid). This chemical is used extensively to prevent broadleaf weeds (which are eudicots) from growing in fields of cereal crops such as corn (which are monocots). By an unknown mechanism, 2,4-D causes an abnormal burst of growth in which eudicot stems elongate more than 10 times faster than normal— much faster than the plant can support metabolically.

Auxin Transport. To exert their far-reaching effects on plant tissues, auxins must travel away from their main synthesis sites in shoot meristems and young leaves. Yet xylem and phloem sap usually do not contain auxins. Moreover, experiments have shown that although IAA moves through plant tissues slowly—roughly 1 cm/hr— this rate is 10 times faster than could be explained by simple diffusion. How, then, is auxin transported?

Plant physiologists adapted the agar block method pioneered by Went to trace the direction and rate of auxin movements in different kinds of tissues. A research team led by Winslow Briggs at Stanford University determined that the shaded side of a shoot tip contains more IAA than the illuminated side. Hypothesizing that light causes IAA to move laterally from the illuminated to the shaded side of a shoot tip, the team then inserted a vertical barrier (a thin slice of mica) between the shaded and the illuminated sides of a shoot tip. IAA could not cross the barrier, and when the shoot tip was illuminated, it did not bend. In addition, the concentrations of IAA in the two sides of the shoot tip remained about the same. When the barrier was shortened so that the separated sides of the tip again touched, the concentration of IAA in the shaded portion increased significantly, and the tip *did* bend. The study confirmed that IAA initially moves laterally in the shoot tip, from the illuminated side to the shaded side, where it triggers the elongation of cells and curving of the tip toward light. Subsequent research showed that IAA then moves downward in a shoot by way of a top-to-bottom mechanism called **polar transport**. That is, IAA in a coleoptile or shoot tip travels from the apex of the tissue to its base, such as from the tip of a developing leaf to the stem. **Figure 31.6** outlines the experimental method that demonstrated polar transport. When IAA reaches roots, it moves toward the root tip.

Inside a stem, IAA appears to be transported via parenchyma cells adjacent to vascular bundles. IAA again moves by polar transport as it travels through and between cells: It enters at one end by diffusing passively through cell walls and exits at the opposite end by active transport across the plasma membrane. There is increasing evidence that auxin also may travel rapidly through plants in the phloem. As this work continues, researchers will undoubtedly gain a clearer

Figure 31.5

The effect of auxin treatment on a gardenia (*Gardenia*) cutting. Four weeks after an auxin was applied to the base of the cutting on the left, its stem and roots have elongated, but the number of leaves is unchanged. The plant cutting on the right was not treated.

Treated with auxin   Untreated

Kingsley R. Stern

understanding of how plants distribute this crucial hormone to their growing parts.

Possible Mechanisms of IAA Action. Ever since auxin was discovered, researchers have actively sought to understand how IAA stimulates cell elongation. As a plant cell elongates, the cellulose meshwork of the cell wall is first loosened and then stretched by turgor pressure. Several hormones, and auxin especially, apparently increase the plasticity (irreversible stretching) of the cell wall. Two major hypotheses seek to explain this effect, and both may be correct.

Plant cell walls grow much faster in an acid environment—that is, when the pH is less than 7. The **acid-growth hypothesis** suggests that auxin causes cells to secrete acid (H^+) into the cell wall by stimulating the plasma membrane **H^+ pumps** to move hydrogen ions from the cell interior into the cell wall; the increased acidity activates proteins called *expansins*, which penetrate the cell wall and disrupt bonds between cellulose microfibrils in the wall **(Figure 31.7)**. In the laboratory, it is easy to measure an increase in the rate at which coleoptiles or stem tissues release acid when they are treated with IAA. Activation of the plasma membrane H^+ pump also produces a membrane potential that pulls K^+ and other cations into the cell; the resulting osmotic gradient draws water into the cell, increasing turgor pressure and helping to stretch the "loosened" cell walls.

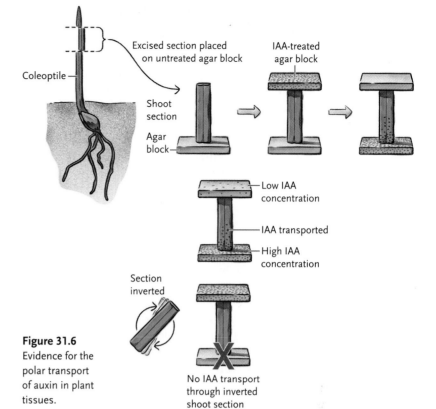

Figure 31.6
Evidence for the polar transport of auxin in plant tissues.

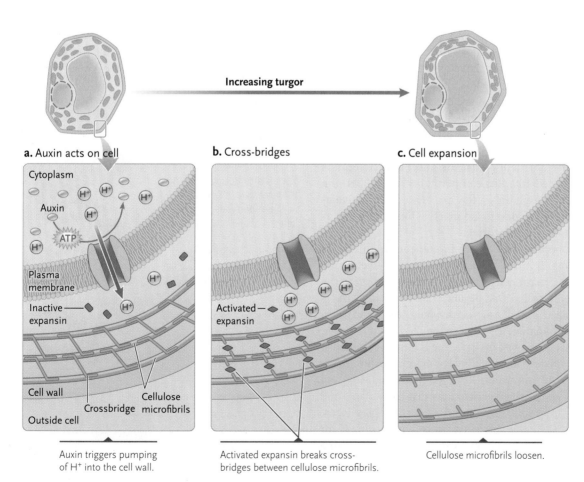

a. Auxin acts on cell
Cytoplasm
Auxin
ATP
Plasma membrane
Inactive expansin
Cell wall
Crossbridge
Cellulose microfibrils
Outside cell
Auxin triggers pumping of H^+ into the cell wall.

b. Cross-bridges
Activated expansin
Activated expansin breaks cross-bridges between cellulose microfibrils.

c. Cell expansion
Cellulose microfibrils loosen.

Increasing turgor

Figure 31.7
How auxin may regulate expansion of plant cells. According to the acid-growth hypothesis, plant cells secrete acid (H^+) when auxin stimulates the plasma membrane H^+ pumps to move hydrogen ions into the cell wall **(a)**; the increased acidity activates enzymes called *expansins*, which disrupt bonds between cellulose microfibrils in the wall **(b).** As a result, the wall becomes extensible, and the cell can expand **(c).**

A second hypothesis, also supported by experimental evidence, suggests that auxin triggers the expression of genes encoding enzymes that play roles in the synthesis of new wall components. Plant cells exposed to IAA don't show increased growth if they are treated with a chemical that inhibits protein synthesis. However, researchers have identified mRNAs that rapidly increase in concentration within 10 to 20 minutes after stem sections have been treated with auxin, although they still do not know exactly which proteins these mRNAs encode.

31.1b Gibberellins Also Stimulate Growth, Including the Elongation of Stems

In the early 1920s, a researcher in Japan, Eiichi Kurosawa, was studying a rice plant disease that the Japanese called *bakanae*—the "foolish seedling" disease. Stems of rice seedlings that had become infected with the fungus *Gibberella fujikuroi* elongated twice as much as uninfected plants. The lanky stems were weak and eventually toppled over before the plants could produce seeds. Kurosawa discovered that extracts of the fungus also could trigger the disease. Eventually, other investigators purified the fungus's disease-causing substance, naming it **gibberellin** (GA).

Gibberellins stimulate several aspects of plant growth. Perhaps most apparent to humans is their ability to promote the lengthening of plant stems by stimulating both cell division and cell elongation. Synthesized in shoot and root tips and young leaves, gibberellins, like auxin, modify the properties of plant cell walls in ways that promote expansion (although the gibberellin mechanism does not involve acidification of the cell wall). Perhaps both hormones affect expansins or are functionally linked in some other way yet to be discovered. Gibberellins have other known effects as well, such as helping to break the dormancy of seeds and buds. Scientists have isolated 100-plus compounds of the gibberellin family, although only a few are biologically active as hormones. The others are inactive forms or serve as precursors to active forms.

Gibberellins are active in eudicots and in a few monocots. In most plant species that have been analyzed, the main controller of stem elongation is the gibberellin called GA_1 **(Figure 31.8).** Normally, GA_1 is synthesized in small amounts in young leaves and transported throughout the plant in the phloem. When GA_1 synthesis goes awry, the outcome is a dramatic change in the plant's stature. For example, experiments with a dwarf variety of peas (*Pisum sativum*) and some other species show that these plants and their taller relatives differ at a single gene locus. Normal plants make an enzyme required for gibberellin synthesis; dwarf plants of the same species lack the enzyme, and their internodes elongate very little.

Another stark demonstration of the effect gibberellins can have on internode growth is **bolting**, growth of a floral stalk in plants that form vegetative rosettes, such as cabbages (*Brassica oleracea*) and iceberg lettuce (*Lactuca sativa*). In a rosette plant, stem internodes are so short that the leaves appear to arise from a single node. When these plants flower, however, the stem elongates rapidly, and flowers develop on the new stem parts. An experimenter can trigger exaggerated bolting by spraying a plant with gibberellin **(Figure 31.9).** In nature, external cues such as increasing day length or warming after a cold snap stimulate gibberellin synthesis, and bolting occurs soon afterward. This observation supports the hypothesis that in rosette plants and possibly some others, gibberellins switch on internode lengthening when environmental conditions favour a shift from vegetative growth to reproductive growth.

Other experiments using gibberellins have turned up a striking number of additional roles for this hormone family. For example, one gibberellin helps stimulate buds and seeds to break dormancy and resume growth in the spring. Research on barley embryos showed that gibberellin provides signals during germination that lead to the enzymatic breakdown of endosperm, releasing nutrients that nourish the developing seedling (see Chapter 30). In monoecious species, which have flowers of both sexual types on the same plant, applications of gibberellin seem to encourage proportionately more "male" flowers to develop. Why would this be a benefit to the plant? The more "male" flowers present, the more pollen is

Figure 31.9
A dramatic example of bolting in cabbage (*Brassica oleracea*), a plant commonly grown as a winter vegetable. The rosette form (left) reflects the plant's growth habit when days are short (and nights are long). Gibberellin was applied to the plants at the right, triggering the rapid stem elongation and subsequent flowering characteristic of bolting.

Two untreated cabbages (controls)　　Cabbages treated with gibberellins

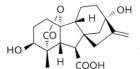

Figure 31.8
Structure of GA_1.

Figure 31.10
Effect of gibberellin on seedless grapes (*Vitis vinifera*). The grapes on the right developed on vines that were treated with a gibberellin.

available to pollinate "female" flowers, and, eventually, more fruits are produced. A gibberellin used by commercial grape growers promotes fruit set and lengthens the stems on which fruits develop, allowing space for individual grapes to grow larger. One result is fruit with greater consumer appeal **(Figure 31.10)**.

31.1c Cytokinins Enhance Growth and Retard Aging

Cytokinins play a major role in stimulating cell division (hence the name, which refers to cytokinesis). These hormones were first discovered during experiments designed to define the nutrient media required for plant tissue culture. Researchers found that in addition to a carbon source such as sucrose or glucose, minerals, and certain vitamins, cells in culture also required two other substances. One was auxin, which promoted the elongation of plant cells but did not stimulate the cells to divide. The other substance could be coconut milk, which is actually liquid endosperm, or it could be DNA that had been degraded into smaller molecules by boiling. When either was added to a culture medium along with an auxin, the cultured cells would begin dividing and grow normally.

We now know that the active ingredients in both boiled DNA and endosperm are cytokinins, which have a chemical structure similar to that of the nucleic acid base adenine. The most abundant natural cytokinin is zeatin, so called because it was first isolated from the endosperm of young corn seeds (*Zea mays*) **(Figure 31.11)**. In endosperm, zeatin probably promotes the burst of cell division that takes place as a fruit matures. As you might expect, cytokinins also are abundant in

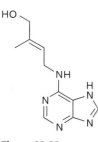

Figure 31.11
Structure of zeatin.

the rapidly dividing meristem tissues of root and shoot tips. Cytokinins occur not only in flowering plants but also in many conifers, mosses, and ferns. They are also synthesized by many soil-dwelling bacteria and fungi and may be crucial to the growth of mycorrhizas, which help nourish thousands of plant species (see Chapter 24). Conversely, *Agrobacterium* and other microbes that cause plant tumours carry genes that regulate the production of cytokinins.

Cytokinins are synthesized largely (although not only) in root tips and apparently are transported through the plant in xylem sap. Besides promoting cell division, they have a range of effects on plant metabolism and development, probably by regulating protein synthesis. For example, cytokinins promote the expansion of young leaves (as leaf cells expand), cause chloroplasts to mature, and retard leaf aging. Another cytokinin effect—coordinating the growth of roots and shoots, in concert with auxin—underscores the point that plant hormones often work together to evoke a particular response. Investigators culturing tobacco tissues found that the relative amounts of auxin and a cytokinin strongly influenced not only growth but also development **(Figure 31.12)**. When the concentrations of the two hormones were approximately equal, the growing tissue did not differentiate but instead

Figure 31.12
Effects of varying ratios of auxin and cytokinin on tobacco tissues (*Nicotiana tabacum*) grown in culture. The method starts with a block of stem pith, essentially a core of ground tissue removed from the centre of a stem. The callus growing on the pith is a disorganized mass of undifferentiated cells.

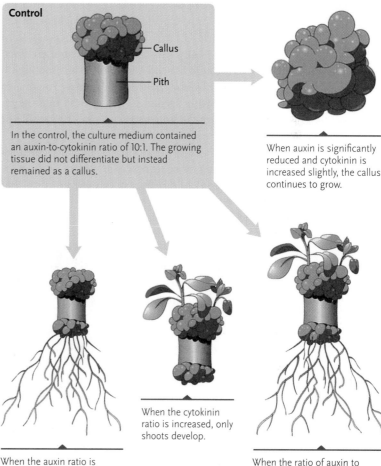

Control

Callus
Pith

In the control, the culture medium contained an auxin-to-cytokinin ratio of 10:1. The growing tissue did not differentiate but instead remained as a callus.

When auxin is significantly reduced and cytokinin is increased slightly, the callus continues to grow.

When the cytokinin ratio is increased, only shoots develop.

When the auxin ratio is greater than 10:1, the cultured tissue produces roots but no differentiated shoot.

When the ratio of auxin to cytokinin is intermediate between the high and low values, both shoots and roots develop.

remained as a loose mass of cells, or *callus*. When the relative auxin concentration was increased slightly, the callus produced roots. When the relative concentration of the cytokinin was increased, chloroplasts in the callus cells matured, the callus became green and more compact, and it produced shoots. In nature, the interaction of a cytokinin and auxin may produce the typical balanced growth of roots and shoots, with each region providing the other with key nutrients.

Natural cytokinins can prolong the life of stored vegetables. Similar synthetic compounds are already widely used to prolong the shelf life of lettuces and mushrooms and to keep cut flowers fresh.

31.1d Ethylene Regulates a Range of Responses, Including Senescence

Most parts of a plant can produce **ethylene**, which is present in fruits, flowers, seeds, leaves, and roots. In different species, it helps regulate a wide variety of plant physiological responses, including seed and bud dormancy, seedling growth, stem elongation, the ripening of fruit, and the eventual separation of fruits, leaves, and flowers from the plant body. Ethylene is an unusual hormone, in part because it is structurally simple **(Figure 31.13)** and in part because it is a gas at normal temperature and pressure.

Before a bean or pea seedling emerges from the soil, ethylene simultaneously slows elongation of the stem and stimulates cell divisions that increase stem girth **(Figure 31.14).** These alterations push the curved hypocotyl through the soil and into the air (see Figure 31.14). Such ethylene-induced horizontal growth also can help a growing seedling "find its way" into the air if the seed happens to germinate under a pebble or some other barrier.

Ethylene also governs the biologically complex process of aging, or **senescence**, in plants. Senescence is a closely controlled process of deterioration that leads to the death of plant cells. In autumn, the leaves of deciduous trees senesce, often turning yellow or red as chlorophyll and proteins break down, so that other pigments become more noticeable. Ethylene triggers the expression of genes, leading to the synthesis of chlorophyllases and proteases, enzymes that launch the breakdown process. In many plants, senescence is associated with **abscission**, the dropping of flowers, fruits, and leaves in response to environmental signals. In this process, ethylene apparently stimulates the activity of enzymes that digest cell walls

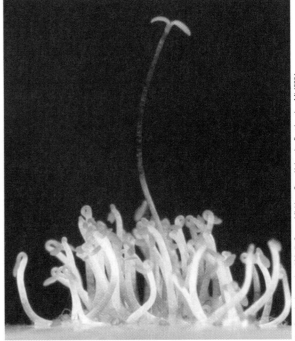

Figure 31.14

Wild-type seedlings and one ethylene-insensitive mutant of *Arabidopsis thaliana* grown in an atmosphere containing ethylene. The wild-type seedlings show the reduced elongation characteristic for plants treated with ethylene. The ethylene-insensitive mutant elongated normally, just as wild-type seedlings would do in an atmosphere without ethylene.

in an abscission zone—a localized region at the base of the petiole. The petiole detaches from the stem at that point **(Figure 31.15).**

For some species, the funnelling of nutrients into reproductive parts may be a cue for senescence of leaves, stems, and roots. When the drain of nutrients is halted by removing each newly emerging flower or seed pod, a plant's leaves and stems stay green and vigorous much longer **(Figure 31.16).** Gardeners routinely remove flower buds from many plants to maintain vegetative growth. Senescence requires other cues,

Figure 31.13
Structure of ethylene.

Figure 31.15
Abscission zone in a maple (*Acer*). This longitudinal section at the left is through the base of the petiole of a leaf.

Abscission zone at base of leaf where it joins the stem

Control plant
(pods not removed)

Experimental plant
(pods removed)

Figure 31.16
Experimental results showing that the removal of seed pods from a soybean plant (*Glycine max*) delays its senescence.

however. For instance, when a cocklebur is induced to flower under winterlike conditions, its leaves turn yellow regardless of whether the nutrient-demanding young flowers are left on or pinched off. It is as if a "death signal" forms that leads to flowering and senescence when there are fewer hours of daylight (typical of winter days). This observation underscores the general theme that many plant responses to the environment involve the interaction of multiple molecular signals.

Fruit ripening is a special case of senescence. Although the precise mechanisms are not well understood, ripening begins when a fruit starts to synthesize ethylene. The ripening process may involve the conversion of starch or organic acids to sugars, the softening of cell walls, or the rupturing of the cell membrane and loss of cell fluid. The same kinds of events occur in wounded plant tissues, which also synthesize ethylene.

Ethylene from an outside source can stimulate senescence responses, including ripening, when it binds to specific protein receptors on plant cells. The ancient Chinese observed that they could induce picked fruit to ripen faster by burning incense; later, it was found that the incense smoke contains ethylene. Today, ethylene gas is widely used to ripen tomatoes, pineapples, bananas, honeydew melons, mangoes, papayas, and other fruit that has been

picked and shipped while still green. Ripening fruit itself gives off ethylene, which is why placing a ripe banana in a closed sack of unripe peaches (or some other green fruit) often can cause the fruit to ripen. Oranges and other citrus fruits may be exposed to ethylene to brighten the colour of their rind. Conversely, limiting fruit exposure to ethylene can delay ripening. Apples will keep for months without rotting if they are exposed to a chemical that inhibits ethylene production or if they are stored in an environment that inhibits the hormone's effects—including low atmospheric pressure and a high concentration of CO_2, which may bind ethylene receptors.

31.1e Brassinosteroids Regulate Plant Growth Responses

The dozens of steroid hormones classed as **brassinosteroids (Figure 31.17)** all appear to be vital for normal growth in plants because they stimulate cell division and elongation in a wide range of plant cell types. Confirmed as plant hormones in the 1980s, brassinosteroids now are the subject of intense research on their sources and effects. Although brassinosteroids have been detected in a wide variety of plant tissues and organs, the highest concentrations are found in shoot tips and in developing seeds and embryos—all examples of young, actively developing parts. In laboratory studies, the hormone has different effects depending on the tissue where it is active. For example, it has been found to promote cell elongation, differentiation of vascular tissue, and elongation of a pollen tube after a flower is pollinated. By contrast, it inhibits the elongation of roots. First isolated from the pollen of a plant in the mustard family, *Brassica napus* (a type of canola), under natural conditions, brassinosteroids seem to regulate the expression of genes associated with a plant's growth responses to light.

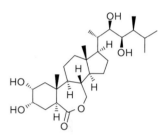

Figure 31.17
Structure of a brassinosteroid.

31.1f Abscisic Acid Suppresses Growth and Influences Responses to Environmental Stress

Plant scientists ascribe a variety of effects to the hormone **abscisic acid (ABA)**, many of which represent evolutionary adaptations to environmental challenges. Plants apparently synthesize ABA **(Figure 31.18)** from carotenoid pigments inside plastids in leaves and possibly other plant parts. In general, we can group its effects into changes in gene expression that result in long-term inhibition of growth and rapid, short-term physiological changes that are responses to immediate stresses, such as a lack of water, in a plant's surroundings. As its name suggests, at one time, ABA was thought to play a major role in abscission. As already

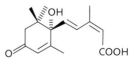

Figure 31.18
Structure of abscisic acid.

CHAPTER 31 CONTROL OF PLANT GROWTH AND DEVELOPMENT |

Figure 31.19
Bud scales, here on a perennial corn-flower bud (*Centaurea montana*).

described, however, abscission is largely the domain of ethylene. So what are the functions of ABA?

Suppressing Growth in Buds and Seeds. Operating as a counterpoint to growth-stimulating hormones such as gibberellins, ABA inhibits growth in response to environmental cues, such as seasonal changes in temperature and light. This growth suppression can last for many months or even years. For example, one of ABA's major growth-inhibiting effects is apparent in perennial plants, in which the hormone promotes dormancy in leaf buds—an important adaptive advantage in places where winter cold can damage young leaves. If ABA is applied to a growing leaf bud, the bud's normal development stops, and instead, protective *bud scales*—modified, nonphotosynthetic leaves that are small, dry, and tough—form around the apical meristem and insulate it from the elements **(Figure 31.19)**. After the scales develop, most cell metabolic activity shuts down, and the leaf bud becomes dormant.

In some plants that produce fleshy fruits, such as apples and cherries, abscisic acid is associated with the dormancy of seeds as well. As the seed develops, ABA accumulates in the seed coat, and the embryo does not germinate even if it becomes hydrated. Before such a seed can germinate, it usually will require a long period of cool, wet conditions, which stimulate the breakdown of ABA. The buildup of ABA in developing seeds does more than simply inhibit development, however. As early development draws to a close, ABA stimulates the transcription of certain genes, and large amounts of their protein products are synthesized. These proteins are thought to store nitrogen and other nutrients that the embryo will use when it eventually does germinate. ABA and related growth inhibitors are often applied to plants slated to be shipped to plant nurseries. Dormant plants suffer less shipping damage, and the effects of the inhibitors can be reversed by applying a gibberellin.

Responses to Environmental Stress. ABA also triggers plant responses to various environmental stresses, including cold snaps, high soil salinity, and drought. A great deal of research has focused on how ABA influences plant responses to a lack of water. When a plant is water-stressed, ABA helps prevent excessive water loss by stimulating stomata to close. As described in Chapter 29, flowering plants depend heavily on the proper functioning of stomata. When a lack of water leads to wilting, mesophyll cells in wilted leaves rapidly synthesize and secrete ABA. The hormone diffuses to guard cells, where an ABA receptor binds it. Binding stimulates the release of K^+ and water from the guard cells, and within minutes, the stomata close.

31.1g Jasmonates and Oligosaccharins Regulate Growth and Have Roles in Defence

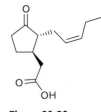

Figure 31.20
Structure of jasmonic acid.

In recent years, studies of plant growth and development have helped define the roles—or revealed the existence—of several other hormonelike compounds in plants. Like the well-established plant hormones just described, these substances are organic molecules, and only tiny amounts are required to alter some aspect of a plant's functioning. Some have long been known to exist in plants, but the extent of their signalling roles has only recently become better understood. This group includes **jasmonates**, a family of about 20 compounds derived from fatty acids **(Figure 31.20)**. Experiments with *Arabidopsis* and other plants have revealed numerous genes that respond to jasmonate, including genes that help regulate root growth and seed germination. Jasmonate also appears to help plants "manage" stresses due to deficiencies of certain nutrients (such as K^+). The jasmonate family is best known, however, as part of the plant arsenal to limit damage by pathogens and predators, the topic of the following section.

Some other substances also are drawing keen interest from plant scientists, but because their signalling roles are still poorly understood, they are not widely accepted as confirmed plant hormones. A case in point involves the complex carbohydrates that are structural elements in the cell walls of plants and some fungi. Several years ago, researchers observed that in some plants, some of these oligosaccharides could serve as signalling molecules. Such compounds were named **oligosaccharins**, and one of their known roles is to defend the plant against pathogens. In addition, oligosaccharins have been proposed as growth regulators that adjust the growth and differentiation of plant cells, possibly by modulating the influences of growth-promoting hormones such as auxin. At this writing, researchers in many laboratories are pursuing a deeper understanding of this curious subset of plant signalling molecules.

STUDY BREAK

1. Which plant hormones promote growth, and which inhibit it?
2. Give examples of how some hormones have both promoting and inhibiting effects in different parts of the plant at different times of the life cycle.

31.2 Signal Responses at the Cellular Level

Auxin and the other hormones do not directly cause the plant responses outlined above instead, they alter a target cell's gene expression and elicit a cellular response, which leads to a change in growth or physiology. For decades, plant physiologists have looked avidly for clues about how those signals are converted into a chemical message that produces a change in cell metabolism or growth. Some of the basic mechanisms that have been discovered for animal cells also apply to plant cells (see Chapter 8).

31.2a Several Signal Response Pathways Operate in Plants

Hormones (and environmental stimuli, which we consider later in this chapter) alter the behaviour of target cells, which have receptors to which specific signal molecules can bind and elicit a cellular response. By means of a response pathway, a signal can induce changes in the cell's shape and internal structure or influence the transport of ions and other substances into and out of cells. Some signals cause cells to alter gene activation and the rate of protein synthesis; others set in motion events that modify existing cell proteins. Here, we briefly consider how signal molecules may operate in plants.

Certain hormones bind to receptors at the target cell's plasma membrane, on its endoplasmic reticulum (ER), or in the cytoplasm. For example, ethylene receptors are on the ER, and the auxin receptor is a protein in the cytoplasm. Research in several laboratories recently confirmed that auxin binds directly to this protein, setting in motion events that inhibit transcription. As a result, previously repressed genes are turned on. Thus, binding of a hormone triggers a complex pathway that leads to the cell response—the opening of ion channels, activation of transport proteins, or some other event.

Only some cells can respond to a particular signalling molecule because not all cells have the same types of receptors. For example, particular cells in ripening fruits and developing seeds have ethylene receptors, but few, if any, cells in stems do. Different signals also may have different effects on a single cell and may exert those effects by way of different response pathways. One type of signal might stimulate transcription, and another might inhibit it. In addition, as we've seen, some genes controlled by particular receptors encode proteins that regulate still *other* genes.

In plants, we know the most about pathways involving auxin, ethylene, salicylic acid, and blue light. **Figure 31.21** diagrams a general model for these response pathways in plant cells. As the figure shows, the response may lead to a change in the cell's structure, its metabolic activity, or both, either directly or by altering the expression of one or more genes.

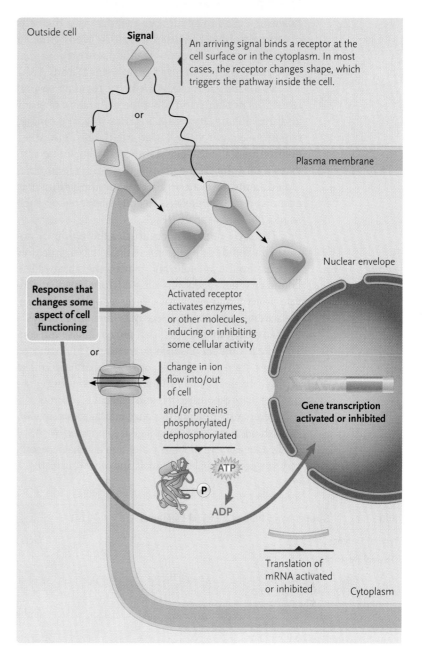

Figure 31.21
Signal response pathways in plant cells.

31.2b Second-Messenger Systems Enhance the Plant Cell's Response to a Hormone's Signal

We can think of plant hormones and other signalling molecules as external *first messengers* that deliver the initial physiological signal to a target cell. Often, as with salicylic acid, binding of the signal molecule triggers the synthesis of internal *second messengers* (see Chapter 8). These intermediary molecules diffuse rapidly through the cytoplasm and provide the main chemical signal that alters cell functioning.

Second messengers usually are synthesized in a sequence of chemical reactions that converts an external signal into internal cell activity. For many years, the details of plant second-messenger systems were sketchy and hotly debated. More recently, however, reaction sequences that occur in the cells of animals and some fungi have also been found in plants. The following example describes reactions that close plant stomata in response to a signal from ABA.

As discussed above, ABA helps regulate several responses in plants, including the maturation of seeds and the closing of stomata. ABA's role in stomatal closure—triggered by water stress or some other environmental cue—begins when the hormone activates a receptor in the plant cell plasma membrane. Experiments have shown that this binding ultimately stimulates the synthesis of second messengers, such as inositol triphosphate (IP_3).

The second messenger diffuses through the cytoplasm and binds with calcium channels in cell structures such as the ER, vacuole, and plasma membrane. The bound channels open, releasing calcium ions that activate protein kinase enzymes in the cytoplasm. In turn, the activated protein kinases activate their target proteins (by phosphorylating them). Each protein kinase can convert a large number of substrate molecules into activated enzymes, transport proteins, open ion channels, and so forth. Soon the number of molecules representing the final cellular response to the initial signal is enormous.

Recent experimental evidence indicates that, in similar fashion, auxin's hormonal signal is conveyed by cAMP (cyclic adenosine monophosphate), another major second messenger in the cells of animals and other organisms.

In addition to the basic pathways described here, other routes may exist that are unique to plant cells. Light is the driving force for photosynthesis, and it may not be far-fetched to suppose that plants have evolved other unique light-related biochemical pathways as well. For instance, exciting experiments are extending our knowledge of how plant cells respond to blue light, which, as we have discussed, triggers some photoperiod responses such as the opening and closing of stomata.

STUDY BREAK

1. Summarize the various ways that chemical signals reaching plant cells are converted to changes in cell functioning.
2. What basic task does a second messenger accomplish?

31.3 Plant Chemical Defences

Plants don't have immune systems like those that have evolved in animals (discussed in Chapter 44). Even so, over the millennia, plants have been constantly exposed to predation by herbivores, and this onslaught of pathogens has resulted in a striking array of chemical defences that ward off or reduce damage to plant tissues from infectious bacteria, fungi, worms, or plant-eating insects (Table 31.2).

Table 31.2	Summary of Plant Chemical Defences	
Type of Defence	**Effects**
General Defences	
Jasmonate (JA) responses to wounds/injury by pathogens; pathways often include other hormones, such as ethylene	Synthesis of defensive chemicals, such as protease inhibitors
Hypersensitive response to infectious pathogens (e.g., fungi, bacteria)	Physically isolates infection site by surrounding it with dead cells
PR (pathogenesis-related) proteins	Enzymes, other proteins that degrade cell walls of pathogens
Salicylic acid (SA)	Mobilized during other responses and independently; induces the synthesis of PR proteins, operates in systemic acquired resistance
Systemin (in tomato)	Triggers JA response
Secondary Metabolites	
Phytoalexins	Antibiotic
Oligosaccharins	Trigger synthesis of phytoalexins
Systemic acquired resistance (SAR)	Long-lasting protection against some pathogens; components include SA and PR proteins that accumulate in healthy tissues
Specific Defences	
Gene-for-gene recognition of chemical features of specific pathogens (by binding with receptors coded by R genes)	Triggers defensive response (e.g., hypersensitive response, PR proteins) against pathogens
Other	
Heat-shock responses (encoded by heat-shock genes)	Synthesis of chaperone proteins that reversibly bind other plant proteins and prevent denaturing due to heat stress
"Antifreeze" proteins	In some species, stabilize cell proteins under freezing conditions

You will discover in this section that as with the defensive strategies of animals, plant defences include both general responses to any type of attack and specific responses to particular threats. Some get under way almost as soon as an attack begins, whereas others help promote the plant's long-term survival. And more often than not, multiple chemicals interact as the response unfolds.

31.3a Jasmonates and Other Compounds Interact in a General Response to Wounds

When an insect begins feeding on a leaf or some other plant part, the plant may respond to the resulting wound by launching what in effect is a cascade of chemical responses. These complex signalling pathways often rely on interactions among jasmonates, ethylene, or some other plant hormone. As the pathway unfolds, it triggers expression of genes, leading to chemical and physical defences at the wound site. For example, in some plants, jasmonate induces a response leading to the synthesis of protease inhibitors, which disrupt an insect's capacity to digest proteins in the plant tissue. The protein deficiency, in turn, hampers the insect's growth and functioning.

A plant's capacity to recognize and respond to the physical damage of a wound apparently has been a strong selection pressure during plant evolution. When a plant is wounded experimentally, numerous defensive chemicals can be detected in its tissues in relatively short order. One of these, **salicylic acid**, or **SA** (a compound similar to aspirin, which is acetyl-salicylic acid), seems to have multiple roles in plant defences, including interacting with jasmonates in signalling cascades (see *Molecule Behind Biology*).

Researchers are regularly discovering new variations of hormone-induced wound responses in plants. For example, experiments have elucidated some of the steps in an unusual pathway that thus far is known only in tomato (*Solanum lycopersicum*) and a few other plant species. As diagrammed in **Figure 31.22,** the wounded plant rapidly synthesizes **systemin**, the first peptide hormone to be discovered in plants. (Various animal hormones are peptides, a topic covered in Chapter 35.) Systemin enters the phloem and is transported throughout the plant. Although various details of the signalling pathway have yet to be worked out, when receptive cells bind systemin, their plasma membranes release a lipid that is the chemical precursor of jasmonate. Next, jasmonate is synthesized, and it, in turn, sets in motion the expression of genes that encode protease inhibitors, which protect the plant against attack, even in parts remote from the original wound.

31.3b The Hypersensitive Response and PR Proteins Are Other General Defences

Often a plant that becomes infected by pathogenic bacteria or fungi counters the attack by way of a **hypersensitive response**—a defence that physically

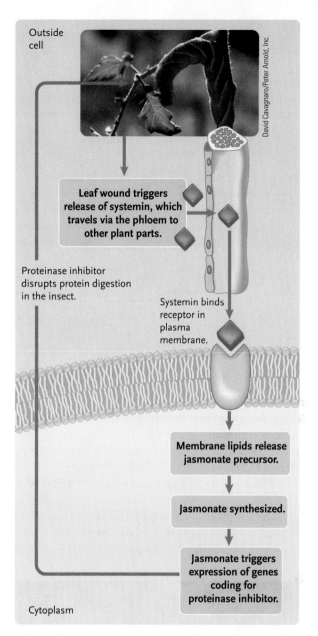

Figure 31.22

The system in response to wounding. When a plant is wounded, it responds by releasing the protein hormone systemin. Transported through the phloem to other plant parts, in receptive cells, systemin sets in motion a sequence of reactions that lead to the expression of genes encoding protease inhibitors—substances that can seriously disrupt an insect predator's capacity to digest protein.

cordons off an infection site by surrounding it with dead cells. Initially, cells near the site respond by producing a burst of highly reactive oxygen–containing compounds (such as hydrogen peroxide, H_2O_2) that can break down nucleic acids, inactivate enzymes, or have other toxic effects on cells. Enzymes in the cell's plasma membrane catalyze the burst of reactive oxygen compounds. It may begin the process of killing cells close to the attack site, and as the response advances, programmed cell death may also come into play. In short order, the "sacrificed" dead cells wall off the infected area from the rest of the plant. Thus denied an ongoing supply of nutrients, the invading pathogen dies. A common sign of a successful hypersensitive response is a dead spot surrounded by healthy tissue **(Figure 31.23)**.

While the hypersensitive response is under way, salicylic acid triggers other defensive responses by an infected plant. One of its effects is to induce the synthesis of **pathogenesis-related proteins**, or **PR - proteins**. Some PR proteins are hydrolytic enzymes

Figure 31.23
Evidence of the hypersensitive response. The dead spots on these leaves of a strawberry plant (*Fragaria* species) are sites where a pathogen invaded, triggering the defensive destruction of the surrounding cells.

Nigel Cattlin/Photo Researchers, Inc.

that break down components of a pathogen's cell wall. Examples are chitinases that dismantle the chitin in the cell walls of fungi and so kill the cells. In some cases, plant cell receptors also detect the presence of fragments of the disintegrating wall and set in motion additional defence responses.

31.3c Secondary Metabolites Defend against Pathogens and Herbivores

Many plants counter bacteria and fungi by making **phytoalexins**, biochemicals of various types that function as antibiotics. When an infectious agent breaches a plant part, genes encoding phytoalexins begin to be transcribed in the affected tissue. For instance, when a fungus begins to invade plant tissues, the enzymes it secretes may trigger the release of oligosaccharins. In addition to their roles as growth regulators (described in Section 31.1), these substances also can promote the production of phytoalexins, which have toxic effects on a variety of fungi. Plant tissues may also synthesize phytoalexins in response to attacks by viruses.

Phytoalexins are among many *secondary metabolites* produced by plants. Such substances are termed "secondary" because they are not routinely synthesized in all plant cells as part of basic metabolism. A wide range of plant species deploy secondary metabolites as defences against feeding herbivores. Examples are alkaloids such as caffeine, cocaine, and the poison strychnine (in the seeds of the *nux vomica* tree, *Strychnos nux-vomica*), tannins such as those in oak acorns, and various terpenes. The terpene family includes insect-repelling substances in conifer resins and cotton and essential oils produced by sage and basil plants. Because these terpenes are volatile—they easily diffuse out of the plant and into the surrounding air—they also can provide indirect defence to a plant. Released from the wounds created by a munching insect, they attract other insects that prey on the herbivore. Chapter 46 looks in detail at the interactions between plants and herbivores.

31.3d Gene-for-Gene Recognition Allows Rapid Responses to Specific Threats

One of the most interesting questions with respect to plant defences is how plants first sense that an attack is under way. In some instances, plants apparently can detect an attack by a specific predator through a mechanism called **gene-for-gene recognition**. This term refers to a matchup between the products of the dominant alleles of two types of genes: a so-called *R* gene (for "resistance") in a plant and an *Avr* gene (for "avirulence") in a particular pathogen. Thousands of *R* genes have been identified in a wide range of plant species. Dominant R alleles confer enhanced resistance to plant pathogens, including bacteria, fungi, and nematode worms that attack roots.

The basic mechanism of gene-for-gene recognition is simple: The dominant R allele encodes a receptor in plasma membranes of a plant's cells, and the dominant pathogen Avr allele encodes a molecule that can bind the receptor. "Avirulence" implies "not virulent," and binding of the *Avr* gene product triggers an immediate defence response in the plant. Trigger molecules run the gamut from proteins to lipids to carbohydrates that have been secreted by the pathogen or released from its surface **(Figure 31.24)**. Experiments have demonstrated a rapid-fire sequence of early biochemical changes that follow binding of the Avr-encoded molecule; these include changes in ion concentrations inside and outside plant cells and the production of biologically active oxygen compounds that heralds the hypersensitive response. In fact, of the instances of gene-for-gene recognition plant scientists have observed thus far, most trigger the hypersensitive response and the ensuing synthesis of PR proteins, with their antibiotic effects.

31.3e Systemic Acquired Resistance Can Provide Long-Term Protection

The defensive response to a microbial invasion may spread throughout a plant, so that the plant's healthy tissues become less vulnerable to infection. This phenomenon is called **systemic acquired resistance**, and experiments using *Arabidopsis* plants have shed light on how it comes about **(Figure 31.25, p. 752)**. In a key early step, SA builds up in the affected tissues. By some route, probably through the phloem, the SA passes from the infected organ to newly forming organs such as leaves, which begin to synthesize PR proteins—again,

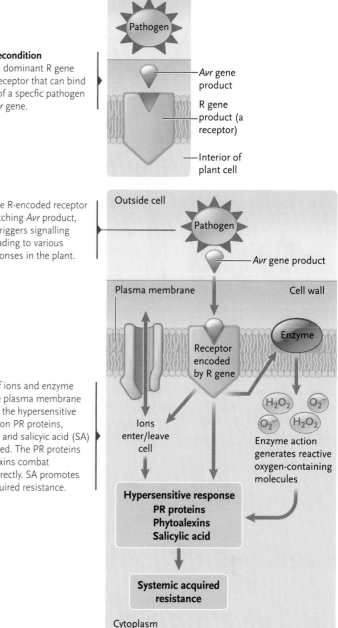

Required precondition
A plant has a dominant R gene encoding a receptor that can bind the product of a specfic pathogen dominant *Avr* gene.

— *Avr* gene product

— R gene product (a receptor)

— Interior of plant cell

1 When the R-encoded receptor binds its matching *Avr* product, the binding triggers signalling pathways, leading to various defence responses in the plant.

2 Fluxes of ions and enzyme activity at the plasma membrane contribute to the hypersensitive response. Soon PR proteins, phytoalexins, and salicyic acid (SA) are synthesized. The PR proteins and phytoalexins combat pathogens directly. SA promotes systemic acquired resistance.

Outside cell

Pathogen

Avr gene product

Plasma membrane

Cell wall

Enzyme

Receptor encoded by R gene

Ions enter/leave cell

H_2O_2 O_2^-
O_2^- H_2O_2

Enzyme action generates reactive oxygen-containing molecules

Hypersensitive response
PR proteins
Phytoalexins
Salicylic acid

Systemic acquired resistance

Cytoplasm

Figure 31.24
Model of how gene-for-gene resistance may operate. For resistance to develop, the plant must have a dominant *R* gene, and the pathogen must have a corresponding dominant *Avr* gene. The products of such "matching" genes can interact physically, rather like the lock-and-key mechanism of an enzyme and its substrate. Most *R* genes encode receptors at the plasma membranes of plant cells. As diagrammed in step 1, when one of these receptors binds an *Avr* gene's product, the initial result may be changes in the movements of specific ions into or out of the cell and the activation of membrane enzymes that catalyze the formation of highly reactive oxygen–containing molecules. Such events help launch other signalling pathways that lead to a variety of defensive responses, including the hypersensitive response (step 2).

providing the plant with a "homegrown" antimicrobial arsenal. How does the SA exert this effect? It seems that when enough SA accumulates in a plant cell's cytoplasm, a regulatory protein called NPR-1 (for *non*-expressor of *p*athogenesis-related genes) moves from the cytoplasm into the cell nucleus. There it interacts

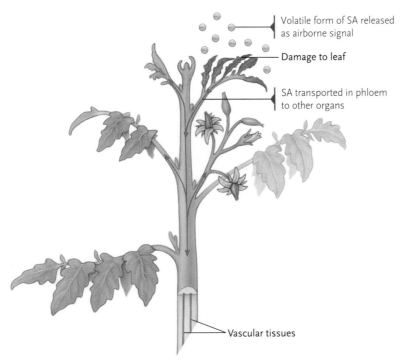

Volatile form of SA released as airborne signal

Damage to leaf

SA transported in phloem to other organs

Vascular tissues

Figure 31.25

A proposed mechanism for systemic acquired resistance. When a plant successfully fends off a pathogen, the defensive chemical salicylic acid (SA) is transported in the phloem to other plant parts, where it may help protect against another attack by stimulating the synthesis of PR proteins. In addition, the plant synthesizes and releases a slightly different, more volatile form of SA. This chemical may serve as an airborne signal to other parts of the plant, as well as to neighbouring plants.

with factors that promote the transcription of genes encoding PR proteins.

In addition to synthesizing SA that will be transported internally in a plant's vascular system, the damaged leaf also synthesizes a chemically similar compound, methyl salicylate. This substance is volatile, and researchers speculate that it may serve as an airborne "harm" signal, promoting defence responses in the plant that synthesized it and possibly in nearby plants as well.

STUDY BREAK

1. Which plant chemical defences are general responses to attack, and which are specific to a particular pathogen?
2. Why is salicylic acid considered to be a general systemic response to damage?
3. How is the hypersensitive response integrated with other chemical defences?

31.4 Plant Responses to the Environment: Movements

Although a plant cannot move from place to place as external conditions change, plants can and do alter the orientation of their body parts in response to environmental stimuli. As noted earlier in the chapter, growth toward or away from a unidirectional stimulus, such as light or gravity, is called a tropism. Tropic movement involves permanent changes in the plant body because cells in particular areas or organs grow differentially in response to the stimulus. Plant physiologists do not fully understand how tropisms occur, but they are fascinating examples of the complex abilities of plants to adjust to their environment. This also touches on two other kinds of movements: developmental responses to physical contact and position changes that are not related to the location of the stimulus.

31.4a Phototropisms Are Responses to Light

As you learned in Chapter 1, light is a key environmental stimulus for many kinds of organisms. Phototropisms, which we have already discussed in the section on auxins, are growth responses to a directional light source. As the Darwins discovered, if light is more intense on one side of a stem, the stem may curve toward the light **(Figure 31.26a)**. Phototropic movements are extremely adaptive for photosynthesizing organisms because they help maximize the exposure of photosynthetic tissues to sunlight.

How do auxins influence phototropic movements? In a coleoptile that is illuminated from one side, IAA moves by polar transport into the cells on the shaded side **(Figure 31.26b–d)**. Phototropic bending occurs because cells on the shaded side elongate more rapidly than do cells on the illuminated side.

The main stimulus for phototropism is blue light. Experiments on corn coleoptiles have shown that a molecule called phototropin can absorb blue light, and it may play a role in stimulating the initial lateral transport of IAA to the dark side of a shoot tip. Studies with *Arabidopsis* suggest that there is more than one blue light receptor, however. One is a light-absorbing protein called **cryptochrome**, which is sensitive to blue light and may also be an important early step in the various light-based growth responses. As you will read later, cryptochrome appears to have a role in other plant responses to light as well.

31.4b Gravitropism Orients Plant Parts to the Pull of Gravity

Plants show growth responses to Earth's gravitational pull, a phenomenon called **gravitropism**. After a seed germinates, the primary root curves down, toward the "pull" (positive gravitropism), and the shoot curves up (negative gravitropism).

Several hypotheses seek to explain how plants respond to gravity. The most widely accepted hypothesis proposes that plants detect gravity much as animals do—that is, particles called **statoliths** in certain cells move in the direction gravity pulls them. In the

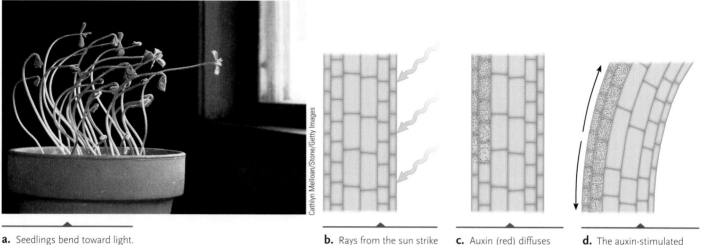

a. Seedlings bend toward light.

b. Rays from the sun strike one side of a shoot tip.

c. Auxin (red) diffuses down from the shoot tip to cells on its shaded side.

d. The auxin-stimulated cells elongate more quickly, causing the seedling to bend.

Figure 31.26

Phototropism in seedlings. **(a)** Tomato seedlings grown in darkness; their right side was illuminated for a few hours before they were photographed. **(b–d)** Hormone-mediated differences in the rates of cell elongation bring about the bending toward light.

semicircular canals of human ears, tiny calcium carbonate crystals serve as statoliths; in most plants, the statoliths are amyloplasts, modified plastids that contain starch grains. In eudicot angiosperm stems, amyloplasts often are present in one or two layers of cells just outside the vascular bundles. In monocots such as cereal grasses, **amyloplasts** are located in a region of tissue near the base of the leaf sheath. In roots, amyloplasts occur in the root cap. If the spatial orientation of a plant cell is shifted experimentally, its amyloplasts sink through the cytoplasm until they come to rest at the bottom of the cell **(Figure 31.27)**.

How do amyloplast movements translate into an altered growth response? The full explanation appears to be fairly complex, and there is evidence that somewhat different mechanisms operate in stems and roots. In stems, the sinking of amyloplasts may provide a mechanical stimulus that triggers a gene-guided redistribution of IAA. **Figure 31.28** shows what happens when a potted sunflower seedling is turned on its side in a dark room. Within 15 to 20 minutes, cell elongation decreases markedly on the upper side of the growing horizontal stem but increases on the lower side. With the adjusted growth pattern, the stem curves upward, even in the absence of light. Using different types of tests, researchers have been able to document the shifting of IAA from the top to the bottom side of the stem. The changing auxin gradient correlates with the altered pattern of cell elongation.

In roots, a high concentration of auxin has the opposite effect—it inhibits cell elongation. If a root is placed on its side, amyloplasts in the root cap accumulate near the side wall that now is the bottom side of the cap. In some way, this stimulates cell elongation in the opposite wall, and within a few hours, the root once again curves downward. In the root tips of many

a. Root oriented vertically **b.** Root oriented horizontally

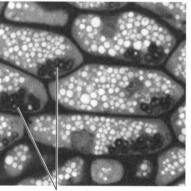

Statoliths   Statoliths

Figure 31.27

Evidence that supports the statolith hypothesis. When a corn root was laid on its side, amyloplasts—statoliths—in cells from the root cap settled to the bottom of the cells within 5 to 10 minutes. Statoliths may be part of a gravity-sensing mechanism that redistributes auxin through a root tip. Micrographs courtesy of Randy Moore, from "How Roots Respond to Gravity," M. L. Evans, R. Moore, and K. Hasenstein, Scientific American, December 1986.

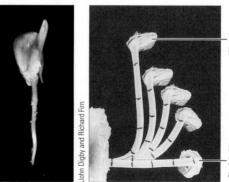

Position 2 hours later

Position 30 minutes after turn

Figure 31.28

Gravitropism in a young shoot. A newly emerged sunflower seedling was grown in the dark for five days. Then it was turned on its side and marked at 0.5 cm intervals. Negative gravitropism turned the stem upright in 2 hours.

plants, however, especially eudicots, researchers have not been able to detect a shift in IAA concentration that correlates with the changing position of amyloplasts. One hypothesis is that IAA is redistributed over extremely short distances in root cells and therefore is difficult to measure. Root cells are much more sensitive to IAA than are cells in stem tissue, and even a tiny shift in IAA distribution could significantly affect their growth.

Along with IAA, calcium ions (Ca^{2+}) appear to play a major role in gravitropism. For example, if Ca^{2+} is added to an otherwise untreated agar block that is then placed on one side of a root cap, the root will bend toward the block. In this way, experimenters have been able to manipulate the direction of growth so that the elongating root forms a loop. Similarly, if an actively bending root is deprived of Ca^{2+}, the gravitropic response abruptly stops. By contrast, the negative gravitropic response of a shoot tip is inhibited when the tissue is exposed to excess calcium.

Just how Ca^{2+} interacts with IAA in gravitropic responses is unknown. One hypothesis posits that calcium plays a role. Calcium binds to a small protein called *calmodulin*, activating it in the process. Activated calmodulin, in turn, can activate a variety of key cell enzymes in many organisms, both plants and animals. One possibility is that calcium-activated calmodulin stimulates cell membrane pumps that enhance the flow of both IAA and calcium through a gravity-stimulated plant tissue.

Some of the most active research in plant biology focuses on the intricate mechanisms of gravitropism. For example, there is increasing evidence that in many plants, cells in different regions of stem tissue are more or less sensitive to IAA and that gravitropism is linked in some fundamental way to these differences in auxin sensitivity. In a few plants, including some cultivated varieties of corn and radish, the direction of the gravitropic response by a seedling's primary root is influenced by light. Clearly, there is much more to be learned.

31.4c Thigmotropism and Thigmomorphogenesis Are Responses to Physical Contact

Varieties of peas, grapes, and some other plants demonstrate **thigmotropism** (*thigma* = touch), which is growth in response to contact with a solid object. Thigmotropic plants typically have long, slender stems and cannot grow upright without physical support. They often have *tendrils*, modified stems or leaves that can rapidly curl around a fencepost or the sturdier stem of a neighbouring plant. If one side of a grapevine stem grows against a trellis, for example, specialized epidermal cells on that side of the stem tendril shorten, whereas cells on the other side of the tendril rapidly elongate. Within minutes, the tendril starts to

curl around the trellis, forming tight coils that provide strong support for the vine stem. **Figure 31.29** shows thigmotropic twisting in the passionflower (*Passiflora*). Auxin and ethylene may be involved in thigmotropism, but most details of the mechanism remain elusive.

The rubbing and bending of plant stems caused by frequent strong winds, rainstorms, grazing animals, and even farm machinery can inhibit the overall growth of plants and can alter their growth patterns. In this phenomenon, called **thigmomorphogenesis**, a stem stops elongating and instead adds girth when it is regularly subjected to mechanical stress. Merely shaking some plants daily for a brief period will inhibit their upward growth **(Figure 31.30).** But although such plants may be shorter, their thickened stems will be stronger. Thigmomorphogenesis helps explain why plants growing outdoors are often shorter, have somewhat thicker stems, and are not as easily blown over as plants of the same species grown indoors. Trees growing near the snowline of windswept mountains show an altered growth pattern that reflects this response to wind stress.

Figure 31.29
Thigmotropism in a passionflower (*Passiflora*) tendril, which is twisted around a support.

a. b. c.

Figure 31.30
Effect of mechanical stress on tomato plants (*Lycopersicon esculentum*). **(a)** This plant was the control; it was grown in a greenhouse, protected from wind and rain. **(b)** Each day for 28 days, this plant was mechanically shaken for 30 seconds at 280 rpm. **(c)** This plant received the same shaking treatment, but twice a day for 28 days.

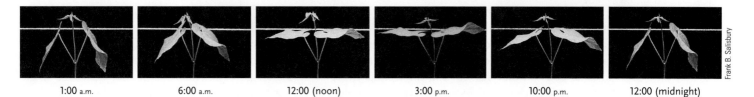

| 1:00 a.m. | 6:00 a.m. | 12:00 (noon) | 3:00 p.m. | 10:00 p.m. | 12:00 (midnight) |

Frank B. Salisbury

Figure 31.31

Nastic sleep movements in the leaves of a bean plant. Although this plant was kept in constant darkness for 23 hours, its sleep movements continued independently of sunrise (6 a.m.) and sunset (6 p.m.). Folding the leaves closer to the stem may prevent phytochrome from being activated by bright moonlight, which could interrupt the dark period necessary to trigger flowering. Or perhaps it helps slow heat loss from leaves otherwise exposed to the cold night air.

Research on the cellular mechanisms of thigmomorphogenesis has begun to yield tantalizing clues. In one study, investigators repeatedly sprayed *Arabidopsis* plants with water and imposed other mechanical stresses and then sampled tissues from the stressed plants. The samples contained as much as double the usual amount of mRNA for at least four genes, which had been activated by the stress. The mRNAs encoded calmodulin and several other proteins that may have roles in altering *Arabidopsis* growth responses. The test plants were also short, generally reaching only half the height of unstressed controls.

31.4d Nastic Movements Are Nondirectional

Tropisms are responses to directional stimuli, such as light striking one side of a shoot tip, but many plants also exhibit **nastic movements** (*nastos* = pressed close together)—reversible responses to nondirectional stimuli, such as mechanical pressure or humidity. We see nastic movements in leaves, leaflets, and even flowers. For instance, certain plants exhibit nastic sleep movements, holding their leaves (or flower petals) in roughly horizontal positions during the day but folding them closer to the stem at night **(Figure 31.31)**. Tulip flowers "go to sleep" in this way.

Many nastic movements are temporary and result from changes in cell turgor. For example, the daily opening and closing of stomata in response to changing light levels are nastic movements, as is the traplike closing of the lobed leaves of the Venus flytrap when an insect brushes against hairlike sensory structures on the leaves. The leaves of *Mimosa pudica*, the sensitive plant, also close in a nastic response to mechanical pressure. Each *Mimosa* leaf is divided into pairs of leaflets **(Figure 31.32a)**. Touching even one leaflet at the leaf tip triggers a chain reaction in which each pair of leaflets closes up within seconds **(Figure 31.32b)**.

In many turgor-driven nastic movements, water moves into and out of the cells in **pulvini** (*pulvinus* = cushion), thickened pads of tissue at the base of a leaf or petiole. Stomatal movements depend on changing concentrations of ions within guard cells, and pulvinar cells drive nastic leaf movements in *Mimosa* and numerous other plants by the same mechanism **(Figure 31.32c)**.

How is the original stimulus transferred from cells in one part of a leaf to cells elsewhere? The answer lies in the polarity of charge across cell plasma membranes (see Chapter 6). Touching a *Mimosa* leaflet triggers an **action potential**—a brief reversal in the polarity of the membrane charge. When an action potential occurs at the plasma membrane of a pulvinar

a.

David Sieren/Visuals Unlimited

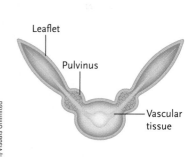

Leaflet

Pulvinus

Vascular tissue

b.

David Sieren/Visuals Unlimited

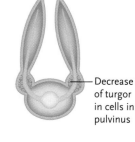

Decrease of turgor in cells in pulvinus

Figure 31.32

Nastic movements in the leaflets of *Mimosa pudica*, the sensitive plant. **(a)** In an undisturbed plant, the leaflets are open. If a leaflet near the leaf tip is touched, changes in turgor pressure in pulvini at the base cause the leaf to fold closed. **(b)**. The diagrams show a cross-section of this folding movement. Other leaflets close in sequence as action potentials transmit the stimulus along the leaf.

cell, the change in polarity causes potassium ion (K^+) channels to open, and ions flow out of the cell, setting up an osmotic gradient that draws water out as well. As water leaves by osmosis, turgor pressure falls, pulvinar cells become flaccid, and the leaflets move together. Later, when the process is reversed, the pulvinar cells regain turgor, and the leaflets spread apart. Action potentials travel between parenchyma cells in the pulvini via plasmodesmata at the rate of about 2 cm/sec. Animal nerves conduct similar changes in membrane polarity along their plasma membranes (see Chapter 33). These changes in polarity, which are also called action potentials, occur much more rapidly—at velocities between 1 and 100 m/sec.

Stimuli other than touch also can trigger action potentials leading to nastic movements. Cotton, soybean, sunflower, and some other plants display *solar tracking*, nastic movements in which leaf blades are oriented toward the east in the morning and then steadily change their position during the day, following the sun across the sky. Such movements maximize the amount of time that leaf blades are perpendicular to the sun, which is the angle at which photosynthesis is most efficient.

STUDY BREAK

1. What is the direct stimulus for phototropisms? For gravitropism?
2. Explain how nastic movements differ from tropic movements.

31.5 Plant Responses to the Environment: Biological Clocks

Like all eukaryotic organisms, plants have internal time-measuring mechanisms called **biological clocks** that adapt the organism to recurring environmental changes. In plants, biological clocks help adjust both daily and seasonal activities.

31.5a Circadian Rhythms Are Based on 24-Hour Cycles

Some plant activities occur regularly in cycles of about 24 hours, even when environmental conditions remain constant. These are **circadian rhythms** (*circa* = around; *dies* = day). In Chapter 29, we noted that stomata open and close on a daily cycle, even where plants are kept in total darkness. Nastic sleep movements, described earlier, are another example of a circadian rhythm. Even when such a plant is kept in constant light or darkness for a few days, it folds its leaves into the "sleep" position at roughly 24-hour intervals. In some way, the plant measures time without sunrise

(light) and sunset (darkness). Such experiments demonstrate that internal controls, rather than external cues, largely govern circadian rhythms.

Circadian rhythms and other activities regulated by a biological clock help ensure that plants of a single species do the same thing, such as flowering, at the same time. For instance, flowers of the aptly named four o'clock plant (*Mirabilis jalapa*) open predictably every 24 hours—in nature, in the late afternoon. Such coordination can be crucial for successful pollination. Although some circadian rhythms can proceed without direct stimulus from light, many biological clock mechanisms are influenced by the relative lengths of day and night.

31.5b Photoperiodism Involves Seasonal Changes in the Relative Length of Night and Day

Obviously, environmental conditions in a 24-hour period are not the same in summer as they are in winter. In North America, for instance, winter temperatures are cooler and winter day length is shorter. Experimenting with tobacco and soybean plants in the early 1900s, two American botanists, Wightman Garner and Henry Allard, elucidated a phenomenon they called **photoperiodism**, in which plants respond to changes in the relative lengths of light and dark periods in their environment during each 24-hour period. Through photoperiodism, the biological clocks of plants (and animals) make seasonal adjustments in their patterns of growth, development, and reproduction.

In plants, we now know that a blue-green pigment called **phytochrome** often serves as a switching mechanism in the photoperiodic response, signalling the plant to make seasonal changes. Plants synthesize phytochrome in an inactive form, P_r, which absorbs the light of red wavelengths. Sunlight contains relatively more red light than far-red light. During daylight hours, when red wavelengths dominate, P_r absorbs red light. Absorption of red light triggers the conversion of phytochrome to an active form designated P_{fr}, which absorbs the light of far-red wavelengths. At sunset, at night, or even in shade, where far-red wavelengths predominate, P_{fr} reverts to P_r **(Figure 31.33)**.

In nature, a high concentration of P_{fr} "tells" a plant that it is exposed to sunlight, an adaptation that is vital given that, over time, sunlight provides favourable conditions for leaf growth, photosynthesis, and flowering. The exact mechanism of this crucial transfer of environmental information is still not fully understood. Botanists suspect that P_{fr} controls the types of enzymes being produced in particular cells—and different enzymes are required for seed germination, stem elongation and branching, leaf expansion, and the formation of flowers, fruits, and seeds. When plants adapted to full sunlight are grown in darkness,

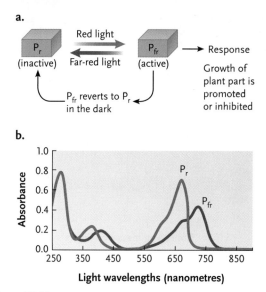

a.

P_r (inactive) — Red light / Far-red light → P_fr (active) → Response

Growth of plant part is promoted or inhibited

P_fr reverts to P_r in the dark

b.

Absorbance vs. Light wavelengths (nanometres)

Figure 31.33
The phytochrome switching mechanism, which can promote or inhibit the growth of different plant parts. **(a)** Interconversion of phytochrome from the active form (P_{fr}) to the inactive form (P_r). **(b)** The absorption spectra associated with the interconversion of P_r and P_{fr}.

they put more resources into stem elongation and less into leaf expansion or stem branching **(Figure 31.34)**.

Phytochrome also plays an important role in shade avoidance by plants. When seedlings germinate, they have a limited nutrient supply to support them until they can start to feed themselves by photosynthesis. They need to find a location with abundant light as soon as possible. Shade is rich in far-red light, which converts phytochrome to the P_r form, causing rapid elongation of the shoot, helping the seedling grow out of the shade and into sunlight.

Dwight Kuhn

Figure 31.34
Effects of the absence of light on young bean plants (*Phaseolus*). The two plants at the right, the control group, were grown in a greenhouse. The other two were grown in darkness for eight days. Note that the dark-grown plants are yellow; they could form carotenoid pigments but not chlorophyll in darkness. They have longer stems, smaller leaves, and smaller root systems than the controls.

Cryptochrome—which, recall, is sensitive to blue light and appears to influence light-related growth responses—also interacts with phytochromes in producing circadian responses. Researchers recently discovered that cryptochrome occurs not only in plants but also in animals such as fruit flies and mice (see *Molecule Behind Biology*). Does cryptochrome mediate a variety of light responses in animals as well as in plants? Recent research indicates that this may be the case. For example, cryptochromes are involved in bird navigation during migration. Migratory birds use a magnetic compass to orient themselves, and it appears that cryptochromes in the retinas of these birds allow the birds to "see" magnetic fields. Cryptochromes also play a role in photosensitive behaviour in animals that do not have eyes or other specialized light-sensing organs; for example, during the full moon in late spring, corals of the Great Barrier Reef undergo a mass spawning. Although biologists knew that changes in moonlight were one of the triggers for this mass spawning, they did not know how the corals were able to detect the light. Now a group of researchers from Australia and the United Kingdom have demonstrated that cryptochromes are present in these animals and that expression of one cryptochrome gene varies with the full moon.

31.5c Cycles of Light and Dark Often Influence Flowering

Photoperiodism is especially apparent in the flowering process. Like other plant responses, flowering is often keyed to changes in day length through the year and to the resulting changes in environmental conditions. Corn, soybeans, peas, and other annual plants begin flowering after only a few months of growth. Roses and other perennials typically flower every year or after several years of vegetative growth. Carrots, cabbages, and other biennials typically produce roots, stems, and leaves the first growing season; die back to soil level in autumn; and then grow a new flower-forming stem in the second season.

In the late 1930s, Karl Hamner and James Bonner grew cocklebur plants (*Xanthium strumarium*) in chambers in which the researchers could carefully control environmental conditions, including photoperiod. They made an unexpected discovery: flowering occurred only when the test plants were exposed to at least a single night of 8.5 hours of uninterrupted darkness. The length of the "day" in the growth chamber did not matter, but if light interrupted the dark period for even a minute or two, the plant would not flower at all. Subsequent research confirmed that for most angiosperms, the length of darkness, not light, controls flowering.

Kinds of Flowering Responses. The photoperiodic responses of flowering plants are so predictable that botanists have long used them to categorize plants

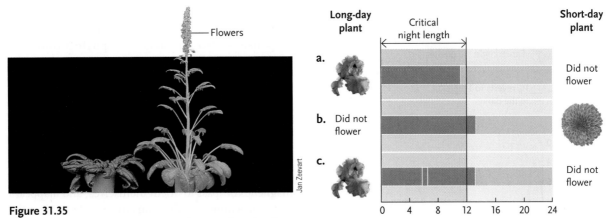

Flowers

Figure 31.35
Effect of day length on spinach (*Spinacia oleracea*), a long-day plant.

Long-day plant | Critical night length | Short-day plant

a. — Did not flower

b. Did not flower —

c. — Did not flower

Time being measured (hours)

Figure 31.36
Experiments showing that short-day and long-day plants flower by measuring night length. Each horizontal bar signifies 24 hours. Blue bars represent night, and yellow bars represent day. **(a)** Long-day plants, such as bearded irises, flower when the night is shorter than a critical length, whereas **(b)** short-day plants, such as chrysanthemums, flower when the night is longer than a critical value. **(c)** When an intense red flash interrupts a long night, both kinds of plants respond as if it were a short night; the irises flowered, but the chrysanthemums did not.

(Figure 31.35). The categories, which refer to day length, reflect the fact that scientists recognized the phenomenon of photoperiodic flowering responses long before they understood that darkness, not light, was the cue. **Long-day plants**, such as irises, daffodils, and corn, usually flower in spring, when dark periods become shorter and day length becomes longer than some critical value—usually 9 to 16 hours. **Short-day plants**, including cockleburs, chrysanthemums, and potatoes, flower in late summer or early autumn, when dark periods become longer and day length becomes shorter than some critical value. Intermediate-day plants, such as sugarcane, flower only when day length falls between the values for long-day and short-day plants. **Day-neutral plants**, such as dandelions and roses, flower whenever they become mature enough to do so, without regard to photoperiod.

Experiments demonstrate what happens when plants are grown under the "wrong" photoperiod regimens. For instance, spinach, a long-day plant, flowers and produces seeds only if it is exposed to no more than 10 hours of darkness each day for 2 weeks (see Figure 31.27). **Figure 31.36** illustrates the results of an experiment to test the responses of short-day and long-day plants to night length. In this experiment, bearded iris plants (*Iris* species), which are long-day plants, and chrysanthemums, which are short-day plants, were exposed to a range of light conditions. In each case, when the researchers interrupted a critical dark period with a pulse of red light, the light reset the plants' clocks. The experiment showed clearly that short-day plants flower only when nights are longer than a critical value, and long-day plants flower only when nights are shorter than a critical value.

Chemical Signals for Flowering. When photoperiod conditions are right, what sort of chemical message stimulates a plant to develop flowers? In the 1930s, botanists began postulating the existence of "florigen," a hypothetical hormone that served as the flowering signal. In a somewhat frustrating scientific quest, researchers spent the rest of the twentieth century seeking this

substance in vain. Recently, however, molecular studies using *Arabidopsis* plants have defined a sequence of steps that may collectively provide the internal stimulus for flowering. Here again, we see one of the recurring themes in plant development—major developmental changes guided by several interacting genes.

Figure 31.37 traces the steps of the proposed flowering signal. To begin with, a gene called *CONSTANS* is expressed in a plant's leaves in tune with the daily light/ dark cycle, with expression peaking at dusk (step 1). The gene encodes a regulatory protein called CO (not to be confused with carbon monoxide). As days lengthen in spring, the concentration of CO rises in leaves, and as a result, a second gene is activated (step 2). The product of this gene, a protein called FT, travels in the phloem to shoot tips (step 3). Once there, the mRNA is translated into a second regulatory protein (step 4) that in some way interacts with yet a third regulatory protein that is synthesized only in shoot apical meristems (step 5). The encounter apparently sparks the development of a flower (step 6) by promoting the expression of floral organ identity genes in the meristem tissue (see Section 34.5).

Vernalization and Flowering. Flowering is more than a response to changing night length. Temperatures also change with the seasons in most parts of the world, and they, too, influence flowering. For instance, unless the buds of some biennials and perennials are exposed to low winter temperatures, flowers do not form on stems in spring. Low-temperature stimulation of flowering is called **vernalization** ("making springlike").

In 1915, the plant physiologist Gustav Gassner demonstrated that it was possible to influence the flowering

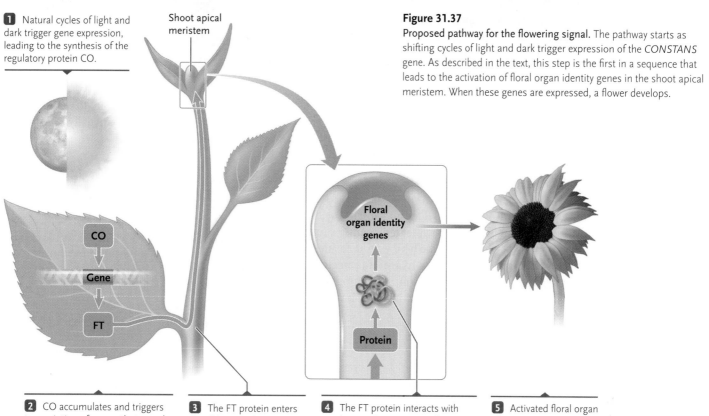

1 Natural cycles of light and dark trigger gene expression, leading to the synthesis of the regulatory protein CO.

Shoot apical meristem

Figure 31.37
Proposed pathway for the flowering signal. The pathway starts as shifting cycles of light and dark trigger expression of the *CONSTANS* gene. As described in the text, this step is the first in a sequence that leads to the activation of floral organ identity genes in the shoot apical meristem. When these genes are expressed, a flower develops.

CO

Gene

FT

Floral organ identity genes

Protein

2 CO accumulates and triggers transcription of a gene that encodes a second regulatory protein called FT.

3 The FT protein enters the phloem and is transported to the shoot apex.

4 The FT protein interacts with another regulatory protein, forming a complex that can promote transcription of floral organ identity genes.

5 Activated floral organ identity genes initiate development of a flower.

of cereal plants by controlling the temperature of seeds while they were germinating. In one case, he maintained germinating seeds of winter rye (*Secale cereale*) at just above freezing (1°C) before planting them. In nature, winter rye seeds planted in soil germinate during the winter, giving rise to a plant that flowers months later, in summer. Plants grown from Gassner's test seeds, however, flowered the same summer even when the seeds were planted in the late spring. Home gardeners can induce flowering of daffodils and tulips by putting the bulbs (technically, *corms*) in a freezer for several weeks before early spring planting. Commercial growers use vernalization to induce millions of plants, such as Easter lilies, to flower just in time for seasonal sales.

31.5d Dormancy Is an Adaptation to Seasonal Changes or Stress

As autumn approaches and days grow shorter, growth slows or stops in many plants even if temperatures are still moderate, the sky is bright, and water is plentiful. When a perennial or biennial plant stops growing under conditions that seem (to us) quite suitable for growth, it has entered a state of **dormancy**. Ordinarily, its buds will not resume growth until early spring.

Short days and long nights—conditions typical of winter—are strong cues for dormancy. In one experiment, in which a short period of red light interrupted the long dark period for Douglas firs, the plants

responded as if the nights were shorter and the days were longer; they continued to grow taller **(Figure 31.38)**. Conversion of P_r to P_{fr} by red light during the dark

Figure 31.38
Effect of the relative length of day and night on the growth of Douglas firs (*Pseudotsuga menziesii*). The young tree at the left was exposed to alternating periods of 12 hours of light followed by 12 hours of darkness for a year; its buds became dormant because day length was too short. The tree at the right was exposed to a cycle of 20 hours of light and 4 hours of darkness; its buds remained active, and growth continued. The middle plant was exposed each day to 12 hours of light and 11 hours of darkness, with a 1-hour light in the middle of the dark period. This light interruption of an otherwise long dark period also prevented buds from going dormant.

CHAPTER 31 CONTROL OF PLANT GROWTH AND DEVELOPMENT

period prevented dormancy. In nature, buds may enter dormancy because less P_{fr} can form when day length shortens in late summer. Other environmental cues are at work also. Cold nights, dry soil, and nitrogen deficiency apparently also promote dormancy.

The requirement for multiple dormancy cues has adaptive value. For example, if temperature were the only cue, plants might flower and seeds might germinate in warm autumn weather—only to be killed by winter frost.

A dormancy-breaking process is at work between fall and spring. Depending on the species, breaking dormancy probably involves gibberellins and abscisic acid, and it requires exposure to low winter temperatures for specific periods **(Figure 31.39)**. The temperature needed to break dormancy varies greatly among species. Generally, trees growing in Canada or Sweden require longer cold exposure than those growing in Italy or the southern United States.

STUDY BREAK

1. Summarize the switching mechanism that operates in plant responses to changes in photoperiod.
2. Give some examples of how relative lengths of dark and light can influence flowering.
3. Explain why dormancy is an adaptive response to a plant's environment.

Potted plant grown inside a greenhouse did not flower.

Branch exposed to cold outside air flowered.

Figure 31.39
Effect of cold temperature on dormant buds of a lilac (*Syringa vulgaris*). In this experiment, a branch of the plant was positioned so that it grew out of a hole in a greenhouse during winter; the rest of the plant was inside, at warm temperatures. Only the buds on the branch exposed to low outside temperatures resumed growth in spring. This experiment suggests that low-temperature effects are localized.

31.6 Plant Responses to the Environment: Responses to Temperature Extremes

In general, plants have limited ability to regulate their temperature, so their temperature usually mirrors that of their environment.

31.6a Extremes of Heat and Cold Elicit Protective Chemical Responses

Plants use evaporative cooling—loss of water from leaves by evaporation and transpiration—to regulate their leaf temperature. If water becomes limiting, as on a hot, dry day in the summer, a plant's stomates will close, reducing its ability to cool itself by evaporative cooling. Although most plants can survive a brief exposure to high temperatures, prolonged exposure to such temperatures is lethal, largely due to the detrimental effects of high temperatures on enzymes. As do other organisms, plant cells contain **heat-shock proteins (HSPs)**, a type of protein that binds and stabilizes other proteins, including enzymes, which might otherwise stop functioning if they were to become denatured by rising temperature. Plant cells may rapidly synthesize HSPs in response to a sudden temperature rise. For example, experiments with the cells and seedlings of soybean (*Glycine max*) showed that when the temperature rose 10° to 15°C, in less than 5 minutes, mRNA transcripts coding for as many as 50 different HSPs were present in the cells. When the temperature returns to a normal range, HSPs release bound proteins, which can then resume their usual functions. Further studies have revealed that HSPs help protect plant cells subjected to other environmental stresses as well, including drought, salinity, and cold.

Like extreme heat, freezing can also be lethal to plants. If ice crystals form in cells, they can literally tear the cell apart. In many cold-resistant species, dormancy is the long-term strategy for dealing with cold, but in the short term, such as an unseasonable cold snap, some species also undergo a rapid shift in gene expression that equips cold-stressed cells with so-called antifreeze proteins. Like HSPs, these molecules are thought to help maintain the structural integrity of other cell proteins.

Researchers are actively investigating mechanisms that regulate plant response to extreme temperatures as these offer promise for the development of new crop lines that can survive in harsh habitats.

Do plants have a "backup" copy of their genome?

As described at the beginning of this chapter, land plants manifest adaptations that allow them to survive and reproduce in unfavourable or hostile conditions. Adaptations include changes in growth and development reflecting responses to environmental fluctuations that occur naturally during the normal life cycle of plants. Being physically anchored in one place has driven plant adaptation so that changes in the plant body can facilitate survival. It is also possible, however, that the sessile existence of land plants may have selected for unusual adaptive strategies. Might plants have devised a strategy to utilize previously unknown genetic resources and thereby expand their potential repertoire of adaptive responses? Recent findings demonstrating the existence of a previously unknown mechanism of genetic instability suggest that such a strategy may indeed have been in place during the evolution of land plants. These findings suggest that, at least in *Arabidopsis thaliana*, a "backup" copy of the genome exists that can be accessed under unfavourable conditions.

Why have a backup copy of the genome? Simply put, if the system crashes, it can be restored. By analogy, the genome could be considered the "operating system" stored on the "hard drive" of the organism. If that operating system becomes corrupted, for example, by a devastating power surge or a computer virus, a global systems failure might occur. However, if a backup copy were maintained at least in a subset of the population, then, under conditions that might lead to extinction, the backup copy could be used to "restore" the system and increase the chances of survival for that organism or population. In other words, the genome could adapt using the stored information.

An intriguing possibility is that such a backup genome might exist in the form of RNA. The fact that backup copies have not been found using conventional DNA-based detection methods or classical genetic approaches leaves open the exciting possibility that RNA might serve as the storage medium for this information. In a sense, having the information stored in an alternative chemical form (analogous to a different computer language or code) might also make it less susceptible to corruption. Furthermore, it may be that this backup genome is a remnant of an ancestral condition in which the genome was RNA based.

How would you go about testing these different possibilities? First, the findings would have to be independently verified and the existence of a "restoration" mechanism would have to be confirmed by other research groups working on *Arabidopsis* or other plant species. Second, the source and chemical nature of the backup information would need to be identified. Where is it, and is it RNA, DNA, protein, or a combination of these? The question of mechanism would also need to be addressed. How is the system restored, and when does it happen? The question of how global this phenomenon is would also need to be considered. Do all plant species maintain a backup copy, and do organisms outside the plant kingdom have a backup genome?

Susan Lolle is associate professor of biology at the University of Waterloo. Her research interests include plant development, genetics, and genome biology. To learn more, go to http://www.biology.uwaterloo.ca.

Review

Go to CENGAGENOW™ at http://hed.nelson.com/ to access quizzing, animations, exercises, articles, and personalized homework help.

31.1 Plant Hormones

- At least seven classes of hormones govern flowering plant development, including germination, growth, flowering, fruit set, and senescence.
- Auxins, mainly IAA, promote elongation of cells in the coleoptile and stem.
- Gibberellins promote stem elongation and help seeds and buds break dormancy.
- Cytokinins stimulate cell division, promote leaf expansion, and retard leaf aging.
- Ethylene promotes fruit ripening and abscission.
- Brassinosteroids stimulate cell division and elongation.
- Abscisic acid (ABA) promotes stomatal closure and may trigger seed and bud dormancy.
- Jasmonates regulate growth and have roles in defence.

31.2 Signal Responses at the Cellular Level

- Hormones and environmental stimuli alter the behaviour of target cells, which have receptors to which signal molecules can bind. By means of a response pathway that ultimately alters gene expression, a signal can induce changes in the cell's shape or internal structure or influence its metabolism or the transport of substances across the plasma membrane.
- Some plant hormones and growth factors may bind to receptors at the target cell's plasma membrane, changing the receptor's shape. This binding often triggers the release of internal second messengers that diffuse through the cytoplasm and provide the main chemical signal that alters gene expression.
- Second messengers usually act by way of a reaction sequence that amplifies the cell's response to a signal. An activated receptor, in turn, activates a series of proteins, including G proteins and enzymes that stimulate the synthesis of second messengers (such as IP_3) that bind ion channels on endoplasmic reticulum.
- Binding releases calcium ions, which enter the cytoplasm and activate protein kinases, enzymes that activate specific proteins that produce the cell response.

31.3 Plant Chemical Defences

- Plants have diverse chemical defences that limit damage from bacteria, fungi, worms, or plant-eating insects.
- The hypersensitive response isolates an infection site by surrounding it with dead cells. During the response, salicylic acid (SA) induces the synthesis of PR (pathogenesis-related) proteins.

- Oligosaccharins can trigger the synthesis of phytoalexins, secondary metabolites that function as antibiotics.
- Gene-for-gene recognition enables a plant to chemically recognize a pathogen and mount defences against it.
- Systemic acquired resistance provides long-term protection against some pathogens. Salicylic acid passes from the infected organ to newly forming organs such as leaves, which then synthesize PR proteins

31.4 Plant Responses to the Environment: Movements

- Plants adjust their growth patterns in response to environmental rhythms and unique environmental circumstances. These responses include tropisms.
- Phototropisms are growth responses to a directional light source. Blue light is the main stimulus for phototropism.
- Gravitropism is a growth response to Earth's gravitational pull. Stems exhibit negative gravitropism, growing upward, whereas roots show positive gravitropism.
- Some plants or plant parts demonstrate thigmotropism, growth in response to contact with a solid object.
- Mechanical stress can cause thigmomorphogenesis, which causes the stem to add girth.
- In nastic leaf movements, water enters or exits the cells of a pulvinus, a pad of tissue at the base of a leaf or petiole, in response to action potentials.

31.5 Plant Responses to the Environment: Biological Clocks

- Plants have biological clocks, internal time-measuring mechanisms with a biochemical basis. Environmental cues can "reset" the clocks, enabling plants to make seasonal adjustments in growth, development, and reproduction.

- In photoperiodism, plants respond to a change in the relative length of daylight and darkness in a 24-hour period. A switching mechanism involving the pigment phytochrome promotes or inhibits germination, growth, and flowering and fruiting.
- Phytochrome is converted to an active form (P_{fr}) during daylight, when red wavelengths dominate. It reverts to an inactive form (P_r) at sunset, at night, or in shade, when far-red wavelengths predominate. P_{fr} may control the types of metabolic pathways that operate under specific light conditions.
- Long-day plants flower in spring or summer, when day length is long relative to night. Short-day plants flower when day length is relatively short, and intermediate-day plants flower when day length falls between the values for long-day and short-day plants. Flowering of day-neutral plants is not regulated by light. In vernalization, a period of low temperature stimulates flowering.
- The direct trigger for flowering may begin in leaves, when the regulatory protein CO triggers the expression of the *FT* gene. The resulting mRNA transcripts move in phloem to apical meristems, where translation of the mRNAs yields a second regulatory protein, which, in turn, interacts with a third. This final interaction activates genes that encode the development of flower parts.
- Senescence is the sum of processes leading to the death of a plant or plant structure.
- Dormancy is a state in which a perennial or biennial stops growing even though conditions appear to be suitable for continued growth.

31.6 Plant Responses to the Environment: Responses to Temperature Extremes

- Heat-shock proteins can reversibly bind enzymes and other proteins in plant cells and prevent them from denaturing when the plant is under heat stress.
- Some plants can synthesize "antifreeze" proteins that stabilize cell proteins when cells are threatened with freezing.

Questions

Self-Test Questions

1. Which of the following plant hormones does *not* stimulate cell division?
   a. auxins
   b. cytokinins
   c. ethylene
   d. gibberellins
   e. abscisic acid

2. Which is the correct pairing of a plant hormone and its function?
   a. salicylic acid: triggers synthesis of general defence proteins
   b. brassinosteroids: promote responses to environmental stress
   c. cytokinins: stimulate stomata to close in water-stressed plants
   d. gibberellins: slow seed germination
   e. ethylene: promotes formation of lateral roots

3. Fruit bowls and hanging wire fruit baskets often have many holes or open spaces. The major advantage of these spaces is that they
   a. prevent gibberellins from causing bolting or the formation of rosettes on the fruit.
   b. allow the evaporation of ethylene and thus slow ripening of the fruit.

   c. allow oxygen in the air to stimulate the production of ethylene, which hastens the abscission of fruits.
   d. allow oxygen to stimulate brassinosteroids, which hasten the maturation of seeds in/on the fruits.
   e. allow carbon dioxide in the air to stimulate the production of cytokinins, which promotes mitosis in the fruit tissue and hastens ripening.

4. Which of the following is *not* an example of a plant chemical defence?
   a. ABA inhibits leaves from budding if conditions favour attacks by sap-sucking insects.
   b. Jasmonate activates plant genes encoding protease inhibitors that prevent insects from digesting plant proteins.
   c. Acting against fungal infections, the hypersensitive response allows plants to produce highly reactive oxygen compounds that kill selected tissue, thus forming a dead tissue barrier that walls off the infected area from healthy tissues.
   d. Chitinase, a PR hydrolytic protein produced by plants, breaks down chitin in the cell walls of fungi and thus halts the fungal infection.
   e. Attack by fungi or viruses triggers the release of oligosaccharins, which, in turn, stimulate the production of phytoalexins with antibiotic properties.

5. Which of the following statements about plant responses to the environment is true?
   a. The heat-shock response induces a sudden halt to cellular metabolism when an insect begins feeding on plant tissue.
   b. In gravitropism, amyloplasts sink to the bottom of cells in a plant stem, causing the redistribution of IAA.
   c. The curling of tendrils around a twig is an example of thigmotropism.
   d. Phototropism results when IAA moves first laterally and then downward in a shoot tip when one side of the tip is exposed to light.
   e. Nastic movements, such as the sudden closing of the leaves of a Venus flytrap, are examples of a plant's ability to respond to specific directional stimuli.

6. In nature, the poinsettia, a plant native to Mexico, blooms only in or around the month of December. This pattern suggests that
   a. the long daily period of darkness (short day) in December stimulates the flowering.
   b. vernalization stimulates the flowering.
   c. the plant is dormant for the rest of the year.
   d. phytochrome is not affecting the poinsettia flowering cycle.
   e. a circadian rhythm is in effect.

7. Which of the following steps is *not* part of the sequence that is thought to trigger flowering?
   a. Cycles of light and dark stimulate the expression of the *CONSTANS* gene in a plant's leaves.
   b. CO proteins accumulate in the leaves and trigger expression of a second regulatory gene.
   c. mRNA transcribed during expression of a second regulatory gene moves via the phloem to the shoot apical meristem.
   d. Interactions among several regulatory proteins promote the expression of floral organ identity genes in meristem tissue.
   e. CO proteins in the floral meristem interact with florigen, a so-called flowering hormone, which provides the final stimulus for expression of floral organ identity genes.

8. Damage from an infectious bacterium, fungus, or worm may trigger a plant defensive response when the pathogen or a substance it produces binds to
   a. a receptor encoded by the plant's *avirulence* (*Avr*) gene.
   b. an *R* gene in the plant cell nucleus.
   c. a receptor encoded by a dominant *R* gene.
   d. PR proteins embedded in the plant cell plasma membrane.
   e. salicylic acid molecules released from the besieged plant cell.

Questions for Discussion

1. You work for a plant nursery and are asked to design a special horticultural regimen for a particular flowering plant. The plant is native to northern Spain, and in the wild, it grows a few long, slender stems that produce flowers each July. Your boss wants the nursery plants to be shorter, with thicker stems and more branches, and she wants them to bloom in early-December in time for holiday sales. Outline your detailed plan for altering the plant's growth and reproductive characteristics to meet these specifications.

2. Synthetic auxins such as 2,4-D can be weed killers because they cause an abnormal growth burst that kills the plant within a few days. Suggest reasons why such rapid growth might be lethal to a plant.

3. In experiments, the shoots of mutant plants lacking differentiated endodermis in their root and shoot tissue don't respond normally to gravity, but the roots of such plants do respond normally. Explain this finding, based on your reading in this chapter.

4. In *A. thaliana* plants carrying a mutation called *pickle (pkl)*, the primary root meristem retains characteristics of embryonic tissue—it spontaneously regenerates new embryos that can grow into mature plants. However, when the mutant root tissue is exposed to a gibberellin (GA), this abnormal developmental condition is suppressed. Explain why this finding suggests that additional research is needed on the fundamental biological role of GA.

Appendix A
Answers to Self-Test Questions

Chapter 17
1. c 2. b 3. c 4. d 5. b 6. e 7. a 8. b 9. c 10. d

Chapter 18
1. e 2. e 3. c 4. b 5. b 6. e 7. c 8. a 9. a 10. b

Chapter 19
1. b 2. b 3. a 4. d 5. b 6. e 7. a 8. a 9. e 10. d

Chapter 20
1. b 2. b 3. d 4. b 5. c 6. b 7. a 8. b 9. d 10. d

Chapter 21
1. a 2. d 3. e 4. e 5. b 6. d

Chapter 22
1. c 2. a 3. d 4. a 5. e 6. b 7. a

Chapter 23
1. d 2. b 3. c 4. b 5. a 6. c

Chapter 24
1. a 2. d 3. d 4. e 5. c 6. c 7. e

Chapter 25
1. b 2. d 3. e 4. e 5. a 6. d 7. b 8. a

Chapter 26
1. c. 2. d. 3. e. 4. d. 5. b.

Chapter 27
1. a 2. c 3. d 4. b 5. a 6. c 7. c 8. d 9. c 10. a

Chapter 28
1. d 2. c 3. b 4. c 5. a 6. d 7. b

Chapter 29
1. b 2. d 3. a 4. e 5. a 6. b 7. e 8. d 9. c 10. b

Chapter 30
1. c 2. a 3. b 4. e 5. d

Chapter 31
1. e 2. a 3. b 4. b 5. b 6. a 7. d 8. c

abdomen The region of the body that contains much of the digestive tract and sometimes part of the reproductive system; in insects, the region behind the thorax.

abscisic acid (ABA) A plant hormone involved in the abscission of leaves, flowers, and fruits; dormancy of buds and seeds; and closing of stomata.

abscission In plants, the dropping of flowers, fruits, and leaves in response to environmental signals.

absorptive nutrition Mode of nutrition in which an organism secretes digestive enzymes into its environment and then absorbs the small molecules thus produced.

acid-growth hypothesis A hypothesis to explain how the hormone auxin promotes the growth of plant cells; it suggests that auxin stimulates H pumps in the plasma membrane to move H from the cell interior into the cell wall, which increases wall acidity, making the wall expandable.

acoelomate A body plan of bilaterally symmetrical animals that lack a body cavity (coelom) between the gut and the body wall.

acorn worms Sedentary marine animals living in U-shaped tubes or burrows in coastal sand or mud.

action potential The abrupt and transient change in membrane potential that occurs when a neuron conducts an electrical impulse.

active transport The mechanism by which ions and molecules move against the concentration gradient across a membrane, from the side with the lower concentration to the side with the higher concentration.

adaptation Characteristic or suite of characteristics that helps an organism survive longer or reproduce more under a particular set of environmental conditions.

adaptation, evolutionary The accumulation of adaptive traits over time.

adaptive trait A genetically based characteristic, preserved by natural selection, that increases an organism's likelihood of survival or its reproductive output.

adductor muscle A muscle that pulls inward toward the median line of the body; in bivalve molluscs, it pulls the shell closed.

adhesion The adherence of molecules to the walls of conducting tubes, as in plants.

adventitious root A root that develops from the stem or leaves of a plant.

aerobe An organism that requires oxygen for cellular respiration.

African emergence hypothesis A hypothesis proposing that modern humans first evolved in Africa and then dispersed to other continents.

agar A gelatinous product extracted from certain red algae or seaweed used as a culture medium in the laboratory and as a gelling or stabilizing agent in foods.

aggregate fruit A fruit that develops from multiple separate carpels of a single flower, such as a raspberry or strawberry.

albumin The most abundant protein in blood plasma, important for osmotic balance and pH buffering; also, the portion of an egg that serves as the main source of nutrients and water for the embryo.

algin Alginic acid, found in the cell walls of brown algae.

allele frequency The abundance of one allele relative to others at the same gene locus in individuals of a population.

allometric growth A pattern of postembryonic development in which parts of the same organism grow at different rates.

allopatric speciation The evolution of reproductive isolating mechanisms between two populations that are geographically separated.

allopolyploidy The genetic condition of having two or more complete sets of chromosomes from different parent species.

alpine tundra A biome that occurs on high mountaintops throughout the world, in which dominant plants form cushions and mats.

alternation of generations The regular alternation of mode of reproduction in the life cycle of an organism, such as the alternation between diploid (sporophyte) and haploid (gametophyte) phases in plants.

altricial Helpless at birth.

amnion In an amniote egg, an extraembryonic membrane that encloses the embryo, forming the amniotic cavity and secreting amniotic fluid, which provides an aquatic environment in which the embryo develops.

amniote (amniotic) egg A shelled egg that can survive and develop on land.

amyloplast Colourless plastid that stores starch in plants.

anaerobic respiration The process by which molecules are oxidized to produce ATP via an electron transport chain and ATP synthase, but unlike aerobic respiration, oxygen is not the final electron acceptor.

anagenesis The slow accumulation of evolutionary changes in a lineage over time.

anapsid (lineage Anapsida) A member of the group of amniote vertebrates with no temporal arches and no spaces on the sides of the skull (includes turtles).

ancestral character A trait that was present in a distant common ancestor.

angiosperm A flowering plant. Its egg-containing ovules mature into seeds within protected chambers called ovaries.

Animalia The taxonomic kingdom that includes all living and extinct animals.

annual A herbaceous plant that completes its life cycle in one growing season and then dies.

annulus In ferns, a ring of thick-walled cells that nearly encircles the sporangium and functions in spore release.

antennal glands Excretory structures at the base of the antennae in some crustaceans.

anterior Indicating the head end of an animal.

antheridium (plural, antheridia) In plants, a structure in which sperm are produced.

Anthocerophyta The phylum comprising hornworts.

Anthophyta The phylum comprising flowering plants.

antigen A foreign molecule that triggers an adaptive immunity response.

apical dominance Inhibition of the growth of lateral buds in plants due to auxin diffusing down a shoot tip from the terminal bud.

apical growth Growth from the tip of a cell or tissue.

apical meristem A region of unspecialized dividing cells at the shoot tips and root tips of a plant.

apicomplexan A group or parasitic organisms with specific structures in their apical complex to penetrate and enter the cells they parasitize.

apomixis In plants, the production of offspring without meiosis or formation of gametes.

apoplastic pathway The route followed by water moving through plant cell walls and intercellular spaces (the apoplast). *Compare* symplastic pathway.

aquaporin A specialized protein channel that facilitates diffusion of water through cell membranes.

arbuscular mycorrhizas Symbiotic association between a glomeromycete fungus and the roots of a wide range of plants, including nonvascular, nonseed, and seed plants.

arbuscule Highly branched hypha produced inside root cells by arbuscular mycorrhizal fungi; nutrient-exchange site between plant and fungus.

Archaea One of two domains of prokaryotes; archaeans have some unique molecular and biochemical traits, but they also share some traits with Bacteria and other traits with Eukarya.

archegonium The flask-shaped structure in which bryophyte eggs form.

archenteron The central endoderm-lined cavity of an embryo at the gastrula stage, which forms the primitive gut.

Archosauromorpha A diverse group of diapsids that comprises crocodilians, pterosaurs, and dinosaurs (including birds).

arctic tundra A treeless biome that stretches from the boreal forests to the polar ice cap in Europe, Asia, and North America.

artificial selection Selective breeding of animals or plants to ensure that certain desirable traits appear at higher frequency in successive generations.

ascocarp A reproductive body that bears or contains asci.

ascospore Spore formed by meiosis in ascus, a saclike cell produced by ascomycete fungi.

ascus (plural, asci) A saclike cell in ascomycetes (sac fungi) in which meiosis gives rise to haploid sexual spores (meiospores).

assumption of parsimony Assumption that the simplest explanation should be the most accurate.

asymmetrical Characterized by a lack of proportion in the spatial arrangement or placement of parts.

atrial siphon A tube through which invertebrate chordates expel digestive and metabolic wastes.

atriopore The hole in the body wall of a cephalochordate through which water is expelled from the body.

atrium (plural, atria) A body cavity or chamber surrounding the perforated pharynx of invertebrate chordates; also one of the chambers that receive blood returning to the heart.

autopolyploidy The genetic condition of having more than two sets of chromosomes from the same parent species.

auxin Any of a family of plant hormones that stimulate growth by promoting cell elongation in stems and coleoptiles; inhibit abscission; govern responses to light and gravity, and have other developmental effects.

Avr **gene** A gene in certain plant pathogens that encodes a product triggering a defensive response in the plant.

axil The upper angle between the stem and an attached leaf.

axopods Slender, raylike strands of cytoplasm supported internally by long bundles of microtubules.

bacteria One of the two domains of prokaryotes; collectively, bacteria are the most metabolically diverse organisms.

bacteriophage A virus that infects bacteria. Also referred to as a *phage*.

balanced polymorphism The maintenance of two or more phenotypes in fairly stable proportions over many generations.

bark The tough outer covering of woody stems and roots, composed of all of the living and nonliving tissues between the vascular cambium and the stem surface.

basal angiosperm Any of the earliest branches of the flowering plant lineage; includes the star anise group and water lilies.

basidiocarp A fruiting body of a basidiomycete; mushrooms are examples.

basidiospore A haploid sexual spore produced by basidiomycete fungi.

basidium (plural, basidia) A small, club-shaped structure in which sexual spores of basidiomycetes arise.

behavioural isolation A prezygotic reproductive isolating mechanism in which two species do not mate because of differences in courtship behaviour; also known as ethological isolation.

biennial A plant that completes its life cycle in two growing seasons and then dies; limited secondary growth occurs in some biennials.

bilateral symmetry The body plan of animals in which the body can be divided into mirror image right and left halves by a plane passing through the midline of the body.

binomial Relating to or consisting of two names or terms.

biofilm A microbial community consisting of a complex aggregation of microorganisms attached to a surface.

biogeochemical cycle Any of several global processes in which a nutrient circulates between the abiotic environment and living organisms.

biogeographic region A major region of Earth that is occupied by distinct evolutionary lineages of plants and animals.

biogeography The study of the geographic distributions of plants and animals.

biological clock An internal time-measuring mechanism that adapts an organism to recurring environmental changes.

biological evolution The process by which some individuals in a population experience changes in their DNA and pass those modified instructions to their offspring.

biological lineage An evolutionary sequence of ancestral organisms and their descendants.

biological research The collective effort of individuals who have worked to understand how living systems function.

Biological Species Concept The definition of species based on the ability of populations to interbreed and produce fertile offspring.

biomass The dry weight of biological material per unit area or volume of habitat.

bioremediation Applications of chemical and biological knowledge to decontaminate polluted environments.

biota The total collection of organisms in a geographic region.

bipedalism The habit in animals of walking upright on two legs.

blade The expanded part of a leaf that provides a large surface area for absorbing sunlight and carbon dioxide.

blastopore The opening at one end of the archenteron in the gastrula that gives rise to the mouth in protostomes and the anus in deuterostomes.

bolting Rapid formation of a floral shoot in plant species that form rosettes, such as lettuce.

book lungs Pocketlike respiratory organs found in some arachnids consisting of several parallel membrane folds arranged like the pages of a book.

boreal forest A biome that is a circumpolar expanse of evergreen coniferous trees in Europe, Asia, and North America.

brassinosteroid Any of a family of plant hormones that stimulate cell division and elongation and differentiation of vascular tissue.

Bryophyta The phylum of nonvascular plants, including mosses and their relatives.

bryophyte A general term for plants (such as mosses) that lack internal transport vessels.

budding A mode of asexual reproduction in which a new individual grows and develops while attached to the parent.

bulk flow The group movement of molecules in response to a difference in pressure between two locations.

callus An undifferentiated tissue that develops on or around a cut plant surface or in tissue culture.

calyx The outermost whorl of a flower, made up of sepals; early in the development of a flower, it encloses all of the other parts, as in an unopened bud.

capsid *See* coat.

carapace A protective outer covering that extends backward behind the head on the dorsal side of an animal, such as the shell of a turtle or lobster.

carnivore An animal that primarily eats other animals.

carpel The reproductive organ of a flower that houses an ovule and its associated structures.

carrageenan A chemical extracted from the red alga *Eucheuma* that is used to thicken and stabilize paints, dairy products such as pudding and ice cream, and many other creams and emulsions.

Casparian strip A thin, waxy impermeable band that seals abutting cell walls in roots; the strip helps control the type and amount of solutes that enter the stele by blocking the apoplastic pathway at the endodermis and forcing substances to pass through cells (the symplast).

catastrophism The theory that Earth has been affected by sudden, violent events that were sometimes world-wide in scope.

cell expansion A mechanism that enlarges the cells in specific directions in a developing organ.

cellular slime mould Any of a variety of primitive organisms of the phylum Acrasiomycota, especially of the genus *Dictyostelium*; the life cycle is characterized by a slimelike amoeboid stage and a multicellular reproductive stage.

cellulose One of the primary constituents of plant cell walls, formed by chains of carbohydrate subunits.

central vacuole A large, water-filled organelle in plant cells that maintains the turgor of the cell and controls movement of molecules between the cytosol and sap.

cephalization The development of an anterior head where sensory organs and nervous system tissue are concentrated.

cephalothorax The anterior section of an arachnid, consisting of a fused head and thorax.

chaperone protein (chaperonin) "Guide" protein that binds temporarily with newly synthesized proteins, directing their conformation toward the correct tertiary structure and inhibiting incorrect arrangements as the new proteins fold.

charophyte A member of the group of green algae most similar to the algal ancestors of land plants.

chelicerae The first pair of fanglike appendages near the mouth of an arachnid, used for biting prey and often modified for grasping and piercing.

chemoautotroph An organism that obtains energy by oxidizing inorganic substances such as hydrogen, iron, sulphur, ammonia, nitrites, and nitrates and uses carbon dioxide as a carbon source.

chemoheterotroph An organism that oxidizes organic molecules as an energy source and obtains carbon in organic form.

chitin A polysaccharide that contains nitrogen and is present in the cell walls of fungi and the exoskeletons of arthropods.

choanocyte One of the inner layer of flagellated cells lining the body cavity of a sponge.

Choanoflagellata A group of minute, single-celled protists found in water; the flask-shaped body has a collar of closely packed microvilli that surrounds the single flagellum by which it moves and takes in food.

circadian rhythm Any biological activity that is repeated in cycles, each about 24 hours long, independently of any shifts in environmental conditions.

circulatory vessel An element of the circulatory system through which fluid flows and carries nutrients and oxygen to tissues and removes wastes.

clade A monophyletic group of organisms that share homologous features derived from a common ancestor.

cladistics An approach to systematics that uses shared derived characters to infer the phylogenetic relationships and evolutionary history of groups of organisms.

cladogenesis The evolution of two or more descendant species from a common ancestor.

cladogram A branching diagram in which the end points of the branches represent different species of organisms, used to illustrate phylogenetic relationships.

claspers A pair of organs on the pelvic fins of male crustaceans and sharks, which help transfer sperm into the reproductive tract of the female.

class A Linnaean taxonomic category that ranks below a phylum and above an order.

classification An arrangement of organisms into hierarchical groups that reflect their relatedness.

cleavage Mitotic cell divisions of the zygote that produce a blastula from a fertilized ovum.

cline A pattern of smooth variation in a characteristic along a geographic gradient.

closed circulatory system A circulatory system in which the fluid, blood, is confined in blood vessels and is distinct from the interstitial fluid.

cnidocyte A prey-capturing and defensive cell in the epidermis of cnidarians.

coat The protective layer of protein that surrounds the nucleic acid core of a virus in free form; also known as a capsid.

coccoid Spherical prokaryotic cell.

coccus (plural, cocci) A spherical prokaryote.

coelom A fluid-filled body cavity in bilaterally symmetrical animals that is completely lined with derivatives of mesoderm.

coelomate A body plan of bilaterally symmetrical animals that have a coelom.

coevolution The evolution of genetically based, reciprocal adaptations in two or more species that interact closely in the same ecological setting.

cohesion The high resistance of water molecules to separation.

cohesion–tension mechanism of water transport A model of how water is transported from roots to leaves in vascular plants; the evaporation of water from leaves pulls water up in the xylem by creating a continuous negative pressure (tension) that extends to roots.

coleoptile A protective sheath that covers the shoot apical meristem and plumule of the embryo in monocots, such as grasses, as it pushes up through soil.

coleorhiza A sheath that encloses the radicle of an embryo until it breaks out of the seed coat and enters the soil as the primary root.

collenchyma One of three simple plant tissues. Flexibly supports rapidly growing plant parts. Its elongated cells are alive at maturity and collectively often form strands or a sheathlike cylinder under the dermal tissue of growing shoot regions and leaf stalks.

colony Multiple individual organisms of the same species living in a group.

companion cell A specialized parenchyma cell that is connected to a mature sieve tube member by plasmodesmata and assists sieve tube members with both the uptake of sugars and the unloading of sugars in tissues.

comparative morphology Analysis of the structure of living and extinct organisms.

complete digestive system A digestive system with a mouth at one end, through which food enters, and an anus at the other end, through which undigested waste is voided.

complete metamorphosis The form of metamorphosis in which an insect passes through four separate stages of growth: egg, larva, pupa, and adult.

compound eye The eye of most insects and some crustaceans, composed of many-faceted, light-sensitive units called ommatidia fitted closely together, each with its own refractive system and each forming a portion of an image.

cone In the vertebrate eye, a photoreceptor in the retina that is specialized for detection of different wavelengths (colours). In cone-bearing plants, a cluster of sporophylls.

conidiophore A fungal hypha that gives rise to conidia.

conidium (plural, conidia) An asexually produced fungal spore.

Coniferophyta The major phylum of cone-bearing gymnosperms, most of which are substantial trees; includes pines, firs, and other conifers.

conodont An abundant, bonelike fossil dating from the early Paleozoic era through the early Mesozoic era, now described as a feeding structure of some of the earliest vertebrates.

conservation biology An interdisciplinary science that focuses on the maintenance and preservation of biodiversity.

continental drift The long-term movement of continents as a result of plate tectonics.

continuous distribution A geographic distribution in which a species lives in suitable habitats throughout a geographic area.

contractile vacuole A specialized cytoplasmic organelle that pumps fluid in a cyclical manner from within the cell to the outside by alternately filling and then contracting to release its contents at various points on the surface of the cell.

convergent evolution The evolution of similar adaptations in distantly related organisms that occupy similar environments.

coral reef A structure made from the hard skeletons of coral animals or polyps; found largely in tropical and subtropical marine environments.

cork A nonliving, impermeable secondary tissue that is one element of bark.

cork cambium A lateral meristem in plants that forms periderm, which in turn produces cork.

corolla The structure formed collectively by the petals of a flower.

corona The ciliated crownlike organ at the anterior end of rotifers used for feeding or locomotion.

cortex Generally, an outer, rindlike layer. In mammals, the outer layer of the brain, the kidneys, or the adrenal glands. In plants, the outer region of tissue in a root or stem lying between the epidermis and the vascular tissue, composed mainly of parenchyma.

cotyledon A leaf of a seed plant embryo; also known as a seed leaf.

courtship display A behaviour performed by males to attract potential mates or to reinforce the bond between a male and a female.

cranium The part of the skull that encloses the brain.

crassulacean acid metabolism (CAM) A biochemical variation of photosynthesis that was discovered in a member of the plant family Crassulaceae. Carbon dioxide is taken up and stored during the night to allow the stomata to remain closed during the daytime, decreasing water loss.

Crenarchaeota A major group of the domain Archaea, separated from the other archaeans based mainly on rRNA sequences.

crista Fold that expands the surface area of the inner mitochondrial membrane.

cryptochrome A light-absorbing protein that is sensitive to blue light and that may also be an important early step in various light-based growth responses.

cuticle The outer layer of plants and some animals, which helps prevent desiccation by slowing water loss.

Cycadophyta A phylum of palmlike gymnosperms known as cycads; the pollen-bearing and seed-bearing cones (strobili) occur on separate plants.

cytokinin A hormone that promotes and controls growth responses of plants.

cytoplasmic streaming Intracellular movement of cytoplasm.

day-neutral plant A plant that flowers without regard to photoperiod.

derivative One of the daughter cells produced when a plant cell divides; it typically divides once or twice and then enters on the path to differentiation.

derived character A new version of a trait found in the most recent common ancestor of a group.

dermal tissue system The plant tissue system that comprises the outer tissues of the plant body, including the epidermis and periderm; it serves as a protective covering for the plant body.

descent with modification Biological evolution.

desert A sparsely vegetated biome that forms where rainfall averages less than 25 cm per year.

determinate cleavage A type of cleavage in protosomes in which each cell's developmental path is determined as the cell is produced.

determinate growth The pattern of growth in most animals in which individuals grow to a certain size and then their growth slows dramatically or stops.

deuterostome A division of the Bilateria in which blastopore forms the anus during development and the mouth appears later (includes Echinodermata and Chordata).

diapsid (lineage Diapsida) A member of a group within the amniote vertebrates with a skull with two temporal arches. Their living descendants include lizards and snakes, crocodilians, and birds.

digestion The splitting of carbohydrates, proteins, lipids, and nucleic acids in foods into chemical subunits small enough to be absorbed into the body fluids and cells of an animal.

digestive tube A tubelike digestive system with two openings that form a separate mouth and anus; the digestive contents move in one direction through specialized regions of the tube, from the mouth to the anus.

dikaryon The life stage in certain fungi in which a cell contains two genetically distinct haploid nuclei.

dikaryotic hyphae Hyphae containing two separate nuclei in one cell.

dioecious Having male flowers and female flowers on different plants of the same species.

diploblastic An animal body plan in which adult structures arise from only two cell layers, the ectoderm and the endoderm.

directional selection A type of selection in which individuals near one end of the phenotypic spectrum have the highest relative fitness.

Discicristates A protist group of single-celled, highly motile organisms that swim by means of flagella and that have characteristic disk-shaped mitochondrial cristae (inner mitochondrial membranes).

disjunct distribution A geographic distribution in which populations of the same species or closely related species live in widely separated locations.

dispersal The movement of organisms away from their place of origin.

disruptive selection A type of natural selection in which extreme phenotypes have higher relative fitness than intermediate phenotypes.

domain In protein structure, a distinct, large structural subdivision produced in many proteins by the folding of the amino acid chain. In systematics, the highest taxonomic category; a group of cellular organisms with characteristics that set it apart as a major branch of the evolutionary tree.

dormancy A period in the life cycle in which biological activity is suspended.

dorsal Indicating the back side of an animal.

double fertilization The characteristic feature of sexual reproduction in flowering plants. In the embryo sac, one sperm nucleus unites with the egg to form a diploid zygote from which the embryo develops, and another unites with two polar nuclei to form the primary endosperm nucleus.

ecdysis Shedding of the cuticle, exoskeleton, or skin; moulting.

ecological isolation A prezygotic reproductive isolating mechanism in which species that live in the same geographic region occupy different habitats.

Ecological Species Concept Defines a species as a group of organisms that share a distinct ecological niche.

ecological succession A somewhat predictable series of changes in the species composition of a community over time.

ecology The study of the interactions between organisms and their environments.

ectoderm The outermost of the three primary germ layers of an embryo, which develops into epidermis and nervous tissue.

ectomycorrhiza A mycorrhiza that grows between and around the young roots of trees and shrubs but does not enter root cells.

ectoparasite A parasite that lives on the exterior of its host organism.

egg cell The female reproductive cell.

electroreceptor A specialized sensory receptor that detects electrical fields.

Elasmobranchii Cartilaginous fishes, including the skates and rays.

element A pure substance that cannot be broken down into simpler substances by ordinary chemical or physical techniques.

embryo An organism in its early stage of reproductive development, beginning in the first moments after fertilization.

embryo sac The female gametophyte of angiosperms, within which the embryo develops; it usually consists of seven cells: an egg cell, an endosperm mother cell, and five other cells with fleeting reproductive roles.

endangered species A species in immediate danger of extinction throughout all or a significant portion of its range.

endemic species A species that occurs in only one place on Earth.

endoderm The innermost of the three primary germ layers of an embryo, which develops into the gastrointestinal tract and, in some animals, the respiratory organs.

endodermis The innermost layer of the root cortex; a selectively permeable barrier that helps control the movement of water and dissolved minerals into the stele.

endosperm Nutritive tissue inside the seeds of flowering plants.

endospore A small, metabolically inactive, asexual spore that develops within some bacterial cells when environmental conditions become unfavourable.

endosporous Pattern of development in some plants (e.g., seed plants) in which the gametophyte develops inside the spore wall.

endotoxin A lipopolysaccharide released from the outer membrane of the cell wall when a bacterium dies and lyses.

enterocoelom In deuterostomes, the body cavity pinched off by outpocketings of the archenteron.

envelope Outer glycoprotein layer surrounding the capsid of some viruses, derived in part from host cell plasma membrane.

enveloped virus A virus that has a surface membrane derived from its host cell.

epicotyl The upper part of the axis of an early plant embryo, located between the cotyledons and the first true leaves.

epidermis A complex tissue that covers an organism's body in a single continuous layer or sometimes in multiple layers of tightly packed cells.

esophagus A connecting passage of the digestive tube.

ethylene A plant hormone that helps regulate seedling growth, stem elongation, the ripening of fruit, and the abscission of fruits, leaves, and flowers.

eudicot A plant belonging to the Eudicotyledones, one of the two major classes of angiosperms; their embryos generally have two seed leaves (cotyledons), and their pollen grains have three grooves.

Eukarya The domain that includes all eukaryotes, organisms that contain a membrane-bound nucleus within each of their cells; all protists, plants, fungi, and animals.

Euryarchaeota A major group of the domain Archaea, members of which are found in different extreme environments. They include methanogens, extreme halophiles, and some extreme thermophiles.

evolutionary developmental biology A field of biology that compares the genes controlling the developmental processes of different animals to determine the evolutionary origin of morphological novelties and developmental processes.

evolutionary divergence A process whereby natural selection or genetic drift causes populations to become more different over time.

excretion The process that helps maintain the body's water and ion balance while ridding the body of metabolic wastes.

exodermis In the roots of some plants, an outer layer of root cortex that may limit water losses from roots and help regulate the absorption of ions.

exoskeleton A hard external covering of an animal's body that blocks the passage of water and provides support and protection.

exotoxin A toxic protein that leaks from or is secreted from a bacterium and interferes with the biochemical processes of body cells in various ways.

experimental data Information that describes the result of a careful manipulation of the system under study.

experimental variable The variable to which any difference in observations of experimental treatment subjects and control treatment subjects is attributed.

extinction The death of the last individual in a species or the last species in a lineage.

extracellular digestion Digestion that takes place outside body cells, in a pouch or tube enclosed within the body.

eye The organ animals use to sense light.

facultative anaerobe An organism that can live in the presence or absence of oxygen, using oxygen when it is present and living by fermentation under anaerobic conditions.

family A Linnaean taxonomic category that ranks below an order and above a genus.

fat Neutral lipid that is semisolid at biological temperatures.

fatty acid One of two components of a neutral lipid, containing a single hydrocarbon chain with a carboxyl group linked at one end.

feather A sturdy, lightweight structure of birds, derived from scales in the skin of their ancestors.

feces Condensed and compacted digestive contents in the large intestine.

fibre In sclerenchyma, an elongated, tapered, thick-walled cell that gives plant tissue its flexible strength.

fibrous root system A root system that consists of branching roots rather than a main taproot; roots tend to spread laterally from the base of the stem.

filament In flowers, the stalk of a stamen, which supports the anther.

fission The mode of asexual reproduction in which the parent separates into two or more offspring of approximately equal size.

flagellum (plural, flagella) A long, threadlike, cellular appendage responsible for movement; found in both prokaryotes and eukaryotes, but with different structures and modes of locomotion.

flower The reproductive structure of angiosperms, consisting of floral parts grouped on a stem; the structure in which seeds develop.

food vacuole A membrane-bound sac used for digestion.

food web A set of interconnected food chains with multiple links.

fossil The remains or traces of an organism of a past geologic age embedded and preserved in Earth's crust.

founder effect An evolutionary phenomenon in which a population that was established by just a few colonizing individuals has only a fraction of the genetic diversity seen in the population from which it was derived.

fragmentation A type of vegetative reproduction in plants in which cells or a piece of the parent break off and then develop into new individuals.

frequency-dependent selection A form of natural selection in which rare phenotypes have a selective advantage simply because they are rare.

fruit A mature ovary, often with accessory parts, from a flower.

fruiting body In some fungi, a stalked, spore-producing structure such as a mushroom.

gallbladder The organ that stores bile between meals, when no digestion is occurring.

gametangiuma A cell or organ in which gametes are produced.

gamete A haploid cell, and egg or sperm. Haploid cells fuse during sexual reproduction to form a diploid zygote.

gametic isolation A prezygotic reproductive isolating mechanism caused by incompatibility between the sperm of one species and the eggs of another; may prevent fertilization.

gametophyte An individual of the haploid generation produced when a spore germinates and grows directly by mitotic divisions in organisms that undergo alternation of generations.

ganglion A functional concentration of nervous system tissue composed principally of nerve cell bodies, usually lying outside the central nervous system.

gastrodermis The derivative of endoderm that lines the gastrovascular cavity of radially symmetrical animals and forms the epithelial lining of the midgut in bilaterally symmetrical anmals.

gastrovascular cavity A saclike body cavity with a single opening, a mouth, which serves both digestive and circulatory functions.

gemma (plural, gemmae) Small cell mass that forms in cuplike growths on a thallus.

gemmules Clusters of cells with a resistant covering that allows them to survive unfavourable conditions.

gene A unit containing the code for a protein molecule or one of its parts, or for functioning RNA molecules such as tRNA and rRNA.

gene flow The transfer of genes from one population to another through the movement of individuals or their gametes.

gene pool The sum of all alleles at all gene loci in all individuals in a population.

gene-for-gene recognition A mechanism in which plants can detect an attack by a specific pathogen; the product of a specific plant gene interacts with the product of a specific pathogen gene, triggering the plant's defensive response.

generalized transduction Transfer of bacterial genes between bacteria using virulent phages that have incorporated random DNA fragments of the bacterial genome.

genetic drift Random fluctuations in allele frequencies as a result of chance events; usually reduces genetic variation in a population.

genetic engineering The use of DNA technologies to alter genes for practical purposes.

genetic equilibrium The point at which neither the allele frequencies nor the genotype frequencies in a population change in succeeding generations.

genotype frequency The percentage of individuals in a population possessing a particular genotype.

genus A Linnaean taxonomic category ranking below a family and above a species.

germ layer The layers (up to three) of cells produced during the early development of the embryo of most animals.

gestation The period of mammalian development in which the embryo develops in the uterus of the mother.

gibberellin Any of a large family of plant hormones that regulate aspects of growth, including cell elongation.

gill A respiratory organ formed as evagination of the body that extends outward into the respiratory medium.

gill arch One of the series of curved supporting structures between the slits in the pharynx of a chordate.

gill slit One of the openings in the pharynx of a chordate through which water passes out of the pharynx.

Ginkgophyta A plant phylum with a single living species, the ginkgo (or maidenhair) tree.

gland A cell or group of cells that produces and releases substances nearby, in another part of the body, or to the outside.

glycogen Energy-providing carbohydrates stored in animal cells.

glycolysis Stage of cellular respiration in which sugars such as glucose are partially oxidized and broken down into smaller molecules.

Gnathostomata The group of vertebrates with movable jaws.

gradualism The view that Earth and its living systems changed slowly over its history.

gradualist hypothesis The hypothesis that large changes in either geologic features or biological lineages result from the slow, continuous accumulation of small changes over time.

Gram stain procedure A procedure of staining bacteria to distinguish between types of bacteria with different cell wall compositions.

Gram-negative Describing bacteria that do not retain the stain used in the Gram stain procedure.

Gram-positive Describing bacteria that appear purple when stained using the Gram stain technique.

gravitropism A directional growth response to Earth's gravitational pull that is induced by mechanical and hormonal influences.

ground meristem The primary meristematic tissue in plants that gives rise to ground tissues, mostly parenchyma.

ground tissue system One of the three basic tissue systems in plants; includes all tissues other than dermal and vascular tissues.

guard cell Either of a pair of specialized crescent-shaped cells that control the opening and closing of stomata in plant tissue.

guttation The exudation of water from leaves as a result of strong root pressure.

gymnosperm A seed plant that produces "naked" seeds not enclosed in an ovary.

H$^+$ pump *See* proton pump.

habitat fragmentation A process in which remaining areas of intact habitat are reduced to small, isolated patches.

half-life The time it takes for half of a given amount of a radioisotope to decay.

Hardy–Weinberg principle An evolutionary rule of thumb that specifies the conditions under which a population of diploid organisms achieves genetic equilibrium.

head The anteriormost part of the body, containing the brain, sensory structures, and feeding apparatus.

head–foot In molluscs, the region of the body that provides the major means of locomotion and contains concentrations of nervous system tissues and sense organs.

heartwood The inner core of a woody stem; composed of dry tissue and nonliving cells that no longer transport water and solutes and may store resins, tannins, and other defensive compounds.

heat-shock protein (HSP) Any of a group of chaperone proteins that are present in all cells in all life forms. They are induced when a cell undergoes various types of environmental stresses such as heat, cold, and oxygen deprivation.

helical virus A virus in which the protein subunits of the coat assemble in a rodlike spiral around the genome.

hemocoel A cavity in the body of some coelomic invertebrates (arthropods and some molluscs) filled with blood. The hemocoel displaces the coelom, which persists as a small chamber surrounding the gonads or heart.

hemolymph The circulatory fluid of invertebrates with open circulatory systems, including molluscs and arthropods.

Hepatophyta The phylum that includes liverworts and their bryophyte relatives.

herbicide A compound that, at proper concentration, kills plants.

herbivore An animal that obtains energy and nutrients primarily by eating plants.

heterochrony Changes in the relative rate of development of morphological characters.

heterosporous Producing two types of spores, "male" microspores and "female" megaspores.

heterotroph An organism that acquires energy and nutrients by eating other organisms or their remains.

heterozygote advantage An evolutionary circumstance in which individuals that are heterozygous at a particular locus have higher relative fitness than either homozygote.

historical biogeography The study of the geographic distributions of plants and animals in relation to their evolutionary history.

Holocephali The chimeras, another group of cartilaginous fishes.

homeobox A region of a homeotic gene that corresponds to an amino acid section of the homeodomain.

homeodomain An encoded transcription factor of each protein that binds to a region in the promoters of the genes whose transcription it regulates.

hominid A member of a monophyletic group of primates, characterized by an erect bipedal stance, that includes modern humans and their recent ancestors.

Hominoidea The monophyletic group of primates that includes apes and humans.

homologous traits Characteristics that are similar in two species because they inherited the genetic basis of the trait from their common ancestor.

homoplasies Characteristics shared by a set of species, often because they live in similar environments, but not present in their common ancestor; often the product of convergent evolution.

homosporous Producing only one type of spore.

hormone A signalling molecule secreted by a cell that can alter the activities of any cell with receptors for it; in animals, typically a molecule produced by one tissue and transported via the bloodstream to another specific tissue to alter its physiological activity.

host A species that is fed upon by a parasite.

host race A population of insects that may be reproductively isolated from other populations of the same species as a consequence of their adaptation to feed on a specific host plant species.

hybrid breakdown A postzygotic reproductive isolating mechanism in which hybrids are capable of reproducing, but their offspring have either reduced fertility or reduced viability.

hybrid inviability A postzygotic reproductive isolating mechanism in which a hybrid individual has a low probability of survival to reproductive age.

hybrid sterility A postzygotic reproductive isolating mechanism in which hybrid offspring cannot form functional gametes.

hybrid zone A geographic area where the hybrid offspring of two divergent populations or species are common.

hybridization When two species interbreed and produce fertile offspring.

hydrogen bond Noncovalent bond formed by unequal electron sharing between hydrogen atoms and oxygen, nitrogen, or sulphur atoms.

hydrolysis Reaction in which the components of a water molecule are added to functional groups as molecules are broken into smaller subunits.

hydrosphere The component of the biosphere that encompasses all of the waters on Earth, including oceans, rivers, and polar ice caps.

hydrostatic skeleton A structure consisting of muscles and fluid that, by themselves, provide support for the animal or part of the animal; no rigid support, such as a bone, is involved.

hyomandibular bones Bones that support the hyoid and throat.

hypersensitive response A plant defence that physically cordons off an infection site by surrounding it with dead cells.

hypertonic Solution containing dissolved substances at higher concentrations than the cells it surrounds.

hypha (plural, hyphae) Any of the threadlike filaments that form the mycelium of a fungus.

hypocotyl The region of a plant embryo's vertical axis between the cotyledons and the radicle.

hypothesis A "working explanation" of observed facts.

hypotonic Solution containing dissolved substances at lower concentrations than the cells it surrounds.

imbibition The movement of water into a seed as the water molecules are attracted to hydrophilic groups of stored proteins; the first step in germination.

imperfect flower A type of incomplete flower that has stamens or carpels, but not both.

inbreeding A special form of nonrandom mating in which genetically related individuals mate with each other.

incisors Flattened, chisel-shaped teeth of mammals, located at the front of the mouth, that are used to nip or cut food.

incomplete metamorphosis In certain insects, a life cycle characterized by the absence of a pupal stage between the immature and adult stages.

incurrent siphon A muscular tube that brings water containing oxygen and food into the body of an invertebrate.

indeterminate cleavage A type of cleavage, observed in many deuterostomes, in which the developmental fates of the first few cells produced by mitosis are not determined as soon as cells are produced.

indeterminate growth Growth that is not limited by an organism's genetic program, so that the organism grows for as long as it lives; typical of many plants. *Compare* determinate growth.

inheritance The transmission of DNA (that is, genetic information) from one generation to the next.

initial A plant cell that remains permanently as part of a meristem and gives rise to daughter cells that differentiate into specialized cell types.

inner boundary membrane Membrane lying just inside the outer boundary membrane of a chloroplast, enclosing the stroma.

inner mitochondrial membrane Membrane surrounding the mitochondrial matrix.

instar The stage between successive moults in insects and other arthropods.

intermediate-day plant A plant that flowers only when day length falls between the values for long-day and short-day plants.

internode The region between two nodes on a plant stem.

intertidal zone The shoreline that is alternately submerged and exposed by tides.

intestinal villus A microscopic, fingerlike extension in the lining of the small intestine.

intestine The portion of digestive system where organic matter is hydrolyzed by enzymes secreted into the digestive tube. As muscular contractions of the intestinal wall move the mixture along, cells lining the intestine absorb the molecular subunits produced by digestion.

intracellular digestion The process in which cells take in food particles by endocytosis.

invagination The process in which cells changing shape and pushing inward from the surface produce an indentation, such as the dorsal lip of the blastopore.

invertebrate An animal without a vertebral column.

ion A positively or negatively charged atom.

iris Of the eye, the coloured muscular membrane that lies behind the cornea and in front of the lens, which by opening or closing determines the size of the pupil and hence the amount of light entering the eye.

isotope A distinct form of the atoms of an element, with the same number of protons but a different number of neutrons.

jasmonate Any of a group of plant hormones that help regulate aspects of growth and responses to stress, including attacks by predators and pathogens.

karyogamy In plants, the fusion of two sexually compatible haploid nuclei after cell fusion (plasmogamy).

keeled sternum The ventrally extended breastbone of a bird to which the flight muscles attach.

kingdom A Linnaean taxonomic category that ranks below a domain and above a phylum.

kingdom Animalia The taxonomic kingdom that includes all living and extinct animals.

kingdom Fungi The taxonomic kingdom that includes all living or extinct fungi.

kingdom Plantae The taxonomic kingdom encompassing all living or extinct plants.

kingdom Protoctista A diverse and polyphyletic group of single-celled and multicellular eukaryotic species.

Korarchaeota A group of Archaea recognized solely on the basis of rRNA coding sequences in DNA taken from environmental samples.

landscape ecology The field that examines how large-scale ecological factors—such as the distribution of plants, topography, and human activity—influence local populations and communities.

larva (larval form) A sexually immature stage in the life cycle of many animals that is morphologically distinct from the adult.

latent phase The time during which a virus remains in the cell in an inactive form.

lateral bud A bud on the side of a plant stem from which a branch may grow.

lateral line system The complex of mechanoreceptors along the sides of some fishes and aquatic amphibians that detect vibrations in the water.

lateral meristem A plant meristem that gives rise to secondary tissue growth. *Compare* primary meristem.

lateral root A root that extends away from the main root (or taproot).

lateral-line system The complex of organs and sensory receptors along the sides of many fishes and amphibians that detects vibrations in water.

leaf primordium A lateral outgrowth from the apical meristem that develops into a young leaf.

lens The transparent, biconvex intraocular tissue that helps bring rays of light to a focus on the retina.

Lepidosauromorpha A monophyletic lineage of diapsids that includes both marine and terrestrial animals, represented today by sphenodontids, lizards, and snakes.

lichen A single vegetative body that is the result of an association between a fungus and a photosynthetic partner, often an alga.

life cycle The sequential stages through which individuals develop, grow, maintain themselves, and reproduce.

light The portion of the electromagnetic spectrum that humans can detect with their eyes.

lignification The deposition of lignin in plant cell walls; it anchors the cellulose fibres in the walls, making them stronger and more rigid, and protects the other wall components from physical or chemical damage.

lignin A tough, rather inert polymer that strengthens the secondary walls of various plant cells and thus helps vascular plants grow taller and stay erect on land.

lipopolysaccharide A large molecule that consists of a lipid and a carbohydrate joined by a covalent bond.

lithosphere The component of the biosphere that includes the rocks, sediments, and soils of the crust.

liver A large organ whose many functions include aiding in digestion, removing toxins from the body, and regulating the chemicals in the blood.

loam Any well-aerated soil composed of a mixture of sand, clay, silt, and organic matter.

long-day plant A plant that flowers in spring when dark periods become shorter and day length becomes longer.

lophophore The circular or U-shaped fold with one or two rows of hollow, ciliated tentacles that surrounds the mouth of brachiopods, bryozoans, and phoronids and is used to gather food.

lung One of a pair of invaginated respiratory surfaces, buried in the body interior where they are less susceptible to drying out; the organs of respiration in mammals, birds, reptiles, and most amphibians.

Lycophyta The plant phylum that includes club mosses and their close relatives.

lysed Refers to a cell that has ruptured or undergone lysis.

lysogenic cycle Cycle in which the DNA of the bacteriophage is integrated into the DNA of the host bacterial cell and may remain for many generations.

lytic cycle The series of events from infection of one bacterial cell by a phage through the release of progeny phages from lysed cells.

macroevolution Large-scale evolutionary patterns in the history of life, producing major changes in species and higher taxonomic groups.

macromolecule A very large molecule assembled by the covalent linkage of smaller subunit molecules.

macronucleus In ciliophorans, a single large nucleus that develops from a micronucleus but loses all genes except those required for basic "housekeeping" functions of the cell and for ribosomal RNAs.

macrophage A phagocyte that takes part in nonspecific defences and adaptive immunity.

magnification The ratio of an object as viewed to its real size.

magnoliids An angiosperm group that includes magnolias, laurels, and avocados; they are more closely related to monocots than to eudicots.

Malpighian tubule The main organ of excretion and osmoregulation in insects, helping them maintain water and electrolyte balance.

mandible In arthropods, one of the paired head appendages posterior to the mouth used for feeding. In vertebrates, the lower jaw.

mantle One or two folds of the body wall that lines the shell and secretes the substance that forms the shell in molluscs.

mantle cavity The protective chamber produced by the mantle in many molluscs.

marsupium An external pouch on the abdomen of many female marsupials, containing the mammary glands, and within which the young continue to develop after birth.

mastax The toothed grinding organ at the anterior of the digestive tract in rotifers.

mating The pairing of a male and a female for the purpose of sexual reproduction.

mating type A genetically defined strain of an organism (such as a fungus) that can only mate with an organism of the opposite mating type; mating types are often designated + and −.

maxilla (plural, maxillae) One of the paired head appendages posterior to the mouth used for feeding in arthropods.

mechanical isolation A prezygotic reproductive isolating mechanism caused by differences in the structure of reproductive organs or other body parts.

medusa (plural, medusae) The tentacled, usually bell-shaped, free-swimming sexual stage in the life cycle of a coelenterate.

megapascal A unit of pressure used to measure water potential.

megaspore A plant spore that develops into a female gametophyte; usually larger than a microspore.

membrane potential An electrical voltage that measures the potential inside a cell membrane relative to the fluid just outside; it is negative under resting conditions and becomes positive during an action potential.

meristem An undifferentiated, permanently embryonic plant tissue that gives rise to new cells forming tissues and organs.

mesenteries Sheets of loose connective tissue, covered on both surfaces with epithelial cells, which suspend the abdominal organs in the coelom and provide lubricated, smooth surfaces that prevent chafing or abrasion between adjacent structures as the body moves.

mesoderm The middle layer of the three primary germ layers of an animal embryo, from which the muscular, skeletal, vascular, and connective tissues develop.

mesoglea A layer of gel-like connective tissue separating the gastrodermis and epidermis in radially symmetrical animals. It contains widely dispersed amoeboid cells.

mesohyl The gelatinous middle layer of cells lining the body cavity of a sponge.

mesophyll The ground tissue located between the two outer leaf tissues, composed of loosely packed parenchyma cells that contain chloroplasts.

metabolism The biochemical reactions that allow a cell or organism to extract energy from its surroundings and use that energy to maintain itself, grow, and reproduce.

metamorphosis A reorganization of the form of certain animals during postembryonic development.

metanephridium (plural, metanephridia) The excretory tubule of most annelids and molluscs.

microevolution Small-scale genetic changes within populations, often in response to shifting environmental circumstances or chance events.

micronucleus In ciliophorans, one or more diploid nuclei that contains a complete complement of genes, functioning primarily in cellular reproduction.

micropyle A small opening at one end of an ovule through which the pollen tube passes prior to fertilization.

microscope Instrument of microscopy with different magnifications and resolutions of specimens.

microscopy Technique for producing visible images of objects that are too small to be seen by the human eye.

microspore A plant spore from which a male gametophyte develops; usually smaller than a megaspore.

microsporidium (plural, microsporidia) A fungal parasite of animals; many mycologists believe that they make up a possible sixth phylum within the kingdom Fungi.

microvilli Fingerlike projections forming a brush border in epithelial cells that cover the villi.

middle ear The air-filled cavity containing three small, interconnected bones: the malleus, incus, and stapes.

middle lamella Layer of gel-like polysaccharides that holds together walls of adjacent plant cells.

migration The predictable seasonal movement of animals from the area where they are born to a distant and initially unfamiliar destination, returning to their birth site later.

minimum viable population size The smallest population size that is likely to survive both predictable and unpredictable environmental variation.

mitochondrion Membrane-bound organelle responsible for synthesis of most of the ATP in eukaryotic cells.

mitosis Nuclear division that produces daughter nuclei that are exact genetic copies of the parental nucleus.

modern synthesis A unified theory of evolution developed in the middle of the twentieth century.

molars Posteriormost teeth of mammals, with a broad chewing surface for grinding food.

mould Asexual, spore-producing stage of many multicellular fungi.

molecular clock A technique for dating the time of divergence of two species or lineages, based on the number of molecular sequence differences between them.

molecule A unit composed of atoms combined chemically in fixed numbers and ratios.

monocot A plant belonging to the Monocotyledones, one of the two major classes of angiosperms; monocot embryos have a single seed leaf (cotyledon) and pollen grains with a single groove.

monoecious Having both "male" flowers (which possess only stamens) and "female" flowers (which possess only carpels).

monomers Identical or nearly identical subunits that link together to form polymers during polymerization.

monophyletic taxon A group of organisms that includes a single ancestral species and all of its descendants.

monotreme A lineage of mammals that lay eggs instead of bearing live young.

morphogenesis Orderly, genetically programmed changes in the size, shape, and proportion of body parts of an organism; the process by which specialized tissues and organs form.

Morphological Species Concept The concept that all individuals of a species share measurable traits that distinguish them from individuals of other species.

mosaic evolution The tendency of characteristics to undergo different rates of evolutionary change within the same lineage.

motif A highly specialized region in a protein produced by the three-dimensional arrangement of amino acid chains within and between domains.

motile Capable of self-propelled movement.

multicellular organism Individual consisting of interdependent cells.

multiple fruit A fruit that develops from several ovaries in multiple flowers; examples are pineapples and mulberries.

Multiregional Hypothesis A hypothesis proposing that after archaic humans migrated from Africa to many regions on Earth, their different populations evolved into modern humans simultaneously.

mutualism A symbiotic interaction between species in which both partners benefit.

mycelium A network of branching hyphae that constitutes the body of a multicellular fungus.

mycobiont The fungal component of a lichen.

mycorrhiza A mutualistic symbiosis in which fungal hyphae associate intimately with plant roots.

nastic movement In plants, a reversible response to nondirectional stimuli, such as mechanical pressure or humidity.

natural history The branch of biology that examines the form and variety of organisms in their natural environments.

natural selection The evolutionary process by which alleles that increase the likelihood of survival and the reproductive output of the individuals that carry them become more common in subsequent generations.

natural theology A belief that knowledge of God may be acquired through the study of natural phenomena.

nematocyst A coiled thread, encapsulated in a cnidocyte, that cnidarians fire at prey or predators, sometimes releasing a toxin through its tip.

nerve A bundle of axons enclosed in connective tissue and all following the same pathway.

nerve cord A bundle of nerves that extends from the central ganglia to the rest of the body, connected to smaller nerves.

nerve net A simple nervous system that coordinates responses to stimuli but has no central control organ or brain.

neutral variation hypothesis An evolutionary hypothesis that some variation at gene loci coding for enzymes and other soluble proteins is neither favoured nor eliminated by natural selection.

nitrogen cycle A biogeochemical cycle that moves nitrogen between the huge atmospheric pool of gaseous molecular nitrogen and several much smaller pools of nitrogen-containing compounds in soils, marine and freshwater ecosystems, and living organisms.

node The point on a stem where one or more leaves are attached.

nondisjunction The failure of homologous pairs to separate during the first meiotic division or of chromatids to separate during the second meiotic division.

nonvascular plant *See* bryophyte.

notochord A flexible rodlike structure constructed of fluid-filled cells surrounded by tough connective tissue, which supports a chordate embryo from head to tail.

nuclear envelope In eukaryotes, membranes separating the nucleus from the cytoplasm.

nucleoid The central region of a prokaryotic cell with no boundary membrane separating it from the cytoplasm, where DNA replication and RNA transcription occur.

nucleoplasm The liquid or semiliquid substance within the nucleus.

nucleotide The monomer of nucleic acids consisting of a five-carbon sugar, a nitrogenous base, and a phosphate.

nucleus The central region of eukaryotic cells, separated by membranes from the surrounding cytoplasm, where DNA replication and messenger RNA transcription occur.

null hypothesis A statement of what would be seen if the hypothesis being tested were wrong.

null model A conceptual model that predicts what one would see if a particular factor had no effect.

nutrition The processes by which an organism takes in, digests, absorbs, and converts food into organic compounds.

obligate aerobe A microorganism that uses oxygen for cellular respiration and requires oxygen in its surroundings to support growth.

obligate anaerobe A microorganism that cannot use oxygen and can grow only in the absence of oxygen.

observational data Basic information on biological structures or the details of biological processes.

oligosaccharin A complex carbohydrate that in plants serves as a signalling molecule and as a defence against pathogens.

open circulatory system An arrangement of internal transport in some invertebrates in which the vascular fluid, hemolymph, is released into sinuses, bathing organs directly, and is not always retained within vessels.

operculum A lid or flap of the bone serving as the gill cover in some fishes.

oral hood Soft fleshy structure at the anterior end of a cephalochordate that frames the opening of the mouth.

order A Linnaean taxonomic category of organisms that ranks above a family and below a class.

organic acid (carboxylic acid) Acid for which the characteristic functional group is a carboxyl group (—COOH).

organic molecule Molecule based on carbon.

orthogenesis An obsolete theory that evolution is goal oriented, striving to perfect organisms.

ostracoderm One of an assortment of extinct, jawless fishes that were covered with bony armour.

outer boundary membrane A smooth membrane that surrounds a chloroplast, enclosing the stroma.

outer membrane In Gram-negative bacteria, an additional boundary membrane that covers the peptidoglycan layer of the cell wall.

outgroup comparison A technique used to identify ancestral and derived characters by comparing the group under study with more distantly related species that are not otherwise included in the analysis.

ovary In animals, the female gonad, which produces female gametes and reproductive hormones. In flowering plants, the enlarged base of a carpel in which one or more ovules develop into seeds.

overexploitation The excessive harvesting of an animal or plant species, potentially leading to its extinction.

ovule In plants, the structure in a carpel in which a female gametophyte develops and fertilization takes place.

paleobiology The study of ancient organisms.

parapatric speciation Speciation between populations with adjacent geographic distributions.

paraphyletic taxon A group of organisms that includes an ancestral species and some, but not all, of its descendants.

parapodia Fleshy lateral extensions of the body wall of aquatic annelids, used for locomotion and gas exchange.

parasite An organism that feeds on the tissues of or otherwise exploits its host.

parasitism A symbiotic interaction in which one species, the parasite, uses another, the host, in a way that is harmful to the host.

parthenogenesis A mode of asexual reproduction in which animals produce offspring by the growth and development of an egg without fertilization.

passive transport The transport of substances across cell membranes without expenditure of energy, as in diffusion.

pathogenesis-related (PR) protein A hydrolytic enzyme that breaks down components of a pathogen's cell wall.

pectoral girdle A bony or cartilaginous structure in vertebrates that supports and is attached to the forelimbs.

pedicellariae Small pincers at the base of short spines in starfishes and sea urchins.

pedipalp The second pair of appendages in the head of chelicerates.

pedomorphosis A common form of heterochrony in which juvenile characteristics are retained in a reproductive adult.

pelagic province The water in a marine biome.

pellicle A layer of supportive protein fibres located inside the cell, just under the plasma membrane, providing strength and flexibility instead of a cell wall.

pelvic girdle A bony or cartilaginous structure in vertebrates that supports and is attached to the hindlimbs.

peptidoglycan A polymeric substance formed from a polysaccharide backbone tied together by short polypeptides, which is the primary structural molecule of bacterial cell walls.

perennial A plant in which vegetative growth and reproduction continue year after year.

perfect flower A flower that has both male (stamen) and female (carpel) sexual organs.

pericarp The fruit wall.

periderm The outermost portion of bark; consists of cork, cork cambium, and secondary cortex.

peritoneum The thin tissue derived from mesoderm that lines the abdominal wall and covers most of the organs in the abdomen.

peroxisome Microbody that produces hydrogen peroxide as a by-product.

petal Part of the corolla of a flower, often brightly coloured.

petiole The stalk by which a leaf is attached to a stem.

phage *See* bacteriophage.

pharynx The throat. In some invertebrates, a protrusible tube used to bring food into the mouth for passage to the gastrovascular cavity; in mammals, the common pathway for air entering the larynx and food entering the esophagus.

phenotypic variation Differences in appearance or function between individual organisms.

phloem The food-conducting tissue of a vascular plant.

phloem sap The solution of water and organic compounds that flows rapidly through the sieve tubes of flowering plants.

phosphate group Group consisting of a central phosphorus atom held in four linkages: two that bind —OH groups to the central phosphorus atom, a third that binds an oxygen atom to the central phosphorus atom, and a fourth that links the phosphate group to an oxygen atom.

phosphorylation The addition of a phosphate group to a molecule.

photoautotroph A photosynthetic organism that uses light as its energy source and carbon dioxide as its carbon source.

photobiont The photosynthetic component of a lichen.

photoheterotroph An organism that uses light as the ultimate energy source but obtains carbon in organic form rather than as carbon dioxide.

photoperiodism The response of plants to changes in the relative lengths of light and dark periods in their environment during each 24-hour period.

photophosphorylation The synthesis of ATP coupled to the transfer of electrons energized by photons of light.

photopigment Light-absorbing pigment.

photopsin One of three photopigments in which retinal is combined with different opsins.

photosynthesis The conversion of light energy to chemical energy in the form of sugar and other organic molecules.

photosystem A large complex into which the light-absorbing pigments for photosynthesis are organized with proteins and other molecules.

photosystem II In photosynthesis, a protein complex in the thylakoid membrane that uses energy absorbed from sunlight to synthesize ATP.

phototropism The tendency of a plant shoot to bend toward a source of light.

PhyloCode A formal set of rules governing phylogenetic nomenclature.

phylogenetic species concept A concept that seeks to delineate species as the smallest aggregate population that can be united by shared derived characters.

phylogenetic tree A branching diagram depicting the evolutionary relationships of groups of organisms.

phylogeny The evolutionary history of a group of organisms.

phylum (plural, phyla) A major Linnaean division of a kingdom, ranking above a class.

physiological respiration The process by which animals exchange gases with their surroundings—how they take in oxygen from the outside environment and deliver it to body cells and remove carbon dioxide from body cells and deliver it to the environment.

phytoalexin A biochemical that functions as an antibiotic in plants.

phytochrome A blue-green pigmented plant chromoprotein involved in the regulation of light-dependent growth processes.

phytoplankton Microscopic, free-flowing aquatic plants and protists.

pigment A molecule that can absorb photons of light.

pinacoderm In sponges, an unstratified outer layer of cells.

pith The soft, spongelike, central cylinder of the stems of most flowering plants, composed mainly of parenchyma.

placenta A specialized temporary organ that connects the embryo and fetus with the uterus in mammals, mediating the delivery of oxygen and nutrients. Analagous structures occur in other animals.

plasmid A DNA molecule in the cytoplasm of certain prokaryotes, which often contains genes with functions that supplement those in the nucleoid and which can replicate independently of the nucleoid DNA and be passed along during cell division.

plasmodesma A minute channel that perforates a cell wall and contains extensions of the cytoplasm that directly connect adjacent plant cells.

plasmodial slime mould A slime mould of the class Myxomycetes.

plasmodium The composite mass of plasmodial slime moulds consisting of individual nuclei suspended in a common cytoplasm surrounded by a single plasma membrane.

plasmogamy The sexual stage of fungi during which the cytoplasms of two genetically different partners fuse.

plasmolysis Condition due to outward osmotic movement of water, in which plant cells shrink so much that they retract from their walls.

plastids A family of plant organelles.

plastron The ventral part of the shell of a turtle.

plate tectonics The geologic theory describing how Earth's crust is broken into irregularly shaped plates of rock that float on its semisolid mantle.

plumule The rudimentary terminal bud of a plant embryo located at the end of the hypocotyl, consisting of the epicotyl and a cluster of tiny foliage leaves.

poikilohydric Having little control over internal water content.

polar nucleus In the embryo sac of a flowering plant, one of two nuclei that migrate into the centre of the sac, become housed in a central cell, and eventually give rise to endosperm.

polar transport Unidirectional movement of a substance from one end of a cell (or other structure) to the other.

pollen grain The male gametophyte of a seed plant.

pollen sac The microsporangium of a seed plant, in which pollen develops.

pollen tube A tube that grows from a germinating pollen grain through the tissues of a carpel and carries the sperm cells to the ovary.

pollination The transfer of pollen to a flower's reproductive parts by air currents or on the bodies of animal pollinators.

pollutant Materials or energy in a form or quantity that organisms do not usually encounter.

polyhedral virus A virus in which the coat proteins form triangular units that fit together like the parts of a geodesic sphere.

polymorphic development The production during development of one or more morphologically distinct forms.

polymorphism The existence of discrete variants of a character among individuals in a population.

polyp The tentacled, usually sessile stage in the life cycle of a coelenterate.

polypeptide The chain of amino acids formed by sequential peptide bonds.

polyphyletic taxa A group of organisms that belong to different evolutionary lineages and do not share a recent common ancestor.

polysaccharide Chain with more than 10 linked monosaccharide subunits.

population All individuals of a single species that live together in the same place and time.

population bottleneck An evolutionary event that occurs when a stressful factor reduces population size greatly and eliminates some alleles from a population.

population genetics The branch of science that studies the prevalence and variation in genes among populations of individuals.

posterior Indicating the tail end of an animal.

postzygotic isolating mechanism A reproductive isolating mechanism that acts after zygote formation.

preadaptation A characteristic evolved by an ancestral species that serves an adaptive but different function in a descendant species or population.

precocial Born with fur and quickly mobile.

prediction A statement about what the researcher expects to happen to one variable if another variable changes.

pregnancy The period of mammalian development in which the embryo develops in the uterus of the mother.

premolars Teeth located in pairs on each side of the upper and lower jaws of mammals, positioned behind the canines and in front of the molars.

pressure flow mechanism In vascular plants, pressure that builds up at the source end of a sieve tube system and pushes solutes by bulk flow toward a sink, where they are removed.

prezygotic isolating mechanism A reproductive isolating mechanism that acts prior to the production of a zygote, or fertilized egg.

primary cell wall The initial cell wall laid down by a plant cell.

primary endosymbiosis In the model for the origin of plastids in eukaryotes, the first event in which a eukaryotic cell engulfed a photosynthetic cyanobacterium.

primary growth The growth of plant tissues derived from apical meristems. *Compare* secondary growth.

primary meristem Root and shoot apical meristems, from which a plant's primary tissues develop. *Compare* lateral meristem.

primary plant body The portion of a plant that is made up of primary tissues.

primary producer An autotroph, usually a photosynthetic organism, a member of the first trophic level.

primary structure The sequence of amino acids in a protein.

primary tissue A plant tissue that develops from an apical meristem.

principle of monophyly A guiding principle of systematic biology that defines monophyletic taxa, each of which contains a single ancestral species and all of its descendants.

principle of parsimony A principle of systematic biology that states that a particular trait is unlikely to evolve independently in separate evolutionary lineages.

prion An infectious agent that contains only protein and does not include a nucleic acid molecule.

procambium The primary meristem of a plant that develops into primary vascular tissue.

proglottid One of the segmentlike repeating units that constitute the body of a tapeworm.

prokaryote Organism in which the DNA is suspended in the cell interior without separation from other cellular components by a discrete membrane.

prokaryotic flagellum A long, threadlike protein fibre that rotates in a socket in the plasma membrane and cell wall to push a prokaryotic cell through a liquid medium.

prophage A viral genome inserted in the host cell DNA.

protein Molecules that carry out most of the activities of life, including the synthesis of all other biological molecules. A protein consists of one or more polypeptides depending on the protein.

protist Organism currently classified in the kingdom Protista.

Protoctista The kingdom that includes all of the eukaryotes that are not fungi, plants, or animals.

protoderm The primary meristem that will produce stem epidermis.

proton Positively charged particle in the nucleus of an atom.

proton pump Pump that moves hydrogen ions across membranes and pushes hydrogen ions across the plasma membrane from the cytoplasm to the cell exterior. Also referred to as H^+ *pump*.

protonema The structure that arises when a liverwort or moss spore germinates and eventually gives rise to a mature gametophyte.

protoplast The cytoplasm, organelles, and plasma membrane of a plant cell.

protostome A division of the Bilateria in which the blastopore forms the mouth during development of the embryo and the anus appears later.

pseudocoelom A fluid- or organ-filled body cavity between the gut (a derivative of endoderm) and the muscles of the body wall (a derivative of mesoderm).

pseudocoelomate A body plan of bilaterally symmetrical animals with a body cavity that lacks a complete lining derived from mesoderm.

pseudopod (plural, pseudopodia) A temporary cytoplasmic extension of a cell.

psychrophile An archaean or bacterium that grows optimally at temperatures in the range of -10 to $-20°C$.

Pterophyta The plant phylum of ferns and their close relatives.

pulvinus (plural, pulvini) A jointlike, thickened pad of tissue at the base of a leaf or petiole; flexes when the leaf makes nastic movements.

punctuated equilibrium hypothesis The evolutionary hypothesis that most morphological variation arises during speciation events in isolated populations at the edge of a species' geographic distribution.

pupa The nonfeeding stage between the larva and adult in the complete metamorphosis of some insects, during which the larval tissues are completely reorganized within a protective cocoon or hardened case.

qualitative variation Variation that exists in two or more discrete states, with intermediate forms often being absent.

quantitative variation Variation that is measured on a continuum (such as height in human beings) rather than in discrete units or categories.

quiescent centre A region in a root apical meristem where there is no cell division.

quorum sensing The use of signalling molecules by prokaryotes to communicate and to coordinate their behaviour.

R gene A resistance gene in a plant; dominant R alleles confer enhanced resistance to plant pathogens.

radial cleavage A cleavage pattern in deuterostomes in which newly formed cells lie directly above and below other cells of the embryo.

radial symmetry A body plan of organisms in which structures are arranged regularly around a central axis, like spokes radiating out from the centre of a wheel.

radicle The rudimentary root of a plant embryo.

radiometric dating A dating method that uses measurements of certain radioactive isotopes to calculate the absolute ages in years of rocks and minerals.

radula The tooth-lined "tongue" of molluscs that scrapes food into small particles or drills through the shells of prey.

receptacle The expanded tip of a flower stalk that bears floral organs.

recognition protein Protein in the plasma membrane that identifies a cell as part of the same individual or as foreign.

recombination The physical exchange of segments between the chromatids of homologous chromosomes or between the chromosomes of prokaryotic cells or viruses.

red tide A growth in dinoflagellate populations that causes red, orange, or brown discoloration of coastal ocean waters.

reinforcement The enhancement of reproductive isolation that had begun to develop while populations were geographically separated.

relative abundance The relative commonness of populations within a community.

relative fitness The number of surviving offspring that an individual produces compared with the number left by others in the population.

reproductive isolating mechanism A biological characteristic that prevents the gene pools of two species from mixing.

respiratory surface A layer of epithelial cells that provides the interface between the body and the respiratory medium.

respiratory system All parts of the body involved in exchanging air between the external environment and the blood.

retina A light-sensitive membrane lining the posterior part of the inside of the eye.

rhizoid A modified hypha that anchors a fungus to its substrate and absorbs moisture.

rhizome A horizontal, modified stem that can penetrate a substrate and anchor the plant.

rhynchocoel A coelomic cavity that contains the proboscis of nemerteans.

ring species A species with a geographic distribution that forms a ring around uninhabitable terrain.

rod In the vertebrate eye, a type of photoreceptor in the retina that is specialized for detection of light at low intensities.

root An anchoring structure in land plants that also absorbs water and nutrients and (in some plant species) stores food.

root cap A dome-shaped cell mass that forms a protective covering over the apical meristem in the tip of a plant root.

root hair A tubular outgrowth of the outer wall of a root epidermal cell; root hairs absorb much of a plant's water and minerals from the soil.

root pressure The pressure that develops in plant roots as the result of osmosis, forcing xylem sap upward and out through leaves. *See also* guttation.

root primordium A rudimentary root.

root system An underground (or submerged) network of roots with a large surface area that favours the rapid uptake of soil water and dissolved mineral ions.

salicylic acid (SA) In plants, a chemical synthesized following a wound that has multiple roles in plant defences, including interaction with jasmonates in signalling cascades.

saprotroph An organism nourished by dead or decaying organic matter.

sapwood The newly formed outer wood located between heartwood and the vascular cambium. Compared with heartwood, it is wet, lighter in colour, and not as strong.

savanna A biome comprising grasslands with few trees, which grows in areas adjacent to tropical deciduous forests.

schizocoelom In protostomes, the body cavity that develops as inner and outer layers of mesoderm separate.

scientific name A two-part name identifying the genus to which a species belongs and designating a particular species within that genus.

sclereid A type of sclerenchyma cell; sclereids typically are short and have thick, lignified walls.

sclerenchyma A ground tissue in which cells develop thick secondary walls, which commonly are lignified and perforated by pits through which water can pass.

sclerotium Tough mass of hyphae, often serving as a survival or overwintering structure.

scolex The anterior (head) of a tapeworm, adapted for fastening the worm to the intestinal epithelium of its host.

secondary cell wall A layer added to the cell wall of plants that is more rigid and may become many times thicker than the primary cell wall.

secondary endosymbiosis In the model for the origin of plastids in eukaryotes, the second event, in which a nonphotosynthetic eukaryote engulfed a photosynthetic eukaryote.

secondary growth Plant growth that originates at lateral meristems and increases the diameter of older roots and stems. *Compare* primary growth.

secondary metabolite Organic compound not required for the growth or survival of an organism; tends to be biologically active.

secondary tissue In plants, the tissue that develops from lateral meristems.

secretion A selective process in which specific small molecules and ions are transported from the body fluids (in animals with open circulatory systems) or blood (in animals with closed circulatory systems) into the excretory tubules.

seed The structure that forms when an ovule matures after a pollen grain reaches it and a sperm fertilizes the egg.

seed coat The outer protective covering of a seed.

segmentation The production of body parts and some organ systems in repeating units.

selectively neutral *See* neutral variation hypothesis.

selectively permeable Membranes that selectively allow, impede, or block the passage of atoms and molecules.

self-incompatibility In plants, the inability of a plant's pollen to fertilize ovules of the same plant.

senescence The biologically complex process of aging in mature organisms that leads to the death of cells and eventually the whole organism.

sensor A tissue or organ that detects a change in an external or internal factor such as pH, temperature, or the concentration of a molecule such as glucose.

sepal One of the separate, usually green parts forming the calyx of a flower.

septum (plural, septa) A thin partition or cross wall that separates body segments.

sessile Unable to move from one place to another.

seta (plural, setae) A chitin-reinforced bristle that protrudes outward from the body wall in some annelid worms.

sex chromosomes Chromosomes that are different in male and female individuals of the same species.

sexual dimorphism Differences in the size or appearance of males and females.

sexual selection A form of natural selection established by male competition for access to females and by the females' choice of mates.

shoot system The stems and leaves of a plant.

short-day plant A plant that flowers in late summer or early autumn when dark periods become longer and light periods become shorter.

sieve tube A series of phloem cells joined end to end, forming a long tube through which nutrients are transported; seen mainly in flowering plants.

sieve tube member Any of the main conducting cells of phloem that connect end to end, forming a sieve tube.

simple fruit A fruit that develops from a single ovary; in many of them, at least one layer of the pericarp is fleshy and juicy.

sink Any region of a plant where organic substances are being unloaded from the sieve tube system and used or stored.

sinus A body space that surrounds an organ.

slime layer A coat typically composed of polysaccharides that is loosely associated with bacterial cells.

social behaviour The interactions that animals have with other members of their species.

solute The molecules of a substance dissolved in water.

solution Substance formed when molecules and ions separate and are suspended individually, surrounded by water molecules.

somatic embryo A plant embryo that is genetically identical to the parent because it arose through asexual means.

soredium (plural, soredia) A specialized cell cluster produced by lichens, consisting of a mass of algal cells surrounded by fungal hyphae; soredia function like reproductive spores and can give rise to a new lichen.

sorus (plural, sori) A cluster of sporangia on the underside of a fern frond; reproductive spores arise by meiosis inside each sporangium.

source In plants, any region (such as a leaf) where organic substances are being loaded into the sieve tube system of phloem.

source population In metapopulation analyses, a population that is either stable or increasing in size.

specialized transduction Transfer of bacterial genes between bacteria using temperate phages that have incorporated fragments of the bacterial genome as they make the transition from the lysogenic cycle to the lytic cycle.

speciation The process of species formation.

species A group of populations in which the individuals are so closely related in structure, biochemistry, and behaviour that they can successfully interbreed.

species cluster A group of closely related species recently descended from a common ancestor.

spinneret A modified abdominal appendage from which spiders secrete silk threads.

spiral cleavage The cleavage pattern in many protostomes in which newly produced cells lie in the space between the two cells immediately below them.

spiral valve A corkscrew-shaped fold of mucous membrane in the digestive system of elasmobranchs, which slows the passage of material and increases the surface area available for digestion and absorption.

spirillum (plural, spirilla) Any flagellated aerobic bacterium twisted helically like a corkscrew.

spongocoel The central cavity in a sponge.

sporangium (plural, sporangia) A single-celled or multicellular structure in fungi and plants in which spores are produced.

spore A haploid reproductive structure, usually a single cell, that can develop into a new individual without fusing with another cell; found in plants, fungi, and certain protists.

sporophyll A specialized leaf that bears sporangia (spore-producing structures).

sporophyte An individual of the diploid generation produced through fertilization in organisms that undergo alternation of generations; it produces haploid spores.

squalene A liver oil found in sharks that is lighter than water, which increases their buoyancy.

stabilizing selection A type of natural selection in which individuals expressing intermediate phenotypes have the highest relative fitness.

stamen A "male" reproductive organ in flowers, consisting of an anther (pollen producer) and a slender filament.

stapes The smallest of three sound-conducting bones in the middle ear of tetrapod vertebrates.

starch Energy-providing carbohydrates stored in plant cells.

statolith A movable starch- or carbonate-containing stonelike body involved in sensing gravitational pull.

stele The central core of vascular tissue in roots and shoots of vascular plants; it consists of the xylem and phloem together with supporting tissues.

steroid A type of lipid derived from cholesterol.

stigma The receptive end of a carpel where deposited pollen germinates.

stoma (plural, stomata) The opening between a pair of guard cells in the epidermis of a plant leaf or stem, through which gases and water vapour pass.

stomach The portion of the digestive system in which food is stored and digestion begins.

strobilus *See* cone.

style The slender stalk of a carpel situated between the ovary and the stigma in plants.

suberin A waxy, waterproof substance present in cork cells.

subspecies A taxonomic subdivision of a species.

substrate The particular reacting molecule or molecular group that an enzyme catalyzes.

succession The change from one community type to another.

surface tension The force that places surface water molecules under tension, making them more resistant to separation than the underlying water molecules.

suspensor In seed plants, a stalklike row of cells that develops from a zygote and helps position the embryo close to the nourishing endosperm.

swim bladder A gas-filled internal organ that helps fish maintain buoyancy.

symbiont An organism living in symbiosis with another organism; the symbionts are not usually closely related.

symbiosis An interspecific interaction in which the ecological relations of two or more species are intimately tied together.

symmetry (adj., symmetrical) Exact correspondence of form and constituent configuration on opposite sides of a dividing line or plane.

sympatric Occupying the same spaces at the same time.

sympatric speciation Speciation that occurs without the geographic isolation of populations.

symplastic pathway The route taken by water that moves through the cytoplasm of plant cells (the symplast). *Compare* apoplastic pathway.

symport The transport of two molecules in the same direction across a membrane. Also referred to as *cotransport*.

synapse A site where a neuron makes a communicating connection with another neuron or an effector such as a muscle fibre or gland.

synapsid One of a group of amniotes with one temporal arch on each side of the head, which includes living mammals.

systematics The branch of biology that studies the diversity of life and its evolutionary relationships.

systemic acquired resistance A plant defence response to microbial invasion; defensive chemicals including salicylic acid may spread throughout a plant, rendering healthy tissues less vulnerable to infection.

systemin A plant peptide hormone that functions in defence responses to wounds.

taiga *See* boreal forest.

taproot system A root system consisting of a single main root from which lateral roots can extend; often stores starch.

taxon (plural, taxa) A name designating a group of organisms included within a category in the Linnaean taxonomic hierarchy.

taxonomic hierarchy A system of classification based on arranging organisms into ever more inclusive categories.

taxonomy The science of the classification of organisms into an ordered system that indicates natural relationships.

temperate rain forest A coniferous forest biome supported by heavy rain and fog, which grows where winters are mild and wet and the summers are cool.

template A nucleotide chain used in DNA replication for the assembly of a complementary chain.

temporal isolation A prezygotic reproductive isolating mechanism in which species live in the same habitat but breed at different times of day or different times of year.

terminal bud A bud that develops at the apex of a shoot.

Tetrapoda A monophyletic lineage of vertebrates that includes animals with four feet, legs, or leglike appendages.

T-even bacteriophage Virulent bacteriophages, T2, T4, and T6, that have been valuable for genetic studies of bacteriophage structure and function.

thallus A plant body not differentiated into stems, roots, or leaves.

thermoregulation The control of body temperature.

thigmomorphogenesis A plant response to a mechanical disturbance, such as frequent strong winds; includes inhibition of cellular elongation and production of thick-walled supportive tissue.

thigmotropism Growth in response to contact with a solid object.

thorax The central part of an animal's body, between the head and the abdomen.

tissue A group of cells and intercellular substances with the same structure that function as a unit to carry out one or more specialized tasks.

tonoplast The membrane that surrounds the central vacuole in a plant cell.

topsoil The rich upper layer of soil where most plant roots are located; it generally consists of sand, clay particles, and humus.

torsion The realignment of body parts in gastropod molluscs that is independent of shell coiling.

totipotent Having the capacity to produce cells that can develop into or generate a new organism or body part.

trachea In insects, an extensively branched, air-conducting tube formed by invagination of the outer epidermis of the animal and reinforced by rings of chitin. In vertebrates, the windpipe, which branches into the bronchi.

tracheal system A branching network of tubes that carries air from small openings in the exoskeleton of an insect to tissues throughout its body.

tracheid A conducting cell of xylem, usually elongated and tapered.

tracheophyte A plant with xylem, phloem, and usually well-developed roots, stems, and leaves.

traditional evolutionary systematics An approach to systematics that uses phenotypic similarities and differences to infer evolutionary relationships, grouping together species that share both ancestral and derived characters.

trait A particular variation in a genetic or phenotypic character.

transduction In cell signalling, the process of changing a signal into the form necessary to cause the cellular response. In prokaryotes, the process in which DNA is transferred from donor to recipient bacterial cells by an infecting bacteriophage.

transfer cell Any of the specialized cells that form when large amounts of solutes must be loaded or unloaded into the phloem; they facilitate the short-distance transport of organic solutes from the apoplast into the symplast.

transmembrane pathway The path followed by water when it enters root cells by crossing across the plasma membrane.

transpiration The evaporation of water from a plant, principally from the leaves.

transport protein A protein embedded in the cell membrane that forms a channel allowing selected polar molecules and ions to pass across the membrane.

trichocyst A dartlike protein thread that can be discharged from a surface organelle for defence or to capture prey.

trichome A single-celled or multicellular outgrowth from the epidermis of a plant that provides protection and shade and often gives the stems or leaves a hairy appearance.

triploblastic An animal body plan in which adult structures arise from three primary germ layers: endoderm, mesoderm, and ectoderm.

trochophore The small, free-swimming, ciliated aquatic larva of various invertebrates, including certain molluscs and annelids.

trophozoite Motile, feeding stage of *Giardia* and other single-celled protists.

tropical forest Any forest that grows between the Tropics of Capricorn and Cancer, a region characterized by high temperature and rainfall and thin, nutrient-poor topsoil.

tropical rain forest A dense tropical forest biome that grows where some rain falls every month, mean annual rainfall exceeds 250 cm, mean annual temperature is at least 25°C, and humidity is above 80%.

tropism The turning or bending of an organism or one of its parts toward or away from an external stimulus, such as light, heat, or gravity.

turgor pressure The internal hydrostatic pressure within plant cells.

turgor pressure The normal fullness or tension produced by the fluid content of plant and animal cells.

tympanum A thin membrane in the auditory canal that vibrates back and forth when struck by sound waves.

undulating membrane In parabasalid protists, a finlike structure formed by a flagellum buried in a fold of the cytoplasm that facilitates movement through thick and viscous fluids. An expansion of the plasma membrane in some flagellates that is usually associated with a flagellum.

uniformitarianism The concept that the geologic processes that sculpted Earth's surface over long periods of time—such as volcanic eruptions, earthquakes, erosion, and the formation and movement of glaciers—are exactly the same as the processes observed today.

unreduced gamete A gamete that contains the same number of chromosomes as a somatic cell.

vagina The muscular canal that leads from the cervix to the exterior.

variable An environmental factor that may differ among places or an organismal characteristic that may differ among individuals.

vascular bundle A cord of plant vascular tissue; often multistranded with both xylem and phloem.

vascular cambium A lateral meristem that produces secondary vascular tissues in plants.

vascular plant *See* tracheophyte.

vascular tissue system One of the three tissue systems in plants that provide the foundation for plant organs; it consists of transport tubes for water and nutrients.

vegetative reproduction Asexual reproduction in plants by which new individuals arise (or are created) without seeds or spores; examples include fragmentation from the parent plant or the use of cuttings by gardeners.

vein In a plant, a vascular bundle that forms part of the branching network of conducting and supporting tissues in a leaf or other expanded plant organ. In an animal, a vessel that carries the blood back to the heart.

veliger A second larva that occurs after the trochophore in some molluscs.

ventral Indicating the lower or "belly" side of an animal.

vernalization The stimulation of flowering by a period of low temperature.

vertebrae The series of bones that form the vertebral column of vertebrate animals.

vertebral column The series of vertebrae that surrounds and protects the dorsal nerve cord and forms the supporting axis of the body.

vertebrate A member of the monophyletic group of tetrapod animals that possess a vertebral column.

vesicle A small, membrane-bound compartment that transfers substances between parts of the endomembrane system.

vessel In plants, one of the tubular conducting structures of xylem, typically several centimetres long; most angiosperms and some other vascular plants have xylem vessels.

vessel member Any of the short cells joined end to end in tubelike columns in xylem.

vestigial structure An anatomical feature of living organisms that no longer retains its function.

vibrio Any of various short, motile, S-shaped or comma-shaped bacteria of the genus *Vibrio*.

vicariance The fragmentation of a continuous geographic distribution by nonbiological factors.

viroid A plant pathogen that consists of strands or circles of RNA, smaller than any viral DNA or RNA molecule, that have no protein coat.

virulent bacteriophage Bacteriophage that kills its host bacterial cells during each cycle of infection.

virus An infectious agent that contains either DNA or RNA surrounded by a protein coat.

visceral mass In molluscs, the region of the body containing the internal organs.

vitamin An organic molecule required in small quantities that the animal cannot synthesize for itself.

viviparous Referring to animals that retain the embryo within the mother's body and nourish it during at least early embryo development.

water potential The potential energy of water, representing the difference in free energy between pure water and water in cells and solutions; it is the driving force for osmosis.

wavelength The distance between two successive peaks of electromagnetic radiation.

wax A substance insoluble in water that is formed when fatty acids combine with long-chain alcohols or hydrocarbon structures.

wetland A highly productive ecotone often at the border between a freshwater biome and a terrestrial biome.

wilting The drooping of leaves and stems caused by a loss of turgor.

wood The secondary xylem of trees and shrubs, lying under the bark and consisting largely of cellulose and lignin.

X chromosome Sex chromosome that occurs paired in female cells and single in male cells.

xylem The plant vascular tissue that distributes water and nutrients.

xylem sap The dilute solution of water and solutes that flows in the xylem.

Y chromosome Sex chromosome that is paired with an X chromosome in male cells.

yeast A single-celled fungus that reproduces by budding or fission.

yolk The portion of an egg that serves as the main energy source for the embryo.

zone of cell division The region in a growing root that consists of the root apical meristem and the actively dividing cells behind it.

zone of elongation The region in a root where newly formed cells grow and elongate.

zone of maturation The region in a root above the zone of elongation where cells do not increase in length but may differentiate further and take on specialized roles.

zooplankton Small, usually microscopic, animals that float in aquatic habitats.

zygospore A multinucleate, thick-walled sexual spore in some fungi that is formed from the union of two gametes.

zygote A fertilized egg.

CHAPTER 17 **373:** © Mark Moffett/Foto Natura/Minden Pictures **374:** (top) The Advertising Archives, London **374:** (a) George Vernard/Foto Natural/Photo Researchers, Inc. **374:** (b) Timothy A. Pearce, Ph.D./Section of Mollusks/Carnegie Museum of Natural History. Photograph by Mindy McNaugher **375:** Arthur Morris/VIREO **376:** (left) Eric Crichton/Bruce Coleman, Inc. **376:** (right) William E. Ferguson **381:** (top) David Neal Parks **381:** (bottom) W. Carter Johnson **382:** Frans Lanting/Minden Pictures **386:** Forrest W. Buchanan/Visuals Unlimited **386:** (top left) Modified from Weis & Abrahamson. 1986. American Naturalist 127 p. 687 **386:** (top right) Gregory K. Scott/Photo Researchers, Inc. **386:** (bottom) Heather Angel/Natural Visions **387:** (left) © 2008 Josef Hlasek **387:** (right) Modified from Andersson. 1982. Nature 299: 818–820 (Figure 1b) **390:** Modified from Cain & Sheppard. 1954. Natural selection in Cepaea. Genetics 39: 89–116. **392:** (top left) Yuri Arcurs/Shutterstock

CHAPTER 18 **395:** © Waterscan **396:** Photo by M.B. Fenton **397:** (top) Ingo Schlupp photo **397:** (bottom) From Evolutionary Ecology: Sex and the Single Killifish by Elizabeth Pennisi, Science, Vol. 313, p. 1381. Reprinted with permission from AAAS. **398:** © David Hosking / Alamy **399:** Photo by B. Clare **400:** COSEWIC **401:** (top right) Reprinted by permission from Macmillan Publishers Ltd: Nature, "Biogeography: Molecular trails from hitch-hiking snails", by Edmund Gittenberger, Dick S. J. Groenenberg, Bas Kokshoorn and Richard C. Preece, vol. 439, p. 409, copyright (2006). **401:** (bottom left) © 4nature.at / Alamy **401:** (bottom right) From Hale et al., "Impact of Landscape Management on the Genetic Structure of Red Squirrel Populations.", Science, Vol. 293, pp. 2246–2248, Sep 21, 2001. Reprinted with permission from AAAS. **402:** (bottom left) Credit: K. Roy, UCSD **402:** (bottom right) From Hale et al., "Impact of Landscape Management on the Genetic Structure of Red Squirrel Populations.", Science, Vol. 293, pp. 2246–2248, Sep 21, 2001. Reprinted with permission from AAAS. **403:** From Michael E. Hellberg, Deborah P. Balch, Kaustuv Roy, "Climate-Driven Range Expansion and Morphological Evolution in a Marine Gastropod", Science, vol. 292, Jun 1, 2001, pp. 1707–1710. Reprinted with permission from AAAS. **403:** From Michael E. Hellberg, Deborah P. Balch, Kaustuv Roy, "Climate-Driven Range Expansion and Morphological Evolution in a Marine Gastropod", Science, vol. 292, Jun 1, 2001, pp. 1707–1710. Reprinted with permission from AAAS. **405:** Courtesy of James E. Lloyd. Miscellaneous Publications of the Museum of Zoology of the University of Michigan, 130:1–195, 1966. **406:** (all photos) Reny Parker **407:** (top left) © DLILLC/Corbis **408:** © DLILLC/Corbis **409:** (left) Patrice Geisel/Visuals Unlimited **409:** (centre) Tom Van Sant/The Geosphere Project, Santa Monica, CA **409:** (right) Fred McConnaughey/Photo Researchers, Inc. **410:** (top left) Yuri Arcurs/Shutterstock **410:** (bottom left) Photo by Jeremy McNeil **410:** (bottom right) Photo by Jeremy McNeil **412:** Dr. Jim Smith, Michigan State University **413:** (left) Andrew Parkinson/Frank Lane Photo Agency **413:** (right) Eric Soder/Foto Natura/Photo Researchers, Inc.

CHAPTER 19 **419:** Photo by M.B. Fenton **420:** (left, a) Edward S. Ross **420:** (left, b) Edward S. Ross **420:** (right, a) Juan M. Renjifo/Animals Animals—Earth Scenes **420:** (right, b) Photo: Gary Fewless **421:** (a) © Peter Arnold, Inc. / Alamy **421:** (b) © imagebroker / Alamy **421:** (c) © OVIA IMAGES / Alamy **421:** (d) Photo © D. Smirnov **421:** (e) Image is courtesy of Angie from St. Paul, Minnesota **422:** (a–c) Photo: Al and Betty Schneider **423:** From Qiang Ji, Zhe-Xi Luo, Chong-Xi Yuan, Alan R. Tabrum, "A Swimming Mammaliaform from the Middle Jurassic and Ecomorphological Diversification of Early Mammals", Science, vol. 311, Feb 24, 2006, pp. 1123–1127. Reprinted with permission from AAAS. **423:** From Qiang Ji, Zhe-Xi Luo, Chong-Xi Yuan, Alan R. Tabrum, "A Swimming Mammaliaform from the Middle Jurassic and Ecomorphological Diversification of Early Mammals", Science, vol. 311, Feb 24, 2006, pp. 1123–1127. Reprinted with permission from AAAS." **423:** Photo by M.B. Fenton **423:** Photo by M.B. Fenton **423:** Photo by M.B. Fenton **423:** Photo by M.B. Fenton **423:** Photo by M.B. Fenton **423:** Photo by M.B. Fenton **423:** Photo by M.B. Fenton **423:** Photo by M.B. Fenton **423:** Photo by M.B. Fenton **423:** Photo: Skulls Unlimited International, Inc. **423:** a) Photo: Professor Dr. Wilhelm Barthlott **424:** Photo by M.B. Fenton **426:** (left) Nature's Images/Photo Researchers, Inc. **426:** (centre) Neil Bowman/Frank Lane Picture Agency **426:** (right) Millard Sharp/Photo Researchers, Inc. **433:** (top left) Yuri Arcurs/Shutterstock **434:** (a) Thomas J. Lemieux, University of Colorado **434:** (b) Sandra Floyd, University of Colorado **436:** (top) From VA Albert, SE Williams, MW Chase, "Carnivorous plants: phylogeny and structural evolution", Science, vol. 257, Sep 11, 1992, pp. 1491–1495. Reprinted with permission from AAAS.

CHAPTER 20 **439:** Photo by M.B. Fenton **440:** C.S. Churcher **442:** Photo by M.B. Fenton **443:** (b) D. Kaleth/Image Bank/Getty Images **443:** (c) William Paton/Foto Natural/Photo Researchers, Inc. **443:** (d) Heather Angel/Natural Visions **446:** (a) © George H. H. Huey/CORBIS **446:** (b) Neville Pledge/South Australian Museum **446:** (c) Jack Koivula/Foto Natural/Photo Researchers, Inc. **446:** (d) Novosti/Photo Researchers, Inc. **447:** (top) From White, "PALEOANTHROPOLOGY: Early Hominids—Diversity or Distortion?", Science, vol. 299, Mar 28, 2003, pp. 1994–1997. Reprinted with permission from AAAS. **447:** (bottom) David Noble/FPG/Getty Images **448:** (top left) Yuri Arcurs/Shutterstock **450:** (all photos) Photo by M.B. Fenton **454:** (all) Alan Cheetham et al, Department of Paleobiology, National Museum of Natural History, Smithsonian Institution, Washington, D.C. **455:** Photo by M.B. Fenton **457:** (top left) David Scott/SREL **457:** (a, b) Gary Head **459:** © Michael D. Shapiro and David Kingsley **461:** Photo by M.B. Fenton **462:** From Irmis et al, "A Late Triassic Dinosauromorph Assemblage from New Mexico and the Rise of Dinosaurs", Science, vol. 317, Jul 20, 2007, pp. 358–361. Reprinted with permission from AAAS.

CHAPTER 21 **465:** Copyright Dennis Kunkel Microscopy, Inc. **466:** (a–c) Tony Brian, David Parker/SPL/, Photo Researchers, Inc. **467:** (a–c) David M. Phillips/Visuals Unlimited **467:** (bottom left) icrobiologybytes.wordpress.com **468:** Copyright Dennis Kunkel Microscopy, Inc. **469:** (a, b) T. J. Beveridge/ Visuals Unlimited **470:** (top left) © Frank Dazzo, Michigan State University **470:** (a) CNRI/SPL/, Photo Researchers, Inc. **470:** (b) Copyright Dennis Kunkel Microscopy, Inc. **470:** (c) Photo: New Scientist **471:** Dr. Ken Macdonald/SPL/Photo Researchers, Inc. **472:** Copyright Dennis Kunkel Microscopy, Inc. **473:** ©Phototake, Inc. **474:** Source: Emerg Infect Dis (c) 2002 Centers for Disease Control and Prevention (CDC) **476:** Hans Reichenbach, Gesellschaft for Biotech-

nologische Forschung, Braunsweig, Germany **477:** (top left) Yuri Arcurs/Shutterstock **477:** (center right) Courtesy of Luke Marshall **477:** (a) Dr. Jeremy Burgess/SPL/Photo Researchers, Inc. **477:** (b, top) Tony Brian/SPL/Photo Researchers, Inc. **477:** (b, bottom) P. W. Johnson and J. McN. Sieburth, University of Rhode Island/Biological Photo Service **478:** (bottom left) David M. Phillips/Visuals Unlimited **478:** (top right) Copyright Dennis Kunkel Microscopy, Inc. **479:** (a) Barry Rokeach **479:** (b) Alan L. Detrick/Science Source/Photo Researchers, Inc. **480:** R. Robinson/Visuals Unlimited

CHAPTER 22 **483:** K. G. Murti/Visuals Unlimited **487:** Eye of Science/Photo Researchers, Inc. **491:** Credit: St. Edward's University **493:** APHIS photo by Dr. Al Jenny **494:** (top left) Yuri Arcurs/Shutterstock

CHAPTER 23 **497:** (a) Copyright Dennis Kunkel Microscopy, Inc. **497:** (b) Photo: Dennis Anderson **498:** (a) Edward S. Ross **498:** (b) Gary W. Grimes and Steven L'Hernault **498:** (c) Daniel Mosquin **498:** (d) Wim van Egmond/Visuals Unlimited **501:** (top left) Wim van Egmond **501:** (top right) MI Walker/Photo Researchers, Inc. **501:** (center right) Redrawn from V. & J. Pearse and M. & R. Buchsbaum, Living Invertebrates, The Boxwood Press, 1987. **501:** (bottom right) © Micropolitan, org **502:** M. Abbey/Visuals Unlimited **503:** (a) Dr. Dennis Kunkel/Visuals Unlimited **503:** (b) The Systematic Biology Biodiversity Collection **503:** (bottom right) Tom E. Adams / Peter Arnold Inc. **504:** Oliver Meckes/Photo Researchers, Inc. **505:** (a) Jacek Gaertig, University of Georgia, Athens **505:** (b) Louis De Vos, Free University of Brussels, BIODIC **506:** (a) Hong Kong Red Tide Information Network/The Agriculture, Fisheries and Conservation Department **506:** (b) Dr. David Phillips/Visuals Unlimited/Getty Images **507:** (left) Mike Sauder **507:** (right) © REEF RELIEF All Rights Reserved **508:** Ariena van Bruggen **509:** (a) Claude Taylor and the University of Wisconsin Dept. of Botany **509:** (b) Heather Angel **509:** (c) W. Merrill **509:** (bottom right) Jan Hinsch/SPL/Photo Researchers, Inc. **510:** (a) Ron Hoham, Dept. of Biology, Colgate University **510:** (b) © Phillip Colla **510:** (c) © Phillip Colla **511:** (centre right) Walter Meayers Edwards/National Geographic/Getty Images **512:** (a) Manfred Kage / Peter Arnold Inc. **512:** (b) Wim van Egmond/ Visuals Unlimited **512:** (c) Courtesy of Allen W. H. Be and David A. Caron **512:** (d) John Clegg/Ardea, London **512:** (e) Redrawn from V. & J. Pearse and M. & R. Buchsbaum, Living Invertebrates, The Boxwood Press, 1987. **513:** Wim van Egmond **514:** (a) Carolina Biological Supply **514:** (b) Carolina Biological Supply **514:** (c) Courtesy Robert R. Kay from R. R Kay, et al, Development, 1989 Supplement, pp. 81–90. ©The Company of Biologists Ltd., 1989 **515:** (top left) Yuri Arcurs/Shutterstock **515:** (top centre) New Scientist **515:** (a) Photo: George Barron **515:** (b) Photo: Greg Thorn **516:** (a) Wim van Egmond/Visuals Unlimited **516:** (b) Douglas Faulkner/Sally Faulkner Collection **517:** (a) Wim van Egmond/Visuals Unlimited **517:** (b) Brian Parker/ Tom Stack and Associates **517:** (c) Manfrage Kage/Peter Arnold, Inc. **518:** Dr. John Clayton, National Institute of Water and Atmospheric Research, New Zealand

CHAPTER 24 **523:** Fritz Polking/ Peter Arnold, Inc. **524:** (a) Tim Flach/Stone/Getty Images **524:** (b) Photo: Alex Wild **524:** (bottom) Robert C. Simpson/Nature Stock **525:** (top left) Yuri Arcurs/Shutterstock **525:** (a–c) From Cameron R. Currie, Michael Poulsen, John Mendenhall, Jacobus J. Boomsma, Johan Billen, "Coevolved crypts and exocrine glands support mutualistic bacteria in fungus-growing ants", Science, Vol 311, 6 January 2006, pp. 81–83. Reprinted with permission from AAAS. **526:** (a) Garry T. Cole, University of Texas,

vier. **651:** (top, a–b) Photo by M.B. Fenton **651:** (centre) D. & V. Blagden/ANT Photo Library **651:** (bottom) Jean Phillipe Varin/Jacana/Photo Researchers, Inc. **652:** (left) Milse, T./Arco Images/ Peter Arnold **652:** (centre) Photo by M.B. Fenton **652:** (right) Photo by M.B. Fenton **653:** (top, a) Theo Allofs/Photonica/Getty Images **653:** (top, b) J. Scott Altenbach, University of New Mexico **653:** (top, c) Leonard Lee Rue III/FPG/Getty Images **653:** (top, d) Martin Harvey/Peter Arnold **653:** (top, e) David Parker/SPL/Photo Researchers, Inc. **653:** (bottom) From Zhe-Xi Luo, John R. Wible, "A Late Jurassic Digging Mammal and Early Mamma-lian Diversification", Science, Apr 1, 2005, vol. 308, pp. 103–107. Reprinted with permission from AAAS. **654:** (top, a–b) From Zhe-Xi Luo, John R. Wible, "A Late Jurassic Digging Mammal and Early Mammalian Diversification", Science, Apr 1, 2005, vol. 308, pp. 103–107. Reprinted with permission from AAAS. **654:** (top, c) Photo by M.B. Fenton **654:** (bottom) From Zhe-Xi Luo, John R. Wible, "A Late Jurassic Digging Mammal and Early Mammalian Diversification", Science, Apr 1, 2005, vol. 308, pp. 103–107. Reprinted with permission from AAAS. **655:** (all photos) M.B. Fenton **656:** (all photos) M.B. Fenton **657:** (left) Photo by M.B. Fenton **657:** (right) Reprinted by permission from Macmillan Publishers Ltd: Nature, "A reversible wet/dry adhesive inspired by mussels and geckos", Haeshin Lee, Bruce P. Lee and Phillip B. Messer-smith, vol. 448, pp. 338–341, copyright (2007). **659:** (left, a) Dr. Donald Johanson, Institute of Human Origins **659:** (left, b) Louise M. Robbins **659:** (right, a) Science VU/NM/Visuals Unlimited **659:** (right, b) AAAC/Tophan/The Image Works **660:** Yuri Arcurs/Shutterstock **661:** From Jun Z. Li, Devin M. Absher, Hua Tang, Audrey M. Southwick, Amanda M. Casto, Sohini Ramachandran, Howard M. Cann, Gregory S. Barsh, Marcus Feldman, Luigi L. Cavalli-Sforza, Richard M. Myers, "Worldwide Human Relationships Inferred from Genome-Wide Patterns of Variation", Science, Feb 22, 2008, vol. 319, pp. 1100–1104. Reprinted with permission from AAAS.

CHAPTER 28 **667:** (inset) Photo: Adrian Jones, IAN Image Library (www.ian.umces.edu/imageli-brary/) **667:** (main) Photo: Isabella M. Gioia **668:** Photo: Brian Ecott **671:** © Biophoto Associates/ Photo Researchers, Inc. **673:** (top left) © Bruce Iverson **673:** (top right) © Mike Clayton/Univer-sity of Wisconsin Department of Botany **673:** (centre left) © Ernest Manewal/ Index Stock Imagery **673:** (centre right) © Darrell Gulin/ Corbis **673:** (bottom left) © Simon Fraser/ Photo Researchers, Inc. **673:** (bottom right) Gary Head **674:** (micrograph) Ed Reschke / Peter Arnold Inc. **675:** (top, a–c) © Biophoto Associates **675:** (bottom left) © Kingsley R. Stern **675:** (bottom right) © D.E. Akin and I.L. Rigsby, Richard B. Russel Agricultural Research Service, U.S. Depart-ment of Agriculture, Athens, Georgia **676:** (bottom left) Alison W. Roberts, University **676:** (bottom centre) H.A. Cote, W.A. Cote and A.C. Day, Wood Structure and Identification, second edition, Syra-cuse University Press **677:** (top left) James D. Mauseth, University of Texas **677:** (centre left) Courtesy of Professor John Main, Pacific Luthern University **677:** (bottom, a) George S. Ellmore **677:** (bottom, b) © Dr. Jeremy Burgess/SPL/ Photo Researchers, Inc **677:** (bottom, c) Courtesy Mark Holland, Salisbury University. **678:** Jakub Jasinski/Visuals Unlimited **679:** (top centre) Robert and Linda Mitchell Photography **679:** (top right) Richard Dute **680:** (top centre) Ray F. Evert **680:** (top right) James W. Perry **680:** (bottom centre) Carolina Biological Supply **680:** (centre right) James W. Perry **681:** (top, a) Mike Hill/Getty Images **681:** (top, b) Wally Eberhart/Visuals Unlimited **681:** (top, c) Joerg Boethling/Peter Arnold, Inc. **681:** (top, d) © Alan & Linda Detrick/ Photo Researchers, Inc. **681:** (top, e) Michael P. Gadomski/Photo Researchers, Inc. **681:** (bottom left) Joseph Devenney/Getty Images **681:** (bottom right) Maxine Adcock/Science Photo Library/ Photo Researchers, Inc. **682:** C.E. Jeffree, et al, Planta 172 (1):20–37, 1987. Reprinted by permis-sion of C.E. Jeffree and Springer-Verlag **683:** Beth

Davidow/Visuals Unlimited **684:** John Limbaugh/ Ripon Microslides, Inc. **685:** (top left) Chuck Brown **685:** (top right) Carolina Biological Supply **685:** (bottom) Omnikron/Photo Researchers, Inc. **687:** Photo: Daniel Mosquin **688:** © George Bernard/SPL/ Photo Researchers, Inc. **689:** (right) Photo: Cliff Ecology Research Group, Department of Integrative Biology, University of Guelph **689:** (top left) Yuri Arcurs/Shutterstock **690:** (top left) © DLILLC/Corbis **690:** bottom, Photo: Raymond G. Milewski

CHAPTER 29 **695:** ©Steve Gschmeissner/ SPL/ Photo Researchers, Inc. **696:** Owaki–Kulla/ CORBIS **697:** Micrograph Chuck Brown **700:** (micrographs) © Claude Nuridsany and Marie Perennou/ Science Photo Library/ Photo Researchers, Inc. **702:** Micrograph Chuck Brown **705:** Dr. John D. Cunningham/Visuals Unlimited **706:** (right, a) T. A. Masefield **706:** (right, b) T. A. Masefield **708:** (top left) BIOS Matt Alexander/ Peter Arnold, Inc. **708:** (top right) Thomas L. Rost **708:** (bottom left) Fritz Polking/Visuals Unlimited **708:** (bottom right) Fritz Polking/Visuals Unlim-ited **709:** (top left) Yuri Arcurs/Shutterstock

CHAPTER 30 **715:** © Ted Kinsman/ SPL/ Photo Researchers, Inc. **716:** (top left) Kashfia Rahman/ StockXchng **716:** (top right) Ian Britton/FreeFoto. com **716:** (centre left) Photographer: David/ www.3d-images.ws **716:** (bottom left) NASA Earth Observatory **717:** (top) Photo: Tom Horton **717:** (inset) Photographer: Allan Carson **719:** (left) Justin Voight/iStockPhoto **719:** (top right) Photo: Doug Waylett **719:** (bottom right) Photo: Doug Waylett **721:** (bottom left) David M. Phillips/ Visuals Unlimited **721:** (bottom centre) Dr. Jeremy Burgess/SPL/Photo Researchers, Inc. **721:** (bottom right) David Scharf/Peter Arnold, Inc. **722:** Photographer: Quimbaya **723:** (top left) Yuri Arcurs/Shutterstock **723:** (centre) William E. Fried-man, University of Georgia **725:** (b) Siegel, R./ Arco Images/Peter Arnold **725:** (c, top) Richard H. Gross **725:** (c, bottom) Andrew Syred/SPL/Photo Researchers, Inc. **725:** (d) Mark Rieger **725:** (e) R. Carr **727:** Dr. John D. Cunningham/Visuals Unlim-ited **728:** Herve Chaumeton/ Agence Nature **729:** (top right) Barry L. Runk/Grant Heilman, Inc. **729:** (centre right) James Mauseth **729:** (bottom right) Ed Reschke/Peter Arnold **730:** (left) R-R/S/Grant Heilman Photography, Inc. **730:** (centre top) Professor Dr. Hans Hanks-Ulrich Koop **730:** (centre bottom) Professor Dr. Hans Hanks-Ulrich Koop **730:** (right) Professor Dr. Hans Hanks-Ulrich Koop

CHAPTER 31 **735:** © Garry Black/ Masterfile **736:** (top left) Source: Christian Krupke, John Ober-meyer, and Larry Bledsoe/Purdue University **736:** (top right) Dr. L. T. Kok, Professor of Entomology, Virginia Tech, Blacksburg, VA **736:** (bottom) Mari-etta College **738:** (top left) Yuri Arcurs/Shutter-stock **738:** (right) William Perlman/ Star Ledger/ Corbis **740:** Kingsley R. Stern **742:** Sylvan H. Wittwer/Visuals Unlimited **743:** Sylvan Wittwer/ Visuals Unlimited **744:** (top) Photo: Kurt Stepnitz, Instructional Media Center, Michigan State University, East Lansing, MI 48824 **744:** (bottom) N.R. Lersten **745:** Larry D. Nooden **746:** Amanda Darcy/Getty Images **749:** David Cavagnaro/Peter Arnold, Inc. **750:** Nigel Cattlin/ Photo Researchers Inc. **753:** (top left) Cathlyn Melloan/Stone/Getty Images **753:** (centre) Micrographs courtesy of Randy Moore, from "How Roots Respond to Gravity," M. L. Evans, R. Moore, and K. Hasen-stein, Scientific American, December 1986. **753:** (bottom left) Michael Clayton, University of Wisconsin **753:** (bottom right) John Digby and Richard Firn **754:** (bottom) Cary Mitchell **755:** (top) Frank B. Salisbury **755:** (centre right) David Sieren/Visuals Unlimited **755:** (bottom right) David Sieren/Visuals Unlimited **757:** Dwight Kuhn **758:** (top left) Jan Zeevart **758:** (top right) Eric Crichton/CORBIS **759:** R. J. Downs **760:** Eric Welzel/Fox Hill Nursery, Freeport, Maine

Icons
People Behind Biology: Yuri Arcurs/Shutterstock
Life on the Edge: © DLILLC/Corbis

Index

wing bones, interspecies comparisons of, 425–426, 426i
wings, as bird characteristic, 428
wings, feathered, evolution of, 427
Woese, Carl R., 434
wolf spider (*Lycosa* species), 607i
wood, **686**, 687i
wood-decay fungi, 524i
wood-eating insects, 502–503
wood spiders (*Nehila*), 461, 461i
woody plant debris, 535
wormlike animals, 420i
wound response and repair
in plants, 703, 749, 749i

Xenoturbella bocki, 617, 620i
Xenoturbellida (phylum), **617, 619**
xerophytes, 707
xylem, 688
   evolution of, **551**
   transport functions of, 711
   water and mineral transport in, **675–676**, 676i, 703–708
   water pathways to, 701–702, 701i
xylem sap, **698**, 703, 705

yellowfin tuna (*Thannus albacores*), 633i
yellow-rumped warbler, 399i
yellow-throated warbler, 399i
yolk, 638
Younis, Jorge J., 415

Zambryski, Patricia, 712
Zamia, 567i
Zauner, Klaus-Peter, **515**
zeatin, 743, 743i
zebras, ancestry of, 451
zebroids, 406
zooplankton, **500**
zygomycetes (Zygomycota), **529–530**
zygospore, **529–530**
zygote
   cell division of, 725, 731, 740
zygotes, formation of, 578

CengageNOW MAKES IT EASIER TO DO WHAT YOU ALREADY DO.

Designed by instructors for instructors, CengageNOW mirrors your natural workflow and provides time-saving, performance-enhancing tools for you and your students—all in one program!

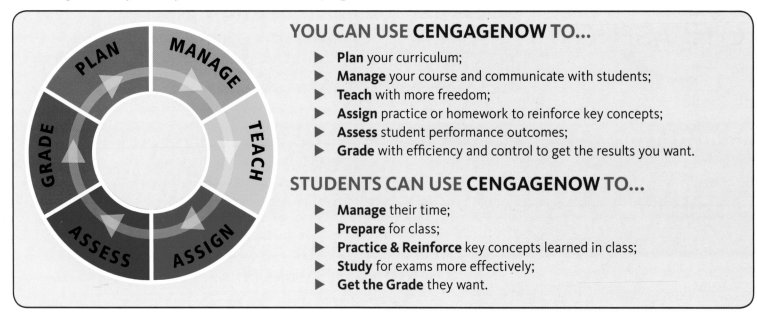

YOU CAN USE **CENGAGENOW** TO...

- ▶ **Plan** your curriculum;
- ▶ **Manage** your course and communicate with students;
- ▶ **Teach** with more freedom;
- ▶ **Assign** practice or homework to reinforce key concepts;
- ▶ **Assess** student performance outcomes;
- ▶ **Grade** with efficiency and control to get the results you want.

STUDENTS CAN USE **CENGAGENOW** TO...

- ▶ **Manage** their time;
- ▶ **Prepare** for class;
- ▶ **Practice & Reinforce** key concepts learned in class;
- ▶ **Study** for exams more effectively;
- ▶ **Get the Grade** they want.

The flexibility of CengageNOW allows you to use a single aspect of the program, or for maximum power and effectiveness, to use all of the teaching and learning resources to create and customize your own material to match your course objectives.

CENGAGENOW SEAMLESSLY INTEGRATES WITH POPULAR COURSE MANAGEMENT PROGRAMS

CengageNOW on Blackboard, WebCT, and eCollege provides students with seamless single sign-on access to CengageNOW through the school's course management system (CMS). After entering a simple access code just once at the beginning of the term, students get seamless access to both their CMS and CengageNOW textbook specific assignments and activities, with results flowing to your Blackboard, WebCT, or eCollege gradebook. Rich content, seamless integration with CengageNOW functionality, and only one gradebook to manage.

INTERESTED IN GIVING **CENGAGENOW** A TEST DRIVE IN YOUR CLASS?

Contact your Cengage Learning sales representative for more information about the **CengageNOW Class Test Program**.